# TEACHER'S EDITION

*Progress*™

**Mathematics**

**5**

**For additional online resources, go to** www.SadlierConnect.com
**and enter the Teacher's Access Code:**

| State | Access Code | State | Access Code |
|---|---|---|---|
| Alabama | SBIP01AL54 | Missouri | SBIP29MO51 |
| Arizona | SBIP04AZ5R | New Jersey | SBIP34NJ5T |
| Arkansas | SBIP05AR52 | New York | SBIP36NY5C |
| California | SBIP06CA56 | North Carolina | SBIP37NC5X |
| Colorado | SBIP08CO5B | Ohio | SBIP39OH5J |
| Connecticut | SBIP09CT5L | Oklahoma | SBIP40OK5P |
| Florida | SBIP12FL51 | Pennsylvania | SBIP42PA54 |
| Georgia | SBIP13GA53 | South Carolina | SBIP45SC5T |
| Illinois | SBIP17IL5I | Tennessee | SBIP47TN59 |
| Kentucky | SBIP21KY52 | Texas | SBIP48TX5K |
| Louisiana | SBIP22LA5C | Virginia | SBIP51VI92 |
| Massachusetts | SBIP25MA5N | Wisconsin | SBIP55WI5X |
| Michigan | SBIP26MI55 | All Other States | SBIPNA25PG |
| Mississippi | SBIP28MS5A | | |

**Sadlier School**

# TEACHER'S EDITION

Progress™
Mathematics

**Cover:** *Series Design:* Studio Montage; *Title design:* Quarasan, Inc. **Photo Credits:** Cover: age fotostock/Keith Levit: *bottom left*. Getty Images/Jupiterimages: *top left*; Siede Preis: *bottom left*. Used under license from Shutterstock/RoboLab: *background*; topseller: *right*. Interior: Corbis/Rob Lewine: T12; Ocean: T17; Dann Tardiff: T09. Used under license from Shutterstock.com/wavebreakmedia: T03; Corbis/Rob Lewine: T12; Ocean: T15 and T17; Dann Tardiff: T07. Used under license from Shutterstock.com/wavebreakmedia: T03; age fotostock/Justus de Cuveland/im: 225; Sonderegger Christof: 39. Alamy/caia images/Moretti/Viant: 8 *top*. Blend Images/Corbis: 38 *top*; GM Visuals: 224 *top*; John Lund/Sam Diephuis: 132 *top*. Corbis/Reuters/ISSEI KATO: 9. Dreamstime.com/Steve Allen: vi *bottom left*; Njnightsky: vi *top right*. Getty Images/Jupiterimages: vi *center*. Masterfile/Royalty Free: 302 *top*. Used under license from Shutterstock.com/Ilya Akinshin: vi *bottom right*; Jana Guothova: 8 *bottom*, 38 *bottom*, 132 *bottom*, 224 *bottom*, 302 *bottom*; koosen: vi *top left*; RoboLab: 1, vi *background*; Ivan Ryabokon: vi *top left*. SuperStock/age fotostock/Steven Bernard: 133; Cusp: 303. **Text Credits:** Common Core State Standards Copyright © 2010. National Governors Association Center for Best Practices and Council of Chief State School Officers. All rights reserved. National Mathematics Advisory Panel. *Foundations for Success: The Final Report of the National Mathematics Advisory Panel,* U.S. Department of Education: Washington, DC, 2008. **Illustrator Credit:** Dave Titus

William H. Sadlier, Inc.
9 Pine Street
New York, NY 10005-4700

Printed in the United States of America.
ISBN: 978-1-4217-3165-0
1 2 3 4 5 6 7 8 9 WEBC 18 17 16 15 14

# Contents

## Access Your Digital Resources

### Get Started

**1. Go to** www.SadlierConnect.com

**2. Log in**

Don't have a username and password? Teachers click "Get Started!" in the Teacher Registration section.

**3. Select your program to begin accessing content.**

With one username and password, you now have access to all your Sadlier Mathematics and English Language Arts content.

# Contents

*continued next page*

T4

# Contents

*continued next page*

# Contents

## Unit 5 Focus on Geometry

## Program Overview

*Progress Mathematics* is a streamlined, yet comprehensive K–8 supplemental mathematics program that provides standards-based instruction, scaffolded practice, and assessment for the critical skills and concepts of each grade level.

**In *Progress Mathematics*, students will:**

- Build understanding of key mathematical concepts using multiple representations of a skill.

- Model mathematics with real-world problems to make sense of math and apply their knowledge.

- Share their thinking and reason mathematically while developing academic vocabulary.

- Use higher-level thinking skills and apply levels of Webb's Depth of Knowledge (DOK) with rigorous, cognitively-demanding independent practice items.

- Regularly apply the National Council of Teachers of Mathematics (NCTM) Process Standards—communication, reasoning, representation, connections, and problem solving—in all aspects of learning mathematics.

**With the support of a comprehensive Teacher's Edition, teachers will be able to:**

- Scaffold student learning with easy-to-use, comprehensive lesson plans.

- Use student assessment data, both observational and formal, to inform and redirect instruction.

- Understand the progression of skills and concepts and how they unfold within a grade level and across the grade levels to help students make connections.

- Support diverse learners, including English language learners, struggling learners, and those needing extended learning opportunities.

- Access online and professional development resources to enhance instruction.

## Built to Support the National Mathematics Advisory Panel (NMAP) Report

The instructional and programmatic features of *Progress Mathematics* were built to support the findings and recommendations of the National Mathematics Advisory Panel (NMAP) in the areas of **Curricular Content**, **Learning Process**, **Instructional Practices**, and **Assessment of Mathematics Learning**.

| NMAP Findings & Recommendations | | How Addressed in *Progress Mathematics* |
|---|---|---|
| Curricular Content | Focused, coherent progression of mathematics learning, with an emphasis on proficiency with key topics, should become the norm in elementary and middle school mathematics curricula. (p. xvi)<br><br>The mathematics curriculum in Grades PreK–8 should be streamlined and should emphasize a well-defined set of the most critical topics in the early grades. (p. xiii) | The table of contents of each grade level is organized around a focused, coherent group of mathematical topics to help build students' understanding of key skills and concepts.<br><br>Lessons at each grade level focus on the Benchmarks for the Critical Foundations of the grade levels as defined by NMAP and the NCTM Curriculum Focal Points.<br><br>*Learning Progression* charts at the beginning of each Unit in both the Student Worktexts and the Teacher's Editions describe how skills and concepts are developed within and across grade levels. |
| Learning Process | To prepare students for Algebra, the curriculum must simultaneously develop conceptual understanding, computational fluency, and problem-solving skills. (p. xix)<br><br>Use should be made of what is clearly known from rigorous research about how children learn, especially by recognizing the mutually reinforcing benefits of conceptual understanding, procedural fluency, and automatic (i.e., quick and effortless) recall of facts. (p. xiv) | Skills and concepts are taught through a consistent lesson design (Guided Instruction, Guided Practice, Independent Practice), which provides routine opportunities with fluency practice, concept development, application problems, and daily formative assessment opportunities.<br><br>The Guided Instruction section focuses on developing conceptual understanding of mathematical skills/concepts through Understand-Connect instructional presentations, often using models to help students visualize math and make connections.<br><br>The Guided Practice offers students an opportunity to practice their newly learned skills with teacher support and to collaborate with other students.<br><br>The Independent Practice section provides intentionally sequenced and scaffolded exercises so that students build knowledge to reach the expectation of the learning objective. Application problems require students to apply the four-step problem-solving model (Read-Plan-Solve-Check) to efficiently and accurately solve problems.<br><br>Daily ongoing review in terms of **fluency practice** is available online at **www.SadlierConnect.com** and is identified at point of use in each lesson of the Teacher's Edition. |

| NMAP Findings & Recommendations | | How Addressed in *Progress Mathematics* |
|---|---|---|
| Instructional Practices | High-quality research does not support the contention that instruction should be either entirely "student centered" or "teacher directed." Research indicates that some forms of particular instructional practices can have a positive impact under specified conditions. (p. xiv)<br><br>High-quality research does not support the exclusive use of either approach. (p. xxii) | *Progress Mathematics* was built on the Gradual Release of Responsibility instructional model (Pearson and Gallagher, 1983). Each lesson incorporates all three steps of the Gradual Release of Responsibility model beginning with direct and guided instruction (I do it.), guided practice (We do it.), peer collaboration (You do it together.), and concludes with independent practice (You do it independently.). |
| Assessment | Teachers' regular use of formative assessments improves their students' learning, especially if teachers have additional guidance on using the assessment results to design and individualize instruction. (p. 47) | *Progress Mathematics* provides a range of formative and summative assessment opportunities to help guide students to mathematical proficiency.<br><br>Observational Assessment suggestions in the Guided Practice section of each lesson in the Teacher's Edition offer formative assessment opportunities to gauge students' conceptual knowledge.<br><br>Each unit introduction includes a *Progress Check* that allows students to focus on the unit's key skills and concepts, self-assess before the learning, and reflect on progress at the end of the unit. It also provides data for teachers to determine if students need additional instruction on precursor content in order to successfully master new content introduced in that unit.<br><br>*Unit Reviews* and *Unit Performance Tasks* also support teachers in determining students' level of mastery. |

## Flexible Program Use

*Progress Mathematics* lessons focus on the grade-level key skills and concepts and combine solid content with a pedagogically-sound lesson design that simplifies the instructional process.

### *Progress Mathematics* can be used as:

• Supplemental lessons in a core Mathematics program.

• Targeted preparation materials for state standardized assessments.

• Support for individual or small group instruction on a particular skill or concept.

## Diverse Grouping Models

The *Progress Mathematics* program employs diverse grouping and instructional models to help teachers provide effective instruction in key mathematical skills/concepts.

**Guided Instruction** The program uses **whole-class** instruction to provide direct skill instruction and think-aloud modeling while the students follow along with the teacher, helping students conceptualize skills and concepts through modeling and reasoning.

**Guided Practice** Students work through scaffolded-practice problems of increasing complexity, independently or in small groups, as the teacher circulates around the classroom to gauge understanding of the concepts and skill being learned.

**Independent Practice** Lessons offer independent application practice requiring students to use their critical-thinking skills and apply their math knowledge.

## Foundational Skill Support and Fluency Practice

Foundational skills lessons and fluency practice are provided in the following ways in *Progress Mathematics*.

• A comprehensive Foundational Skills Handbook, located in the back of this guide as well as in the Student Worktext, provides a review of *all* prerequisite mathematics needed to understand the grade-level concepts and skills.

• Fluency practice is available online providing students with the opportunity to build their skills of performing calculations and solving problems quickly and accurately in order to meet the grade level fluency expectations.

• Problem-Solving Model offers students a four-step model as an approach to solving problems.

## Student Worktext

(in print, eBook, and interactive edition formats)
Organized around a focused, coherent group of mathematical topics, the standards-based instruction includes clearly-stated models, multiple representations of skills, a focus on the critical areas of each grade level, and connections between topics. ▶

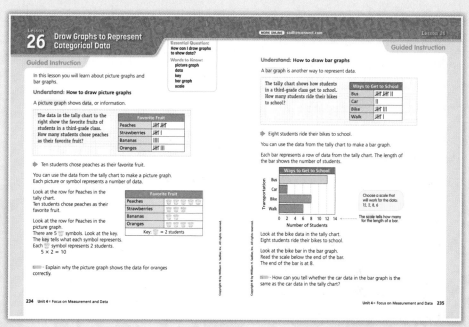

Grade 3 Pages 234–235

## Teacher's Edition ◀

(in print and eBook formats)
Teacher-friendly lesson plans with targeted standards instruction and supportive features suitable for both novice and experienced teachers.

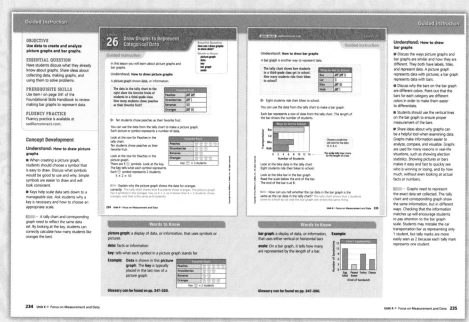

Grade 3 Teacher's Edition Pages 234–235

## Progress Monitor*
### (Optional Purchase)

Four comprehensive Benchmark Assessments to identify instructional needs as benchmarked against grade level mathematical skills and concepts. ▶

*Items are mapped to CCSS.

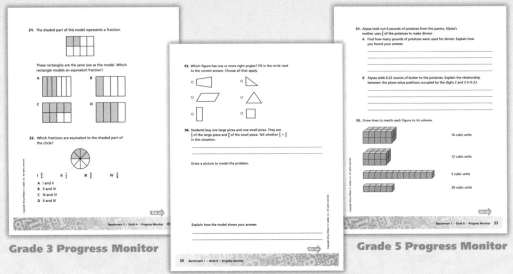

**Grade 3 Progress Monitor**

**Grade 4 Progress Monitor**

**Grade 5 Progress Monitor**

## Online Digital Resources

A rich array of online resources at **www.SadlierConnect.com** supports program implementation and extends learning.

**Home Connect Activities** support family member involvement and help create associations with math in real-world situations. ▼

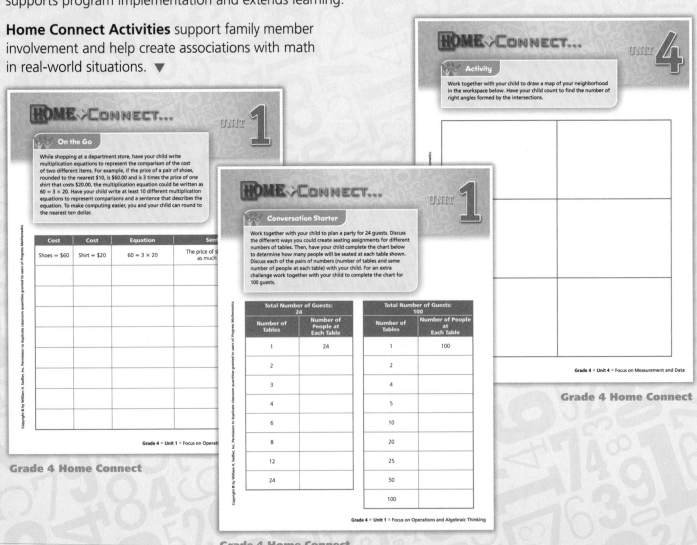

**Grade 4 Home Connect**

**Grade 4 Home Connect**

**Grade 4 Home Connect**

## Unit Performance Tasks

provide practice opportunities for Performance Tasks related to the content of each unit. ▶

## Performance Tasks 1 and 2

allow students to apply their learning and provide teachers with robust evaluation support. These tasks can be used for mid-year and end-of-year assessment purposes. ▼

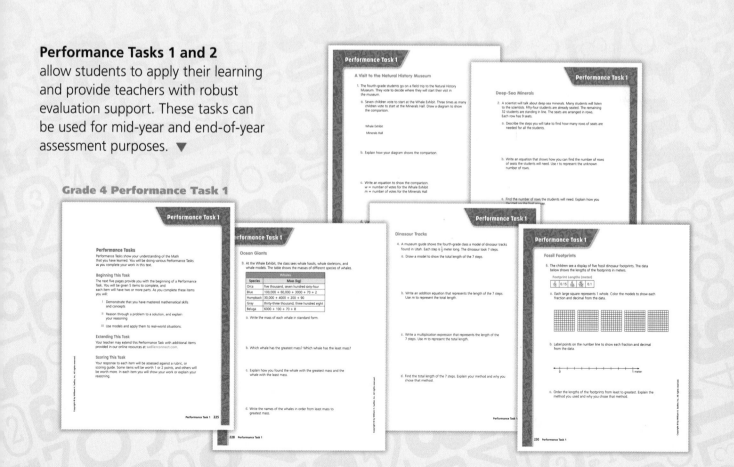

Grade 4 Unit 1 Performance Task

Grade 4 Performance Task 1

**Additional Practice** offers opportunities to augment program practice. ▼

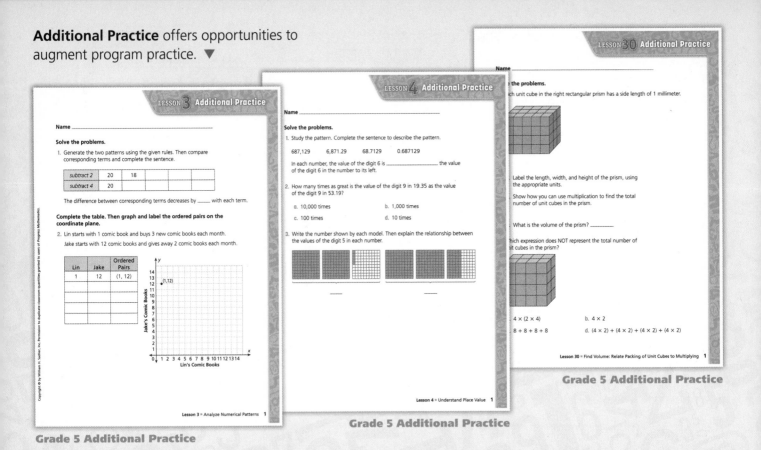

**Grade 5 Additional Practice**

**Grade 5 Additional Practice**

**Grade 5 Additional Practice**

**Fluency Practice** provides opportunities for students to improve speed and accuracy with simple calculations. ▼

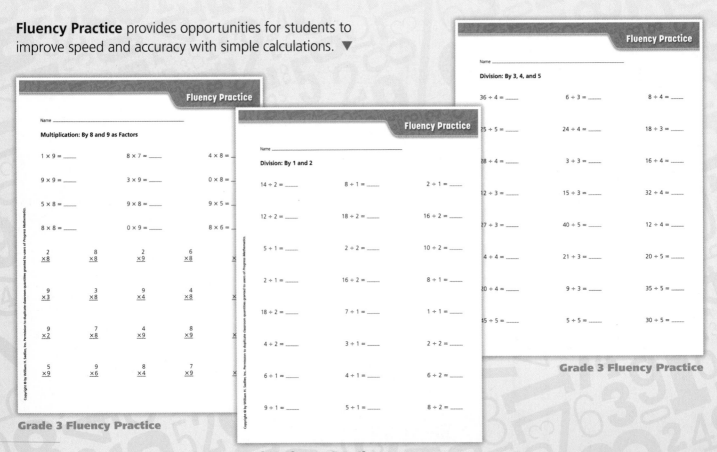

**Grade 3 Fluency Practice**

**Grade 3 Fluency Practice**

**Grade 3 Fluency Practice**

## iProgress Monitor* (Optional Purchase)

This dynamic online assessment system is available to help monitor student progress on grade-level mathematical skills and concepts in real time and customize assignments based on individual needs through its built-in test generator feature. See page T17 for more information about this online assessment system.

*Items are mapped to CCSS.

## eBooks (Optional Purchase)

**Student Worktext eBook** The eBook provides the same quality content as the print Student Worktext. Delivered via Sadlier's one-stop platform at **www.SadlierConnect.com**, the eBook format also provides access to robust tools that allow students to:

- Read Text
- Make notes and highlight important information
- Search for key words
- Zoom in on specific content

**Teacher's Edition eBook** The eBook provides the same quality content as the print Teacher's Edition. Delivered via Sadlier's one-stop platform at **www.SadlierConnect.com**, the eBook format also provides access to robust tools that allow teachers to:

- Toggle between the Student and Teacher's Edition
- Use Full-screen Mode to project the Student Edition onto a whiteboard to focus on instruction
- Assign lessons to an entire class or a specific group of students to take offline (in PDF format)
- View digital resources at point of use
- Make notes and highlight important information
- Search for key words
- Zoom in on specific content

*Progress Mathematics Grade 3 eBook*

*Progress Mathematics* contains many formative and summative assessment opportunities to help teachers gather evidence of students' progress toward mastering grade-level skills and concepts and prepare for the new state-standardized assessments.

## Integrated, Ongoing Assessment Opportunities

**Observational Assessment** opportunities are a routine part of each Lesson Plan in the Teacher's Edition. Common Errors and Teaching Tips features at point of use help teachers identify student misconceptions and provide strategies for solutions. ▶

### Teaching Tips

**Item 16**
Students may have difficulty solving the problem because they do not draw the array correctly. Provide grid paper for those who have difficulty aligning rows and columns.

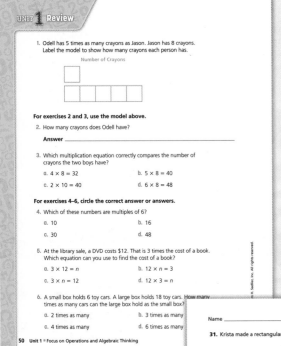

Grade 4 Page 50

◀ **Unit Reviews** assess the mathematical skills and concepts taught within the Unit and expose students to the question types that they might experience on the new state assessments.

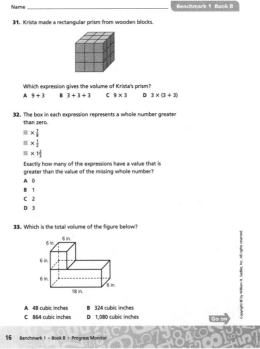

Grade 5 Progress Monitor

◀ **Benchmark Assessments\*** in Progresss Monitor (optional purchase) provide four comprehensive assessments that can be administered periodically throughout the school year to evaluate students' knowledge and skill level relative to grade-level mathematical skills and concepts.

\*Items are mapped to CCSS.

**Unit Performance Tasks**, available online at **www.SadlierConnect.com**, provide practice opportunities for students to solve real-world problems that integrate the skills and concepts within each unit, and often require students to explain and justify their solutions.

**Performance Tasks 1 and 2** ▶ provide tasks that parallel those in standardized assessments. The tasks assess students' conceptual understanding of grade-level skills and concepts and require them to show evidence through application, modeling, and written arguments. Performance Tasks 1 and 2 are also available online at **www.SadlierConnect.com**. They can be used for mid-year and end-of-year assessment purposes. These Performance Tasks play a vital role in helping you determine if students are able to integrate the skills and concepts being taught and to apply them in solving real-world problems.

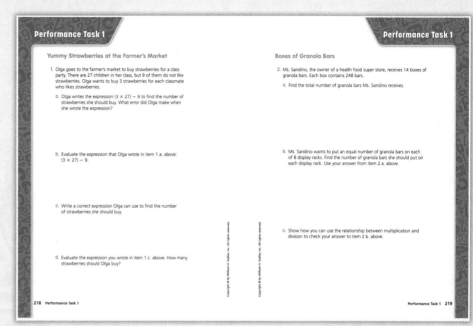

Grade 5 Pages 218–219

## iProgress Monitor* (Optional Purchase)

Augment your assessment resources with customized assignments and test-building power!

With the **iProgress Monitor**, teachers can:

- Assign, evaluate, and monitor student progress with preformatted program assessments in an interactive format.
- Build custom assessments with a built-in test generator.
- Track students' progress and guide instruction with real-time data.

*Items are mapped to CCSS.

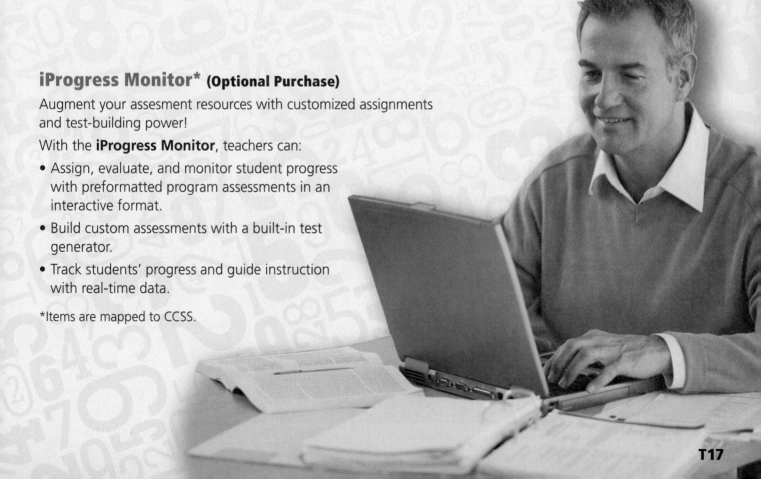

## Student Worktext

With a full-color, engaging design the Student Worktext provides students with the opportunity to:

- Develop proficiency in mathematics through the integration of skills and concepts
- Build conceptual understanding of mathematical content following a gradual release of responsibility model of instruction
- Reason and communicate mathematically
- Develop mathematical arguments and model real-world problems

Organized around a focused, coherent group of mathematical topics, the lessons in the Student Worktext focus on developing conceptual understanding, computational fluency, and problem-solving skills.

## A Unit Introduction That Focuses on Standards

**Grade 3 Page 7**

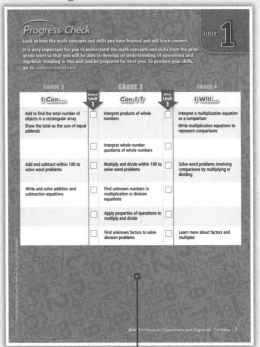

**Progress Check** at the beginning of each unit allows students to focus on the unit's key skills and concepts, self-assess before learning, and reflect on progress at the end of the unit.

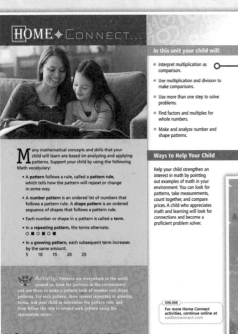

**Grade 4 Page 8**

**Home Connect** activities for each unit provide families a window into their child's learning and encourage them to take an active role.

**Grade 5 Page 9**

An **Essential Question** sets the focus and identifies the big idea for each unit, enhanced with vivid images featuring engaging and relevant content that helps students make connections between math and the real world.

# Gradual Release of Responsibility

Each standard is taught using a gradual release of responsibility instructional model. By gradually decreasing the level of support within each lesson, students can develop the conceptual understanding necessary for solving complex problems and tasks independently.

This gradual release of responsibility instructional model starts with **Guided Instruction**, helping students conceptualize skills and concepts through modeling and reasoning.

## Guided Instruction

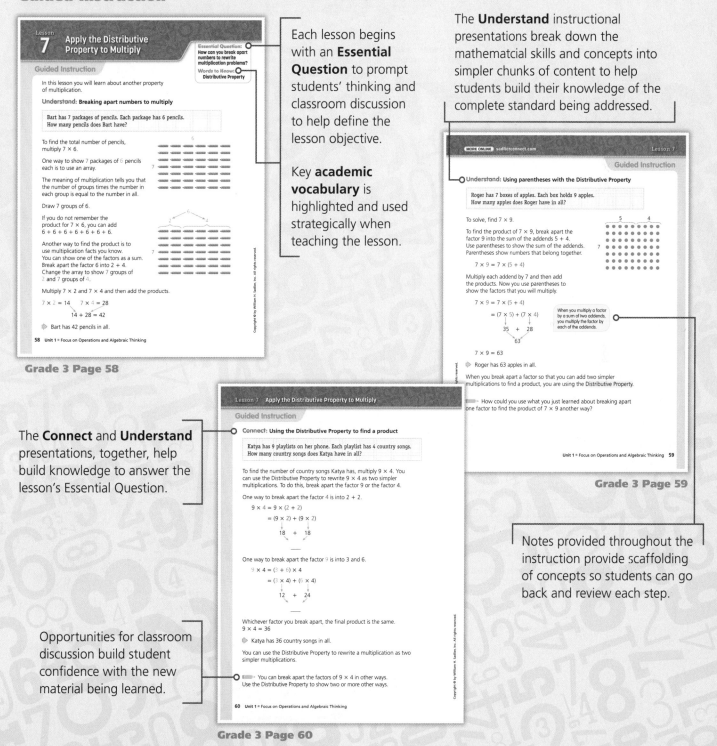

Each lesson begins with an **Essential Question** to prompt students' thinking and classroom discussion to help define the lesson objective.

Key **academic vocabulary** is highlighted and used strategically when teaching the lesson.

The **Understand** instructional presentations break down the mathematcial skills and concepts into simpler chunks of content to help students build their knowledge of the complete standard being addressed.

**Grade 3 Page 58**

**Grade 3 Page 59**

The **Connect** and **Understand** presentations, together, help build knowledge to answer the lesson's Essential Question.

Notes provided throughout the instruction provide scaffolding of concepts so students can go back and review each step.

Opportunities for classroom discussion build student confidence with the new material being learned.

**Grade 3 Page 60**

## Gradual Release of Responsibility

The structure of the lesson continues the gradual release of responsibility model with **Guided Practice**, which allows the opportunity for students to work through problems with the teacher's supervision and assistance.

**Guided Practice**

Scaffolding is gradually removed as students work through the problems on the page(s). This allows students more independence in applying and developing strategies and skills necessary to solve the problems.

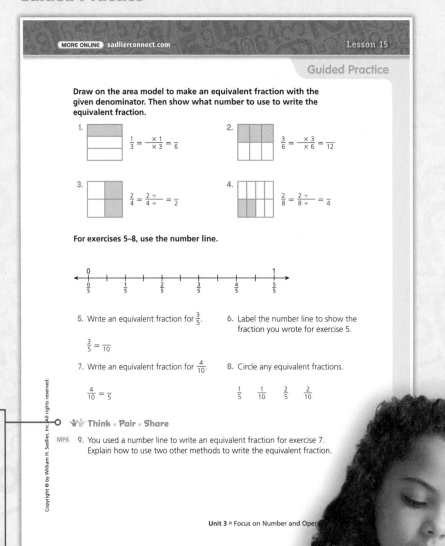

**Think-Pair-Share** opportunities encourage students to think independently about mathematics and then discuss, model, and explain their reasoning while learning from one another.

Grade 4 Page 137

# Overview of the Student Worktext

## Gradual Release of Responsibility

The gradual release of responsibility model culminates with **Independent Practice**, which requires students to use their critical-thinking skills, apply their math knowledge, and respond to problems leveled to Webb's Depth of Knowledge. These independent practice pages can be used independently at home or in class.

### Independent Practice

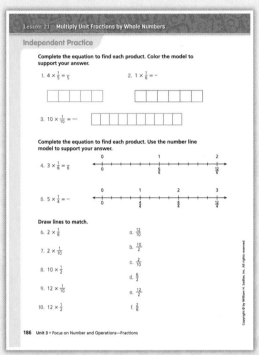

**Grade 4 Page 186**

As the level of scaffolding decreases and students' knowledge and confidence with the material increases, the exercises become more difficult and require higher-order thinking as well as justification of answers.

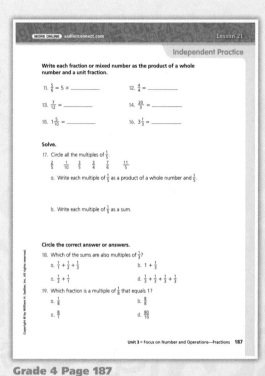

**Grade 4 Page 187**

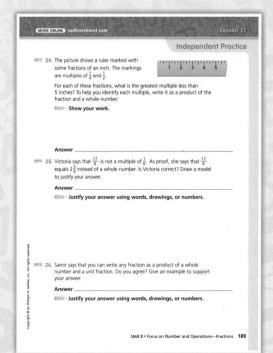

**Grade 4 Page 188**

Students have ample opportunities to model, reason, and justify their answers.

**Grade 4 Page 189**

# Built-In Assessment Practice

Every unit concludes with a **Unit Review** that provides practice with items similar to those students will encounter on state standardized assessments. Covering all of the skills and concepts taught in the unit, the reviews allow teachers to monitor student progress and understanding of each skill/concept.

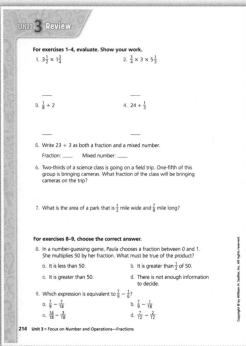

**Grade 5 Page 214**

**Grade 5 Page 215**

**Grade 5 Page 216**

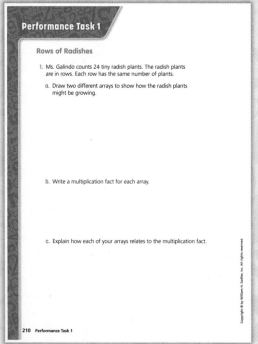

**Grade 3 Page 210**

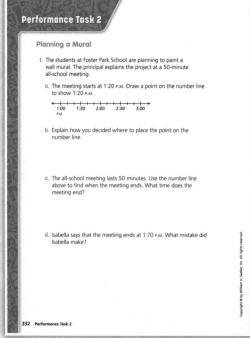

**Grade 3 Page 332**

**Performance Tasks** in a real-world setting provide opportunities for students to demonstrate their mathematical understanding through application, modeling, and written arguments.

## Teacher's Edition

Teacher-friendly, easy-to-use lesson plans support teachers in providing systematic instruction, practice, and application of mathematical skills and concepts. *Progress Mathematics* Teacher's Edition is also available in an eBook format.

## At-a-Glance Unit Introduction Pages

Unit introduction pages, featuring a student self-assessment, a home connection, a planner for understanding key concepts, and learning progressions provide an at-a-glance reference for busy educators!

Each unit begins with support for student self-assessment and connecting to home. The **Progress Check** provides students with a visual roadmap identifying how the skills and concepts are developed and linked across grade levels, emphasizing coherence.

**Home Connect** activities for each unit encourage families to take an active role in their child's learning and connect math to real-world situations.

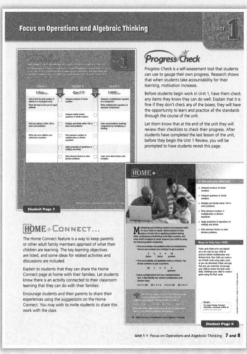

**Grade 3 Teacher's Edition Pages 7 and 8**

## Unit Planner

The **Unit Planner** outlines everything a teacher needs to know to gather unit resources, and identify all lesson objectives, essential questions, and vocabulary.

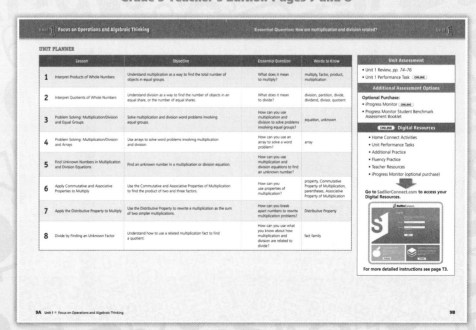

**Grade 3 Teacher's Edition Pages 9A and 9B**

## Learning Progressions

Learning Progressions provide context and background knowledge of the critical skills and skills progression across the years by showing what students learned in the previous grade and connections to what they will learn in the next grade, building coherence within and across grade levels.

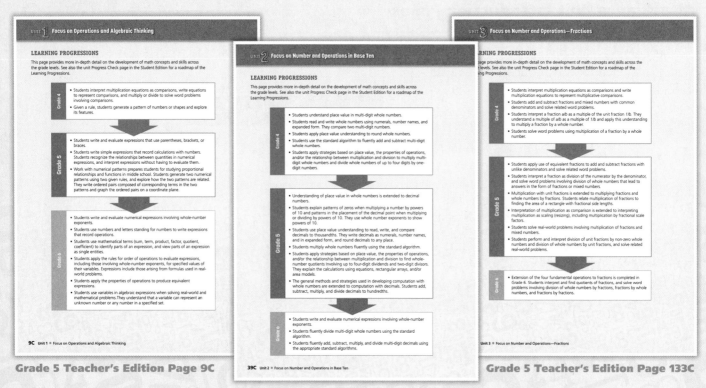

**Grade 5 Teacher's Edition Page 9C**

**Grade 5 Teacher's Edition Page 39C**

**Grade 5 Teacher's Edition Page 133C**

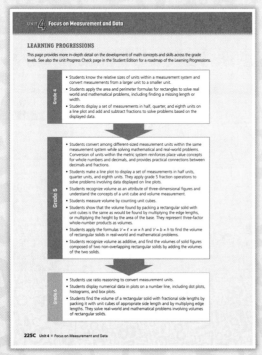

**Grade 5 Teacher's Edition Page 225C**

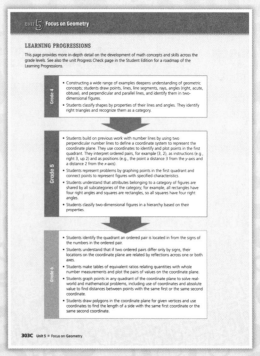

**Grade 5 Teacher's Edition Page 303C**

## On-the-Spot Lesson Support Makes Teachers Mathematical Experts!

Teacher-friendly Lesson Plans provide targeted standards-based instruction and supportive features suitable for both novice and experienced teachers.

### Guided Instruction

Clearly stated objectives provide the focus for each lesson.

**Fluence Practice**, a daily ongoing review, is listed at point-of-use.

Support/Strategies for effectively teaching the lesson's skills/concepts and engaging students in productive learning are provided in the **Concept Development**. Skills and concepts are broken down to help students build knowledge and gain full understanding.

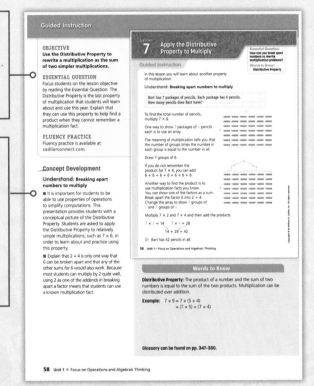

Grade 3 Teacher's Edition Page 58

The Guided Instruction culminates with the **Connect** feature building the students' understanding of the mathematical concept being taught.

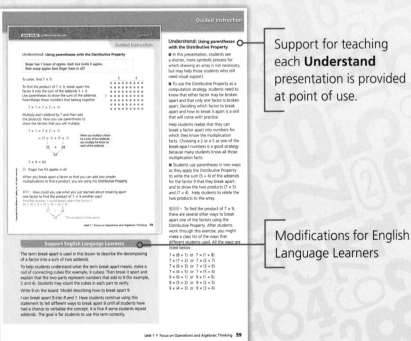

Support for teaching each **Understand** presentation is provided at point of use.

Modifications for English Language Learners

Grade 3 Teacher's Edition Page 59

Grade 3 Teacher's Edition Page 60

## Successive Increase of Student Responsibility Leads to Success

### Guided Practice

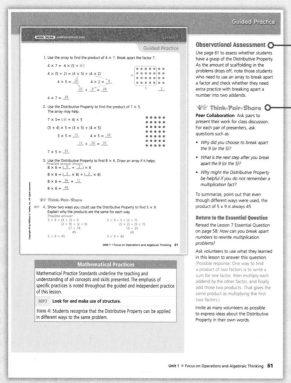

**Grade 3 Teacher's Edition Page 61**

**Observational Assessment** The Guided Practice pages offer teachers an opportunity for formative assessment to gauge student progress.

**Think-Pair-Share** Support for this peer collaboration activity helps teachers to encourage students to work together.

**Return to the Essential Question** In order to help solidify understanding before students begin to work independently, teachers encourage them to return to the Essential Question of the lesson, allowing the students to explain what they have learned in their own words.

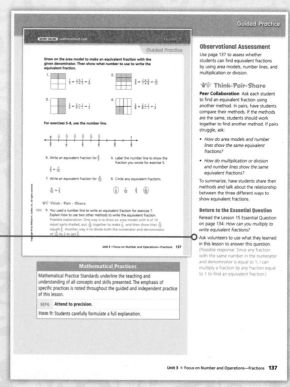

**Grade 4 Teacher's Edition Page 137**

## Scaffolded Practice Makes Independent Application of Skills Accessible

*Progress Mathematics* provides ample opportunity for rigorous independent practice, allowing students to develop procedural fluency together with conceptual understanding.

**Teaching Tip** Point-of-use teaching strategies and Common Error analyses provide help to identify potential areas of confusion or misconceptions.

### Independent Practice

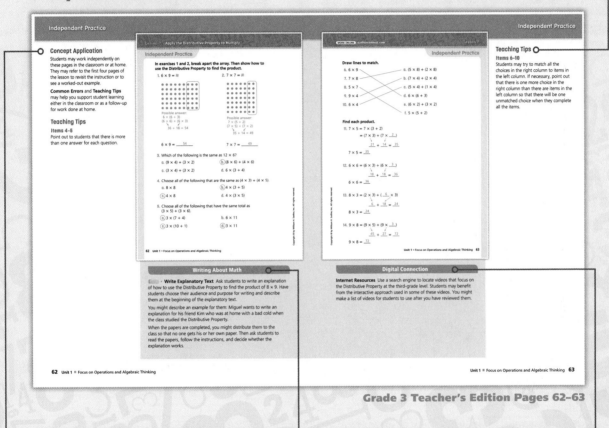

Grade 3 Teacher's Edition Pages 62–63

**Concept Application** Teachers direct students to work independently on increasingly cognitive demanding exercises and tasks.

**Writing About Math** Teacher-directed suggestions for helping students to make connections between concepts and to integrate ELA skills in their math lessons.

Writing activities include:
- Write an Informative Text
- Write an Explanatory Text
- Compare and Contrast
- Write a Narrative Text
- Write an Opinion Text

**Digital Connections** give suggestions for helping students find online resources to enhance their understanding of mathematical concepts.

## Assessment Tools Make Grading Simple

*Progress Mathematics* supports busy teachers by offering easy-to-use rubrics for grading and results charts that outline next steps after grading or assessing.

**Grade 5 Teacher's Edition Pages 214–215**

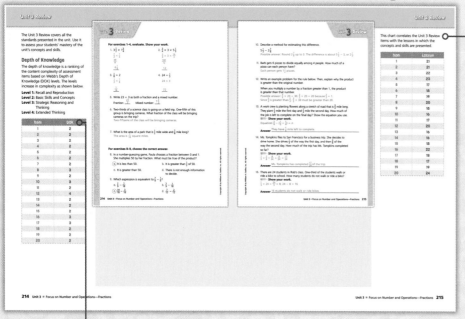

A correlation is provided for each item in the Unit Review, identifying the lesson in which the concepts or skills are presented providing teachers with a quick reference should students require a review of the concepts/skills.

Each item is identified by the DOK level, allowing teachers to quickly identify the level of understanding of each student.

**Grade 3 Teacher's Edition Page 336**

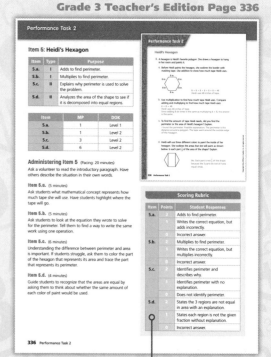

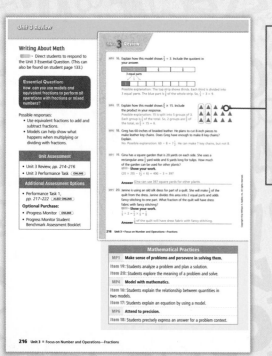

The reviews culminate with higher-order thinking problems and require students to justify their answers in writing.

Additional Assessment options are referenced at point-of-use.

**Performance Task Rubrics** provide clear and thorough guidance on how to evaluate the assessment.

**Grade 5 Teacher's Edition Page 216**

**T28**

# Suggested Planning and Pacing Guide

| Weeks | Student Worktext | Online Resources to Enrich, Support, and Assess |
|---|---|---|
| 1–2 | Unit 1: Focus on Operations and Algebraic Thinking<br>Lessons 1–3; pp. 7–36 | Unit 1 Performance Task; Additional Practice; Fluency Practice; Teacher Resources<br>Optional purchase: iProgress Monitor |
| 3–10 | Unit 2: Focus on Number and Operations in Base Ten<br>Lessons 4–14; pp. 37–130 | Unit 2 Performance Task; Additional Practice; Fluency Practice; Teacher Resources<br>Optional purchase: iProgress Monitor |
| 11–18 | Unit 3: Focus on Number and Operations—Fractions<br>Lessons 15–24; pp. 131–216 | Unit 3 Performance Task; Additional Practice; Fluency Practice; Teacher Resources<br>Optional purchase: iProgress Monitor |
| 19 | Performance Task 1<br>pp. 217–222 | Performance Task 1 |
| 20–27 | Unit 4: Focus on Measurement and Data<br>Lessons: 25–33; pp. 223–300 | Unit 4 Performance Task; Additional Practice; Fluency Practice; Teacher Resources<br>Optional purchase: iProgress Monitor |
| 28–29 | Unit 5: Focus on Geometry<br>Lessons: 34–36; pp. 301–330 | Unit 5 Performance Task; Additional Practice; Fluency Practice; Teacher Resources<br>Optional purchase: iProgress Monitor |
| 30 | Performance Task 2<br>pp. 331–336 | Performance Task 2 |

## Suggested Pacing

To achieve optimum student results, it is suggested that *Progress Mathematics* become an integral part of your math instruction. The multi-part lesson structure provides you with the flexibility you need in order to focus on a particular math skill/concept each day.

| Suggested Timeline | Day 1 | Day 2 | Day 3 | Day 4 | Day 5 |
|---|---|---|---|---|---|
| **Lesson Structure** | Guided Instruction | Guided Practice | Independent Practice | Independent Practice | • Additional Practice Online<br>• iProgress Monitor (optional purchase) Customized Assignments |

*Progress Monitor Student Benchmark Assessments,* an optional purchase, contains four comprehensive Benchmark Assessments that you may administer throughout the school year to track and assess students' mastery of grade-level skills/concepts.

Successful students use the following mathematical practices as they approach their study of mathematics. Using these mathematical practices instills in students the reasoning and problem-solving skills they need to be confident in their ability to learn and use mathematics both in school and in their everyday lives. These Mathematical Practices are fully embedded within the instruction and practice, labeled as MP, and encourage students to develop the habit of reliance on the practices when approaching problems.

## Mathematical Practices in *Progress Mathematics*

The National Council of Teachers of Mathematics (NCTM) Process Standards—communication, reasoning, representation, connections, and problem solving—are integrated in these mathematical practices.

1. **Make sense of problems and persevere in solving them.**
   The Guided Instruction provided in the program offers stepped out approaches to solving problems, helping students develop strategies to use when approaching new problems.

2. **Reason abstractly and quantitatively.**
   Concepts are introduced using the Understand and Connect structure to help students break down the components of the standard and develop the reasoning skills necessary for deep conceptual understanding.

3. **Construct viable arguments and critique the reasoning of others.**
   Whether justifying their reasoning in writing or participating in group discussions about a Think-Pair-Share exercise, there are opportunities in every lesson for students to practice the skills of developing and defending mathematical arguments and communicating their ideas clearly.

4. **Model with mathematics.**
   In addition to the models of real-world situations presented to the students throughout the program to introduce new concepts, students are encouraged to develop their own models when working through the exercises.

5. **Use appropriate tools strategically.**
   Having a solid understanding of the tools available and practicing with those tools during Guided Instruction and Guided Practice, fosters familiarity and fluency using the tools when working independently.

6. **Attend to precision.**
   Students are encouraged to be precise and accurate during each stage of the problem solving process, from using the correct vocabulary to communicate ideas to attending to the units used to express their answers.

7. **Look for and make use of structure.**
   Presenting concepts and skills in a way that reveals mathematical structures, allows students to seek out these patterns on their own.

8. **Look for and express regularity in repeated reasoning.**
   As students work through cognitively-demanding exercises they develop an awareness of repeated reasoning which promotes their ability to apply similar reasoning in real-world situations.

## Progress Check

**Progress Check**

Look at how the math concepts and skills you have learned and will learn connect.

It is very important for you to understand the math concepts and skills from the prior grade level so that you will be able to develop an understanding of operations and algebraic thinking in this unit and be prepared for next year. To practice your skills, go to sadlierconnect.com.

UNIT 1

| GRADE 4 | | Before Unit 1 | GRADE 5 | After Unit 1 | GRADE 6 |
|---|---|---|---|---|---|
| **I Can...** | | | **Can I ?** | | **I Will...** |
| Interpret a multiplication equation as a comparison | | ☐ | Write and evaluate expressions that use parentheses, brackets, or braces | ☐ | Write repeated multiplication expressions as exponential expressions |
| Write multiplication equations to represent multiplicative comparisons | | | | | Evaluate numerical expressions involving exponents |
| Solve word problems involving multiplicative comparisons by multiplying or dividing | | ☐ | Write simple expressions that record calculations with numbers | ☐ | Write expressions that use numbers and letters standing for numbers |
| | | | Interpret numerical expressions without evaluating them | ☐ | Evaluate expressions for given values of their variables |
| Generate a pattern of numbers or shapes that follows a given rule | | ☐ | Generate two numerical patterns using two given rules, and explore how the two patterns are related | ☐ | Generate equivalent expressions |
| Explore and explain features of patterns generated from given rules | | | | | Use variables and expressions when solving a real-world or mathematical problem |

Unit 1 ■ Focus on Operations and Algebraic Thinking

**Student Page 7**

Progress Check is a self-assessment tool that students can use to gauge their own progress. Research shows that when students take accountability for their learning, motivation increases.

Before students begin work in Unit 1, have them check any items they know they can do well. Explain that it is fine if they don't check any of the boxes; they will have the opportunity to learn and practice all the standards through the course of the unit.

Let them know that at the end of the unit they will review their checklists to check their progress. After students have completed the last lesson of the unit, before they begin the Unit 1 Review, you will be prompted to have students revisit this page.

## HOME ◆ CONNECT...

The Home Connect feature is a way to keep parents or other adult family members apprised of what their children are learning. The key learning objectives are listed, and some ideas for related activities and discussions are included.

Explain to students that they can share the Home Connect page at home with their families. Let students know there is an activity connected to their classroom learning that they can do with their families.

Encourage students and their parents to share their experiences using the suggestions on the Home Connect. You may wish to invite students to share this work with the class.

### HOME ◆ CONNECT...

**In this unit your child will:**

- Use grouping symbols and evaluate numerical expressions.
- Write and interpret numerical expressions.
- Analyze numerical patterns.

**Ways to Help Your Child**

As your child's math lessons become more challenging, be sure to avoid making negative comments such as "I was never good at math," or "I don't like math." A positive attitude is important to your child's academic success. And if your child is learning math in ways that are new to you, learn together.

**Y**our child has used the Order of Operations to evaluate numerical expressions. This year they will be asked to interpret a real-world problem and find its solution by writing a numerical expression or equation. These problems will involve more than one operation, which often requires your child to use more than one grouping symbol.

You can help your child by recalling the purpose of the Order of Operations and its definition: a set of a rules that is used to evaluate mathematical expressions given more than one operation.

**The Order of Operations:**

- Evaluate inside grouping symbols.
  parentheses ( )
  brackets [ ]
  braces { }
- Multiply or divide from left to right.
- Add or subtract from left to right.

**On the Go:** The next time you and your child have extra time, challenge him or her to write numerical expressions for ones you say aloud. For example, you could say "add six and nine, and then double the sum" or ask "What is two less than the quotient of fifteen and three?"

**ONLINE**
For more Home Connect activities, continue online at sadlierconnect.com

8 Unit 1 ■ Focus on Operations and Algebraic Thinking

**Student Page 8**

# UNIT 1 Focus on Operations and Algebraic Thinking

## UNIT PLANNER

| Lesson | Objective |
|---|---|
| **1** Use Grouping Symbols and Evaluate Numerical Expressions | Use grouping symbols to write and to evaluate numerical expressions. |
| **2** Write and Interpret Numerical Expressions | Write and interpret numerical expressions that represent calculations with numbers. |
| **3** Analyze Numerical Patterns | Generate two numerical patterns and identify relationships between their corresponding terms. |

**Essential Question:** How can you apply the properties of operations to represent, interpret, and evaluate numerical expressions?

UNIT 1

| Essential Question | Words to Know |
|---|---|
| How do grouping symbols affect the values of numerical expressions? | numerical expression<br>parentheses<br>grouping symbols<br>evaluate<br>brackets<br>braces |
| How do you write and interpret numerical expressions? | |
| How can you identify relationships between corresponding terms of two numerical patterns? | numerical pattern<br>corresponding terms<br>coordinate plane<br>*x*-axis<br>*y*-axis<br>origin<br>ordered pair<br>coordinates |

## Unit Assessment

- Unit 1 Review, *pp. 34–36*
- Unit 1 Performance Task  ONLINE

## Additional Assessment Options

**Optional Purchase:**
- iProgress Monitor  ONLINE
- Progress Monitor Student Benchmark Assessment Booklet

## ONLINE  Digital Resources

- Home Connect Activities
- Unit Performance Tasks
- Additional Practice
- Fluency Practice
- Teacher Resources
- iProgress Monitor (optional purchase)

**Go to SadlierConnect.com to access your Digital Resources.**

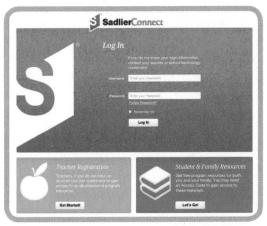

**For more detailed instructions see page T3.**

## LEARNING PROGRESSIONS

This page provides more in-depth detail on the development of math concepts and skills across the grade levels. See also the unit Progress Check page in the Student Edition for a roadmap of the Learning Progressions.

**Grade 4**

- Students interpret multiplication equations as comparisons, write equations to represent comparisons, and multiply or divide to solve word problems involving comparisons.
- Given a rule, students generate a pattern of numbers or shapes and explore its features.

**Grade 5**

- Students write and evaluate expressions that use parentheses, brackets, or braces.
- Students write simple expressions that record calculations with numbers. Students recognize the relationships between quantities in numerical expressions, and interpret expressions without having to evaluate them.
- Work with numerical patterns prepares students for studying proportional relationships and functions in middle school. Students generate two numerical patterns using two given rules, and explore how the two patterns are related. They write ordered pairs composed of corresponding terms in the two patterns and graph the ordered pairs on a coordinate plane.

**Grade 6**

- Students write and evaluate numerical expressions involving whole-number exponents.
- Students use numbers and letters standing for numbers to write expressions that record operations.
- Students use mathematical terms (sum, term, product, factor, quotient, coefficient) to identify parts of an expression, and view parts of an expression as single entities.
- Students apply the rules for order of operations to evaluate expressions, including those involving whole-number exponents, for specified values of their variables. Expressions include those arising from formulas used in real-world problems.
- Students apply the properties of operations to produce equivalent expressions.
- Students use variables in algebraic expressions when solving real-world and mathematical problems. They understand that a variable can represent an unknown number or any number in a specified set.

# Focus on Operations and Algebraic Thinking

UNIT 1

**Essential Question:**
How can you apply the properties of operations to represent, interpret, and evaluate numerical expressions?

**Essential Question:**
How can you apply the properties of operations to represent, interpret, and evaluate numerical expressions?

As students become involved with the Essential Question they will use order of operations to evaluate expressions and use number sense to answer questions about expressions and equations.

## Conversation Starters

Have students discuss the photograph.

Ask questions such as: *What different types of fish do you see in the tank? How would you describe these fish? Which type of fish is most numerous? What methods could you use to determine how many of each type of fish there are?*

Look at all the fish in the tank. *How would you write an expression that represents all the fish in the tank?* (List the numbers for each type of fish and add them.)

Suppose three of the ray type of fish were taken out of the tank. *How would that change your expression?* (There would be three fewer total fish. I could subtract 3 from the number of rays.)

Look at the smaller fish at the bottom of the aquarium. The aquarium has decided to double the number of this fish. *How would you determine how many of these fish there would be now? What would you need to do to find the total number of fish in the aquarium?* (I would multiply the current number of the fish by two. I would replace the old number with this new number in the expression.)

Let students work in pairs to discuss how to find the total number of fish in the aquarium. Lead them to see that using numeric expressions is a good strategy to find the total number.

## Activity

Have students imagine they are stocking different aquariums of fish. Small fish are in groups of 4. Medium fish are in groups of 2. Large fish are single. All of the aquariums contain each type of fish and there may be more than one correct answer.

Aquarium A has 20 fish with more medium fish than small fish and more small fish than large fish. Aquarium B has 15 fish with more small fish than medium fish and more medium fish than large fish.

Let volunteers explain their work. Students may have in Aquarium A—5 groups of medium fish (10 fish), 2 groups of small fish (8 fish), and 2 large fish (2 fish); Aquarium B—2 groups of small fish (8 fish), 3 groups of medium fish (6 fish), and 1 large fish (1 fish).

## OBJECTIVE
Use grouping symbols to write and to evaluate numerical expressions.

## ESSENTIAL QUESTION
Students begin working with expressions in a more formal manner at the start of Grade 5. It is important for students to understand that grouping symbols affect the value of an expression by changing the order in which the operations are performed.

## FLUENCY PRACTICE
Fluency practice is available at **sadlierconnect.com**.

## Concept Development

## Understand: Order of Operations and parentheses

■ Expect that students will be able to evaluate numerical expressions that have grouping symbols and write simple numerical expressions that record calculations with numbers.

■ A numerical expression does not include variables and has just one possible value.

▪ Have students interpret this expression within the context of the problem.

---

**Lesson 1**

# Use Grouping Symbols and Evaluate Numerical Expressions

**Essential Question:** How do grouping symbols affect the values of numerical expressions?

**Words to Know:**
numerical expression
parentheses
grouping symbols
evaluate
brackets
braces

## Guided Instruction

In this lesson you will write and evaluate expressions that have parentheses and other grouping symbols.

**Understand:** Order of Operations and parentheses

> Mr. Jay's class wins 10 books for its library. 3 books are nonfiction, 5 books are fiction, and the remaining books are reference books. Write and evaluate an expression to find the number of reference books.

To find the number of reference books, you add to find the total number of nonfiction and fiction books, and then subtract the sum from the total number of books. Write a numerical expression to model this.

*A numerical expression is a mathematical phrase containing only numbers and one or more operation symbols.*

Use parentheses, ( ), to show that the addition is done before the subtraction. Parentheses are grouping symbols. They group part of an expression together to show that it should be evaluated first.

| total number of books the class wins | | number of nonfiction books | | number of fiction books |
|---|---|---|---|---|
| 10 | − | (3 | + | 5) |

Now, evaluate, or find the value of, the expression to find the number of reference books. Do the calculations inside parentheses first.

10 − (3 + 5) ← Numerical expression.
10 − 8 ← Add inside parentheses.
2 ← Subtract.

➡ Two of the books the class wins are reference books.

**Remember!**
Order of Operations:
• Evaluate inside grouping symbols.
• Multiply or divide from left to right.
• Add or subtract from left to right.

▪ Zak wrote the expression 10 − 3 + 5 to represent the problem. Explain why the expression Zak wrote is not correct.
Possible answer: In Zak's expression, the number of nonfiction books is subtracted from the total and then the number of fiction books is added. This gives the incorrect answer 12. The correct expression, 10 − (3 + 5), uses parentheses to show that the numbers of nonfiction books and fiction books are added first, and then the sum is subtracted from the total.

---

## Words to Know

**numerical expression:** a mathematical phrase containing only numbers and one or more operation symbols

**parentheses:** ( ) symbols used to group terms within expressions and equations

**grouping symbols:** Parentheses, brackets, and braces are examples. These symbols group parts of a mathematical expression together to show which part to evaluate first.

**Glossary can be found on pp. 347–350.**

**MORE ONLINE** sadlierconnect.com

Lesson 1

Guided Instruction

### Understand: Using more than one set of grouping symbols

A baking company makes 634 loaves of bread each day. They sell 350 loaves to supermarkets and 275 loaves to restaurants. They donate the rest to a local shelter. Write and evaluate an expression to find the number of loaves the company donates over a 5-day workweek.

**Step 1**

Write an expression for the number of loaves the company sells each day.

$$\underset{\text{loaves sold to supermarkets}}{350} \quad + \quad \underset{\text{loaves sold to restaurants}}{275}$$

**Step 2**

Subtract that sum from 634 to represent the number of loaves the company donates each day.

> Use parentheses to show that the addition is done first.

$$\underset{\text{loaves made each day}}{634} \quad - \quad \underset{\text{loaves sold each day}}{(350 + 275)}$$

**Step 3**

Multiply the expression from Step 2 by 5 to represent the number of loaves the company donates in 5 days. You need to use another set of grouping symbols to show that the expression in Step 2 is evaluated *before* the multiplication. When you need to put one set of grouping symbols inside another, use brackets, [ ], for the outside set.

$$\underset{\text{loaves donated each day}}{[634 - (350 + 275)]} \quad \times \quad \underset{\text{Number of days}}{5}$$

**Step 4**

Evaluate the expression. When there is more than one set of grouping symbols in an expression, work from the inside out.

$[634 - (350 + 275)] \times 5$ ← Numerical expression.
$[634 - 625] \times 5$ ← Add inside the parentheses.
$9 \times 5$ ← Subtract inside the brackets.
$45$ ← Multiply.

➡ The baking company donates 45 loaves of bread during a 5-day workweek.

Unit 1 ■ Focus on Operations and Algebraic Thinking **11**

---

### Understand: Using more than one set of grouping symbols

■ If students have difficulty understanding the meaning of the problem, suggest that they work in small groups to act out or model the problem.

■ Explain to students that the expression within the innermost set of grouping symbols (the parentheses) is evaluated first. Then, the resulting expression in the outermost set of grouping symbols (the brackets) is evaluated.

■ Encourage students to discuss other ways to write the expression without changing its value, such as changing the order of the addends or placing the factor, 5, in front of the expression. Encourage students to recall that addition and multiplication are commutative; therefore, the order of the factors or addends does not change the solution.

---

## Words to Know

**evaluate:** to find the value of an expression

**Example:** Evaluate $4 \times (9 - 3)$. $4 \times (9 - 3) = 4 \times 6 = 24$.

**brackets:** [ ] symbols used to group terms within expressions and equations

**braces:** { } symbols used to group terms within expressions and equations

**Glossary can be found on pp. 347-350.**

**Connect: What you know about grouping symbols and evaluating expressions** Use this page to help students understand how to evaluate numerical expressions with grouping symbols.

■ Remind students that if an expression contains more than one set of grouping symbols, the expression in the innermost set is evaluated first.

■ To assist visual learners, use various colors or highlighting to show the transition from one step to the next. For example, in the first step, write the expression within the parentheses including the parentheses, $(\frac{5}{6} + \frac{2}{6})$, in red. Then in the next step, write its value, $\frac{7}{6}$, in red to show that it has replaced the expression in the parentheses.

■ Ask students why the fractions $\frac{7}{6}$, $\frac{28}{6}$, and $\frac{30}{6}$ were not simplified in Steps 2, 3, and 4. Explain that it would not be wrong to do this; however, waiting until the final answer to simplify makes the computations easier.

✏ Ask students if there is another expression that can be written for the problem and if so, to explain why it is correct. One expression is 32 + (10 − 6). Compare this expression to (10 − 6) + 32. Have students identify that the Commutative Property of Addition can be used to show that these are equivalent expressions.

---

## Guided Instruction

**Connect: What you know about grouping symbols and evaluating expressions**

Evaluate: $\{\frac{2}{6} + [4 \times (\frac{5}{6} + \frac{2}{6})]\} \div 5$

The expression $\{\frac{2}{6} + [4 \times (\frac{5}{6} + \frac{2}{6})]\} \div 5$ contains three sets of grouping symbols: parentheses, brackets, and braces { }.

To evaluate an expression with more than one set of grouping symbols, work from the inside set of grouping symbols (the parentheses) out.

$\{\frac{2}{6} + [4 \times (\frac{5}{6} + \frac{2}{6})]\} \div 5$ ← Numerical expression.

$\{\frac{2}{6} + [4 \times \frac{7}{6}]\} \div 5$ ← Add inside the parentheses.

$\{\frac{2}{6} + \frac{28}{6}\} \div 5$ ← Multiply inside the brackets.

$\frac{30}{6} \div 5$ ← Add inside the braces.

$5 \div 5 = 1$ ← Divide.

➡ The value of $\{\frac{2}{6} + [4 \times (\frac{5}{6} + \frac{2}{6})]\} \div 5$ is 1.

✏ Sam and Raj wrote expressions for the following problem:

Olivia's grandfather gave her $10 for mowing his lawn. She spent $6 of her earnings on a movie and added the rest to $32 she already had saved. How much in total has she saved?

Sam wrote (10 − 6) + 32, and Raj wrote 10 − 6 + 32. Explain why both expressions are correct.
Possible answer: To solve this problem, you subtract 6 from 10 and then add the result to 32. Both expressions show this. In Sam's expression, we know to subtract first because the subtraction is in parentheses. Raj's expression has no parentheses, so we do the addition and subtraction from left to right. This means we subtract 6 from 10 first and then add 32, just as we did in Sam's expression. The parentheses are not needed.

---

## Support English Language Learners

The term *evaluate* may be confusing to some students. To help students gain a greater understanding of this term, write the words *evaluate* and *value* next to each on the board, and read both words aloud. Explain that evaluating an expression means finding its value. To evaluate an expression, follow the Order of Operations to perform all the operations until you get a single value.

Lesson 1

Guided Practice

**Complete the operations within the grouping symbols first to evaluate each expression.**

1. $[1,225 - (568 - 203)] \times 10$

$[1,225 - \underline{365}] \times 10$

$\underline{860} \times 10$

$\underline{8,600}$

2. $\frac{2}{5} + (4\frac{4}{5} - 3)$

$\frac{2}{5} + 1\frac{4}{5}$

$1\frac{6}{5}$ or $2\frac{1}{5}$

**Solve the problem.**

3. Amy has twenty \$1 bills and twelve \$10 bills. Kevin has forty-two \$1 bills and eighteen \$5 bills. How much more money than Kevin does Amy have?

a. Insert grouping symbols to write a numerical expression that models this problem.

Amy:      Kevin:

$[(20 \times 1) + (12 \times 10)] - [(42 \times 1) + (18 \times 5)]$

b. Evaluate the expression and answer the question.

$[(20) + (120)] - [(42) + (90)] = 140 - 132 = 8$

Amy has \$8 more than Kevin.

### Think • Pair • Share

MP7  4. Compare expressions a–d. Then evaluate each and tell which two expressions are equivalent. Explain your reasoning.

a. $36 - \{[15 + (3 \times 10)] \div 5\}$

b. $36 - [15 + (3 \times 10 \div 5)]$

c. $36 - [(15 + 3) \times (10 \div 5)]$

d. $36 - 15 + 3 \times 10 \div 5$

Students should note that placement (or absence) of the grouping symbols ultimately determines the value of the expression. Although each expression has the same numbers and the same operations, the order of performing operations will change for each. Expressions a and d have a value of 27. They are equivalent. Expression b has a value of 15. Expression c has a value of 0.

Unit 1 ■ Focus on Operations and Algebraic Thinking  **13**

## Mathematical Practices

Mathematical Practice Standards underline the teaching and understanding of all concepts and skills presented. The emphasis of specific practices is noted throughout the guided and independent practice of this lesson.

**MP7  Look for and make use of structure.**

**Item 4:** Students evaluate the structures of similar expressions and use this information to determine equivalent expressions.

## Observational Assessment

Use page 13 to assess whether students are able to evaluate numerical expressions that include grouping symbols. Make sure students understand and apply the Order of Operations when evaluating the expressions. Encourage struggling students to first explain the situations for each person in problem 3, and then use the grouping symbols to give the proper meaning to the numerical expression.

### Think•Pair•Share

**Peer Collaboration** Place students into groups of four. Ask groups to discuss how the expressions are alike and different. Have each student evaluate a different expression in parts **a–d**. Then have students take turns explaining to the group how they evaluated each expression. After all groups have finished sharing, ask:

• How are these numerical expressions alike? How are they different?

• How did the grouping symbols affect the values of the numerical expressions?

### Return to the Essential Question

Reread the Lesson 1 Essential Question on page 10: How do grouping symbols affect the values of numerical expressions?

Ask volunteers to use what they learned in this lesson to answer this question. (Possible responses: They determine which operation to do first.)

Ask for volunteers to give an example of two numerical expressions that have the same numbers and operation(s) in the same order. One should have grouping symbols and the other should not. Have them explain how the grouping symbols change the value of the expression.

## Concept Application

Students may work independently on these pages in the classroom or at home. They may refer to the first four pages of the lesson to revisit the instruction or to see a worked-out example.

**Common Errors** and **Teaching Tips** may help you support student learning either in the classroom or as a follow-up for work done at home.

## Common Errors

### Item 8

Some students may immediately begin evaluating the two expressions without reading the directions. Encourage students to read the directions first. Ask students to describe how the grouping symbols change the value of each expression.

## Teaching Tips

### Items 1–4

Remind students that the blanks in each exercise represent the value of the part of the expression within the grouping symbols in the previous step.

### Items 5–6

Have students refer to the Remember box on page 10 if they need assistance with the Order of Operations.

---

### Independent Practice

**Evaluate each expression.**

1. $15 - (7 + 6)$

   $15 - \underline{13}$

   $\underline{2}$

2. $(24 - 10) \div (2 + 5)$

   $\underline{14} \div \underline{7}$

   $\underline{2}$

3. $[100 - (58 + 16)] \times 91$

   $[100 - \underline{74}] \times 91$

   $\underline{26} \times 91$

   $\underline{2{,}366}$

4. $\frac{3}{8} - [(1 + 1\frac{1}{8}) - \frac{7}{8} \times 2]$

   $\frac{3}{8} - [\underline{2\frac{1}{8}} - \frac{7}{8} \times 2]$

   $\frac{3}{8} - [\underline{2\frac{1}{8}} - \underline{\frac{14}{8}}]$

   $\frac{3}{8} - \underline{\frac{3}{8}}$

   $0$

**List the operations in the order they should be performed.**

5. $160 - [9 \div (12 \times 4) + 6]$

   multiplication

   division

   addition

   subtraction

6. $\{[(18 - 3) \div 3] + 2\} \times 7$

   subtraction

   division

   addition

   multiplication

7. Which expression is equivalent to $[8 + (2 \times 7) + 12] \div 2$?

   a. $8 + 2 \times 7 + 12 \div 2$

   b. $[8 + (2 \times 7 + 12) \div 2]$

   (c.) $(8 + 2 \times 7 + 12) \div 2$

   d. $(8 + 2) \times 7 + 12 \div 2$

**MP2** 8. Interpret the two expressions below without evaluating them.

$19 - (6 + 6)$ and $19 - 6 + 6$

Possible answer: The first expression has grouping symbols, and the second expression does not. In the first expression, add inside the parentheses and then subtract, because evaluating inside parentheses is first in the order of operations. In the second expression, subtract first and then add, because without grouping symbols, addition and subtraction are done from left to right. Students may recognize with mental math that the first expression will have a lesser value than the second expression.

| Mathematical Practices | |
|---|---|
| MP2 | **Reason abstractly and quantitatively.** |
| **Item 8:** Students use properties of operations to interpret expressions. | |

MORE ONLINE sadlierconnect.com

Lesson 1

## Independent Practice

**Evaluate each expression. Show your work.**

9. $(4 + 11) \times 9$
   $15 \times 9$
   $135$

10. $52 \div (\frac{1}{2} + 3\frac{1}{2})$
    $52 \div 4$
    $13$

11. $(9 + 7) \times 10 + 145$
    $16 \times 10 + 145$
    $160 + 145$
    $305$

12. $[(5\frac{4}{8} - 5\frac{3}{8}) \times (19 - 11)] \times 16$
    $[\frac{1}{8} \times 8] \times 16$
    $1 \times 16$
    $16$

13. $205 \div [14 \times (2 + 1) - 37]$
    $205 \div [14 \times 3 - 37]$
    $205 \div [42 - 37]$
    $205 \div 5$
    $41$

14. $2 \times [5\frac{1}{6} - (3\frac{1}{6} + 1\frac{5}{6})]$
    $2 \times [5\frac{1}{6} - 5]$
    $2 \times \frac{1}{6}$
    $\frac{2}{6} = \frac{1}{3}$

**For exercises 15–17, circle the correct answer.**

15. A bouquet of flowers contains 4 carnations, 3 roses, and 5 tulips. Which expression represents how many flowers are in 10 bouquets?

    **a.** $10 \times (4 + 3 + 5)$ *(circled)*
    **b.** $10 \times 4 + 3 + 5$
    **c.** $(10 \times 4) + 3 + 5$
    **d.** $4 + 3 + 5 \times 10$

16. Don has 45 yards of fabric. He uses $5\frac{3}{4}$ yards to make a blanket and $1\frac{1}{4}$ yards to make a pillow. If Don makes 4 blankets and 4 pillows, which expression represents how many yards of fabric will he have left?

    **a.** $45 - 5\frac{3}{4} + 1\frac{1}{4} \times 4$
    **b.** $4 \times (5\frac{3}{4} + 1\frac{1}{4}) - 45$
    **c.** $45 - [(5\frac{3}{4} + 1\frac{1}{4}) \times 4]$ *(circled)*
    **d.** $(45 - 4) \times (5\frac{3}{4} + 1\frac{1}{4})$

17. Lucia and Matteo want to buy a basketball that costs $17 and a backboard that costs $85. Lucia babysat for 5 hours last week and earned $6 per hour. Matteo babysat for 7 hours and earned $5 per hour. If they combine their babysitting money, which expression represents how much more money they will need to buy the basketball and backboard?

    **a.** $(5 \times 6 + 7 \times 5) - (17 + 85)$
    **b.** $[(17 + 85) - 5 \times 6 + 7]$
    **c.** $5 \times [6 + (7 \times 5)] - (17 + 85)$
    **d.** $(17 + 85) - (5 \times 6 + 7 \times 5)$ *(circled)*

Unit 1 ▪ Focus on Operations and Algebraic Thinking  **15**

## Common Errors

### Items 15–17
Remind students that they are not being asked to evaluate the expressions. Students should read each problem carefully before determining which expression represents the situation.

## Teaching Tips

### Items 9–14
Remind students to write each step as they evaluate the numerical expressions.

## Math-to-Language Arts Connection

**Summarize a Text** Ask students to prepare a summary of what they learned in this lesson. Give them the options of presenting their summary by reading it aloud to the class, presenting it through media, or a combination of these options. Students should include the following in their summary:

- a description of what was learned

- new terms used in the lesson and their meaning

- examples of the new terms

- reasoning as to why this lesson is important

Students should sequence their presentations logically and use appropriate facts and relevant examples to support their presentations.

# Independent Practice

## Common Errors

### Item 21

Note that some students may write the expression [(12 − 9) + 45] × 3. This expression also results in the correct solution, but it uses two different types of grouping symbols. Remind students to use only parentheses in their expression.

## Teaching Tips

### Item 19

Students may have difficulty identifying the error in the given expression. Suggest that students make a drawing of the four boxes of pencils if they need help visualizing the problem.

---

## Independent Practice

MP2 **18.** Look at the expression below. Without evaluating, tell whether the value of the expression would be the same or different without parentheses. Explain.

$(5 \times 1) + (3 \times 5) + (2 \times 10)$

The value of the expression would be the same. Possible explanation: Multiplication is performed first in the Order of Operations. Therefore, with or without parentheses, all the multiplication in this expression would be performed before the addition.

MP3 **19.** Ari has 4 boxes of pencils. Each box has 6 red pencils and 8 blue pencils. He wants to divide all the pencils equally between his 2 sisters. Ari wrote the expression $(4 \times 6 + 8) \div 2$ and plans to give each sister 16 pencils. Is he correct? Explain.

Ari is not correct. Possible answer: He should have written $[4 \times (6 + 8)] \div 2$. Add the number of red and blue pencils in each box before multiplying by the number of boxes. He should give each sister 28 pencils.

MP1 **20.** Which expression below has the greater value?

a. $\{1,340 - [15 \times (4 + 16)]\} + 18$     b. $1,340 - \{[(15 \times 4) + 16] + 18\}$

**Show your work.**

| $\{1,340 - [15 \times (4 + 16)]\} + 18$ | $1,340 - \{[(15 \times 4) + 16] + 18\}$ |
|---|---|
| $\{1,340 - [15 \times 20]\} + 18$ | $1,340 - \{[60 + 16] + 18\}$ |
| $\{1,340 - 300\} + 18$ | $1,340 - \{76 + 18\}$ |
| $1,040 + 18$ | $1,340 - 94$ |
| $1,058$ | $1,246$ |

**Answer** Expression b has the greater value.

MP2 **21.** Rewrite the expression below inserting parentheses so that the value of the expression is 144.

$12 - 9 + 45 \times 3$

**Show your work.**
$(12 - 9 + 45) \times 3$
$(3 + 45) \times 3$
$48 \times 3$
$144$

**Answer** $(12 - 9 + 45) \times 3$

---

| Mathematical Practices | |
|---|---|
| **MP1** | **Make sense of problems and persevere in solving them.** |
| **Item 20:** Students analyze two numerical expressions and make sense of the grouping symbols and how they are nested. | |
| **MP2** | **Reason abstractly and quantitatively.** |
| **Item 18:** Students use properties of operations to interpret an expression without evaluating. | |
| **Item 21:** Students use properties of operations and grouping symbols to rewrite an expression. | |
| **MP3** | **Construct viable arguments and critique the reasoning of others.** |
| **Item 19:** Students analyze a problem situation and construct an argument. | |

MORE ONLINE sadlierconnect.com                    Lesson 1

## Independent Practice

**MP3  22.** Joseph says that [(5 + 12) × 2] − (9 + 7) is the same as
5 + 12 × 2 − 9 + 7. What is his error?

▶ **Show your work.**

[(5 + 12) × 2] − (9 + 7) = [(17) × 2] − (9 + 7) = [34] − (16) = 18
5 + 12 × 2 − 9 + 7 = 5 + 24 − 9 + 7 = 27

**Answer** Joseph does not understand how the Order of Operations is affected by grouping symbols. Without grouping symbols, you multiply first and then add and subtract from left to right. With grouping symbols, you add inside parentheses first, then multiply inside the brackets, and then subtract.

**Write and evaluate an expression to solve the problem.**

**MP2  23.** Leila uses $1\frac{1}{4}$ cups of orange juice, $2\frac{3}{4}$ cups of cranberry juice, and 3 cups of seltzer to make punch. If Leila wants to serve the punch to 7 people, how many cups of punch will each person get?

▶ **Show your work.**

$(1\frac{1}{4} + 2\frac{3}{4} + 3) ÷ 7$
7 ÷ 7 = 1

**Answer** Each person will get 1 cup of punch.

**MP2  24.** Ralf is packing 180 books. He has 3 large boxes, and each box holds 25 books. He has 2 medium boxes, and each box holds 18 books. He has 5 small boxes, and each box holds 12 books. Can Ralf pack all 180 books with the boxes he has? Explain.

▶ **Show your work.**

(3 × 25) + (2 × 18) + (5 × 12)
75 + 36 + 60
171

**Answer** Ralf cannot pack all the books. The boxes hold 171 books and he has 180 books to pack.

Unit 1 ▪ Focus on Operations and Algebraic Thinking  **17**

## Common Errors

### Item 22

Some students may attempt to evaluate the second expression by working from left to right. Remind students that in the absence of any grouping symbols, all multiplication and division are completed first, working from left to right. Then all addition and subtraction are completed, again working from left to right.

## Teaching Tips

### Item 24

Suggest to students that they write a separate expression for the number of books contained in each type of box. Then ask students to name the operation used to combine the three totals. Finally, have students combine the two steps in one expression.

## Mathematical Practices

| **MP2** | **Reason abstractly and quantitatively.** |
|---|---|

**Items 23–24:** Students use properties of operations to write and evaluate expressions.

| **MP3** | **Construct viable arguments and critique the reasoning of others.** |
|---|---|

**Item 22:** Students critique the reasoning of another student and explain why it is flawed.

## OBJECTIVE
Write and interpret numerical expressions that represent calculations with numbers.

## ESSENTIAL QUESTION
Explain to students that they use language every day that expresses calculations with numbers. For example, when students ask someone for "two more raisins," they are expressing the operation "add 2." Encourage a discussion about different ways of expressing calculations in words. Explain that, in this lesson, students will focus on writing numerical expressions to represent calculations.

## PREREQUISITE SKILLS
Use Item A on page 337 of the Foundational Skills Handbook to review comparing with an unknown factor.

## FLUENCY PRACTICE
Fluency practice is available at **sadlierconnect.com**.

## Concept Development

### Understand: How to write numerical expressions

■ This presentation focuses on the use of grouping symbols in expressions. Point out to students examples of key words and phrases that indicate that parentheses should be used, such as "the result" and "twice the sum."

■ Be sure that students master simple examples prior to tackling a more complex example.

⬛▶ Students should also understand that there is often more than one way to write a numerical expression.

---

Lesson **2**

# Write and Interpret Numerical Expressions

**Essential Question:** How do you write and interpret numerical expressions?

## Guided Instruction

In this lesson you will write expressions to represent calculations with numbers. You will also interpret numerical expressions without evaluating them.

**Understand: How to write numerical expressions**

> Write a numerical expression to represent each of the following phrases.
> "twice the sum of five and seven"
> "three times the result of subtracting four from nine"
> "two less than the result of dividing fifteen by three"
> "one more than five groups of two-fifths"

To write a numerical expression for each phrase, think about what the words mean. Identify the operations, and use numbers, symbols, and parentheses.

- "*twice* the *sum* of five and seven"
  $(5 + 7) \times 2$

- "three *times* the result of *subtracting* four from nine"
  $3 \times (9 - 4)$

- "two *less than* the result of *dividing* fifteen by three"
  $15 \div 3 - 2$

- "one *more than* five *groups of* two-fifths"
  $5 \times \frac{2}{5} + 1$

▶ The numerical expressions for the phrases:
$(5 + 7) \times 2$
$3 \times (9 - 4)$
$15 \div 3 - 2$
$5 \times \frac{2}{5} + 1$

Parentheses are not needed in the last two expressions because multiplication and division are done before addition and subtraction.

⬛▶ What is another way to write "one more than five groups of two-fifths" in words?
Possible answer: one plus the product of five and two-fifths

18  Unit 1 ■ Focus on Operations and Algebraic Thinking

**Remember!**
When necessary, use parentheses to group the operation that needs to be performed first.

---

## Support English Language Learners

Students may not know that *triple* means *three times* and that *double* means *two times*. To help students, first start by modeling these words. Give a student one counter and have the student show the class. Then take three counters and say, *I have triple the number of counters you have* showing the three counters. Then write the sentence on the board: I have _____ times as many counters. Have students read aloud the sentence and fill in the blank with *three* as you show the three counters to the class.

Repeat the same process for *double*.

---

Guided Instruction

**Understand:** How to interpret numerical expressions

> Andrea writes the expression 3 × (235 + 62) to represent the inventory in her store. Jacob writes the expression 235 + 62 to represent the inventory at his store. How does Andrea's inventory compare to Jacob's inventory?

To compare the values of Andrea's and Jacob's expressions without evaluating them, interpret the numbers, operations, and the placement of the parentheses.

Both expressions contain 235 + 62, or the *sum* of 235 and 62. Andrea's expression 3 × (235 + 62), *multiplies* 235 + 62 by 3, or *triples* that sum.

The value of Andrea's expression 3 × (235 + 62) is 3 times as much as the value of Jacob's expression 235 + 62.

➡ Andrea has 3 times as many items in inventory at her store as Jacob has at his store.

There are many ways to compare expressions using words.

| Less | Equal | More |
|---|---|---|
| less than<br>fewer than<br>smaller than | the same as<br>equal to<br>equivalent to | more than<br>greater than<br>larger than<br>times as many |

✏ Interpret the expressions below. Then compare their values without evaluating them.

> Equivalent numerical expressions are numerical expressions with the same value.

   **a.** (30 + 100) ÷ 15 and (100 + 30) ÷ 15

   **b.** $4 + (2\frac{5}{6} - 1\frac{7}{6})$ and $5 + (2\frac{5}{6} - 1\frac{7}{6})$

a.) The order of the numbers in parentheses, 100 + 30 and 30 + 100, does not matter. The sum is the same for both expressions. In both expressions, the sum is divided by 15. Therefore, the expressions are equivalent. b.) The difference of the two numbers in parentheses is the same for both expressions. In the first expression, 4 is added to the difference. In the second expression, 5 is added to the difference. The value of $4 + (2\frac{5}{6} - 1\frac{7}{6})$ is 1 less than $5 + (2\frac{5}{6} - 1\frac{7}{6})$.

Unit 1 ■ Focus on Operations and Algebraic Thinking   **19**

---

**Understand: How to interpret numerical expressions**

■ This presentation has students interpreting and comparing numerical expressions without evaluating them. Be sure students understand that the sum 235 + 62 has the same value in both expressions. It is not necessary to calculate the sum to know that 3 × (235 + 62) is 3 times as much as 235 + 62.

■ Students should understand that not all expressions can be compared without evaluating. Talk about some strategies that can help students determine whether computations are necessary. For example, students can look for parts of the expressions that are the same or equivalent.

✏ To compare the expressions without evaluating them, students should first look for parts of the expressions that are equivalent. It may be necessary to remind students of the Commutative and Associative Properties of Addition.

---

## Math-to-Language Connection

**Synonyms** Remind students that synonyms are different words that have similar meanings. Work with the class to brainstorm a list of synonyms for the four operations. Organize the words in a chart to be displayed in the classroom for future reference. Some common synonyms are listed below.

**Addition:** add, more than, the sum of, the total of, plus

**Subtraction:** subtract, less than, less, the difference of, take away, minus

**Multiplication:** multiply, multiplied by, times, times as much as, the product of

**Division:** divide, divided by, divides, the quotient of

**Connect:** **What you know about writing and interpreting numerical expressions** Use this page to help students apply what they know about writing and interpreting numerical expressions to concrete situations.

■ Prompt students to consider a case of water bottles as one group of 24. So, the number of water bottles in three cases is three groups of twenty-four, or 3 × 24.

■ Next, point out the key words *plus four extra* and *drink two,* and have students explain how to represent these words in their phrases and numerical expressions.

■ Point out that the product of 3 × 24 has the same value in both expressions. The value of Jamal's expression is 4 more than this value, and the value of Katie's expression is 2 less than this value. So, the value of Jamal's expression is greater.

**Connect:** **What you know about writing and interpreting numerical expressions**

> Jamal and Katie bring water bottles to the soccer tournament for the team. Jamal brings three cases of twenty-four bottles, plus four extra bottles. Katie brings three cases of twenty-four bottles, but she and her brother drink two of the bottles on the way to the tournament.
>
> Write numerical expressions to represent how many water bottles Jamal and Katie each bring to the soccer tournament. How does the number of water bottles that Jamal brings compare to the number that Katie brings?

**Step 1**

Write word phrases and numerical expressions to represent how many water bottles Jamal and Katie bring.

Jamal: three *groups of* twenty-four plus four *more.*
3 × 24 + 4

Katie: three *groups of* twenty-four *less* two.
3 × 24 − 2

**Step 2**

Interpret the expressions.

Both expressions contain 3 × 24, or 3 groups of 24.
Jamal's expression is 4 *more than* 3 × 24.
Katie's expression is 2 *less than* 3 × 24.

**Step 3**

Compare the values of the expressions.

The value of 3 × 24 + 4 is *greater than* the value of 3 × 24 − 2.

Both expressions contain 3 × 24, but the value of Jamal's expression is greater than the value of Katie's expression because it adds 4 to 3 × 24 instead of subtracting 2.

➧ Jamal brings 6 more water bottles to the soccer tournament.

**20**  Unit 1 ■ Focus on Operations and Algebraic Thinking

## Math-to-Math Connection

**Arithmetic and Algebra** Interpreting the expressions in this lesson prepares students to work with variables and equations in Algebra.

Choose two expressions that include equivalent parts. Replace the equivalent parts with a symbol, such as a square or rectangle. Then rewrite the expressions. Tell students that the symbol represents the same amount in each expression. By replacing the equivalent parts with a single symbol, students can more easily visualize how the expressions are different.

MORE ONLINE sadlierconnect.com

## Guided Practice

**Write a numerical expression for each phrase. The first two are started for you.**

**1.** eleven plus three and seven-eighths

$11 \underline{\;+\;} 3\frac{7}{8}$

**2.** ten less than one hundred twenty

$120 \underline{\;-\;10\;}$

**3.** five more than eight groups of seven-tenths

$8 \times \frac{7}{10} + 5 \text{ or } 5 + 8 \times \frac{7}{10}$

**4.** eight more than the result of dividing three hundred fifty by two

$8 + (350 \div 2) \text{ or } (350 \div 2) + 8$

**Interpret and explain the two expressions without evaluating them. The first one is started for you.**

**5.** $7 \times (4 + 8)$ and $4 + 8$

$7 \times (4 + 8)$ is 7 times as much as $4 + 8$ because $7 \times (4 + 8)$ means 7 groups of $(4 + 8)$.

**6.** $(19 - 2\frac{3}{4}) + 5$ and $(19 - 2\frac{3}{4}) - 5$

Both expressions contain $19 - 2\frac{3}{4}$, but the value of the first expression is greater than the second because it adds 5 to $(19 - 2\frac{3}{4})$ instead of subtracting 5.

### Think · Pair · Share

MP7 **7.** Two students compared the expressions below.

$12 + 3 - \frac{2}{3}$ and $(12 + 3 - \frac{2}{3}) \times 2$

Tricia says $(12 + 3 - \frac{2}{3})$ is half as much as $(12 + 3 - \frac{2}{3}) \times 2$.

Ava says $(12 + 3 - \frac{2}{3}) \times 2$ is twice as much as $(12 + 3 - \frac{2}{3})$.

Explain why both students are correct.
Possible answer: If one amount is half as much as a second amount, then that second amount is twice as much as the first. Tricia and Ava are both expressing the same comparison, but they are saying it in different ways.

Unit 1 ■ Focus on Operations and Algebraic Thinking **21**

## Mathematical Practices

Mathematical Practice Standards underline the teaching and understanding of all concepts and skills presented. The emphasis of specific practices is noted throughout the guided and independent practice of this lesson.

**MP7  Look for and make use of structure.**

**Item 7:** Students look at the structure of the expressions, identifying parts that are equivalent.

## Observational Assessment

Use page 21 to assess whether students have mastered writing and interpreting numerical expressions. Students are familiar with many everyday words such as *four more* and *twice as many*. To interpret expressions independently, students must also feel comfortable using mathematical language such as *groups of* and *the value of.*

### Think·Pair·Share

**Peer Collaboration** Place students into groups of two. Ask each group to discuss Tricia and Ava's statements. Have each student explain how they determined if Tricia's statement is correct. Then have each student explain how they determined if Ava's statement is correct. Encourage students to include the following:

- *What is the same about these two numerical expressions? What is different?*

- *What is the result when you multiply any number by 2?*

### Return to the Essential Question

Reread the Lesson 2 Essential Question on page 18: *How do you write and interpret numerical expressions?*

Ask volunteers to use what they learned in this lesson to answer this question. (Possible responses: Numbers and operation symbols are used to represent words. Parentheses are sometimes needed to group parts of a numerical expression. If parts of two expressions are equivalent, I can compare the value of the expressions without evaluating them.)

Invite as many volunteers as possible to express ideas about how to identify and use parts of expressions that are equivalent.

## Concept Application

Students may work independently on these pages in the classroom or at home. They may refer to the first four pages of the lesson to revisit the instruction or to see a worked-out example.

**Common Errors** and **Teaching Tips** may help you support student learning either in the classroom or as a follow-up for work done at home.

## Teaching Tips

### Items 3, 4, 7, and 8

To help students become more comfortable using mathematical terminology such as *groups of, the result of dividing, sum,* and *product,* have them read the problems aloud and identify key symbols and words. This strategy will support auditory, visual, and kinesthetic learners.

---

### Independent Practice

**Complete the numerical expression for each phrase.**

1. thirteen multiplied by eight and one half

   $13 \underline{\ \times\ } 8\frac{1}{2}$

2. twenty-one less than two hundred thirty

   $230 \underline{\ -\ } 21$

3. seventeen added to two groups of five

   $17 \underline{\ +\ } 2 \underline{\ \times\ } 5$

4. nine less than the result of dividing twelve by four

   $12 \underline{\ \div\ } 4 \underline{\ -\ } 9$

**Complete the phrase for each numerical expression.**

5. $18 \times (9 - 1)$

   eighteen __times__ the number that is one __less than__ nine

6. $7 + (10 - 4)$

   seven __more__ than ten __minus__ four

7. $(6 + 4\frac{3}{4}) \div 2$

   the __sum__ of six and four and three-fourths __divided__ by two

8. $(4 \times \frac{3}{4}) - 5$

   five __less__ than the __product__ of four and three-fourths

**Without evaluating, compare the two expressions. Tell whether the value of the first expression is *less than*, *greater than*, or *equal to* the value of the second expression.**

9. $7 + \frac{11}{13}$ and $3 \times (7 + \frac{11}{13})$

   __less than__

10. $(8 - 2) \times (5 - 1)$ and $(5 - 1) \times (8 - 2)$

    __equal to__

11. $15\frac{1}{4} \times 2$ and $(15\frac{1}{4} \times 2) \div 3$

    __greater than__

12. $(15 - 6) - 7 \times 2$ and $(15 - 6) - 4 \times 2$

    __less than__

---

## Writing About Math

**Write a Descriptive Text** Show students a photograph, a piece of artwork, or an image with multiple objects displayed within it. Ask students to write a paragraph with numerical expressions that describe the objects in the image. Ask them to make use of mathematical terms, such as *groups of* and *three times as many*.

Ask volunteers to read their paragraphs aloud. Remind students that there is often more than one way to describe and interpret relationships between objects.

Lesson 2

## Independent Practice

**Write a numerical expression for each phrase.**

**13.** twenty minus four and two-thirds plus two

$$20 - 4\frac{2}{3} + 2$$

**14.** seven less than the product of five and sixty

$$(5 \times 60) - 7$$

**15.** eighteen and five-sixths divided by three

$$18\frac{5}{6} \div 3$$

**16.** twice the sum of three and nineteen

$$2 \times (3 + 19)$$

**Write a word phrase for each numerical expression.**

**17.** $5 + 10 - 2$
Possible answer: five plus the difference of ten and two

**18.** $903 \times (1 + 7)$
Possible answer: nine hundred three times the sum of one and seven

**19.** $(13\frac{2}{3} + 3) \div 8$
Possible answer: thirteen and two-thirds added to three and then divided by eight

**20.** $17 - (12 \div 6)$
Possible answer: seventeen minus the result of dividing 12 by 6

**Interpret and explain the two expressions without evaluating them.**

**21.** $3 + (16 \div 2)$ and $16 \div 2$
Both expressions contain $16 \div 2$. The first expression is greater since 3 is added to $16 \div 2$.

**22.** $(10 - 4\frac{3}{4}) + 9$
and $9 + (10 - 4\frac{3}{4})$
The expressions have the same value. In both expressions, 9 is added to $(10 - 4\frac{3}{4})$. The order of the addends does not matter.

## Common Errors

### Item 16

Students frequently forget to use parentheses when writing numerical expressions that are grouped. Encourage them to look for key words like *the sum of, the product of, the result of,* or *groups of,* to help them remember to use parentheses.

## Digital Connection

**Internet Resources** Have students use the Internet to research unfamiliar numerical terms. Assign a term to each group of students, for example a *score* is 20, and a *gross* is 12 dozen, or 12 times 12. Encourage students to share their results with the class by reading aloud the definition and a verbal description that uses the term. Students can then write a numerical expression to represent the verbal description. For example, "four score and seven years ago" can be written as $4 \times 20 + 7$.

## Independent Practice

## Common Errors

### Item 23
Students frequently confuse the divisor and the dividend when interpreting statements involving division. Remind them that the divisor (the number we are dividing by) is stated second when saying *divided by* and first when saying *divided into*.

## Teaching Tips

### Items 23–25
Be sure that students break up these problems into three steps: (1) Write the word phrases as numerical expressions; (2) Look for equivalent expressions or equivalent parts of expressions; (3) Compare the expressions.

## Independent Practice

**Solve the problems.**

MP3   **23.** Luke said that "three divided by twenty-one" is the same as "twenty-one divided by three". Is Luke correct? Explain why or why not.
No. Possible explanation: The phrase "three divided by twenty-one" is written as $3 \div 21$. The phrase "twenty-one divided by three" is written as $21 \div 3$. Since $3 \div 21 \neq 21 \div 3$, the phrases are not the same.

MP3   **24.** Is "seven and one seventh less than the product of two times five" the same as "two multiplied by five and then decreased by seven and one seventh"? Explain why or why not.
Yes. Possible explantation: The phrase "seven and one-seventh less than the product of two times five" is written as $2 \times 5 - 7\frac{1}{7}$. The phrase "two multiplied by five and then decreased by seven and one-seventh" is written as $2 \times 5 - 7\frac{1}{7}$. Because the numerical expressions are the same, the phrases are the same.

MP2   **25.** Tyrone has $(17 + 2) \times 100$ baseball cards. Evelyn has $17 + 2$ baseball cards. Without evaluating, explain how the number of Tyrone's baseball cards compares to the number of Evelyn's baseball cards.
Tyrone has 100 times more baseball cards than Evelyn. Possible explantation: The value of the expression $(17 + 2) \times 100$ is 100 times as much as the value of the expression $17 + 2$ since $(17 + 2) \times 100$ means 100 groups of $17 + 2$.

MP7   **26.** Jaime has $14 \div 2 - 3\frac{1}{3}$ feet of string. Charlotte has $14 \div 2$ feet of string. Without evaluating, compare the expressions to tell who has more string. Explain.
Jaime has $3\frac{1}{3}$ fewer feet of string than Charlotte. Possible explanation: Both expressions include $14 \div 2$, but $(14 \div 2) - 3\frac{1}{3}$ means $3\frac{1}{3}$ less than $(14 \div 2)$.

| Mathematical Practices | |
|---|---|
| **MP2** | **Reason abstractly and quantitatively.** |
| **Item 25:** Students identify quantities and their relationships to compare numerical expressions. | |
| **MP3** | **Construct viable arguments and critique the reasoning of others.** |
| **Item 23:** Students evaluate a claim involving numerical expressions and share their reasoning with others. | |
| **Item 24:** Students explain why two verbal expressions represent the same numerical calculations. | |
| **MP7** | **Look for and make use of structure.** |
| **Item 26:** Students recognize identical patterns in order to compare the value of numerical expressions. | |

Lesson 2

## Independent Practice

**MP2 27.** Petra and Billy have stamp collections. Petra has three groups of one hundred stamps, plus nine more. Billy has three groups of one hundred stamps.

Write numerical expressions to show how many stamps Petra and Billy have. How do the expressions compare? Who has more stamps?

**Answer** Petra: $3 \times 100 + 9$; Billy: $3 \times 100$; Petra has more stamps than Billy.

▸ **Justify your answer using words, drawings, or numbers.**
Possible justification: Both expressions include $3 \times 100$, but $3 \times 100 + 9$ means 9 more than $3 \times 100$, so Petra has more stamps.

**MP2 28.** Rajit and Samantha are playing a game. Rajit scored seven hundred plus the result of subtracting eleven from two hundred nineteen points. Samantha scored the result of subtracting eleven from two hundred nineteen, increased by seven hundred points.

Write numerical expressions to represent each player's score. How do the expressions compare? Who scored more points?

**Answer** Rajit: $700 + (219 - 11)$; Samantha: $(219 - 11) + 700$; Rajit and Samantha had the same score.
▸ **Justify your answer using words, drawings, or numbers.**
Possible justification: Both expressions have 700 added to $219 - 11$. The order of the addends does not matter. The value of each expression is the same, so Rajit and Samantha have the same score.

**MP3 29.** Janelle says that "two groups of nine, plus four and two-thirds" is the same as "nine plus four and two-thirds, multiplied by two." What is her error?
Janelle did not interpret her words correctly. "Two groups of nine, plus four and two-thirds" is written as $(2 \times 9) + 4\frac{2}{3}$ and "nine plus four and two-thirds, multiplied by two" is written as $2 \times (9 + 4\frac{2}{3})$. The expressions $(2 \times 9) + 4\frac{2}{3}$ and $2 \times (9 + 4\frac{2}{3})$ are not the same.

Unit 1 ■ Focus on Operations and Algebraic Thinking **25**

### Teaching Tips
**Item 29**
Encourage students to draw a model to visualize how the expressions differ.

## Mathematical Practices

| MP2 | **Reason abstractly and quantitatively.** |
|---|---|

**Items 27–28:** Students write numerical expressions to represent two real-world quantities and use the expressions to compare the quantities.

| MP3 | **Construct viable arguments and critique the reasoning of others.** |
|---|---|

**Item 29:** Students evaluate a claim involving numerical expressions and share their reasoning with others.

## OBJECTIVE
Generate two numerical patterns and identify relationships between their corresponding terms.

## ESSENTIAL QUESTION
Explain that analyzing the corresponding terms of two patterns can help students understand important relationships. For example, this skill can help students determine how much more money they will have at the end of the summer if they save $2 a week rather than $1 a week.

## PREREQUISITE SKILLS
Use Item B on page 337 of the Foundational Skills Handbook to review number patterns and pattern rules.

## FLUENCY PRACTICE
Fluency practice is available at **sadlierconnect.com**.

## Concept Development

### Understand: How to generate and analyze two numerical patterns

■ This presentation introduces the term, *corresponding terms*. Explain to students that they will use two rules to generate two lists of terms. Then they will match the first terms, the second terms, the third terms, and so on. The two terms in each of these pairs are corresponding terms.

■ The comparison between Ana's savings and Carlos's savings after 4 weeks can be expressed in two ways: Ana has saved $8 more than Carlos, and Ana has saved 3 times as much as Carlos. Be sure to discuss both comparisons.

---

### Lesson 3 · Analyze Numerical Patterns

Essential Question:
How can you identify relationships between corresponding terms of two numerical patterns?
Words to Know:
  numerical pattern
  corresponding terms
  coordinate plane
  *x*-axis
  *y*-axis
  origin
  ordered pair
  coordinates

#### Guided Instruction

In this lesson you will generate two numerical patterns using two rules. You will identify relationships between them and graph corresponding terms of the two patterns.

**Understand:** How to generate and analyze two numerical patterns

> Carlos saves $1 each week. Ana saves $3 each week. After 4 weeks, how does the amount Ana saved compare to the amount Carlos saved?

To find how the amounts Carlos and Ana save increase each week, generate numerical patterns. A numerical pattern is a list of numbers that follows a constant rule. This rule is an expression that tells how to complete the numerical pattern.

Carlos saves $1 the first week and then adds $1 to his savings each week. So, to generate a pattern for Carlos's savings, start with 1 and use the rule: *add 1*.

Carlos: 1, 2, 3, 4, 5, ...  (+1 +1 +1 +1)

Ana saves $3 the first week and then adds $3 to her savings each week. So, to generate a pattern for Ana's savings, start with 3 and use the rule: *add 3*.

Ana: 3, 6, 9, 12, 15, ...  (+3 +3 +3 +3)

Corresponding terms are terms that are in the same position in the two patterns. Pairs of corresponding terms are circled below.

Carlos: (1, (2, (3, (4, (5
Ana: 3), 6), 9), 12), 15)

Notice that all the terms in Ana's pattern are three times the corresponding terms in Carlos's pattern.

To compare the amounts saved after four weeks, look at the fourth pair of corresponding terms. Carlos saved $4 and Ana saved $12. You can find how much more Ana saved than Carlos by subtracting: $12 − $4 = $8.

3 × $4 = $12 shows that Ana saved three times as much as Carlos.

➡ Ana saved $8 more than Carlos, or three times as much as Carlos.

---

## Words to Know

**numerical pattern:** a list of numbers that follows a constant rule

**Example:**   3, 6, 9, 12, 15, ...  (+3 +3 +3 +3)

**corresponding terms:** terms that are in the same position in two patterns

**Example:**   Pairs of corresponding terms are circled in green below.

(1, (2, (3, (4, (5
3), 6), 9), 12), 15)

**Glossary can be found on pp. 347–350.**

## Guided Instruction

**Understand:** How to graph ordered pairs of corresponding terms from two patterns

Below are Carlos and Ana's patterns with corresponding terms circled.

Carlos: ①, ②, ③, ④, ⑤
Ana: ③, ⑥, ⑨, ⑫, ⑮

Write the corresponding terms as ordered pairs and graph them on a coordinate plane. Describe the pattern of points.

Ordered pairs are pairs of numbers in the form (x, y), in which the order of the numbers is important. Below are ordered pairs for Carlos and Ana's patterns. Notice that Carlos's value comes first in each pair.

(1, 3)     (2, 6)     (3, 9)     (4, 12)     (5, 15)

The numbers in an ordered pair are called coordinates. The first number is called the *x*-coordinate, and the second is called the *y*-coordinate. Carlos's values are the *x*-coordinates, and Ana's are the *y*-coordinates.

On a coordinate plane, ordered pairs are located using a horizontal number line, called the *x*-axis, and a vertical number line, called the *y*-axis. The *x*-axis and *y*-axis intersect to form perpendicular number lines. The two number lines meet at their 0 points. This intersection point is called the origin, or (0, 0).

Here, the *x*-axis represents Carlos's savings and the *y*-axis represents Ana's savings.

To graph an ordered pair, start at the origin, or (0, 0), and move right the number of units indicated by the *x*-coordinate, and then move up the number of units indicated by the *y*-coordinate. For example, to graph (3, 9), move right 3 units and up 9 units.

➤ The ordered pairs for Carlos and Ana's patterns are shown on the coordinate plane. The points follow a straight-line pattern that moves upward from left to right.

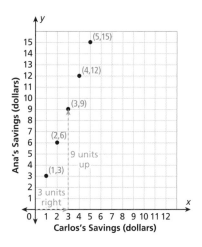

Unit 1 ■ Focus on Operations and Algebraic Thinking   **27**

**Understand: How to graph ordered pairs of corresponding terms from two patterns**

■ The basics of coordinate graphing are introduced here so that students can graph pairs of corresponding terms from two patterns.

■ Students form ordered pairs consisting of corresponding terms from the two patterns.

■ As students graph the points on the coordinate plane, make the connection between the pairs and the numerical patterns. Discuss with students that they move right on the coordinate plane for *x*-coordinates and move up for the *y*-coordinates.

■ Point out that to move from one ordered pair to the next, they move 1 unit to the right based on the rule *Add 1*, and move 3 units up based on the rule *Add 3*.

## Words to Know

**coordinate plane:** a grid formed by intersecting perpendicular number lines

**x-axis:** the horizontal number line on the coordinate plane

**y-axis:** the vertical number line on the coordinate plane

**origin:** The point at which the *x*-axis and *y*-axis of a coordinate plane intersect. The coordinates of the origin are (0, 0).

**ordered pair:** pairs of numbers in the form (x, y) used to locate a point on a coordinate plane

**coordinates:** the numbers in an ordered pair used to locate a point on a coordinate plane

**Glossary can be found on pp. 347–350.**

**Connect:** **What you know about generating and relating two numerical patterns** Use this page to help students apply what they know about generating and relating two numerical patterns to find relationships between corresponding pairs.

■ Have students look for relationship in both the table and the graph.

■ Be sure that students understand that there is more than one way to describe the relationships between the corresponding pairs.

■ Relate the relationships they observe in the table to the relationships they observe in the graph. This will help students develop their ability to find relationships on a coordinate plane.

## Guided Instruction

**Connect:** **What you know about generating and relating two numerical patterns**

> A baker uses 3 cups of flour and 2 cups of berries in each loaf of blueberry bread. Generate numerical patterns to show how the number of cups of flour and berries used changes as the number of loaves increases.
>
> Describe how the corresponding terms of the two patterns are related, and graph the pairs on a coordinate plane.

You can show the patterns in a table, where corresponding pairs are in the same column. There are 3 cups of flour in the first loaf, and 3 more cups for each additional loaf. The rule is *add 3*. There are 2 cups of berries in the first loaf, and 2 more cups for each additional loaf. The rule is *add 2*.

| Cups of Flour: *add 3* | 3 | 6 | 9 | 12 | 15 |
| Cups of Berries: *add 2* | 2 | 4 | 6 | 8 | 10 |

Look for relationships in the corresponding terms. Here are some relationships:

The difference in the first pair of terms, 3 and 2, is 1. The differences of the next four pairs are 2, 3, 4, 5. The difference increases by 1 each time.

The sums of the pairs are 5, 10, 15, 20, and 25. The sum increases by 5 each time.

➡ Graph the ordered pairs (3, 2), (6, 4), (9, 6), (12, 8), and (15, 10). Notice that the points form a straight-line pattern that moves upward from left to right.

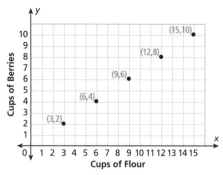

## Support English Language Learners

Some students may understand the meaning of *pattern* when it is used to describe shape, color, and other visual attributes. However, they may be less certain about the meaning of *numerical pattern.* Start by modeling non-numerical patterns by drawing a sequence of dots on the board. Start with a column of two dots, and then draw two columns of two dots, and then three columns of two dots. Ask a volunteer to draw the next arrangement of dots in the pattern. The student should draw four columns of two dots.

Write the numbers 2, 4, and 6 under the first three dot drawings to represent the number of dots in each. Then ask, *which number comes next.* Have the whole class say *eight.* Ask students to describe the similarities between the two patterns. Finally, have students repeat with you that the pattern involving numbers is called a *numerical pattern.*

Lesson 3

## Guided Practice

1. Each fruit basket contains 3 apples and 1 orange. Use the rules to complete numerical patterns that show how the total number of apples and oranges increases with each basket.

| Apples: add 3 | Oranges: add 1 |
|---|---|
| 3 | 1 |
| 6 | 2 |
| 9 | 3 |
| 12 | 4 |

2. Describe two ways the corresponding terms in the patterns in exercise 1 are related:

Each number of apples is __3__ times the corresponding number of oranges.

Each number of oranges is the corresponding number of apples divided by __3__.

3. Write the corresponding terms in the pattern from exercise 1 as ordered pairs.

(3, 1)    (6, 2)

(__9__, 3)    (12, __4__)

4. Graph the ordered pairs from exercise 3 on the coordinate plane.

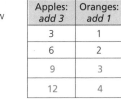

### ☝♔ Think · Pair · Share

MP7  5. Two numerical patterns are shown below.

0, 8, 16, 24, 32, . . .
0, 4, 8, 12, 16, . . .

Analyze the patterns. Tell how they are the same and how they are different. Explain the relationship between the corresponding terms. Possible answer: Each pattern starts with 0. The first pattern uses the rule "Add 8" to complete the pattern. The second pattern uses the rule "Add 4." Each number in the first pattern is twice the number in the second pattern. Each number in the second pattern is half the number (the number divided by 2) in the first pattern.

Unit 1 ■ Focus on Operations and Algebraic Thinking  **29**

## Mathematical Practices

Mathematical Practice Standards underline the teaching and understanding of all concepts and skills presented. The emphasis of specific practices is noted throughout the guided and independent practice of this lesson.

**MP7  Look for and make use of structure.**

**Item 5:** Students recognize relationships in numerical patterns and relationships between the corresponding terms of two numerical patterns.

## Observational Assessment

Use page 29 to assess whether students understand how to recognize corresponding terms, write them as ordered pairs, and identify relationships between them. Remind students of the position of *x*- and *y*-coordinates in the tables, within the parentheses, and on the graph.

### ☝♔ Think·Pair·Share

**Peer Collaboration** Have pairs of students use tables, ordered pairs, and graphs to represent the numerical patterns. For each visual representation, ask:

- *What relationship do you observe within each numerical pattern?*

- *What relationships do you observe between corresponding terms?*

- *What visual representation do you find most helpful in analyzing the relationship?*

To summarize, explain that different tools can help us identify and analyze patterns within numerical patterns and between corresponding terms.

### Return to the Essential Question

Reread the Lesson 3 Essential Question on page 26: *How can you identify relationships between corresponding terms of two numerical patterns?*

Ask volunteers to use what they learned in this lesson to answer this question. (Possible responses: Record corresponding terms in a table and look for a relationship across rows (or down columns). Write corresponding terms as ordered pairs and graph them.)

Invite as many volunteers as possible to express ideas about identifying relationships between corresponding terms in their own words.

## Independent Practice

## Concept Application

Students may work independently on these pages in the classroom or at home. They may refer to the first four pages of the lesson to revisit the instruction or to see a worked-out example.

**Common Errors** and **Teaching Tips** may help you support student learning either in the classroom or as a follow-up for work done at home.

## Common Errors

### Items 5–6

Students often reverse the position of *x*-coordinates and *y*-coordinates when writing ordered pairs. Writing ordered pairs is particularly challenging for children with dyslexia, and other disabilities that involve difficulty with visual processing. Encourage students to use two different colored highlighters to identify *x*-coordinates and *y*-coordinates as they write out the ordered pairs.

## Independent Practice

**Generate patterns using the two rules. Then, complete the statement about how the corresponding terms in each pair are related.**

1. Rule 1: *add 4.*     0, 4, _8_, _12_, _16_

   Rule 2: *add 12.*     0, 12, _24_, _36_, _48_

   **Relationship:** Each term in the Rule 2 pattern is _3_ times the corresponding term in the Rule 1 pattern.

2. Rule 1: *subtract 1.*     10, 9, _8_, _7_, _6_

   Rule 2: *subtract 2.*     10, 8, _6_, _4_, _2_

   **Relationship:** The difference between the Rule 1 term and the corresponding Rule 2 term increases by _1_ with each term.

3. Rule 1: *add 10.*     0, 10, _20_, _30_, _40_

   Rule 2: *add 100.*     0, 100, _200_, _300_, _400_

   **Relationship:** Possible answer: Each term in the Rule 2 pattern is 10 times the corresponding term in the Rule 1 pattern.

4. Rule 1: *add 5.*     20, 25, _30_, _35_, _40_

   Rule 2: *add 10.*     20, 30, _40_, _50_, _60_

   **Relationship:** Possible answer: The difference between the Rule 2 term and the corresponding Rule 1 term increases by 5 with each term.

**The numbers in the first two columns in each table are generated using a different rule. Identify the rule for the pattern in each column, and then complete the table. Form ordered pairs for the corresponding terms.**

5. Pens: *add 10.* Pencils: _add 8_.

| Pens | Pencils | (Pens, Pencils) |
|---|---|---|
| 10 | 8 | (10, 8) |
| 20 | 16 | (20, 16) |
| 30 | 24 | (30, 24) |
| 40 | 32 | (40, 32) |
| 50 | 40 | (50, 40) |

6. Points: _add 6_. Penalties: _subtract 2_.

| Points | Penalties | (Points, Penalties) |
|---|---|---|
| 12 | 10 | (12, 10) |
| 18 | 8 | (18, 8) |
| 24 | 6 | (24, 6) |
| 30 | 4 | (30, 4) |
| 36 | 2 | (36, 2) |

## Writing About Math

> **Write an Informative Text** Ask students about patterns in the real world. Do these patterns follow strict rules, such as *Add 3?* Have students research and write about a pattern in the real world. Some examples are tides, sunrise/sunset times, moon phases, art design patterns, money growth in savings accounts, and musical patterns. Students should explain whether their pattern follows a strict rule.

Ask volunteers to read their paragraphs aloud. Explain to students that even when a real-life event does not follow a strict rule, it is helpful to find an approximate rule. We can use these approximations to make predictions and prepare for the future.

The first two columns of each table show two patterns and their rules. In the third column, write the corresponding terms of the patterns as ordered pairs. Then graph the ordered pairs on the coordinate plane.

7.

| Rule 1: add 1 | Rule 2: add 2 | Ordered Pairs (Rule 1, Rule 2) |
|---|---|---|
| 1 | 2 | (1, 2) |
| 2 | 4 | (2, 4) |
| 3 | 6 | (3, 6) |
| 4 | 8 | (4, 8) |
| 5 | 10 | (5, 10) |

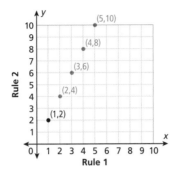

8.

| Rule 1: add 1 | Rule 2: subtract 2 | (Rule 1, Rule 2) |
|---|---|---|
| 1 | 10 | (1, 10) |
| 2 | 8 | (2, 8 ) |
| 3 | 6 | (3, 6) |
| 4 | 4 | (4, 4) |
| 5 | 2 | (5, 2) |

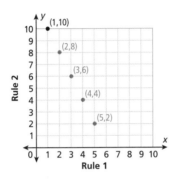

MP2 **9.** How are the patterns of points in exercises 7 and 8 the same? And, how are they different?
Possible answer: In both exercises, the points form a straight-line pattern. In exercise 7 the pattern slants upward. In exercise 8, it slants downward.

Unit 1 ■ Focus on Operations and Algebraic Thinking  **31**

**Teaching Tips**

**Items 7-8**
Students often confuse *x*- and *y*-coordinates when they graph ordered pairs. Show students how to highlight the *x*-axis and *x*-coordinates with a yellow highlighter and the *y*-axis and *y*-coordinates with a blue highlighter to help them graph ordered pairs.

## Mathematical Practices

| MP2 | **Reason abstractly and quantitatively.** |
|---|---|

**Item 9:** Students compare and contrast the linear pattern formed by ordered pairs in two different graphs.

## Teaching Tips

### Item 11

Some students may have difficulty completing problems that involve multiple steps. Have these students list each step separately and check it off as it is completed.

---

### Independent Practice

MP8 **10.** Chandra and Joey are mountain biking. Chandra bikes 8 miles every hour. Joey bikes 9 miles every hour. After biking for 4 hours, how many miles have Chandra and Joey each traveled? Complete the table and find the answer.

| Number of Hours | 1 | 2 | 3 | 4 | 5 |
|---|---|---|---|---|---|
| Chandra (Miles Biked) | 8 | 16 | 24 | 32 | 40 |
| Joey (Miles Biked) | 9 | 18 | 27 | 36 | 45 |

**Answer** Chandra: 32 miles; Joey: 36 miles

▪️ **Justify your answer using words, drawings, or numbers.**
I used the rule *add 8* to complete the pattern for Chandra. I used the rule *add 9* to complete the pattern for Joey. The corresponding terms for 4 hours are 32 and 36, so Chandra has biked 32 miles and Joey has biked 36 miles.

MP8 **11.** Complete the order pairs for the points on the graph, and then complete the columns for Rule 1 and Rule 2. Give the rules for the patterns. Explain how you found the rules.

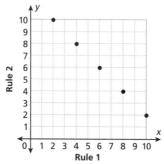

| Ordered Pairs | Rule 1:<br>*add 2* | Rule 2:<br>*subtract 2* |
|---|---|---|
| (2, 10) | 2 | 10 |
| (4, 8 ) | 4 | 8 |
| (6 , 6) | 6 | 6 |
| (8, 4 ) | 8 | 4 |
| (10, 2) | 10 | 2 |

Possible answer: After I filled in the columns for Rule 1 (*x*) and Rule 2 (*y*), I could see that the *x* values increased by 2 with each row, and the *y* values decreased by 2.

---

### Mathematical Practices

**MP8**  **Look for and express regularity in repeated reasoning.**

**Item 10:** Students generate two numerical patterns by applying the same rules repeatedly and then compare corresponding terms to find the solution.

**Item 11:** Students record ordered pairs for the points in a graph in a table, and then write rules for the patterns in the columns of *x*- and *y*-coordinates.

MORE ONLINE sadlierconnect.com                    Lesson 3

**Independent Practice**

MP4 **12.** Rita starts with $10 and saves $5 each month. Tara starts with $50 and spends $5 each month. Complete the tables. The ordered pairs for Rita's table are shown on the coordinate plane. Use a different color to add the points for Tara's table.

Are there any months when Rita and Tara have the same amount of money? Explain.

| Month | Rita |
|-------|------|
| 0 | 10 |
| 1 | 15 |
| 2 | 20 |
| 3 | 25 |
| 4 | 30 |
| 5 | 35 |

| Month | Tara |
|-------|------|
| 0 | 50 |
| 1 | 45 |
| 2 | 40 |
| 3 | 35 |
| 4 | 30 |
| 5 | 25 |

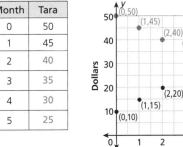

Yes. The graphs for Rita and Tara both contain the point (4, 30), which means that both Rita and Tara have $30 after 4 months.

**Solve the problem.**

MP8 **13.** Kerry is making shapes out of toothpicks. She uses 3 toothpicks to make one shape, 6 toothpicks to make two shapes, 9 toothpicks to make three shapes, and so on. How many toothpicks does Kerry need to make five shapes?

**Answer** Kerry needs 15 toothpicks to make five shapes.

**Justify your answer using words, drawings, or numbers.**
Each number of toothpicks used to form the shapes is 3 more than the previous number. To complete the pattern, Kerry will need 12 toothpicks to make four shapes, and 15 toothpicks to make five shapes.

Unit 1 ■ Focus on Operations and Algebraic Thinking   **33**

---

**Item 13**

Some students may have trouble applying mathematical concepts that they have mastered to new situations. Help students create a table to organize the data. Some students may need assistance determining that the number of shapes created is one coordinate and that the number of toothpicks is the other coordinate.

**Return to the**

Remind students to return to the Progress Check self-assessment, page 7, to check off additional items they have mastered during the unit.

---

| **Mathematical Practices** |
|---|
| **MP4**   **Model with mathematics.** |
| **Item 12:** Students use tables and a graph to analyze and compare the spending and saving habits of two individuals. |
| **MP8**   **Look for and express regularity in repeated reasoning.** |
| **Item 13:** Students generate two numerical patterns and compare corresponding terms to find the solution. |

The Unit 1 Review covers all the standards presented in the unit. Use it to assess your students' mastery of the unit's concepts and skills.

## Depth of Knowledge

The depth of knowledge is a ranking of the content complexity of assessment items based on Webb's Depth of Knowledge (DOK) levels. The levels increase in complexity as shown below.

**Level 1:** Recall and Reproduction
**Level 2:** Basic Skills and Concepts
**Level 3:** Strategic Reasoning and Thinking
**Level 4:** Extended Thinking

| Item | DOK |
|------|-----|
| 1 | 2 |
| 2 | 2 |
| 3 | 1 |
| 4 | 1 |
| 5 | 1 |
| 6 | 2 |
| 7 | 2 |
| 8 | 2 |
| 9 | 2 |
| 10 | 2 |
| 11 | 3 |
| 12 | 2 |
| 13 | 2 |
| 14 | 3 |
| 15 | 4 |
| 16 | 2 |

UNIT **1** Review

**For exercises 1–2, evaluate the expression. Show your work.**

1. $27 \div 3 + [38 - (6 \times 4)]$
   $27 \div 3 + [38 - 24]$
   $27 \div 3 + 14$
   $9 + 14$

   Answer _____23_____

2. $125 - (12 \times 5) + 75$
   $125 - 60 + 75$
   $[65 + 75]$

   Answer _____140_____

**For exercises 3–4, list the operations in the order they should be performed. Do not evaluate.**

3. $\{[(50 - 44) \div 2] + 10\} \times 5$

   _____subtraction_____
   _____division_____
   _____addition_____
   _____multiplication_____

4. $75 - [60 \div (5 \times 2) + 32]$

   _____multiplication_____
   _____division_____
   _____addition_____
   _____subtraction_____

5. Which numerical expression represents the phrase fourteen less than the product of five and thirty?

   a. $5 + 30 - 14$   b.) $5 \times 30 - 14$

   c. $14 - 5 \times 30$   d. $14 - 5 \times 30$

6. Write a numerical expression for the phrase. twelve times the result of dividing 20 by 2
   $12 \times (20 \div 2)$

7. Generate the two patterns using the given rules. Then compare corresponding terms and complete the sentence.

| add 4 | 2 | 6 | 10 | 14 | 18 |
|-------|---|---|----|----|----|
| add 8 | 2 | 10 | 18 | 26 | 34 |

   The difference between corresponding terms increases by __4__ with each term.

This chart correlates the Unit 1 Review items with the lessons in which the concepts and skills are presented.

8. Pam had $20 to spend at the museum. She bought an admission ticket for $8, a tote bag for $6, and spent the rest for lunch. Which expression shows how much she spent for lunch?

  a. $(8 + 6) - 20$          b. $20 - 8 + 6$

  c. $(20 - 8) + 6$          (d.) $20 - (8 + 6)$

MP2 9. Write and evaluate an expression to solve the problem.
A large packing box holds 20 toy cars. A small box holds 8 toy cars. How many toy cars can be shipped in 15 large boxes and 30 small boxes?

**Expression:** $15 \times 20 + 30 \times 8$

**Evaluate:** $15 \times 20 + 30 \times 8 = 300 + 240 = 540$

**Answer** 540 toy cars can be shipped in the boxes.

10. Which expression has the least value?

  a. one more than five groups of two          b. two more than the result of dividing 15 by 3

  (c.) two less than the result of dividing 15 by 3          d. three times the result of subtracting four from nine

11. Do these expressions have the same value? Explain your answer and show the expressions in numerical form.

"twenty less than the product of fifteen and six"

"six multiplied by fifteen and then decreased by twenty"
Yes. The first is $(15 \times 6) - 20$. The second is $(6 \times 15) - 20$. Since $15 \times 6$ equals $6 \times 15$, the two expressions have the same value.

12. Generate the two patterns using the given rules. Then write the corresponding terms of the two patterns as ordered pairs.

| multiply by 2 | 16 | 32 | 64 | 128 | 256 |
| divide by 2 | 16 | 8 | 4 | 2 | 1 |

**Ordered pairs:** (16, 16), (32, 8), (64, 4), (128, 2), (256, 1)

| Item | Lesson |
|---|---|
| 1 | 1 |
| 2 | 1 |
| 3 | 1 |
| 4 | 1 |
| 5 | 2 |
| 6 | 2 |
| 7 | 3 |
| 8 | 1 |
| 9 | 1 |
| 10 | 2 |
| 11 | 2 |
| 12 | 3 |
| 13 | 1 |
| 14 | 2 |
| 15 | 1 |
| 16 | 3 |

## Writing About Math

✏️ Direct students to respond to the Unit 1 Essential Question. (This can also be found on student page 9.)

**Essential Question:**
How can you apply the properties of operations to represent, interpret, and evaluate numerical expressions?

Possible responses:
- Use the properties of operations to write equivalent expressions.
- Apply the Order of Operations to expressions to find and compare solutions.

### Unit Assessment

- Unit 1 Review, *pp. 34–36*
- Unit 1 Performance Task ( ONLINE )

### Additional Assessment Options

**Optional Purchase:**
- iProgress Monitor ( ONLINE )
- Progress Monitor Student Benchmark Assessment Booklet

---

**MP2 13.** A gift basket of fruit contains 3 oranges, 2 peaches, and 3 bananas. How many pieces of fruit are there in 5 gift baskets? Write and evaluate an expression to solve.

**Expression:** $5 \times (3 + 2 + 3) = 5 \times 8 = 40$

**Answer** There are 40 pieces of fruit in 5 gift baskets.

**MP2 14.** There are 16 boys and 18 girls in Ms. Watkins' fifth grade class. Ms. Watkins gave each person 3 pencils and 6 stickers. Write expressions for the number of pencils and stickers. Compare the expressions without evaluating them.

**Pencils:** $3 \times (16 + 18)$     **Stickers:** $6 \times (16 + 18)$
Possible answer: 6 is twice as large as 3. So, there are twice as many stickers as pencils.

**MP3 15.** Explain how you can evaluate the expression mentally.
$(61 - 19) \times [16 \times (8 - 8)] \div (54 + 72)$
8 − 8 is 0, so the product in brackets is 0. This means the entire expression on the left side of the division symbol equals 0. Dividing 0 by anything gives 0. So, the value of the entire expression is 0.

**Complete the table. Then graph the ordered pairs on the coordinate plane.**

**MP4 16.** Drama club starts with 2 members and adds 2 members each week. Debate club starts with 12 members and loses 3 members each week.

| Drama Club | Debate Club | Ordered Pairs |
|---|---|---|
| 2 | 12 | (2, 12) |
| 4 | 9 | (4, 9) |
| 6 | 6 | (6, 6) |
| 8 | 3 | (8, 3) |
| 10 | 0 | (10, 0) |

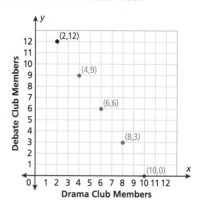

---

## Mathematical Practices

| MP2 | **Reason abstractly and quantitatively.** |
|---|---|
| **Item 9:** Use more than one way to represent problems using symbols. | |
| **Item 13:** Students use properties of operations to find a solution. | |
| **Item 14:** Students represent problems using symbols. | |
| MP3 | **Construct viable arguments and critique the reasoning of others.** |
| **Item 15:** Students explain an approach to a given problem. | |
| MP4 | **Model with mathematics.** |
| **Item 16:** Students interpret the solution in the context of a situation. | |

## Progress Check

Look at how the math concepts and skills you have learned and will learn connect.

It is very important for you to understand the math concepts and skills from the prior grade level so that you will be able to develop an understanding of number and operations in base ten in this unit and be prepared for next year. To practice your skills, go to sadlierconnect.com.

| GRADE 4 | Before Unit 2 | GRADE 5 | After Unit 2 | GRADE 6 |
|---|---|---|---|---|
| **I Can...** | | **Can I ?** | | **I Will...** |
| Understand place value in whole numbers | ☐ | Understand place value in whole numbers and decimal numbers | ☐ | |
| Understand place value in whole numbers | ☐ | Explain patterns when multiplying or dividing whole numbers and decimals by powers of 10 | ☐ | Write repeated multiplication expressions as exponential expressions |
| | | Use whole number exponents to show powers of 10 | ☐ | Evaluate numerical expressions involving exponents |
| Read, write, and compare whole numbers | ☐ | Read, write, and compare decimals to thousandths | ☐ | |
| Round whole numbers to any place | ☐ | Round decimals to any place | ☐ | |
| Multiply whole numbers | ☐ | Fluently multiply whole numbers | ☐ | |
| Divide whole numbers by one-digit divisors | ☐ | Divide whole numbers by two digit divisors | ☐ | Fluently divide multi-digit whole numbers |
| Add two fractions with denominators of 10 and 100 | ☐ | Add, subtract, multiply, and divide decimals to hundredths | ☐ | Fluently add, subtract, multiply, and divide multi-digit decimals |
| Add, subtract, multiply, and divide whole numbers | ☐ | | | |

Unit 2 ■ Focus on Number and Operations in Base Ten

**Student Page 37**

## Progress Check

Progress Check is a self-assessment tool that students can use to gauge their own progress. Research shows that when students take accountability for their learning, motivation increases.

Before students begin work in Unit 2, have them check any items they know they can do well. Explain that it is fine if they don't check any of the boxes; they will have the opportunity to learn and practice all the standards through the course of the unit.

Let them know that at the end of the unit they will review their checklists to check their progress. After students have completed the last lesson of the unit, before they begin the Unit 2 Review, you will be prompted to have students revisit this page.

# HOME ◆ CONNECT...

The Home Connect feature is a way to keep parents or other adult family members apprised of what their children are learning. The key learning objectives are listed, and some ideas for related activities and discussions are included.

Explain to students that they can share the Home Connect page at home with their families. Let students know there is an activity connected to their classroom learning that they can do with their families.

Encourage students and their parents to share their experiences using the suggestions on the Home Connect. You may wish to invite students to share this work with the class.

# HOME ◆ CONNECT...

### In this unit your child will:

- Understand place value.
- Use patterns and whole-number exponents.
- Read, write, and compare decimals to thousandths.
- Round decimals using place value.
- Multiply fluently with multi-digit numbers.
- Divide whole numbers using place value and properties of operations.
- Add, subtract, multiply, and divide decimals to hundredths.

Place value and number sense have been a big part of your child's mathematics instruction. This understanding will now serve as the foundation for working with decimal numbers.

In our base-ten system, the value of a digit depends on its place in the number. Look at the place-value chart below. The number one hundred eleven and twenty-three thousandths is shown.

| hundreds | tens | ones | . | tenths | hundredths | thousandths |
|---|---|---|---|---|---|---|
| 1 | 1 | 1 | . | 0 | 2 | 3 |

The value of each place is *ten times* the value of the place to its right. The value of each place is also *one tenth* the value of the place to its left. Therefore, one hundred is *ten times* the value of ten, and ten is *one tenth* the value of one hundred.

**Activity:** You can think of hundredths as cents when you are talking about a sum of money. There are 100 cents in a dollar, so if you have $10.53, the 3 in the hundredths place represents 3 cents. Play a game with your child in which you round the prices of items from a circular to the nearest hundredth, tenth, or whole number.

### Ways to Help Your Child

Remember not to give your child the answer to a problem. It is very important that your child learn to persevere in solving problems and think independently. Mistakes are an important part of the learning process. They can help your child and their teacher to determine where misunderstandings have occurred.

**ONLINE**
For more Home Connect activities, continue online at sadlierconnect.com

38    Unit 2 ■ Focus on Number and Operations in Base Ten

**Student Page 38**

## UNIT PLANNER

| Lesson | Objective |
|---|---|
| **4** Understanding Place Value | Recognize the relationship between adjacent places in the base-ten system. |
| **5** Powers of 10: Use Patterns and Whole-Number Exponents | Use an understanding of place value to multiply and divide by powers of ten. |
| **6** Read and Write Decimals to Thousandths | Read and write decimals to thousandths. |
| **7** Compare Decimals to Thousandths | Use place value to compare decimals to thousandths. |
| **8** Round Decimals: Use Place Value | Round decimal numbers to the nearest whole, tenth, or hundredth, using place-value charts and number lines. |
| **9** Multiply Fluently with Multi-Digit Numbers | Use the standard algorithm to multiply multi-digit numbers. |
| **10** Divide Whole Numbers: Use Place Value Strategies | Use different methods for dividing a multi-digit number by a two-digit number. |
| **11** Divide Whole Numbers: Use Properties of Operations | Use properties of operations and the relationship between multiplication and division to divide whole numbers. |
| **12** Add and Subtract Decimals to Hundredths | Add and subtract decimal numbers. |
| **13** Multiply Decimals to Hundredths | Learn how to multiply decimal numbers. |
| **14** Divide Decimals to Hundredths | Learn methods to divide decimal numbers. |

**Essential Question:** How can you use place value understanding to perform all operations fluently using whole numbers and decimals?

UNIT 2

| Essential Question | Words to Know |
|---|---|
| What is the relationship between adjacent places in the base-ten system? | |
| How can place value patterns help you multiply and divide by powers of 10? | power of 10<br>base<br>exponent |
| How can you express a decimal to thousandths in different forms? | |
| How can you compare decimal numbers? | |
| How do you use place value to round decimal numbers? | |
| How can you multiply multi-digit numbers by using the standard algorithm? | partial product |
| How can you use place value strategies to divide whole numbers? | partial quotient |
| How can you use properties of operations to divide whole numbers? | |
| How do you add and subtract decimal numbers? | |
| How do you multiply decimal numbers? | |
| How do you divide decimal numbers? | |

## Unit Assessment

- Unit 2 Review, *pp. 128–130*
- Unit 2 Performance Task  ONLINE

## Additional Assessment Options

**Optional Purchase:**
- iProgress Monitor  ONLINE
- Progress Monitor Student Benchmark Assessment Booklet

## ONLINE Digital Resources

- Home Connect Activities
- Unit Performance Tasks
- Additional Practice
- Fluency Practice
- Teacher Resources
- iProgress Monitor (optional purchase)

**Go to SadlierConnect.com to access your Digital Resources.**

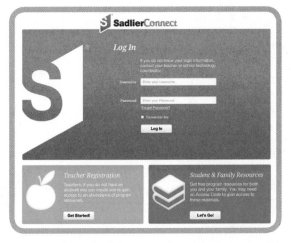

**For more detailed instructions see page T3.**

# LEARNING PROGRESSIONS

This page provides more in-depth detail on the development of math concepts and skills across the grade levels. See also the unit Progress Check page in the Student Edition for a roadmap of the Learning Progressions.

**Grade 4**

- Students understand place value in multi-digit whole numbers.

- Students read and write whole numbers using numerals, number names, and expanded form. They compare two multi-digit numbers.

- Students apply place value understanding to round whole numbers.

- Students use the standard algorithm to fluently add and subtract multi-digit whole numbers.

- Students apply strategies based on place value, the properties of operations, and/or the relationship between multiplication and division to multiply multi-digit whole numbers and divide whole numbers of up to four digits by one-digit numbers.

**Grade 5**

- Understanding of place value in whole numbers is extended to decimal numbers.

- Students explain patterns of zeros when multiplying a number by powers of 10 and patterns in the placement of the decimal point when multiplying or dividing by powers of 10. They use whole number exponents to show powers of 10.

- Students use place value understanding to read, write, and compare decimals to thousandths. They write decimals as numerals, number names, and in expanded form, and round decimals to any place.

- Students multiply whole numbers fluently using the standard algorithm.

- Students apply strategies based on place value, the properties of operations, and/or the relationship between multiplication and division to find whole-number quotients Involving up to four-digit dividends and two-digit divisors. They explain the calculations using equations, rectangular arrays, and/or area models.

- The general methods and strategies used in developing computation with whole numbers are extended to computation with decimals. Students add, subtract, multiply, and divide decimals to hundredths.

**Grade 6**

- Students write and evaluate numerical expressions involving whole-number exponents.

- Students fluently divide multi-digit whole numbers using the standard algorithm.

- Students fluently add, subtract, multiply, and divide multi-digit decimals using the appropriate standard algorithms.

# Focus on Number and Operations in Base Ten

Essential Question:
How can you use place value understanding to perform all operations fluently using whole numbers and decimals?

Unit 2 ■ Focus on Number and Operations in Base Ten  **39**

## Activity

Tell students that 12 skiers are going on a ski trip. Each skier has one pair of skis. They want an extra pair of skis for every 6 skiers. Each van can bring 5 skiers with the necessary equipment. An adult will drive each van.

Explain how many pairs of skis will be taken on the trip. How many vans will be needed and how many people in all will go on the trip?

Have a whole-class discussion in which students share and explain their work. Students may say to add the 12 pairs that each person brings to the number of extra skis. The number of extra pairs of skis will be $12 \div 6 = 2$. So there will be 14 pairs of skis. Divide 12 skiers by 5 since each van can hold 5 skiers to determine that 3 vans are needed. Add the number of skiers to the number of adults. There are 12 skiers and 3 adults, which is 15 people.

### Essential Question:
How can you use place value understanding to perform all operations fluently using whole numbers and decimals?

As students become involved with the Essential Question they will use place value understanding to compute fluently using both whole numbers and decimals. They will learn how to compare the value of digits in a number and use the four operations with both whole numbers and decimals.

## Conversation Starters

Have students discuss the photograph.

Ask questions such as: *What are the skiers doing in the picture? How high do you think they are off the ground? Do you think you could tell which skier is farther off the ground? How fast do you think the skiers are traveling?*

Have students look at the three skiers. *Suppose the skier that is farthest from the ground is 3 meters off the ground and the one that is closest to the ground is 2 meters off the ground. How far off the ground might the other skier be?* (The skier would be more than 2 meters and less than 3 meters.)

*Suppose these three skiers were in a race. What if you know the time it took each skier to finish the race. How could you use the amount of time each took to tell which place each skier came in?* (Put the times in order. The one with the shortest time would be the winner.)

Let students work in pairs to discuss how to compare the skiers using place value. Lead them to see that using place value is a good strategy for ordering things.

## OBJECTIVE
Recognize the relationship between adjacent places in the base-ten system.

## ESSENTIAL QUESTION
After reading the essential question, introduce the topic of place value by asking students to say the names of 100, 10, 1, 0.1, and 0.01 aloud. Some vocabulary terms that could require a brief explanation are *adjacent* and *base-ten system*.

## FLUENCY PRACTICE
Fluency practice is available at **sadlierconnect.com**.

## Concept Development

### Understand: The relationships between $1$, $\frac{1}{10}$, and $\frac{1}{100}$

■ Students learn the relationships among $1$, $\frac{1}{10}$, and $\frac{1}{100}$ (in decimal form, among 1, 0.1, and 0.01). This will help them understand the relationships between the values of adjacent places in decimal numbers.

■ Students have not computed $1 \div 10$ or $\frac{1}{10} \div 10$ in previous grades. By comparing the areas of the base-ten models for $1$, $\frac{1}{10}$, and $\frac{1}{100}$, students can see visually that $1 \div 10 = \frac{1}{10}$ and $\frac{1}{10} \div 10 = \frac{1}{100}$.

■ Using related multiplication and division equations may also help some students understand why $1 \div 10 = \frac{1}{10}$ and $\frac{1}{10} \div 10 = \frac{1}{100}$. Because $10 \times \frac{1}{10} = 1$, it is also true that $1 \div 10 = \frac{1}{10}$, and, because $10 \times \frac{1}{100} = \frac{10}{100} = \frac{1}{10}$, it is also true that $\frac{1}{10} \div 10 = \frac{1}{100}$.

---

# Understand Place Value

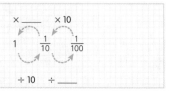

## Guided Instruction

In this lesson you will learn about how the values of adjacent places in a number are related.

**Understand: The relationships between** $1$, $\frac{1}{10}$, **and** $\frac{1}{100}$

Fill in the blanks to show how $1$, $\frac{1}{10}$, and $\frac{1}{100}$ are related.

Compare the area models for $1$, $\frac{1}{10}$, and $\frac{1}{100}$.

$$1 \qquad \frac{1}{10} \qquad \frac{1}{100}$$

**Compare 1 and** $\frac{1}{10}$.

The $\frac{1}{10}$ model has one tenth the area of the 1 model. $\longrightarrow 1 \div 10 = \frac{1}{10}$

The 1 model has ten times the area of the $\frac{1}{10}$ model. $\longrightarrow 10 \times \frac{1}{10} = 1$

**Compare** $\frac{1}{10}$ **and** $\frac{1}{100}$.

The $\frac{1}{100}$ model has one tenth the area of the $\frac{1}{10}$ model. $\longrightarrow \frac{1}{10} \div 10 = \frac{1}{100}$

The $\frac{1}{10}$ model has ten times the area of the $\frac{1}{100}$ model. $\longrightarrow 10 \times \frac{1}{100} = \frac{1}{10}$

This diagram shows the same relationship but with decimals.

---

## Support English Language Learners

The difference between words like *hundreds* and *hundredths* can be unclear to some students. Point out that the suffix *-ths* is used with fractions. Review reading and writing fractions such as fourths, fifths, sixths, and sevenths. Have students compare the position of tens/tenths and hundreds/hundredths in the place-value chart. Create flashcards with these words on one side and the number on the other for quick reference.

### Understand: Decimal place values

> Give the value of each digit in the number 76.54.

The chart below shows decimal place values through hundredths. Just as for whole numbers, the value of each place is ten times the value of the place to its right and one tenth the value of the place to its left.

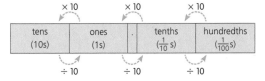

| tens (10s) | ones (1s) | . | tenths ($\frac{1}{10}$ s) | hundredths ($\frac{1}{100}$ s) |
|---|---|---|---|---|

Write 76.54 in the place-value chart.

| tens | ones | . | tenths | hundredths |
|---|---|---|---|---|
| 7 | 6 | . | 5 | 4 |

The 7 is in the tens place, so it represents 7 tens. Its value is $7 \times 10 = 70$.

The 6 is in the ones place, so it represents 6 ones. Its value is $6 \times 1 = 6$.

The 5 is in the tenths place, so it represents 5 tenths. Its value is $5 \times \frac{1}{10} = \frac{5}{10}$.

The 4 is in the hundredths place, so it represents 4 hundredths. Its value is $4 \times \frac{1}{100} = \frac{4}{100}$.

➡ The value of each digit in the number 76.54 is 7 tens, 6 ones, 5 tenths, and 4 hundredths.

✏ Express the values of the digits 5 and 4 in the number 76.54 as decimals. The value of the 5 is 0.5. The value of the 4 is 0.04.

## Understand: Decimal place values

■ In previous grade levels, students investigated the relationships between the values of adjacent places for whole numbers. Help students see the continuity of the pattern over the decimal point.

■ The place-value chart can help students name the place value for each digit. It may help to have students place the digits into the chart starting at the decimal point and moving left and right placing one digit in each box.

■ Repeat the activity shown in the presentation with 33.33 to focus attention on the place value of each digit, instead of the value of each digit.

■ Students should understand the relationships among the values of the places of multi-digit numbers. As they move to the right, the value of each place is divided by 10 with each step. As they move left, the value of each place is multiplied 10 with each step. Explain that this is the basis for the base-ten system mentioned in the Essential Question.

✏ After students have answered this question, ask a few volunteers to share their answers aloud. Be sure students clearly state that 0.5 is read as *five tenths* and 0.04 is read as *four hundredths*.

## Math-to-Science Connection

**Microscopes** Students may have worked with microscopes in the past. Explain to students that microscopes use mirrors and refraction to magnify objects through an eyepiece. Tell students that some microscopes can magnify objects 10 or 100 times as large when viewing through the eyepiece.

If possible, take students to the science lab to investigate, or research microscopes on the Internet. Provide students with some lengths of tiny insects or other objects expressed to the hundredths place. Encourage the class to discuss the size of the image under a magnification of 10 or 100 times.

# Guided Instruction

## Connect: What you know about place value relationships

This presentation will help students understand the place value of a digit and how the place value changes as the digit moves right or left.

■ Lead students to make the connection between 1, $\frac{1}{10}$, and $\frac{1}{100}$ and the parallel connection between 7, $\frac{7}{10}$, and $\frac{7}{100}$.

■ Point out that finding $\frac{1}{10}$ of a number is the same as dividing that number by 10.

■ Provide a similar example with whole numbers to reinforce the concepts taught in the presentation. Discuss how the place value of 7 changes in the numbers 721, 75, and 7.

✏ ▸ After students have answered this question, ask a few volunteers to read their explanations aloud. Also, ask students to speculate about Kami's thinking: What mistake could Kami be making? Extend the question by asking the place value of the 1 in 0.15 and the 0s in 0.05. Then have students find the number that is 10 times as great as 0.05.

## Guided Instruction

### Connect: What you know about place value relationships

> The digit 7 appears in a different place in each number below.
>
> 7          3.7          0.57
>
> Each time 7 moves right one place, how does its place value change? Each time 7 moves left one place, how does its place value change?

Use a place-value chart to identify the place value of the digit 7 in each number.

| ones | . | tenths | hundredths |
|------|---|--------|------------|
| 7 | . | | | ←— 7 ones = 7 |
| 3 | . | 7 | | ←— 7 tenths = $\frac{7}{10}$ = 0.7 |
| 0 | . | 5 | 7 | ←— 7 hundredths = $\frac{7}{100}$ = 0.07 |

**Look at how the value changes as 7 moves right:**

A tenth is $\frac{1}{10}$ as much as a one, so 7 tenths is $\frac{1}{10}$ as much as 7 ones.

A hundredth is $\frac{1}{10}$ as much as a tenth, so 7 hundredths is $\frac{1}{10}$ as much as 7 tenths.

**Look at how the value changes as 7 moves left:**

A tenth is 10 times as much as a hundredth, so 7 tenths is 10 times as much as 7 hundredths.

A one is 10 times as much as a tenth, so 7 ones is 10 times as much as 7 tenths.

▶ Each time 7 moves right one place, its value is divided by 10. Each time 7 moves left one place, its value is multiplied by 10.

✏ ▸ Kami says that the value of the digit 5 in 0.15 is greater than the value of the digit 5 in 0.05 because the value of the 5 in 0.15 is ten times the value of the 5 in 0.05. Is she correct? Explain.
Kami is not correct. Possible explanation: In both 0.15 and 0.05, the digit 5 is in the hundredths place. Therefore, the digit 5 has the same value in both decimal amounts.

**Remember!**
Finding $\frac{1}{10}$ of a number is the same as dividing that number by 10.

## Math-to-Money Connection

**Dollars, Dimes, Pennies** Have students look for patterns in money by creating a chart and determining the relationships between pennies and dimes, pennies and dollars, and dimes and dollars. For example, students should include that the value of a dollar is 10 times the value of a dime. Encourage students to also express the inverse of this relationship: The value of a dime is $\frac{1}{10}$ the value of a dollar.

Lesson 4

## Guided Practice

**For exercises 1–4, use the place-value chart to complete the sentences using *ten times* or *one tenth*.**

| ones | . | tenths | hundredths |
|------|---|--------|------------|
| 1 | . | 1 | 1 |

1. One tenth is __ten times__ the value of one hundredth.

2. One hundredth is __one tenth__ the value of one tenth.

3. One tenth is __one tenth__ the value of one.

4. One is __ten times__ the value of one tenth.

**For exercises 5–7, use the place-value chart to complete the statements about the number 26.13.**

| tens | ones | . | tenths | hundredths |
|------|------|---|--------|------------|
| 2 | 6 | . | 1 | 3 |

5. The digit 3 is in the __hundredths__ place, so its value is $3 \times \frac{1}{100}$, or $\frac{3}{100}$.

6. The digit 2 is in the __tens__ place, so its value is $2 \times 10$, or $20$.

7. The digit 1 is in the __tenths__ place, so its value is $1 \times \frac{1}{10}$, or $\frac{1}{10}$.

### Think • Pair • Share

MP3   8. Liam says the model at the right shows thirty hundredths. Anne says the model shows three tenths. Who is correct? Explain your reasoning.
Both Liam and Anne are correct. Possible explanation: There are one hundred squares, of which thirty are shaded, showing thirty hundredths. There are 10 columns of squares and 3 columns are shaded, showing three tenths.

Unit 2 ■ Focus on Number and Operations in Base Ten   **43**

## Mathematical Practices

Mathematical Practice Standards underline the teaching and understanding of all concepts and skills presented. The emphasis of specific practices is noted throughout the guided and independent practice of this lesson.

| MP3 | **Construct viable arguments and critique the reasoning of others.** |
|-----|---|

**Item 8:** Students analyze the work of two classmates and find that they named the same fractional part of a model.

## Observational Assessment

Use page 43 to assess whether students are able to describe relationships between the values of adjacent places in a decimal number. The exercises on this page also assess whether students are able to connect the correct word (hundredths, tenths, ones, tens) to its associated value ($\frac{1}{100}$, $\frac{1}{10}$, 1, 10).

### Think•Pair•Share

**Peer Collaboration** Have students work in pairs. Have one student work with thirty hundredths and the other student work with three tenths. Both partners should write their numbers in a place-value chart and as a fraction. Then partners should compare their results. After students have finished, ask:

• *How can you write a fraction with a denominator of 10 as an equivalent fraction with a denominator of 100?*

• *Do the numbers 0.3 and 0.30 have the same value?*

Ask for volunteers to share their reasoning for the problem.

### Return to the Essential Question

Reread the Lesson 4 Essential Question on page 40: *What is the relationship between adjacent places in the base-ten system?*

Ask volunteers to use what they learned in this lesson to answer this question. (Possible responses: In a multi-digit number, if I move right one place, the value of the place is multiplied by $\frac{1}{10}$ (or divided by 10) and if I move left one place, the value of the place is multiplied by 10. The value of each place is $\frac{1}{10}$ the value of the place to its left and 10 times the value of the place to its right.)

# Independent Practice

## Concept Application

Students may work independently on these pages in the classroom or at home. They may refer to the first four pages of the lesson to revisit the instruction or to see a worked-out example.

**Common Errors** and **Teaching Tips** may help you support student learning either in the classroom or as a follow-up for work done at home.

## Common Errors

### Item 6

Students may not notice the phrase *one tenth* in the problem statement and may jump to the number 0.7. Ask them to read the problem statement carefully. It may help to write the number that needs to be shaded, 0.07.

## Teaching Tips

### Items 1–5

Verify students' answers to exercise 1 are correct and help them recognize how to use the models in exercise 1 to express the relationship between each pair of numbers in exercises 2–5.

---

### Independent Practice

1. Shade the models below to show 2, 0.2, and 0.02.

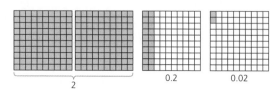

For exercises 2–5, use the models you shaded above to complete the sentences using *ten times* or *one tenth*.

2. 0.2 is ___ten times___ as much as 0.02.

3. 0.2 is ___one tenth___ as much as 2.

4. 0.02 is ___one tenth___ as much as 0.2.

5. 2 is ___ten times___ as much as 0.2.

6. Sam shaded a model to show one tenth of 0.7. Is he correct? Explain.

 Sam is not correct. Possible answer: He shaded 0.7, but one tenth of 0.7 is 0.07. He should have shaded 7 squares to show 7 hundredths.

**For exercises 7–8, use the number 6,125.89.**

7. Which digit is in the hundredths place?
   a. 1
   b. 2
   c. 8
   d. 9 ⟵

8. Which digit is in the tens place?
   a. 9
   b. 8
   c. 5
   d. 2 ⟵

---

## Writing About Math

✏ **Write Explanatory Text** Ask students to write a paragraph giving an explanation of how to determine the place value of a particular digit in a given multi-digit number. Have them describe what the value of that digit would be in an adjacent spot to the right or left. When writing their explanation, students should use precise language and appropriate vocabulary.

Ask a few volunteers to read their paragraphs aloud.

## Independent Practice

**For exercises 9–13, use the place-value chart to answer the questions.**

| tens | ones | . | tenths | hundredths |
|------|------|---|--------|------------|
| 3 | 0 | | | |
| | 3 | | | |
| | 0 | . | 3 | |
| | 0 | . | 0 | 3 |

9. Which number is one tenth as much as 0.3? __0.03__

10. Which number is ten times as much as 0.3? __3__

11. Which number is ten times as much as 0.03? __0.3__

12. Which number is one tenth as much as 3? __0.3__

13. Which number is ten times as much as 3? __30__

14. Which model shows one tenth the value of 5 tenths?

a.

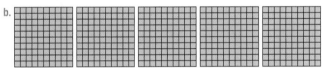
b.

c.

## Teaching Tips

### Items 9–13

If students are struggling, have them label the table like the first table shown on page 41. Ask them to verbalize the list of numbers and state the mathematical process needed to get from one value to the other moving in both directions.

## Digital Connection

**Interactive Whiteboard** Use four numbers and a decimal point, such as 3, 5, 0, and 2 and have students follow directions to create numbers. Some suggested activities are:

• Create the largest number you can.

• Create the smallest number you can.

• Create a number greater than 30.

• Create a number greater than 500.

• Create a number that so that the value of the 5 is 10 times greater than the value of the 5 in the number 35.02.

# Independent Practice

## Teaching Tips

### Items 16-17, 19-20
To see how the place value of the given digit changes, it may help to first record the digit's place value in each number.

### Items 21-22
Suggest to students that they write the place value of each digit before completing the exercises: 60, 6, $\frac{6}{10}$, $\frac{6}{100}$.

## Independent Practice

**Study the pattern. Complete the sentences to describe the pattern.**

138.49        1,384.9        13,849        138,490

15. Reading the numbers from left to right, the digits shift __left__ one place with each number.

16. In each number, the value of the digit 4 is __one tenth__ the value of the digit 4 in the number to its right.

17. In each number, the value of the digit 8 is __ten times__ the value of the digit 8 in the number to its left.

**Study the pattern. Complete the sentences to describe the pattern.**

218,760        21,876        2,187.6        218.76

18. Reading the numbers from left to right, the digits shift __right__ one place with each number.

19. In each number, the value of the digit 1 is __ten times__ the value of the digit 1 in the number to its right.

20. In each number, the value of the digit 6 is __one tenth__ the value of the digit 6 in the number to its left.

**For exercises 21–22, use the place-value chart below.**

| tens | ones | . | tenths | hundredths |
|---|---|---|---|---|
| 6 | 6 | . | 6 | 6 |

21. Write two equations to show how the place values of the digits in the tens and ones place are related.
    60 ÷ 10 = 6
    6 × 10 = 60

22. Write two equations to show how the place values of the digits in the tenths and hundredths places are related.
    $\frac{6}{10} \div 10 = \frac{6}{100}$
    $\frac{6}{100} \times 10 = \frac{6}{10}$

46    Unit 2 ■ Focus on Number and Operations in Base Ten

## Math-to-Science Connection

**Metric Measurement System**  Students will learn how to convert within the metric measurement system in Unit 5. Understanding the relationship between the value of digits and the value of the same digits to the right or left will benefit students when converting within the metric measurement system. The metric measurement system uses a base-ten model; therefore, each unit is 10 times the size of the next smallest unit. For example, 1 meter is 10 times the length of 1 decimeter.

MP6  **23.** Use the model below to show each number. Then explain the relationship between the values of the digit 3 in the numbers.

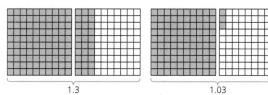

1.3                    1.03

Possible response: The value of the digit 3 in 1.3 is 10 times the value of the digit 3 in 1.03.

MP7  **For exercises 24–27, match each set of clues with the correct secret number. The key number is 13.57.**

**24.** The value of the digit 5 in the secret number has one tenth the value of the digit 5 in the key number.

**25.** The value of the digit 3 in the secret number has ten times the value of the digit 3 in the key number.

**26.** The value of the digit 1 in the secret number has one tenth the value of the digit 1 in the key number.

**27.** The value of the digit 7 in the secret number has ten times the value of the digit 7 in the key number.

a. 71.53

b. 53.71

c. 35.17

d. 17.35

MP7  **28.** Explain the relationship between the values of the digit 7 in these numbers: 270.5, 27.05, 2.70.
Possible answer: The value of the digit 7 in each number is one tenth the value of the digit 7 in the number to its left.

Unit 2 ■ Focus on Number and Operations in Base Ten  **47**

## Common Errors

### Item 28
Students may assume this question is just asking for the place value of 7 in each number. But it is asking them to go further and explain the relationship between the values of the digit 7 in the numbers. Encourage students to think about the place value of a digit as it moves to the right and to the left in a multi-digit number.

## Teaching Tips

### Items 24-27
Ensure that students notice the key number given in the direction line so that they can look for the proper relationship between the secret number and the key number.

| Mathematical Practices | |
| --- | --- |
| MP6 | **Attend to precision.** |

**Item 23:** Students use a model to help explain the relationship between the values of a specified digit in two different numbers.

| MP7 | **Look for and make use of structure.** |
| --- | --- |

**Items 24–27:** Students look for patterns in the relationships between the secret numbers and the key number.

**Item 28:** Students describe the pattern in values of a digit in 3 different given numbers.

## OBJECTIVE
Use an understanding of place value to multiply and divide by powers of ten.

## ESSENTIAL QUESTION
Explain to students that the *powers of 10* are the numbers 10, 100, 1,000, 10,000, and so on. In this lesson, students will learn how to use place-value patterns to multiply and divide by powers of 10.

## FLUENCY PRACTICE
Fluency practice is available at **sadlierconnect.com**.

## Concept Development

### Understand: Powers of 10

■ In this lesson, students will use whole-number exponents to denote powers of 10. Using this notation will help students recognize patterns when multiplying and dividing by powers of ten.

■ Have students practice describing examples of powers of 10 using the terms *base, exponent, factor,* and *to the power of*.

■ Point out that because multiplying 4 by $10^5$ is the same as multiplying by five factors of 10, the product is 4 followed by five zeros.

✏ Extend the activity by providing multiplication expressions and having students write a power of 10, such as $10 \times 10 \times 10 \times 10 \times 10 = 10^5$.

---

**Lesson 5**

# Powers of 10: Use Patterns and Whole-Number Exponents

**Essential Question:**
How can place value patterns help you multiply and divide by powers of 10?

**Words to Know:**
power of 10
base
exponent

## Guided Instruction

In this lesson you will use your understanding of place value to help you multiply and divide by powers of ten.

### Understand: Powers of 10

> Lily reads in a science article that the average distance from Earth to the moon is about $4 \times 10^5$ kilometers. What does $10^5$ represent? What is the average distance from Earth to the moon written as a whole number?

$4 \times 10^5$ kilometers is a multiplication expression representing a number.

$10^5$ is a power of 10. A power of 10 is written with a base number of 10 and an exponent. The exponent tells how many times the base number is used as a factor. In $10^5$, the exponent is 5.

$10^5$ is read as "ten to the fifth power."

$$10^5 \quad \overset{\text{exponent}}{\underset{\text{base}}{}}$$

$$\overset{\text{5 factors of 10.}}{10^5 = 10 \times 10 \times 10 \times 10 \times 10}$$
$$= 100,000$$

$$4 \times 10^5 = 4 \times 10 \times 10 \times 10 \times 10 \times 10$$
$$= 4 \times 100,000$$
$$= 400,000$$

➡ $10^5$ is the product of five factors of 10. The average distance from Earth to the moon is about 400,000 kilometers.

✏ For each power of 10 below, write the equivalent multiplication expression.

1. $10^3$ _____ $10 \times 10 \times 10$ _____

2. $10^7$ _____ $10 \times 10 \times 10 \times 10 \times 10 \times 10 \times 10$ _____

3. $10^4$ _____ $10 \times 10 \times 10 \times 10$ _____

---

## Words to Know

**power of 10:** a number with a base number of 10 and an exponent

**Example:** $10^2$

**base:** the number used as a factor in exponential form

**exponent:** the number of times the base is used as a factor

**Example:** $10^2$: 10 is the base. 2 is the exponent.

**Glossary can be found on pp. 347–350.**

Lesson 5

## Guided Instruction

**Understand:** How to multiply whole numbers by powers of 10

In this chart, 24 is multiplied by increasing powers of 10. What pattern do you see? Why does this pattern occur?

| Muliplication Expression | Factors | Product |
|---|---|---|
| $24 \times 10^1$ | $24 \times 10$ | 240 |
| $24 \times 10^2$ | $24 \times 10 \times 10$ | 2,400 |
| $24 \times 10^3$ | $24 \times 10 \times 10 \times 10$ | 24,000 |
| $24 \times 10^4$ | $24 \times 10 \times 10 \times 10 \times 10$ | 240,000 |

$24 \times 10^1$ is 240, which has 1 zero.
$24 \times 10^2$ is 2,400, which has 2 zeros.
$24 \times 10^3$ is 24,000, which has 3 zeros.
$24 \times 10^4$ is 240,000, which has 4 zeros.

**Remember!**
The value of each place is *10 times* the value of the place to the right.

The number of zeros in the product is the same as the exponent, which is the number of factors of 10. This pattern occurs because each time you multiply by 10, the place values of 2 and 4 are multiplied by 10, so they each shift left to the next greater place.

**Understand:** How to divide whole numbers by powers of 10

In this chart, 37 is divided by increasing powers of 10. What pattern do you see? Why does this pattern occur?

| Division Expression | Dividend ÷ Divisor | Quotient |
|---|---|---|
| $37 \div 10^1$ | $37 \div 10$ | 3.7 |
| $37 \div 10^2$ | $37 \div (10 \times 10)$ | 0.37 |
| $37 \div 10^3$ | $37 \div (10 \times 10 \times 10)$ | 0.037 |

$37 \div 10^1 = 3.7$, so the digits shift right one place.
$37 \div 10^2 = 0.37$, so the digits shift right 2 places.
$37 \div 10^3 = 0.037$, so the digits shift right 3 places.

**Remember!**
The value of each place is *one tenth* the value of the place to the left.

The exponent is the number of places 3 and 7 shift to the right. This pattern occurs because each time you divide by 10, the place values of 3 and 7 are divided by 10, so they shift right to the next smaller place.

Unit 2 ▪ Focus on Number and Operations in Base Ten  **49**

**Understand:** How to multiply whole numbers by powers of 10

■ Students should be able to describe the pattern: When a whole number is multiplied by a power of ten, the exponent determines the number of places each digit in the first factor is shifted to the left in the product.

■ Students may informally explain that to multiply by a power of 10, you write the first factor and then write the number of zeros equal to the exponent.

■ Some students may incorrectly think that the number of zeros in the product is the same as the exponent. This is true only if the first factor does not contain a 0. Give an example such as $20 \times 10^1 = 200$. Students should be very precise in their language.

**Understand:** How to divide whole numbers by powers of 10

■ Students should be able to describe the pattern: When a whole number is divided by a power of ten, the exponent determines the number of places each digit in the first factor is shifted to the right in the quotient.

■ If students have trouble understanding how the digits shift when a numbers is divided by a power of 10, use larger whole numbers, such as 370 or 3,700 as the dividends.

## Support English Language Learners

In this lesson, *ten to the power of five, ten to the fifth power,* and *ten to the fifth* are all used to convey the same numerical concept. Write $10^5$ on the board. Say each description aloud, and have students repeat what you say. Help students understand that each phrase means the $10^5$ pointing to the base and the exponent.

Write another example of a power of 10, such as $10^6$. Have students express this power of 10 in words in three different ways. Prompt students as needed. Repeat with other powers of 10 until students have become comfortable with expressing the numbers in their own words.

**Connect:** **What you know about multiplying and dividing by powers of 10 to decimals** This presentation will help students extend what they know about multiplying and dividing whole numbers by powers of 10 to multiplying and dividing decimals by powers of 10.

■ Be sure that students understand the placement of decimal points in whole numbers. For example, 8 can be written as 8.0 without changing its value.

■ Show students how to use zeros as placeholders. Sometimes they will need to add a zero to get the correct answer. Demonstrate this in Step 1 for the product of $5.26 \times 10^3$. Then ask students to explain how and why zeros are used as placeholders in Step 2.

■ Point out that the exponent tells them how many places the digits shift. Some students may get confused about which direction to shift the digits. Encourage them to use number sense to evaluate their results.

■ Have students think about when they multiply a number by 10, will the product be larger or smaller than the original number? When they divide a number by 10, will the quotient be larger or smaller than the original number?

■ Use this presentation to reinforce understanding from the previous lesson that the place value of a digit in one place represents 10 times as much as it represents in the place to its right and $\frac{1}{10}$ of what it represents in the place to its left.

---

**Connect:** **What you know about multiplying and dividing by powers of 10 to decimals**

Find the products and quotients.

$5.26 \times 10^1 =$ _____     $5.26 \div 10^1 =$ _____

$5.26 \times 10^2 =$ _____     $5.26 \div 10^2 =$ _____

$5.26 \times 10^3 =$ _____     $5.26 \div 10^3 =$ _____

The same patterns you found when multiplying and dividing whole numbers by powers of 10 apply to multiplying and dividing decimals by powers of 10.

**Step 1**

Multiply. Think about how many 10s you are multiplying by each time.

Each time you multiply a number by 10, the digits of that number shift left to the next greater place.

| | | |
|---|---|---|
| $5.26 \times 10^1 = 5.26 \times 10$ | $= 52.6$ | The digits shift left 1 place. |
| $5.26 \times 10^2 = 5.26 \times 10 \times 10$ | $= 526$ | The digits shift left 2 places. |
| $5.26 \times 10^3 = 5.26 \times 10 \times 10 \times 10$ | $= 5,260$ | The digits shift left 3 places. |

**Step 2**

Divide. Think about how many 10s you are dividing by each time.

Each time you divide a number by 10, the digits of that number shift right to the next smaller place.

| | | |
|---|---|---|
| $5.26 \div 10^1 = 5.26 \div 10$ | $= 0.526$ | The digits shift right 1 place. |
| $5.26 \div 10^2 = 5.26 \div (10 \times 10)$ | $= 0.0526$ | The digits shift right 2 places. |
| $5.26 \div 10^3 = 5.26 \div (10 \times 10 \times 10)$ | $= 0.00526$ | The digits shift right 3 places. |

➡ $5.26 \times 10^1 = 52.6$      $5.26 \div 10^1 = 0.526$

$5.26 \times 10^2 = 526$       $5.26 \div 10^2 = 0.0526$

$5.26 \times 10^3 = 5,260$      $5.26 \div 10^3 = 0.00526$

✏ Evaluate $4.5 \times 1,000$ and $4.5 \div 100$ using mental math. Explain your reasoning.
Possible explanation: $4.5 \times 1,000 = 4,500$; $1,000 = 10^3$, so I shifted the digits left 3 places. $4.5 \div 100 = 0.045$; $100 = 10^2$, so I shifted the digits right 2 places.

**50** Unit 2 ■ Focus on Number and Operations in Base Ten

---

## Math-to-Science Connection

**Scientific Notation** Scientists use powers of ten to write measurements that are very large and very small. When a scientist uses a power of ten to represent measurement, that measurement is said to be written in *scientific notation*. The table shows the distances between a few planets and the sun. Have students write each distance in standard form.

| Planet | Average Distance to Sun (in miles) |
|---|---|
| Mercury | $3.6 \times 10^7$ |
| Venus | $6.71 \times 10^7$ |
| Mars | $1.415 \times 10^8$ |
| Neptune | $2.7943 \times 10^9$ |

Guided Practice

**Complete the expression for each power of 10, and find its value. Then complete how the power is read in words.**

1. $10^1 =$ __10__                    "ten to the ____first____ power"

2. $10^2 =$ __10__ × __10__ = __100__        "ten to the ___second___ power"

3. $10^3 =$ __10__ × __10__ × __10__ = __1,000__    "ten to the ____third____ power"

**Place the decimal point in each product. Add zeros if needed.**

4. $2.5 \times 10^2 = 2\,5\,0$

5. $32.69 \times 10^3 = 3\,2,6\,9\,0$

6. $1.94 \times 10 = 1\,9.4$

7. $4 \times 10^3 = 4,0\,0\,0$

**Place the decimal point in each quotient. Add zeros if needed.**

8. $19 \div 10^2 = 0.1\,9$

9. $52.6 \div 10 = 5.2\,6$

10. $13,205 \div 10^3 = 1\,3.2\,0\,5$

11. $5 \div 10^2 = 0.0\,5$

**Think • Pair • Share**

MP3  12. Explain why you had to add zeros in the answers to exercises 7 and 11.
Possible answer: In exercise 7, the 4 shifts 3 places left to the thousands place, so zeros need to be added in the hundreds, tens, and ones places. In exercise 11, the 5 shifts 2 places right to the hundredths place, so a zero needs to be added in the tenths place.

Unit 2 ■ Focus on Number and Operations in Base Ten    **51**

## Observational Assessment

Use page 51 to assess whether students understand how to apply place value patterns to multiply and divide by the powers of ten. Encourage students to draw arrows to determine the placement of the decimal points as they multiply and divide by the powers of ten.

### Think•Pair•Share

**Peer Collaboration** Groups students into pairs. Have one student explain why zeros need to be added in the answer to exercise 7. Have the other student provide the explanation for exercise 11. Ask each pair of students to identify what is the same about their explanations and what is different. Guide student discussion by asking:

- *What is the purpose of the zeros in 4,000?*

- *What is the purpose of the zeros in 0.05?*

To summarize, explain that when multiplying or dividing by powers of 10, the exponent tells how many places to shift the digits. Sometimes it is necessary to add a zero as a placeholder to shift the digits the appropriate number of places.

### Return to the Essential Question

Reread the Lesson 5 Essential Question on page 48: *How can place value patterns help you multiply and divide by powers of 10?*

Ask volunteers to use what they learned in this lesson to answer this question. (Possible responses: Each time you multiply a number by 10, the digits of that number shift one place value to the left. Each time you divide a number by 10, the digits of that number shift one place value to the right.)

Invite as many volunteers as possible to express ideas about multiplying and dividing by powers of 10 in their own words.

## Mathematical Practices

Mathematical Practice Standards underline the teaching and understanding of all concepts and skills presented. The emphasis of specific practices is noted throughout the guided and independent practice of this lesson.

| MP3 | **Construct viable arguments and critique the reasoning of others.** |
|---|---|

**Item 12:** Students construct an argument based on place value patterns.

## Concept Application

Students may work independently on these pages in the classroom or at home. They may refer to the first four pages of the lesson to revisit the instruction or to see a worked-out example.

**Common Errors** and **Teaching Tips** may help you support student learning either in the classroom or as a follow-up for work done at home.

## Teaching Tips

### Items 5 and 7

Encourage students to look at the nonzero digit in the known factor and in the product and then determine how many places that digit shifts. This will tell them which power of 10 is the unknown factor.

### Items 6 and 8

Encourage students to look at the nonzero digit in the dividend and in the quotient and then determine how many places that digit shifts. This will tell them which power of 10 is the divisor.

### Items 9–12

Have students draw arrows to help them place the decimal point in each product or quotient.

---

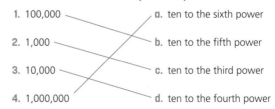

**Independent Practice**

**Match each number to its equivalent power of ten.**

1. 100,000        a. ten to the sixth power

2. 1,000        b. ten to the fifth power

3. 10,000        c. ten to the third power

4. 1,000,000        d. ten to the fourth power

**For exercises 5–8, choose the correct factor or divisor.**

5. $30 \times \blacksquare = 300$

   a. $10^7$        b. $10^1$        c. $10^2$        d. $10^3$

6. $4,000 \div \blacksquare = 40$

   a. $10^4$        b. $10^1$        c. $10^2$        d. $10^3$

7. $0.05 \times \blacksquare = 50$

   a. $10^4$        b. $10^1$        c. $10^2$        d. $10^3$

8. $80 \div \blacksquare = 0.08$

   a. $10^5$        b. $10^1$        c. $10^2$        d. $10^3$

**Place the decimal point in each product or quotient. Add zeros if needed.**

9. $15 \div 10^2 = 0 . 1 \ 5$

10. $32.63 \times 10 = 3 \ 2 \ 6 . 3$

11. $723,356 \div 10^3 = 7 \ 2 \ 3 . 3 \ 5 \ 6$

12. $35,526 \times 10^2 = 3 , 5 \ 5 \ 2 , 6 \ 0 \ 0$

52   Unit 2 ■ Focus on Number and Operations in Base Ten

---

## Writing About Math

✐ **Write Explanatory Text** Have students write an explanation of how to use place value to multiply and divide by powers of 10. They should describe how patterns and rules are used to find products and quotients. Students may include illustrations or models to reinforce their explanations.

Ask volunteers to read their paragraphs aloud. Remind students that there is often more than one way to describe and interpret relationships. Some students may describe how digits shift to the left or to the right, while others may describe moving the decimal point to the left or to the right.

MORE ONLINE sadlierconnect.com

## Independent Practice

**For exercises 13–16, write each product or quotient in the place-value chart. Include zeros only where needed.**

**13.** $5.1 \times 10^3$

| ten thousands | thousands | hundreds | tens | ones | . | tenths | hundredths |
|---|---|---|---|---|---|---|---|
| | 5 | 1 | 0 | 0 | | | |

**14.** $51 \div 10^2$

| ten thousands | thousands | hundreds | tens | ones | . | tenths | hundredths |
|---|---|---|---|---|---|---|---|
| | | | | 0 | . | 5 | 1 |

**15.** $0.51 \times 10^2$

| ten thousands | thousands | hundreds | tens | ones | . | tenths | hundredths |
|---|---|---|---|---|---|---|---|
| | | | 5 | 1 | | | |

**16.** $510{,}000 \div 10^3$

| ten thousands | thousands | hundreds | tens | ones | . | tenths | hundredths |
|---|---|---|---|---|---|---|---|
| | | 5 | 1 | 0 | | | |

**For exercises 17–24, find each product or quotient.**

**17.** $83 \times 10^2 = $ ___8,300___

**18.** $0.34 \times 10^3 = $ ___340___

**19.** $37.5 \times 10^1 = $ ___375___

**20.** $0.08 \times 10^2 = $ ___8___

**21.** $978 \div 10 = $ ___97.8___

**22.** $15{,}334 \div 10^3 = $ ___15.334___

**23.** $88 \div 10^2 = $ ___0.88___

**24.** $2{,}734 \div 10^1 = $ ___273.4___

Unit 2 ■ Focus on Number and Operations in Base Ten **53**

## Common Errors

### Items 17–24

When students first begin multiplying and dividing by powers of 10, they frequently move digits in the wrong direction. Help students develop their number sense by comparing the product or quotient to the factor or dividend.

## Digital Connection

**Interactive Whiteboard** Using a random number generator, select a number between 0 and 99 including place values to the hundredths. This number will be one factor of a power-of-10 multiplication problem. Ask the students to choose a number between 1 and 4. This number will be the exponent in the power-of-10 multiplication problem. Write the power-of-10 multiplication problem on the whiteboard. Ask a volunteer to demonstrate how the digits shift when multiplying by a power of 10.

Extend this activity by creating power-of-10 division problems.

# Independent Practice

## Common Errors

### Item 25

As students begin to work with decimals, they may misunderstand the value of zeros by counting from the leading zero (the zero to the left of the decimal point in a number less than 1). Help students distinguish between place-holding zeros and leading zeros.

## Teaching Tips

### Item 29

Some students will benefit by rewriting 30.05 as 30.050, so that both numbers have the same number of digits. Make sure students understand that you can write a zero to the right of the last digit in a decimal number without changing the value.

### Independent Practice

25. What happens to the digits 2 and 4 when finding the product of $0.0024 \times 10^4$? What is the product?
The digits move four places to the left. The product is 24.

26. Where do you put the decimal point in the quotient for $99,999.99 \div 10^5$? Explain.
The digits shift 5 places to the right, so I move the decimal point five places to the left. The quotient is 0.9999999.

**For exercises 27–29, choose the correct factor or divisor.**

27. $0.22 \times \blacksquare = 22$

    a. $10^4$      b. $10^3$      (c.) $10^2$      d. $10^1$

28. $908.7 \div \blacksquare = 0.9087$

    a. $10^1$      b. $10^6$      c. $10^5$      (d.) $10^3$

29. $30.05 \times \blacksquare = 30,050$

    (a.) $10^3$      b. $10^5$      c. $10^2$      d. $10^7$

**Solve the problems.**

MP3   30. Last year, Josh earned $200 a month running errands for neighbors. He wants to earn $2,000 for a summer vacation. If he starts in January, will Josh earn enough by summer for his vacation? Explain your thinking.
No, Josh will not earn enough by summer. Possible explanation: It will take Josh 10 months, or from January to October, to earn $2,000 if he earns $200 a month. Summer will be over by then.

MP1   31. Ms. Andrews earned $64,000 last year. She spent one tenth of her earnings on medical expenses. How much did Ms. Andrews spend on medical expenses? Explain how you determined the answer.
Ms. Andrews spent $6,400. Possible explanation: To find one tenth divide by 10. This moves the digits one place to the right.

## Mathematical Practices

| | |
|---|---|
| **MP1** | **Make sense of problems and persevere in solving them.** |
| **Item 31:** Students use place-value patterns to solve a real-world problem. | |
| **MP3** | **Construct viable arguments and critique the reasoning of others.** |
| **Item 30:** Students formulate an argument based on place value and share their reasoning with others. | |

## Independent Practice

**MP3** **32.** Kent says that $360,534 \div 10^2 = 36,053.4$. Explain the error Kent made. Then give the correct answer.

**Answer** Kent divided by $10^1$, not $10^2$. The correct answer is 3605.34

**✏ Justify your answer using words, drawings, or numbers.**
$360,534 \div 10^2 = 360,534 \div 100 = 3,6\ 0\ 5.3\ 4. = 3,605.34$

**MP6** **33.** What is the value of the expression below?

$$(3 \times 1,000 + 4 \times 100 + 2 \times 10 + 5) \times 10^3$$

**Answer** 3,425,000

**✏ Justify your answer using words, drawings, or numbers.**
$3 \times 1,000 + 4 \times 100 + 2 \times 10 + 5 = 3,000 + 400 + 20 + 5 = 3,425$
$3,425 \times 10^3 = 3\ 4\ 2\ 5.0\ 0\ 0. = 3,425,000$

**MP7** **34.** Marisa divides a number by a power of ten and the quotient is 1.4. She says that if she multiplies the number by the same power of ten, the product is 14,000. What was the dividend in Marisa's original problem? Use patterns to explain your thinking.

**Answer** The dividend in Marisa's original problem is 140.

**✏ Justify your answer using words, drawings, or numbers.**
Possible justification: I used patterns and inverse operations to find the answer. To find possible dividends, I multiplied because multiplication is the inverse of division: $1.4 \times 10 = 14$; $1.4 \times 10^2 = 140$ and $1.4 \times 10^3 = 1,400$. Then I used division to find a quotient that matches the product. $14,000 \div 10 = 1,400$; $14,000 \div 10^2 = 140$. I got 140 as the same answer when using $10^2$, so 140 is the answer.

## Teaching Tips

**Item 33**
Be sure that students are familiar with the Order of Operations when solving problems that involve multiple operations. Tell students that the expression inside the parentheses should be simplified first.

**Item 34**
It is acceptable for students to use the guess-and-check strategy here to find the original number. Once the original number is found, it will help students explain the pattern.

## Mathematical Practices

| | |
|---|---|
| **MP3** | **Construct viable arguments and critique the reasoning of others.** |

**Item 32:** Students explain an error made when dividing by a power of 10.

| | |
|---|---|
| **MP6** | **Attend to precision.** |

**Item 33:** Students evaluate a numerical expression when multiplying by a power of 10.

| | |
|---|---|
| **MP7** | **Look for and make use of structure.** |

**Item 34:** Students justify their solution by identifying a place-value pattern.

## OBJECTIVE
**Read and write decimals to thousandths.**

## ESSENTIAL QUESTION
Explain to students that they will use several tools such as models, words, and expanded form to read and write decimals. Use and extend students' decimal knowledge from Grade 4 to include knowledge of decimals to the thousandths place.

## FLUENCY PRACTICE
Fluency practice is available at **sadlierconnect.com**.

## Concept Development

### Understand: How to express decimals to hundredths in more than one way

■ Students will use words and models to express decimals to the hundredths place by relating the decimal part to one or more fractions that have denominators of 10 and 100. Make sure students understand that a decimal to hundredths place can be modeled two different ways.

■ Point out that the expanded form shows each place value of a decimal, even though models sometimes represent the entire decimal part, such as $\frac{45}{100}$ in the example above.

✏ A common mistake students make when there is a 0 in the tenths place and a digit 1–9 in the hundredths place is to express the decimal as tenths. Other students may also mistakenly say *three hundreds*. Correct this mispronunciation by connecting their knowledge of fractions to 0.03.

---

**Essential Question:**
How can you express a decimal to thousandths in different forms?

### Guided Instruction

In this lesson you will learn how to read and write decimals to thousandths in different forms.

**Understand: How to express decimals to hundredths in more than one way**

> Andre jogs a distance of 1.45 miles. Express this distance in words, with a model, and in expanded form.

➡ You can express Andre's jogging distance the following ways.

**In words:** Think of the decimal part as a fraction. The decimal 1.45 is the same as $1\frac{45}{100}$, and it is written and read as "one *and* forty-five hundredths."

**With a model:**

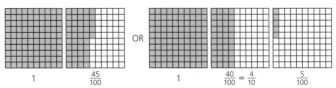

| 1 | $\frac{45}{100}$ | OR | 1 | $\frac{40}{100} = \frac{4}{10}$ | $\frac{5}{100}$ |

**In expanded form:** Use a place-value chart or a model to help you.

| ones | . | tenths | hundredths |
|------|---|--------|------------|
| 1 | . | 4 | 5 |

Below are four ways to write 1.45 in expanded form.
1.45 = 1 one + 4 tenths + 5 hundredths
$1.45 = 1 \times 1 + 4 \times \frac{1}{10} + 5 \times \frac{1}{100}$
$1.45 = 1 \times 1 + 4 \times 0.1 + 5 \times 0.01$
$1.45 = 1 + 0.4 + 0.05$

✏ Express 0.03 in words and as a fraction.
Words: *three hundredths*; Fraction: $\frac{3}{100}$

---

## Support English Language Learners

To help students understand that tenths and hundredths describe fractional parts of a whole, have them work with a partner to write decimal numbers. Provide students with an initial example: The number 10.32 can be expressed in words as ten and thirty-two hundredths. Emphasize to students that *and* is used to indicate the placement of the decimal.

Have each pair alternate writing a decimal in number form and expressing it in word form. Then have each pair alternate providing a decimal in word form and expressing it in number form.

Lesson 6

**Understand:** How to express decimals to thousandths in more than one way

> Express 0.417 in words, with a model, and in expanded form.

⇨ **In words:** The decimal 0.417 is equivalent to the fraction $\frac{417}{1,000}$.
It is written and read as "four hundred seventeen thousandths."

**With a model:**

  OR

$\frac{417}{1,000}$   $\frac{400}{1,000} = \frac{4}{10}$   $\frac{10}{1,000} = \frac{1}{100}$   $\frac{7}{1,000}$

**In expanded form:** Use a place-value chart or a model to help you.

| ones | . | tenths | hundredths | thousandths |
|------|---|--------|-----------|-------------|
| 0 | . | 4 | 1 | 7 |

Below are four ways to write 0.417 in expanded form.

0.417 = 4 tenths + 1 hundredth + 7 thousandths

$0.417 = 4 \times \frac{1}{10} + 1 \times \frac{1}{100} + 7 \times \frac{1}{1,000}$

$0.417 = 4 \times 0.1 + 1 \times 0.01 + 7 \times 0.001$

$0.417 = 0.4 + 0.01 + 0.007$

➤ How would you write the decimal 63.076 in words?
*sixty-three and seventy-six thousandths*

---

**Understand:** How to express decimals to thousandths in more than one way

■ In this presentation, students will extend their understanding of decimals to include the thousandths place. Provide opportunities for students to read decimals using the *value* in the numerator of a fraction and the tenths, hundredths, or thousandths *place value* of the denominator.

■ The expanded form of the decimal will help to reinforce that each adjacent place value is one-tenth the value of the place value to the left.

■ Be sure students understand that when the value of a place is zero, it is included in the place-value chart and in the expanded form of the decimal, but it is not included when expressing the decimal in words.

➤ After students have answered this question, ask volunteers to describe how they approached the problem. Hold a class discussion about the different approaches students used. As an extension, have students write the number 63,076 in words. Discuss the similarities and differences between 63,076 and 63.076.

---

## Math-to-Physical Education Connection

**Time Trials** Have students use a stopwatch and work in pairs to record to the nearest thousandth the time it takes each volunteer to run a hundred-yard dash. Each volunteer should run twice. Have each student use a place-value chart to thousandths to record his or her fastest time and then express that time in words, in expanded form, and as a fraction.

**Connect: What you know about reading and writing decimal numbers to thousandths** Use this page to help students strengthen their understanding of the multiple ways decimal numbers can be represented.

■ A key understanding is that a fraction and an equivalent decimal name the same amount. The question in the problem leads students to reinforce their understanding of the connection between decimals and fractions as they begin to solve the problem.

■ In Step 2, make sure students can explain why it is necessary to place a zero in the tenths place in the place-value chart for the decimal 0.048.

■ Once students have completed Step 3, ask volunteers to share which expanded form of a decimal they prefer to use. Ask students if their preference is based on mathematical efficiency or a familiar structure they may have encountered in the past.

---

## Guided Instruction

**Connect: What you know about reading and writing decimal numbers to thousandths**

> Alice planted a packet of 1,000 tomato seeds in her garden. After a week, 48 of them sprouted. In what ways can you express the fraction of the seeds that sprouted?

**Step 1**

Write a fraction.

48 out of 1,000 seeds sprouted, so the fraction of seeds that sprouted is $\frac{48}{1,000}$.

**Step 2**

Write a decimal.

$\frac{48}{1,000}$ written as a decimal is 0.048.

Show the decimal in a place-value chart.

| ones | . | tenths | hundredths | thousandths |
|---|---|---|---|---|
| 0 | . | 0 | 4 | 8 |

**Step 3**

Express the decimal number in expanded form.

Below are four ways to do this.

0.048 = 0 tenths + 4 hundredths + 8 thousandths

$0.048 = 0 \times \frac{1}{10} \quad + 4 \times \frac{1}{100} \quad + 8 \times \frac{1}{1,000}$

$0.048 = 0 \times 0.1 + 4 \times 0.01 \quad + 8 \times 0.001$

$0.048 = 0 \qquad + 0.04 \qquad + 0.008$

**Step 4**

Write the fraction or its decimal equivalent in words.

$\frac{48}{1,000}$, or 0.048, is written as "forty-eight thousandths."

 You can express the fraction of the plants that sprouted in more than one way: as a fraction, as a decimal, in expanded form, and in words.

---

## Math-to-Sports Connection

**Olympics** Decimals are used to express time in Olympic events. Explain that for some races, the times are so close that they are measured in fractions of a second. Demonstrate how long one second is using the second hand on a clock.

Have students research the finishing times for the men and women's 50-m Olympic track events. Assign a different Olympic year to each student, or group of students, and have them write each of the top three fastest decimal times in a place-value chart, as a fraction, and in words.

---

### Guided Practice

**Write each fraction in decimal form.**

1. $\frac{23}{100}$
   0.23

2. $35\frac{9}{100}$
   35.09

3. $200\frac{103}{1,000}$
   200.103

**Write each decimal in fraction form.**

4. 0.203
   $\frac{203}{1,000}$

5. 0.01
   $\frac{1}{100}$

6. 5.099
   $5\frac{99}{1,000}$

**Write the expanded form to show each decimal.**

7. 0.35    Possible answer: $3 \times \frac{1}{10} + 5 \times \frac{1}{100}$

8. 0.326   Possible answer: $3 \times \frac{1}{10} + 2 \times \frac{1}{100} + 6 \times \frac{1}{1,000}$

**Write the decimal that represents the expanded form of the number.**

9. $5 \times 10 + 0 \times 1 + 1 \times \frac{1}{10} + 4 \times \frac{1}{100} + 2 \times \frac{1}{1,000}$
   50.142

**Express each decimal in words.**

10. 12.76     twelve and seventy-six hundredths

11. 0.029     twenty-nine thousandths

12. 384.9     three hundred eighty-four and nine tenths

13. 9.802     nine and eight hundred two thousandths

#### ⛤ Think • Pair • Share

MP3  14. Patrick says that 0.500 is greater than 0.50 and 0.5. Is he correct? Explain your reasoning.

No, all three express the same amount since $0.500 = \frac{500}{1,000}$, $0.50 = \frac{50}{100}$, and $0.5 = \frac{5}{10}$. Possible explanation: Using a place-value chart or model, you can see they are all equivalent.

---

### Mathematical Practices

Mathematical Practice Standards underline the teaching and understanding of all concepts and skills presented. The emphasis of specific practices is noted throughout the guided and independent practice of this lesson.

| MP3 | **Construct viable arguments and critique the reasoning of others.** |
|---|---|

**Item 14:** Students evaluate the validity of a statement about place value of decimal numbers and explain their reasoning.

---

### Observational Assessment

Use page 59 to assess whether students have an understanding of decimals to the thousandths place. This page also provides opportunities for students to show their comprehension and accuracy when representing decimals in fraction form, expanded form, and in words. Take note of those students who struggle representing decimals as fractions, especially in exercises involving mixed numbers. Encourage students to use place-value charts as needed to organize their decimals.

### ⛤⛤ Think•Pair•Share

**Peer Collaboration** Ask student pairs to evaluate the three decimals in the problem. Once student pairs answer the question, ask volunteers to share the process they used to compare the three values.

- *How did you represent the decimals?*

- *Once you represented each decimal, what process did you use to compare them and reach a conclusion?*

- *How did the zeros affect the value of each decimal?*

To summarize, point out that each process used results in the conclusion that the three decimals are all equivalent.

### Return to the Essential Question

Reread the Lesson 6 Essential Question on page 56: *How can you express a decimal to thousandths in different forms?*

Ask volunteers to use what they learned in this lesson to answer this question. (Possible response: I can use models, place-value charts, words, and expanded forms to represent a decimal to thousandths.)

Ask volunteers to describe the way of representing decimals that they think is most useful and explain why.

# Independent Practice

## Concept Application

Students may work independently on these pages in the classroom or at home. They may refer to the first four pages of the lesson to revisit the instruction or to see a worked-out example.

**Common Errors** and **Teaching Tips** may help you support student learning either in the classroom or as a follow-up for work done at home.

## Common Errors

### Item 8

Students may fail to write the zero in the tenths place of the decimal. Show students how using a place-value chart may help them to reduce errors.

### Independent Practice

**Which decimal does each model represent?**

1.

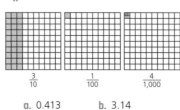

$\frac{3}{10}$          $\frac{1}{100}$          $\frac{4}{1,000}$

   a. 0.413     b. 3.14

   (c.) 0.314    d. 4,130

2.

$\frac{1}{10}$          $\frac{3}{100}$          $\frac{1}{1,000}$

   (a.) 0.131    b. 13.1

   c. 1.31      d. 131

**For exercises 3–6, write the decimals in expanded form.**

3. 0.59

Possible answer: $5 \times \frac{1}{10} + 9 \times \frac{1}{100}$

4. 9.099

Possible answer: $9 \times 1 + 0 \times \frac{1}{10} + 9 \times \frac{1}{100} + 9 \times \frac{1}{1,000}$

5. 21.121

Possible answer: $2 \times 10 + 1 \times 1 + 1 \times \frac{1}{10} + 2 \times \frac{1}{100} + 1 \times \frac{1}{1,000}$

6. 100.930

Possible answer: $1 \times 100 + 0 \times 10 + 0 \times 1 + 9 \times \frac{1}{10} + 3 \times \frac{1}{100} + 0 \times \frac{1}{1,000}$

**Write the fractions as decimals.**

7. $\frac{41}{100}$

   0.41

8. $87\frac{33}{1,000}$

   87.033

9. $1\frac{570}{1,000}$

   1.570 or 1.57

10. $356\frac{242}{1,000}$

   356.242

## Talking About Math

**Collaborative Conversations** Have students work in pairs. Give students three decimals such as 0.8, 0.61, and 0.309. Listen as each student explains to his or her partner how to write each decimal in a place-value chart, in words, and as a fraction. Students should verify that their partners' explanations are correct.

**Write each word phrase as a decimal.**

11. forty-nine hundredths
    0.49

12. fourteen and ninety-nine thousandths
    14.099

13. two hundred thirty-one thousandths
    0.231

14. six hundred nine and two hundred and three thousandths
    609.203

15. eight hundredths
    0.08

16. one and four hundred seventy-three thousandths
    1.473

**Write each decimal in words.**

17. 0.01
    one hundredth

18. 11.011
    eleven and eleven thousandths

19. 0.719
    seven hundred nineteen thousandths

20. 216.231
    two hundred sixteen and two hundred thirty-one thousandths

21. 0.910
    ninety-one hundredths

22. 0.005
    five thousandths

23. What is the decimal that represents ninety hundredths?

    a. 0.09

    b. 9.00

    c. 0.90

    d. 0.009

## Teaching Tips

### Item 23

Encourage students struggling with this item to first write the decimal as a fraction.

## Digital Connection

**Fraction and Decimal Calculators** Use a search engine to find a Fraction to Decimal Calculator and a Decimal to Fraction Calculator. Have students list several fractions with denominators of 10, 100, and 1,000, and list several decimals with place values to tenths, hundredths, and thousands. Tell students to use these calculators to write a decimal for each fraction on their lists, and write a fraction for each decimal on their lists. When converting a decimal to fraction, have students explain why the calculator might display an answer of $\frac{5}{100}$ as $\frac{1}{20}$.

# Independent Practice

## Teaching Tips

### Item 25

Remind students to consider the relationship between adjacent place values in any number when they approach this item.

### Items 26-28

Encourage students to consider the reasonableness of their solutions to these problems based on their previous experiences with these types of measures.

---

## Independent Practice

**MP2** **24.** Look at the decimals below. How are they alike? How are they different?

0.8    0.80    0.800

Possible answer: All the numbers are equal in value. The only difference between them is whether they show a zero in the hundredths and/or thousandths place to represent that the value in that place is 0.

**MP2** **25.** Explain how the value of the digit 4 in 0.47 relates to the value of the digit 4 in 0.704.

Possible answer: The digit 4 is in the tenths place in 0.47 and in the thousandths place in 0.704. Each place is 10 times as much as the place to its right, so the value of 4 in 0.47 is 100 times the value of the 4 in 0.704.

**Solve the problems.**

**MP6** **26.** Farukh helps his father put a new part in the engine of his car. The part has a small gap between two pieces of metal. The gap must be no more than $\frac{16}{1,000}$ of an inch. What is this amount represented as a decimal?

0.016

**MP6** **27.** Maria likes to watch Olympic swimmers on TV. In the closest race, her favorite swimmer lost by two thousandths of a second. What is this amount represented as a decimal?

0.002

**MP4** **28.** Out of 100 students surveyed, 40 responded that they had an older brother or sister. What is this amount represented as a decimal?

0.40 or 0.4

**29.** What is the fraction represented by the decimal 0.001?

a. $\frac{1,000}{1}$                         b. $\frac{1}{10}$

c. $\frac{1}{100}$                         (d.) $\frac{1}{1,000}$

---

## Mathematical Practices

| MP2 | **Reason abstractly and quantitatively.** |
|---|---|

**Item 24:** Students make sense of quantities and their relationship to compare three equivalent decimals expressed in different ways.

**Item 25:** Students consider the place of the given digit to determine the value.

| MP4 | **Model with mathematics.** |
|---|---|

**Item 28:** Students apply their understanding of decimal place value to answer a real-world problem about surveys.

| MP6 | **Attend to precision.** |
|---|---|

**Items 26-27:** Students use precision in units of measure to solve the problem.

---

MP3 **30.** Kai tells Juan that a housefly has a mass of twelve thousandths of a gram. Juan writes this as 0.12 grams. What is his error? Explain.

**Answer** Juan did not write the numbers with their digits in the correct place value. He wrote the number 12 after the decimal instead of putting the 1 in the hundredths place and the 2 in the thousandths place.

**· Justify your answer using words, drawings, or numbers.**

twelve thousandths = $0 \times \frac{1}{10} + 1 \times \frac{1}{100} + 2 \times \frac{1}{1,000} = \frac{12}{1,000} = 0.012$

MP5 **31.** Represent the decimal 0.402 using a model, words, a fraction, and expanded form.

**Model:**
Possible representation using a model.

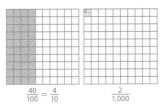

$\frac{40}{100} = \frac{4}{10}$       $\frac{2}{1,000}$

**Words:** four hundred two thousandths

**Fraction:** $\frac{402}{1,000}$

**Expanded form:** Possible answer: $4 \times \frac{1}{10} + 0 \times \frac{1}{100} + 2 \times \frac{1}{1,000}$

## Teaching Tips

### Item 31
Remind students that there are multiple possible expanded forms of the decimal.

| Mathematical Practices | |
|---|---|
| **MP3** | **Construct viable arguments and critique the reasoning of others.** |
| **Item 30:** Students respond to the arguments of others. | |
| **MP5** | **Use appropriate tools strategically.** |
| **Item 31:** Students use a model, words, a fraction, and the expanded form of a decimal to solve a problem. | |

## OBJECTIVE
**Use place value to compare decimals to thousandths.**

## ESSENTIAL QUESTION
Discuss with students when it might be necessary to compare decimal numbers, for example when working with money or with measurements. Students will learn about four ways to compare decimal numbers.

## FLUENCY PRACTICE
Fluency practice is available at **sadlierconnect.com**.

## Concept Development

### Understand: How to use a number line to compare decimal numbers

■ This presentation assists students in comparing two decimals to the thousandths place by comparing their placement on a number line. Explain that selecting and precisely labeling the scale on a number line is imperative when comparing decimals.

■ Review the meanings of the symbols >, <, and =.

### Understand: How to use fractions to compare decimal numbers

■ In this lesson, students write decimals as fractions with common denominators and then compare the fractions.

■ Ask students why it might be easier to compare decimals that have a common denominator. Remind students how to compare fractions with a common denominator.

---

### Guided Instruction

In this lesson you will learn how to compare decimal numbers to thousandths.

**Understand: How to use a number line to compare decimal numbers**

> Sal and Pat store music on their mobile devices. They compare the unused storage each mobile device has left. Sal's mobile device has 9.869 gigabytes left, and Pat's mobile device has 9.863 gigabytes. Whose mobile device has more storage left?

To find whose mobile device has more storage left, plot the gigabyte values from 9.860 to 9.870 on a number line.

Because 9.869 is farther to the right on the number line, 9.869 > 9.863.

▶ Sal's mobile device has more storage left.

**Understand: How to use fractions to compare decimal numbers**

> Tia's batting average is 0.358. Sam's batting average is 0.356. Who has the greater batting average?

To find who has the greater batting average, compare the batting averages using fractions.

Write 0.358 and 0.356 as fractions.

$$0.358 = \frac{358}{1,000} \qquad 0.356 = \frac{356}{1,000}$$

The denominators are the same, so compare the numerators to find which fraction is greater.

$$358 > 356$$
$$\frac{358}{1,000} > \frac{356}{1,000}$$

▶ Tia has the greater batting average.

**64** Unit 2 ■ Focus on Number and Operations in Base Ten

---

## Support English Language Learners

Use this lesson as an opportunity to review terms students encountered in earlier lessons. For this particular lesson, write *decimal numbers, place value,* and *expanded form* on the board and read each term aloud, having students repeat. Then ask students to define each term in their own words, supporting students as needed. For those students who struggle, encourage them to find an example within their book.

## Guided Instruction

**Understand:** How to use place value to compare decimal numbers

> Which is longer, 7.323 inches or 7.385 inches?

To compare 7.323 and 7.385, think about the place values of the digits.

| ones | . | tenths | hundredths | thousandths |
|------|---|--------|------------|-------------|
| 7 | . | 3 | 2 | 3 |
| 7 | . | 3 | 8 | 5 |

Compare the digits of the numbers place by place, starting with the greatest place, until you find digits that are different.

**Compare ones:** 7 ones = 7 ones
**Compare tenths:** 3 tenths = 3 tenths
**Compare hundredths:** 2 hundredths < 8 hundredths

Because 7.385 has more hundredths, it is the greater number. You do not need to check thousandths.

➡ 7.385 inches is longer than 7.323 inches.

**Understand:** How to use expanded form to compare decimal numbers

> A scientist records the lengths of two specimens. Specimen A is 3.452 centimeters long. Specimen B is 3.459 centimeters long. Which specimen is longer?

You can compare the measures using expanded notation.

**Specimen A:** $3.452 = 3 \times 1 + 4 \times \frac{1}{10} + 5 \times \frac{1}{100} + 2 \times \frac{1}{1,000}$

**Specimen B:** $3.459 = 3 \times 1 + 4 \times \frac{1}{10} + 5 \times \frac{1}{100} + 9 \times \frac{1}{1,000}$

Start with the greatest place value and compare. Both numbers have 3 ones, both numbers have 4 tenths, and both numbers have 5 hundredths. Now, compare the thousandths: 2 thousandths is less than 9 thousandths, so 3.452 < 3.459.

➡ Specimen B is longer than Specimen A.

Unit 2 ■ Focus on Number and Operations in Base Ten  **65**

---

**Understand:** How to use place value to compare decimal numbers

■ This presentation walks students through the process of comparing decimal numbers by comparing the digits in each number place by place.

■ Make sure students understand how to use the symbols >, <, and = to compare numbers place by place.

**Understand:** How to use expanded form to compare decimal numbers

■ This presentation shows how writing two decimal numbers in expanded form can help students compare the numbers. Ensure students are starting with the greatest place and comparing each value.

■ Reinforce learning from the previous lesson by having students read assorted decimals in expanded form.

■ For practice, have students write 3.058 in expanded form. Be sure that they include the zero term so that digits with the same place value are compared.

---

## Math-to-Math Connection

**Random Number Generator** Search for a random number generator that simulates the rolling of a number cube 1–6. Have members of small groups take turns simulating the rolling a number cube four times each. After each roll of the cube, instruct each student to secretly choose in which position (ones, tenths, hundredths, or thousandths) to write the digit on a place-value chart. Inform students that they can use each place only once. After the fourth roll, each member of the group will reveal his or her number. Then students will work together to order the decimals from least to greatest.

# Guided Instruction

**Connect: What you know about place value and comparisons** Use this page to help students strengthen their understanding of using place value to compare decimal numbers.

■ In Step 1, discuss that writing a zero to the right of the last digit in a decimal number does not change its value: 0.23 = 0.230. Students should conclude that the zero acts as a placeholder, helping them align the place of each digit. When students begin adding and subtracting decimal numbers, inserting zero placeholders as needed will help students to compute accurately.

■ Have students compare and contrast the method in this presentation with using a place-value chart.

✏ ▸ While students are beginning to grasp the ideas behind comparing decimal numbers, some will make the same mistake as Willa. If students are struggling to explain their reasoning, align the four numbers in columns according to place value. Use this opportunity to reinforce the strategy of writing a zero to the right of the last digit in a decimal number as a placeholder. Then have the students write the numbers from least to greatest and compare.

---

## Guided Instruction

**Connect: What you know about place value and comparisons**

Compare 0.23 and 0.234.

**Step 1**

Write the numbers in a column, lining up like place values. Add a zero to the thousandths column of 0.23 to help you align each digit with its correct corresponding place value.

0.230
0.234

**Step 2**

Compare the digits in the same place, starting from the left. The digits in the ones place are both 0.

0.230
0.234

**Step 3**

Compare the digits in the tenths place. The digits are both 2.

0.230
0.234

**Step 4**

Compare the digits in the hundredths place. The digits are both 3.

0.230
0.234

**Step 5**

Compare the digits in the thousandths place. The digits are different: 0 thousandths < 4 thousandths

0.230
0.234

The number 0.230 is less than 0.234.

➡ 0.23 < 0.234

✏ ▸ Willa says that 0.276 is greater than 0.88 because 276 is greater than 88. Explain why Willa's reasoning is incorrect.
Possible explanation: Willa is not taking into consideration the place values of the digits. If you compare place values of the two numbers, you will see that because 2 tenths is less than 8 tenths, 0.276 < 0.88.

---

## Math-to-Science Connection

**Measurements** Scientists use sophisticated instruments to make precise measurements. A strong understanding of how to read, write, and compare decimals is important when conducting experiments. Using the Internet, have students research some digital instruments, such as balances and thermometers. Encourage a class discussion on the precision of these instruments. The discussion should also include the common uses of the instruments, as well as the place-value range displayed on each instrument.

Lesson 7

Guided Practice

1. Compare 1.237 and 1.234.

   a. Write the decimals in a place-value chart.

| ones | . | tenths | hundredths | thousandths |
|------|---|--------|------------|-------------|
| 1 | . | 2 | 3 | 7 |
| 1 | . | 2 | 3 | 4 |

   Compare the digits starting from the left.

   **Ones:** 1 one = 1 one

   **Tenths:** __2__ tenths = __2__ tenths

   **Hundredths:** ____3 hundredths = 3 hundredths____

   **Thousandths:** ____7 thousandths > 4 thousandths____

   b. Write < or >. 1.237 __>__ 1.234

**For exercises 2–4, compare the numbers using place value.**

2. 0.029 and 0.030

   **Step 1:** Which is the first place from the left that has different digits?

   __hundredths__

   **Step 2:** Which digit is greater? __3__

   **Step 3:** So 0.029 __<__ 0.030

3. 1.109 and 1.019

   1.109 __>__ 1.019

4. 0.27 and 0.269

   0.27 __>__ 0.269

**Ⱶⱶ Think•Pair•Share**

MP2  5. Caleb wants to put three batting averages in order from least to greatest. They are 0.276, 0.283, and 0.279. Explain how he can do this.
Possible answer: He can write the numbers in a column and align like place values. He can then compare the digits starting with the greatest place and see that 0.283 > 0.279 > 0.276.

## Mathematical Practices

Mathematical Practice Standards underline the teaching and understanding of all concepts and skills presented. The emphasis of specific practices is noted throughout the guided and independent practice of this lesson.

| MP2 | **Reason abstractly and quantitatively.** |
|-----|-------------------------------------------|

**Item 5:** Students compare three decimal quantities to each other and write them in ascending order.

## Observational Assessment

Use page 67 to assess whether students understand how to use place value to compare decimals. As the amount of scaffolding in the problems drops off, note those students who need to use a place-value chart to align the digits in the decimal numbers. While place-value charts are useful tools, they can be time-consuming for some students. Suggest a similar method, such as writing the decimal numbers in a column aligned at the decimal point.

**Ⱶⱶ Think•Pair•Share**

**Peer Collaboration** Have pairs of students complete the problem. After each pair has written an explanation, direct pairs to switch their answers with another pair of students. Next, have each pair follow the steps outlined to order the batting averages. Prompt a discussion on comparing three decimal numbers by asking:

- *How is comparing three decimal numbers different than comparing two decimal numbers?*

- *Did your group use the same method to compare the three batting averages as other groups? If not, what steps were done differently?*

To summarize, review each method to compare decimal numbers. Encourage pairs who got an incorrect answer to switch papers with a different pair and follow the outlined steps.

### Return to the Essential Question

Reread the Lesson 7 Essential Question on page 64: *How can you compare decimal numbers?*

Ask volunteers to use what they learned in this lesson to answer the question. (Possible responses: I can compare decimal numbers using a number line, fractions, place-value charts, expanded form, or by writing the decimal numbers in columns. I can compare the digits in each place starting with the greatest place.)

# Independent Practice

## Concept Application

Students may work independently on these pages in the classroom or at home. They may refer to the first four pages of the lesson to revisit the instruction or to see a worked-out example.

**Common Errors** and **Teaching Tips** may help you support student learning either in the classroom or as a follow-up for work done at home.

## Common Errors

### Item 2

Some students may not think it is important to include the zero when writing 0.023 in expanded form. Have students use a different colored pencil to circle each multiplication expression to ensure they are comparing the same place value in both decimals.

## Independent Practice

**Compare using a place-value chart.**

1. Compare 1.135 and 1.153.

    a. Write the decimals in a place-value chart.

    | ones | . | tenths | hundredths | thousandths |
    |------|---|--------|------------|-------------|
    | 1    | . | 1      | 3          | 5           |
    | 1    | . | 1      | 5          | 3           |

    b. Compare the digits in the same place value columns.

    **Ones:** 1 one = 1 one

    **Tenths:** _____ 1 tenth = 1 tenth _____

    **Hundredths:** ___ 3 hundredths < 5 hundredths ___

    c. Since the 3 in the hundredths place of 1.135 is less than the 5 in the hundredths place of 1.153, 1.135 $\underline{<}$ 1.153.

**Compare using expanded form. Show your work.**

2. 0.023 and 0.198

    **Step 1:**
    Write 0.023 in expanded notation.

    $0 \times 1 + 0 \times \frac{1}{10} + \underline{2} \times \frac{1}{100} + 3 \times \frac{1}{1,000}$

    **Step 2:**
    Write 0.198 in expanded notation.

    $0 \times 1 + \underline{1} \times \frac{1}{10} + 9 \times \frac{1}{100} + \underline{8} \times \frac{1}{1,000}$

    **Step 3:**
    Compare the tenths.

    $0 \times \frac{1}{10} \underline{<} 1 \times \frac{1}{10}$

    $0.023 \underline{<} 0.198$

## Writing About Math

▸ **Write an Opinion** Have students review the different methods to compare decicmals taught in this lesson. Tell students to choose the method they prefer and write about why they chose that method. Students should use detailed explanations to justify their choice and include examples. Their writing should also explain why they did not choose one of the other methods.

Encourage volunteers to read their opinions to the class.

Lesson 7

Independent Practice

**Compare. Use place value.**

3. 1.121 and 1.211

1.121 $\leq$ 1.211

4. 0.37 and 0.370

0.37 $=$ 0.370

5. 0.298 and 0.289

0.298 $>$ 0.289

**Compare. Use expanded form.**

6. 3.544 and 3.455

3.544 $>$ 3.455

7. 0.109 and 0.190

0.109 $\leq$ 0.190

8. 0.12 and 0.119

0.12 $>$ 0.119

**Choose the correct answer.**

9. The lengths of two nails are 0.785 inch and 0.768 inch. At which place should you look to decide which nail is longer?

a. ones

(b.) hundredths

c. tenths

d. thousandths

10. For the number 3.124, which of the following correctly shows the place value of the digit 4 in expanded form?

a. $4 \times \frac{1}{10}$

b. $4 \times \frac{1}{100}$

(c.) $4 \times \frac{1}{1,000}$

d. $4 \times 1000$

11. Which of the following decimals is to the left of 0.354 on a number line?

a. 0.355

(b.) 0.35

c. 0.364

d. 1.333

## Teaching Tips

### Item 3–5
Provide grid paper for students to use to help them align decimal numbers correctly and visualize the comparison.

### Item 8
Remind students they may choose to write a zero in the thousandths place of 0.12 before comparing it to 0.119.

### Item 11
Have students draw a number line with a decimal scale of hundredths.

## Digital Connection

**Online Games** There are several online games that involve comparing decimal numbers. Use a search engine to locate some of these games. Many games allow students to choose whether to compare decimal numbers to the tenths, hundredths, or thousandths place. Some students may want to practice comparing to the hundredths place before attempting to compare to the thousandths place.

# Independent Practice

## Common Errors

### Item 12
Students may plot the decimals incorrectly. Provide additional support by reviewing how to plot whole numbers on a number line. To make the connection to plotting decimal numbers, have students visualize the decimal numbers without the decimal points and plot them similarly to plotting whole numbers.

### Item 14
Students may not be able to recognize the error immediately. Prompt students to discuss how decimal numbers are compared by starting with the greatest place value and moving to the right.

## Independent Practice

**Compare the decimals using the number line.**

**12.** 2.543 $\leq$ 2.549

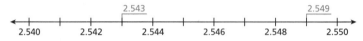

**Solve the problems.**

MP6 **13.** Explain some ways you can compare decimals.
Possible explanation: One way is to use a place value chart and look at digits in each place from left to right. Another way is to use a number line or expanded notation.

MP3 **14.** To compare 5.147 and 5.139, Emily looked at the thousandths place. She said since 9 is greater than 7, 5.139 is greater than 5.147. What is her error? Explain how to correct it.
Emily compared the digits in the thousandths place. She should have compared the digits in the hundredths place, which is the greatest place with different digits. If she compares the digits in the hundredths place, 4 > 3, so 5.147 is greater than 5.139.

MP6 **15.** A quarter is 1.750 millimeters thick. A nickel is 1.950 millimeters thick. Write the sizes as mixed numbers. Which is thicker? Explain.
A quarter is $1\frac{750}{1,000}$ mm thick. A nickel is $1\frac{950}{1,000}$ mm. A nickel is thicker because 1.950 mm > 1.750 mm.

MP6 **16.** A dime has a mass of 2.268 grams. A penny has a mass of 2.500 grams. Write the masses as mixed numbers. Which coin has a greater mass? Explain.
A dime is $2\frac{268}{1,000}$ grams. A penny is $2\frac{500}{1,000}$ grams. A penny has a greater mass because 2.500 grams > 2.268 grams.

## Mathematical Practices

| **MP3** | **Construct viable arguments and critique the reasoning of others.** |
|---|---|

**Item 14:** Students construct an argument on how to properly compare decimal numbers.

| **MP6** | **Attend to precision.** |
|---|---|

**Item 13:** Students communicate their reasoning behind the different methods of comparing decimal numbers.

**Items 15–16:** Students explain how to compare decimal place values to determine which measurement is greater.

MP5 **17.** One gram of anchovies has 0.199 grams of B vitamins. One gram of sturgeon has 0.101 grams of B vitamins. Tuna has more B vitamins than sturgeon but less than anchovies. The number of B vitamins in tuna is a number listed as a, b, or c below. Which number is correct for tuna?

a. 0.099 grams per gram

b. 0.211 grams per gram

c. 0.188 grams per gram

▸ **Show your work. Use a place-value chart.**

| Fish | ones | . | tenths | hundredths | thousandths | |
|------|------|---|--------|------------|-------------|-----|
| anchovies | 0 | . | 1 | 9 | 9 | *most* |
| a. | 0 | . | 0 | 9 | 9 | |
| b. | 0 | . | 2 | 1 | 1 | |
| c. | 0 | . | 1 | 8 | 8 | Tuna |
| sturgeon | 0 | . | 1 | 0 | 1 | *least* |

Tuna has 0.188 grams of B vitamins per gram.

MP4 **18.** Karen wants to drill a hole for a screw. The hole must be a little smaller than the screw. She has three drill bits with diameters of 0.389 inch, 0.362 inch, and 0.352 inch. She has three screws with diameters of 0.385 inch, 0.362 inch, and 0.348 inch. Which are the best drill bit and screw combination that Karen should use? Explain your reasoning.

▸ **Show your work. Use the number line**

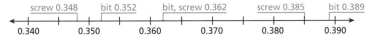

Screw 0.385 < bit 0.389
Screw 0.362 = bit 0.362
Screw 0.362 > bit 0.352
Screw 0.348 < bit 0.352

The number line makes it easier to compare the bit and screw sizes. Because bit 0.389 is larger than any screw, that bit can't be used. Because screw 0.348 is smaller than any bit, that screw cannot be used. Screw 0.362 is the same size as bit 0.362, so that screw cannot be used with that bit. But bit 0.352 is a little smaller than screw 0.362, so that bit and screw are a good combination.

Unit 2 ■ Focus on Number and Operations in Base Ten    **71**

**Teaching Tips**

**Item 17**

Have students first compare the tenths place to eliminate extraneous answer choices. Have students explain why the tenths place should be compared initially.

**Item 18**

Students may wish to order the list of decimals before plotting them on a number line.

| **Mathematical Practices** |
|---|
| **MP4** **Model with mathematics.** |
| **Item 18:** Students use a number line to compare several decimals. |
| **MP5** **Use appropriate tools strategically.** |
| **Item 17:** Students use a place-value chart to determine which decimal is between two given decimals. |

## OBJECTIVE

Round decimal numbers to the nearest whole, tenth, or hundredth, using place-value charts and number lines.

## ESSENTIAL QUESTION

Lead a class discussion on when it is useful to round numbers, for example, when buying an item that costs $1.99. Encourage students to describe when they use rounding in their everyday life.

## FLUENCY PRACTICE

Fluency practice is available at sadlierconnect.com.

## Concept Development

### Understand: How to round decimal numbers to the nearest whole number

■ Students will build on previous knowledge of rounding whole numbers.

■ To round a decimal number students need to be able to identify place values. Review the place-value chart to elicit the understanding that rounding to the nearest whole is the same as rounding to the ones place.

■ Make sure students understand how to interpret the whole numbers and the decimals on the number line.

---

### Lesson 8 — Round Decimals: Use Place Value

## Guided Instruction

In this lesson you will learn how to round decimals using place value.

**Understand: How to round decimal numbers to the nearest whole number**

> A jewelry designer records the mass of a necklace as 32.748 grams. What is the mass of the necklace to the nearest gram?

To find the mass of the necklace to the nearest gram, you can round 32.748 using the same steps you apply to round whole numbers.

Write 32.748 in a place-value chart. Identify the place you are being asked to round to. Rounding to the nearest gram means you are rounding to the nearest *whole number*. So, you are rounding to the ones place.

| tens | ones | . | tenths | hundredths | thousandths |
|------|------|---|--------|------------|-------------|
| 3 | 2 | . | 7 | 4 | 8 |

Use a number line to help you round 32.748 grams to the ones place.

- Draw a number line. Since 32.748 is between **32** and **33**, start and end with these whole numbers. Separate the line into tenths.

- Plot the approximate location of 32.748.

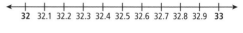

- Identify the whole number closest to 32.748 on the number line. 32.748 is closer to 33 than to 32.

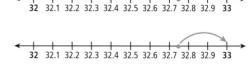

➡ To the nearest gram, the mass of the necklace is 33 grams.

---

## Support English Language Learners

The term *rounding* may be confusing to some students. Students will likely associate *round* as a shape, such as a round ball. Use this knowledge to connect *rounding* with estimating. Say to students, *When we estimate, we want a number that is* **around**, *the exact answer.* Have students repeat your verbalization. Then ask students to estimate the sum of various two-digit numbers that you can write on the board. Repeat this process to help students become familiar with the verbalization.

Lesson 8

Guided Instruction

**Understand: How to round decimal numbers to the nearest tenth**

Now the jewelry designer wants to know what the mass of the necklace, 32.748 grams, is to the nearest tenth of a gram.

Use a number line to help you round 32.748 grams. The answer will be in tenths because you are asked to round to the nearest *tenth* of a gram.

- 32.748 is between the tenths values **32.7** and **32.8**. Divide the interval from 32.7 to 32.8 into ten parts to show hundredths.

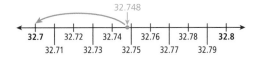

- The point for 32.748 is closer to 32.7 than 32.8.

- 32.748 rounded to the nearest *tenth* is 32.7.

➡ To the nearest tenth of a gram, the mass of the necklace is 32.7 grams.

**Understand: How to round decimal numbers to the nearest hundredth**

Round 32.748 grams to the nearest hundredth of a gram.

Use a number line to help you round 32.748 grams. The answer will be in hundredths because you are asked to round to the nearest *hundredth* of a gram.

- 32.748 is between the hundredths values **32.74** and **32.75**. Divide the interval between these numbers into ten parts to show thousandths.

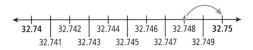

- The point for 32.748 is closer to 32.75 than 32.74.

- 32.748 rounded to the nearest *hundredth* is 32.75.

➡ To the nearest hundredth of a gram the mass is 32.75 grams.

**Understand: How to round decimals to the nearest tenth**

■ This presentation shows how to use a number line to round a decimal number to the tenths place. In this case, it might be helpful to review metric weights and how they are all related to the gram. Ask students to explain how a decimal number can always be between two other decimal numbers.

**Understand: How to round decimals to the nearest hundredth**

■ Prompt students to remember from Lesson 6 that a digit in the thousandths place represents one tenth of what it represents in the hundredths place.

■ Have student pairs discuss how rounding decimals to different places is the same and how it differs.

## Math-to-Math Connection

**Irrational Numbers** The decimal value of an irrational number is nonrepeating and nonterminating. Pi ($\pi$) is perhaps the most common irrational number. It is used to express the ratio of the circumference of a circle to its diameter. Since pi is an irrational number, it must be rounded when used in a calculation. It is typical to round pi to two decimal places, using 3.14 in calculations. If the $\pi$ button on a calculator is used, the value of pi will be rounded to the greatest number of digits the calculator can hold.

**Connect: What you know about place value and rounding decimal numbers** Use this page to help students strengthen their understanding of rounding decimal numbers to any place.

■ In this presentation, students round to the nearest centimeter. Make sure students understand that a centimeter is the whole unit, so they are rounding to the ones place. Some students may know that a centimeter is $\frac{1}{100}$ of a meter and round to the nearest hundredth. It is important that students consider the units within the context of the problem.

■ Remind students to look to the right of the specified place value to make rounding decisions. Reiterate that the rules for rounding decimal numbers are the same as for rounding whole numbers. If students are struggling, have them review and discuss the Remember! feature found on the student page.

---

## Guided Instruction

**Connect: What you know about place value and rounding decimal numbers**

A biologist records the lengths of three lizards in centimeters.

What is the length of lizard A to the nearest centimeter?
What is the length of lizard B to the nearest tenth of a centimeter?
What is the length of lizard C to the nearest hundredth of a centimeter?

| Lizard | Length (cm) |
|--------|-------------|
| A | 14.612 |
| B | 13.844 |
| C | 15.036 |

**Step 1**

To find the length of lizard A to the nearest centimeter, round 14.612 to the ones place. The rounding rules for decimals are the same as for whole numbers. Write 14.612 in a place-value chart.

| tens | ones | . | tenths | hundredths | thousandths |
|------|------|---|--------|------------|-------------|
| 1 | 4 | . | 6 | 1 | 2 |

To round to the ones place, look at the digit in the tenths place: 6 > 5, so round 4 up to get 15.

**Remember!**
To round, look at the digit to the right of the rounding place.
• If it is 5 or more, round the digit in the rounding place up.
• If it is less than 5, leave the digit in the rounding place as it is.

**Step 2**

To find the length of lizard B to the nearest tenth of a centimeter, round 13.844 to the tenths place.

Look at the hundredths place: 13.844. Since 4 < 5, leave the number in the tenths place, 8, as it is. 13.844 rounds to 13.8.

**Step 3**

To find the length of lizard C to the nearest hundredth of a centimeter, round 15.036 to the hundredths place.

Look at the digit in the thousandths place: 15.036. Since 6 > 5, round 3 hundredths up to 4 hundredths. 15.036 rounds to 15.04.

➡ To the nearest centimeter, lizard A is 15 cm long. To the nearest tenth of a centimeter, lizard B is 13.8 cm long. To the nearest hundredth of a centimeter, lizard C is 15.04 cm long.

**74** Unit 2 ■ Focus on Number and Operations in Base Ten

---

## Math-to-Shopping Connection

**Rounding Money** Have students create a shopping list for groceries. Using grocery store advertisements, have students round the prices of their items to the nearest tenth and the nearest dollar. Ask students why it might be helpful to know how to round when shopping at a grocery store. Students might respond that rounding is a quick and easy way to determine whether you have enough money to buy the items in your cart, or whether the total cost is reasonable or not. This activity gives students an opportunity to round decimals in a real-world situation.

MORE ONLINE sadlierconnect.com

Lesson 8

Guided Practice

**For exercises 1–2, use the number line given to complete the sentences and round each number.**

1. 8.215 to the nearest whole number

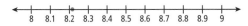

8.215 is closer to __8__ than __9__ on the number line.

8.215 rounded to the nearest whole number is __8__.

2. 19.837 to the nearest hundredth

19.837 is closer to ___19.84___ than ___19.83___ on the number line.

19.837 rounded to the nearest hundredth is ___19.84___.

**Use the place-value chart to round 0.376 to the nearest tenth and nearest hundredth.**

3.

| ones | . | tenths | hundredths | thousandths |
|------|---|--------|------------|-------------|
| 0 | . | 3 | 7 | 6 |

Nearest tenth: _0.4_

Nearest hundredth: _0.38_

👐 Think • Pair • Share

MP2 4. Explain why 1.999 rounded to the nearest hundredth is 2.
Possible explanation: When you round 1.999 to the hundredths place, you must round up 9 hundredths as 10 hundredths, or 1 tenth and 0 hundredths. Since there is also a 9 in the tenths place in 1.999, you add the 1 tenth to 9 tenths to get 10 tenths, or 1 one and 0 tenths. Since there is also a 1 in the ones place, the resulting rounded number is 2.

## Observational Assessment

Use page 75 to assess students' understanding of how to round by finding the closer number on the number line. Ensure that students carefully read to which place value to round. Students must also follow the rules for rounding when rounding decimal numbers.

### 👐 Think•Pair•Share

**Peer Collaboration** Ask students to first complete the problem on their own. Then, have students compare their explanations with a partner. Partners should discuss any differences in their explanations and write one explanation for the pair. Ask for volunteers to share their answers. Extend the discussion with the following questions.

• *What is another way to say ten hundredths? ten tenths?*

• *How could you use a number line to justify your answer?*

To summarize, tell students that there is more than one way to explain their thinking. They can use words, place-value charts, or number lines.

### Return to the Essential Question

Reread the Lesson 8 Essential Question on page 72: *How do you use place value to round decimal numbers?*

Ask volunteers to use what they learned in this lesson to answer this question. (Possible responses: I can round a decimal number by looking at the digit in the place to the right. I can use place value to plot the number on a number line and then round to the nearest number. The place value tells me what scale to use on the number line.)

---

## Mathematical Practices

Mathematical Practice Standards underline the teaching and understanding of all concepts and skills presented. The emphasis of specific practices is noted throughout the guided and independent practice of this lesson.

**MP2  Reason abstractly and quantitatively.**

**Item 4:** Students use quantitative reasoning to explain that rounding a digit up to 10 from 9 moves the digit into the next greater place value.

## Concept Application

Students may work independently on these pages in the classroom or at home. They may refer to the first four pages of the lesson to revisit the instruction or to see a worked-out example.

**Common Errors** and **Teaching Tips** may help you support student learning either in the classroom or as a follow-up for work done at home.

## Common Errors

### Item 5

If students choose an incorrect answer choice, they may have missed the word NOT in the problem statement. Remind students that it is important to read all questions carefully.

## Teaching Tips

### Items 1–2

Help students recognize that they are choosing the tenth or hundredth closest to the given number. Encourage students to underline the number at each end of the number line to which they are rounding.

---

### Independent Practice

**Use the number line to help you round the number.**

1. 0.762 to the nearest tenth

   0.7  0.71  0.72  0.73  0.74  0.75  0.76  0.77  0.78  0.79  0.8

   0.762 rounded to the nearest tenth is __0.8__.

2. 6.308 to the nearest hundredth

   6.30  6.301  6.302  6.303  6.304  6.305  6.306  6.307  6.308  6.309  6.31

   6.308 rounded to the nearest hundredth is __6.31__.

**Use the place-value charts to round each decimal to the nearest whole number, nearest tenth, and nearest hundredth.**

3. 67.822

| tens | ones | . | tenths | hundredths | thousandths |
|------|------|---|--------|------------|-------------|
| 6 | 7 | . | 8 | 2 | 2 |

Nearest whole number: __68__

Nearest tenth: __67.8__

Nearest hundredth: __67.82__

4. 2.467

| ones | . | tenths | hundredths | thousandths |
|------|---|--------|------------|-------------|
| 2 | . | 4 | 6 | 7 |

Nearest whole number: __2__

Nearest tenth: __2.5__

Nearest hundredth: __2.47__

5. Which of the following decimals does NOT round to the nearest tenth as 45.3?

   a. 45.28

   b. 45.331

   (c.) 45.373

   d. 45.317

---

## Writing About Math

▸ **Write an Informative Text** Ask students to write a paragraph explaining how to round to any place in a decimal number. After they are finished, have students trade paragraphs with a partner and follow their partner's directions to round 34.592 to the nearest whole, tenth, and hundredth. Have students revise, edit, rewrite, or try a new approach if their partner cannot round correctly following their directions.

6. Round a, b, c, and d on the number line to the nearest hundredth.

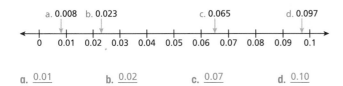

a. <u>0.01</u>          b. <u>0.02</u>          c. <u>0.07</u>          d. <u>0.10</u>

**For exercises 7–10, write the place value that each number was rounded to.**

7. 4.55 rounded to 4.6          8. 0.129 rounded to 0.13
   <u>tenths</u>                   <u>hundredths</u>

9. 66.4 rounded to 66          10. 583.476 rounded to 583.48
   <u>ones</u>                      <u>hundredths</u>

**For exercises 11–14, round the decimals to the nearest one, tenth, and hundredth.**

|        | one | tenth | hundredth |
|--------|-----|-------|-----------|
| 11. 0.344 | 0 | 0.3 | 0.34 |
| 12. 1.545 | 2 | 1.5 | 1.55 |
| 13. 9.624 | 10 | 9.6 | 9.62 |
| 14. 89.799 | 90 | 89.8 | 89.80 |

15. Which number rounds up when rounded to the tenths place?

   a. 65.938                    b. 65.527

   c. 65.409                    (d.) 65.152

## Common Errors

### Item 15

Some students may automatically round to the next nearest place value; in this case hundredths. Have students underline the place value for tenths.

## Teaching Tips

### Item 12

Students may not know how to round to a place value when the digit to the right is a 5. Remind them that there are 5 digits for both situations, rounding up and rounding down. Students should start to see a pattern in when to round up and when to round down.

## Digital Connection

**Spreadsheets** Using a simple spreadsheet program on a computer, show students that you can set spreadsheets to round to a certain number of decimal places. Type a decimal number to several decimal places into a spreadsheet cell. Use the tools in the spreadsheet to change the number of places that are displayed. Show how the program can round up as well as down, depending on the settings.

# Independent Practice

## Teaching Tips

### Item 17
Students should see that the problem requires them to determine what place value was used to round. Encourage students to think about how they would round 8.557 to the nearest hundredth, tenth, and one.

### Item 18
Be sure students can verbalize that when a number is rounded down, it is less than the original number, so rounding an estimate down will result in an underestimation.

## Independent Practice

16. The mass of a sample at the start of a science experiment is 10.951 grams. What is the sample's mass rounded to the nearest tenth of a gram?

    a. 10.0 grams

    b. 10.9 grams

    c. 10.95 grams

    (d.) 11.0 grams ·

**Solve the problems.**

MP2 17. Explain how 8.557 can be rounded correctly to 9, 8.6, or 8.56.
Possible response: 8.557 rounded to the nearest whole number is 9. Rounded to the nearest tenth, it is 8.6. Rounded to the nearest hundredth, it is 8.56.

MP3 18. Mia has exactly $10.25. She wants to buy a box of pens for $6.49 and a notebook for $4.28. She rounds both prices to the nearest dollar to get $6 and $4. She thinks, "When I add the rounded prices I get $10. I have more than enough money." Is Mia correct? Explain.
Mia is incorrect. Possible explanation: The actual total price is more than $10.25, so $10.25 is not enough to buy the items. When Mia rounded down and added, her estimated total of $10 was $0.49 + $0.28 less than the actual total. That is more than $0.25, so she does not have enough money.

MP7 19. A rectangular yard has a length of 7.3 meters and a width of 4.8 meters. Use rounding to estimate the perimeter and area of the yard.

    **Show your work.**
    Perimeter: $2 \times 7 + 2 \times 5 = 24$
    Area: $7 \times 5 = 35$

    **Answer** The perimeter is about 24 meters. The area is about 35 square meters.

## Mathematical Practices

| | |
|---|---|
| **MP2** | **Reason abstractly and quantitatively.** |

**Item 17:** Students think and explain how the same number can be rounded as three different numbers by exploring the value of each digit in the number.

| | |
|---|---|
| **MP3** | **Construct viable arguments and critique the reasoning of others.** |

**Item 18:** Students analyze a problem situation and share their opinions on how to correctly round money.

| | |
|---|---|
| **MP7** | **Look for and make use of structure.** |

**Item 19:** Students use rounding to estimate the perimeter of a rectangle.

MORE ONLINE sadlierconnect.com

Lesson 8

**Independent Practice**

MP1 **20.** Josie finished a sprinting race in 31.183 seconds. Wynne finished the race in 28.927 seconds. Estimate the difference in times by rounding the times to the nearest tenth of a second and subtracting by using a number line or another method. About how much sooner did Wynne finish?

**▶ Show your work.**
31.183 rounds to 31.2
28.927 rounds to 29.0
$31.2 - 29.0 = 2.2$

**Answer** Wynne finished about 2.2 seconds sooner.

MP3 **21.** Pam bought a box of cereal for $4.39 and a gallon of milk for $3.42. Sam bought a carton of orange juice for $3.59 and a loaf of bread for $3.65. Estimate the amount each person paid by rounding the prices to the nearest dollar and adding. Then find the actual total each person paid. Whose estimated total is greater? Whose actual total is greater? Why do you think this happens?

**▶ Show your work.**
Pam's estimated total: $4 + $3 = $7; Pam's actual total: $4.39 + $3.42 = $7.81
Sam's estimated total: $4 + $4 = $8; Sam's actual total: $3.59 + $3.65 = $7.24

**Answer** Sam's estimated total is greater. Pam's actual total is greater. Possible explanation: This happens because we are rounding both values way up to get Sam's estimate and way down to get Pam's estimate. So, the estimates of the sums are not very close to the actual values.

MP1 **22.** Use the hints below to identify the missing digit in the decimal number.

27.■62

• When rounded to the nearest whole number, the number is 27.

• When rounded to the nearest tenth, the number is 27.4.

**Answer** 27.362

**Independent Practice**

## Teaching Tips

### Item 20
As a class, review subtracting decimals on the board if students struggle to find the correct answer.

### Item 22
Help students see that the first clue tells them that the missing number is less than 5 since the digit in the ones places does not change. The second clue tells them that the 6 will cause the missing digit to round up to 4.

## Mathematical Practices

| MP1 | **Make sense of problems and persevere in solving them.** |
|---|---|

**Items 20 and 22:** Students analyze the problem and think about an approach to solving before attempting to solve.

| MP3 | **Construct viable arguments and critique the reasoning of others.** |
|---|---|

**Item 21:** Students use their knowledge of rounding and deductive reasoning to analyze each part of the problem before explaining a general rule in rounding.

## OBJECTIVE
Use the standard algorithm to multiply multi-digit numbers.

## ESSENTIAL QUESTION
Read the essential question to students. Explain that they will use a standard algorithm, which is a set of steps to solve a mathematical problem, and their knowledge of products of one-digit numbers to find the product of multi-digit numbers. Using partial products will allow students to break the problem into smaller, more manageable parts.

## FLUENCY PRACTICE
Fluency practice is available at **sadlierconnect.com**.

## Concept Development

### Understand: How to multiply a multi-digit number by a one-digit number.

■ Students need to understand that the three digits of a three-digit number represent amounts of hundreds, tens, and ones. For example 729, equals 7 hundreds, 2 tens, and 9 ones. After multiplying 9 times 6 in the first step, it may be helpful to stress the place values of the digits in the product 54 and that you are recording 5 tens over the tens places.

■ Students may struggle with the shift between multiplying the factors and then adding the tens or hundred that were regrouped in the previous step. Reading the steps aloud and using place value in your explanations will help students grasp how the algorithm works.

---

### Lesson 9 — Multiply Fluently with Multi-Digit Numbers

**Essential Question:** How can you multiply multi-digit numbers by using the standard algorithm?

**Words to Know:** partial product

**Guided Instruction**

In this lesson you will multiply multi-digit numbers by using the standard algorithm.

**Understand:** How to multiply a multi-digit number by a one-digit number

> The path around the town park is 729 yards long. Cam ran around the park 6 times. How many yards did he run?

To find the distance Cam ran, multiply 729 by 6. You can use the standard multiplication algorithm.

$$\begin{array}{r} 5 \\ 729 \\ \times\ \ \ 6 \\ \hline 4 \end{array}$$

Multiply 9 ones by 6. You get 54 ones, or 5 tens and 4 ones.

Write 4 in the ones place of the answer and record the 5 tens over the tens place to be added in at the next step.

$$\begin{array}{r} 1\ 5 \\ 729 \\ \times\ \ \ 6 \\ \hline 74 \end{array}$$

Multiply 2 tens by 6. You get 12 tens. Add the 5 tens from the previous step to get 17 tens, or 1 hundred and 7 tens.

Write 7 in the tens place of the answer and record the 1 hundred over the hundreds place to be added in the next step.

$$\begin{array}{r} 1\ 5 \\ 729 \\ \times\ \ \ 6 \\ \hline 4,374 \end{array}$$

Multiply 7 hundreds by 6. You get 42 hundreds. Add the 1 hundred from the previous step to get 43 hundreds or 4 thousands and 3 hundreds.

Write 3 in the hundreds place of the answer and write 4 in the thousands place of the answer.

➡ Cam ran 4,374 yards in all.

---

### Words to Know

**partial product:** numbers that are formed by multiplying the value of each digit by a factor

**Example:** The partial products are in red.

$$\begin{array}{r} 3 \\ 2 \\ 24 \\ \times\ \ 86 \\ \hline 144 \leftarrow 6 \times 24 \\ +1{,}920 \leftarrow 80 \times 24 \\ \hline 2{,}064 \end{array}$$

**Glossary can be found on pp. 347–350.**

**Guided Instruction**

## Understand: How to multiply a two-digit number by a two-digit number

> A health club orders 86 boxes of protein bars. Each case contains 24 bars. How many protein bars does the health club order in all?

To find the total number of protein bars, multiply 86 by 24.

This area model shows that 86 × 24 can be calculated by adding the products of 6 × 24 and 80 × 24. Each of these products is called a partial product.

This idea can help you understand how to use the standard algorithm to multiply by a two-digit number.

$$\begin{array}{r} 2 \\ 24 \\ \times\ 86 \\ \hline 144 \end{array}$$

**Multiply 24 by 6.**
This will give you the first partial product. Follow the same steps used to multiply by a one-digit number on the previous page.

$$\begin{array}{r} 3 \\ 2 \\ 24 \\ \times\ 86 \\ \hline 144 \\ 1{,}920 \end{array}$$

**Multiply 24 by 80.**
This will give you the second partial product.

Remember that 80 × 24 is 10 times as much as 8 × 24. So, calculate the product just as you would calculate 8 × 24, but shift the digits in the partial product one place to the left. Put a 0 in the ones place.

> 8 × 24 = 192, so
> 80 × 24 = 1,920

$$\begin{array}{r} 3 \\ 2 \\ 24 \\ \times\ 86 \\ \hline 144 \\ +1{,}920 \\ \hline 2{,}064 \end{array}$$

**Add the partial products to get the product of 24 × 86.**

144 ← 6 × 24
+1,920 ← 80 × 24

➡ The health club orders 2,064 protein bars in all.

Unit 2 ■ Focus on Number and Operations in Base Ten   **81**

## Understand: How to multiply a two-digit number by a two-digit number

■ After examining the area model, help students to make the connection between the area model shown and the partial products derived using the standard algorithm. The product for each area is represented by one of the lines of the standard algorithm. In the last step of the algorithm, the two partial products are added.

■ Remind students that this presentation shows the same steps as were used on the previous page when multiplying by a one-digit number. When multiplying by a two-digit number, apply the steps twice. Point out the blue zero in the second step to reinforce that you are multiplying by 80.

■ Tell students that once they have multiplied by 6, they can cross out the 20 ones that were regrouped as 2 tens in the tens column. Otherwise, when they have to regroup 30 ones as 3 tens in the next step, some students may try to add both 2 and 3 to the partial product.

■ Another way to use partial products is to multiply each digit separately by place value: multiply 6 × 4 = 24, 6 × 20 = 120, 80 × 4 = 320, and 80 × 20 = 1,600. To find the product, add the partial products: 24 + 120 + 320 + 1,600 = 2,064. The accompanying model would show 24 broken into the factors 20 and 4.

## Support English Language Learners

Help students understand that the word *partial,* as used in math, means "part of something." Explain that putting the partial products together completes the product of a multi-digit number multiplication. Demonstrate *partial* first by covering up half of a picture. Say, "This is a partial picture, not the whole picture." Then cover the other half. Say, "This is also a partial picture." Then show the whole picture and say, "When we put the two parts together, we have the whole picture."

Continue demonstrating the concept by showing the standard algorithm for multiplication,  labeling the partial products and adding them to get the product. Write more multi-digit multiplications on the board. Invite students to take turns labeling the partial products and identifying the product.

## Guided Instruction

**Connect: How to multiply numbers using the standard algorithm** Use this page to help students strengthen their understanding of the steps used to multiply multi-digit numbers.

■ The area model is a visual reminder of the place value when multiplying each digit of the second factor.

■ Encourage the class to explain each step as students work through the problem. Verbalizing students' thinking helps strengthen their understanding and gives you a chance to identify errors.

■ Show how to break up the factors by place value: 115 = 100 + 10 + 5 and 36 = 30 + 6. Draw a corresponding area model. Then find the partial products.

---

### Guided Instruction

**Connect: How to multiply numbers using the standard algorithm**

A resort hotel has 36 floors. Each floor has 115 guest rooms. How many guest rooms are in the hotel?

To find how many guest rooms are in the hotel, multiply 115 guest rooms on each floor by 36 floors. Use the standard algorithm.

The model shows that the product of 36 × 115 is the sum of the products of 6 × 115 and 30 × 115.

| | 115 |
|---|---|
| 30 | 30 × 115 |
| 6 | 6 × 115 |

**Step 1**

$$\begin{array}{r} {}^{3}\phantom{0} \\ 115 \\ \times\ 36 \\ \hline 690 \end{array}$$

**Multiply 115 by 6.**
This will give you the first partial product.

**Step 2**

$$\begin{array}{r} 1\phantom{0} \\ {}^{3}\phantom{0} \\ 115 \\ \times\ 36 \\ \hline 690 \\ 3,450 \end{array}$$

**Multiply 115 by 30.**
This will give you the second partial product.

Remember that 30 × 115 is 10 times as much as 3 × 115. So, calculate the product just as you would calculate 3 × 115, but shift the digits in the partial product one place to the left. Put a 0 in the ones place.

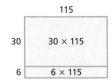

**Remember!**
3 × 115 = 345, so
30 × 115 = 3,450

**Step 3**

$$\begin{array}{r} 1\phantom{0} \\ {}^{3}\phantom{0} \\ 115 \\ \times\ 36 \\ \hline 690 \leftarrow 6 \times 115 \\ +3,450 \leftarrow 30 \times 115 \\ \hline 4,140 \end{array}$$

**Add the partial products to get the product of 36 × 115.**

➤ The hotel has 4,140 guest rooms.

---

## Math-to-Math Connection

**Arithmetic and Geometry** Area models are often used to model multiplication. Ask students how multiplication is related to the formula for area: Area = length × width. Tell students they can use area models to model any multiplication, as they did when they modeled the Distributive Property. Have students compare and contrast the Distributive Property and partial products.

Lesson 9

## Guided Practice

**Label the area model to show the partial products for the given multiplication problem.**

**1.** 32 × 64

```
            64
     ┌──────────────┐
  30 │   30 × 64    │
     ├──────────────┤
   2 │   2  ×  64   │
     └──────────────┘
```

**2.** 84 × 152

```
             152
     ┌──────────────────┐
  80 │   80  ×  152     │
     ├──────────────────┤
   4 │   4   ×  152     │
     └──────────────────┘
```

**The products are calculated using the standard algorithm. Fill in the missing partial products and products.**

**3.**
```
      607
  ×     5
  ───────
    3,035
```

**4.**
```
       74
  ×    52
  ────────
      148   ← 2 × 74
  + 3,700   ← 50 × 74
  ────────
    3,848
```

**5.**
```
       29
  ×    68
  ────────
      232   ← 8 × 29
  + 1,740   ← 60 × 29
  ────────
    1,972
```

**6.**
```
      435
  ×    16
  ────────
    2,610   ← 6 × 435
  + 4,350   ← 10 × 435
  ────────
    6,960
```

### � Think • Pair • Share

**MP3**

**7.** To multiply 225 times 40, Casey breaks apart 225 as 200 and 25. She knows that 25 times 4 is 100, so 25 times 40 is 1,000. Then she multiplies 200 times 40 to get 8,000. Finally, she adds 1,000 and 8,000 to get a final product of 9,000. Is Casey's answer correct? Explain your reasoning. Can you think of another way to break up the factors?
Yes, Casey is correct. Possible answer: You can break apart the factors any way you want as long as they add up to the original factors. Other ways to break up the factors are to break up 225 into 200, 20, and 5, or to break up 40 into 20 and 20.

## Mathematical Practices

Mathematical Practice Standards underline the teaching and understanding of all concepts and skills presented. The emphasis of specific practices is noted throughout the guided and independent practice of this lesson.

| MP3 | **Construct viable arguments and critique the reasoning of others.** |
|-----|----------------------------------------------------------------------|

**Item 7:** Students analyze partial products in writing and determine a correct product.

## Observational Assessment

Use page 83 to assess whether students can solve multi-digit multiplication problems. Note those students needing an area model to break apart a factor. Be sure students can correctly apply the standard algorithm to multiply by a one-digit number before they attempt to multiply by a two-digit number. Also note whether students are accurately regrouping and adding those values in the partial products.

### � Think•Pair•Share

**Peer Collaboration** Have students work in pairs. Tell them to find at least one other way to break up the factors. Students should draw area models to represent Casey's and their own multiplication. Ask students to present their work for class discussion. For each pair of presenters, ask:

- *How do area models help you multiply greater numbers?*

- *How did breaking up the factors make multiplication easier?*

To summarize, discuss how area models are helpful when using partial products to multiply.

### Return to the Essential Question

Reread the Lesson 9 Essential Question on page 80: *How can you multiply multi-digit numbers by using the standard algorithm?*

Ask volunteers to use what they learned in this lesson to answer this question. (Possible responses: I can break apart greater numbers by place value, multiply them, and add the partial products to determine the answer. I can create an area model to represent multiplication of greater numbers by place value, and then add the partial products to determine the answer.)

## Concept Application

Students may work independently on these pages in the classroom or at home. They may refer to the first four pages of the lesson to revisit the instruction or to see a worked-out example.

**Common Errors** and **Teaching Tips** may help you support student learning either in the classroom or as a follow-up for work done at home.

## Common Errors

### Items 1-2

Make sure students set up the multiplication based on the area model. They should break apart the first factor by place value rather than the second factor; otherwise, the area models will not match the partial products.

## Teaching Tips

### Items 5-8

Provide grid paper to help students keep digits aligned in the correct place-value position.

---

### Independent Practice

**Label the area model to show the partial products for the given multiplication problem.**

1. 27 × 51

| | 51 |
|---|---|
| 20 | 20 × 51 |
| 7 | 7 × 51 |

2. 93 × 294

| | 294 |
|---|---|
| 90 | 90 × 294 |
| 3 | 3 × 294 |

**The products are calculated using the standard algorithm. Fill in the missing partial products and products.**

3.
```
    838
  ×   4
  3,352
```

4.
```
    620
  ×   9
  5,580
```

5.
```
      51
  ×   27
     357   ← 7 × 51
+  1,020   ← 20 × 51
   1,377
```
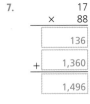

6.
```
     224
  ×   93
     672   ← 3 × 224
+ 20,160   ← 90 × 224
  20,832
```
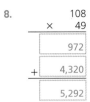

7.
```
      17
  ×   88
     136
+  1,360
   1,496
```

8.
```
     108
  ×   49
     972
+  4,320
   5,292
```

---

## Writing About Math

▪ **Write Explanatory Text** Ask students to write a paragraph that would explain the standard algorithm for multiplication of multi-digit numbers to a person who has never seen it before. Remind them that the order in which they explain it is important, as is the use of proper vocabulary.

Ask students to read each other's paragraphs and highlight key vocabulary terms or highlight areas where vocabulary terms could be inserted.

Lesson 9

Independent Practice

**Multiply. Show your work.**

9. 
$$
\begin{array}{r}
105 \\
\times\ 19 \\
\hline
945 \\
+1{,}050 \\
\hline
1{,}995
\end{array}
$$

10. 
$$
\begin{array}{r}
325 \\
\times\ 25 \\
\hline
1{,}625 \\
+6{,}500 \\
\hline
8{,}125
\end{array}
$$

11. 
$$
\begin{array}{r}
240 \\
\times\ 22 \\
\hline
480 \\
+4{,}800 \\
\hline
5{,}280
\end{array}
$$

12. 
$$
\begin{array}{r}
298 \\
\times\ 56 \\
\hline
1{,}788 \\
+14{,}900 \\
\hline
16{,}688
\end{array}
$$

13. 
$$
\begin{array}{r}
721 \\
\times\ 14 \\
\hline
2{,}884 \\
+\ 7{,}210 \\
\hline
10{,}094
\end{array}
$$

14. 
$$
\begin{array}{r}
386 \\
\times\ 75 \\
\hline
1{,}930 \\
+27{,}020 \\
\hline
28{,}950
\end{array}
$$

**For exercises 15–17, choose the correct answer.**

15. A car company has a large automobile plant that produces 148 cars per hour. The automobile plant operates 24 hours a day. How many cars does the automobile plant produce in a day?

   a. 148                    b. 888

   c. 3,422                  (d.) 3,552

16. A school group is raising money for a trip. The trip will cost $135 per student. If there are 67 students in the group, how much must the group raise?

   a. $9,450                 (b.) $9,045

   c. $8,100                 d. $1,755

17. A catering hall can hold 165 tables. Each table can seat 12 people. How many people can be seated in the catering hall?

   a. 495                    b. 1,650

   c. 1,870                  (d.) 1,980

Unit 2 ■ Focus on Number and Operations in Base Ten  **85**

## Common Errors

### Items 9-14

As students multiply greater numbers, make sure they write each partial product clearly in the correct column. Many students make mistakes when adding the partial products because they write the digits too close together and mistakenly add digits from different columns.

## Teaching Tips

### Items 15-17

Be sure that students are showing their work, writing the three-digit number as the first factor and the two-digit number as the second factor.

## Digital Connection

**Internet** Use a search engine to find Web sites where students are able to work at their own pace to multiply multi-digit numbers. Interactive activities and games are generally very popular with students. These Web sites will generate instant feedback by either keeping score or offering an explanation of the correct response if an answer is not given.

## Common Errors

### Items 20–21

Students will need to be meticulous in recording any values that are regrouped. Encourage students to cross out the regrouped digits once they have been added to the partial products. This is especially true in these exercises because there are multiple values that need to be regrouped, which can lead to several errors.

## Teaching Tips

### Item 18

If students cannot identify the error, have them find the areas in the area model. Then have them estimate the product. They should see that the area model is inaccurate by a factor of 10.

---

**MP4** 18. To multiply 247 by 64, Jacob draws the area model below. What is his error? Explain how he can correct his model.

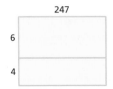

247

6

4

Possible response: Jacob broke apart 64 without paying attention to the place value of each digit. He should have written 60 and 4 for 64.

**MP3** 19. Explain two strategies you can use to find the product of 450 × 50.
Possible response: One strategy is to use the standard algorithm to multiply 450 × 5 and then multiply the result by 10, which would mean shifting the digits left one place and putting a 0 in the ones place. Another strategy is to double 50 to 100 and halve 450 to 225, and then find the product of 225 × 100.

**Solve the problems.**

**MP1** 20. Delilah is making necklaces. Each necklace will have 285 beads. She wants to make 37 necklaces. How many beads will Delilah need?

**▸ Show your work.**

```
  2 1
  5 3
  285
×  37
1,995
+8,550
10,545
```

**Answer** Delilah will need 10,545 beads.

**MP1** 21. Francis counts 863 books in a full bookcase at the library. The library has 95 full bookcases. If each bookcase has 863 books, how many books are in the library?

**▸ Show your work.**

```
  5 2
  3 1
  863
×  95
4,315
77,670
81,985
```

**Answer** There are 81,985 books in the library.

---

| **Mathematical Practices** |
|---|
| **MP1**  **Make sense of problems and persevere in solving them.** |
| **Items 20–21:** Students analyze a problem situation and use the standard algorithm to solve it. |
| **MP3**  **Construct viable arguments and critique the reasoning of others.** |
| **Item 19:** Students construct two different strategies for finding the product of multiplication and justify their conclusion. |
| **MP4**  **Model with mathematics.** |
| **Item 18:** Students multiply by using an area model that represents a problem situation. |

Lesson 9

## Independent Practice

MP8 **22.** A fruit orchard has 65 lemon trees. On average, each lemon tree produces about 407 lemons in 5 years. About how many lemons will the orchard produce in 5 years?

**Show your work.**

```
      4
      3
    407
  ×  65
  2,035
+24,420
 26,455
```

**Answer** The orchard will produce about 26,455 lemons in 5 years.

MP1 **23.** A diner is open for 24 hours a day, every day of the year except for 10 holidays. How many hours is the diner open in a year?

**Answer** The diner is open 8,520 hours in a year.

**Justify your answer using words, drawings, or numbers.**
Possible justification:
There are 365 days in a year, so the diner is open for $365 - 10 = 355$ days a year. $355 \times 24 = 8,520$. So, the diner is open 8,520 hours in a year.

MP8 **24.** A honeybee flaps its wings about 237 times per second. Approximately, how many times does the bee flap its wings in 1 minute?

**Answer** The honeybee flaps its wings approximately 14,220 times in 1 minute.

**Justify your answer using words, drawings, or numbers.**
Possible justification:
One minute is 60 seconds. $237 \times 60 = 14,220$. So, the honeybee flaps its wings 14,220 times in 1 minute.

Unit 2 ■ Focus on Number and Operations in Base Ten **87**

## Teaching Tips

### Items 22–24
Remind students to construct answers in sentence form with the correct units, such as lemons, hours, or times. Often the units can guide them in determining a solution.

### Item 23
Point out to students that some numbers are not given to them in this problem, but they will need to determine what numbers need to be multiplied before solving.

## Mathematical Practices

| MP1 | Make sense of problems and persevere in solving them. |
|---|---|

**Item 23:** Students analyze givens, constraints, and goals of a problem. They may rely on pictures such as an area model to help conceptualize and solve a problem. Finally they may ask if their answer makes sense.

| MP8 | Look for and express regularity in repeated reasoning. |
|---|---|

**Item 22:** Students determine which numbers to multiply to solve the problem.

**Item 24:** Students use the standard algorithm to convert minutes to seconds to solve a problem.

## OBJECTIVE
Use different methods for dividing a multi-digit number by a two-digit number.

## ESSENTIAL QUESTION
Explain that there are different strategies for dividing, just as there are different strategies for other operations. Have students share some of the methods they use to add or multiply and discuss the similarities and differences of the strategies.

## PREREQUISITE SKILLS
Use Item C on page 338 of the Foundational Skills Handbook to review finding quotients with one-digit divisors.

## FLUENCY PRACTICE
Fluency practice is available at **sadlierconnect.com**.

## Concept Development

### Understand: How to divide using an area model

■ In this lesson, students extend division algorithms to two-digit divisors. This presentation demonstrates an area model, which provides a visual representation of division.

■ In this area model, larger sections of the model represent greater place values. When drawing their own models, students do not need to be concerned with the actual size of the section, but rather that each section represents a different place value in the correct order.

---

### Lesson 10 — Divide Whole Numbers: Use Place Value Strategies

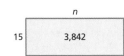

**Essential Question:** How can you use place value strategies to divide whole numbers?

**Words to Know:** partial quotient

In this lesson you will learn methods for dividing a multi-digit number by a two-digit number.

**Understand: How to divide using an area model**

> An aid organization has 3,842 bottles of water to divide equally among 15 shelters. How many bottles will each shelter get?

To find the solution divide: 3,842 bottles ÷ 15 shelters. Because 3,842 is between $15 \times 100 = 1,500$ and $15 \times 1,000 = 15,000$ the quotient is between 100 and 1,000. $15 \times n = 3,842$, so $n = 3,842 \div 15$.

|  | $n$ |
|---|---|
| 15 | 3,842 |

Use an area model. The unknown side length, $n$, is the quotient of $3,842 \div 15$. You will build the quotient place by place, redrawing the rectangle in sections as you go. The quotient for each section is called a partial quotient.

Think: 15 times what hundreds number gives a product closest to 3,842, without going over? $15 \times 200 = 3,000$ and $15 \times 300 = 4,500$, so use 200.

Draw the first section of the rectangle, and write 200 at the top. The area of this section is $15 \times 200 = 3,000$. Subtract 3,000 from 3,842 to find how much area is left, and insert or draw another section for this leftover area.

|  | 200 |  |
|---|---|---|
| 15 | 3,842 −3,000 | 842 |
|  | 842 |  |

Think: 15 times what tens number gives a product closest to 842, without going over? $15 \times 50 = 750$ and $15 \times 60 = 900$, so use 50. Write 50 at the top of the second section, subtract the area of that section from 842, and add a new section.

|  | 200 | 50 |  |
|---|---|---|---|
| 15 | 3,842 −3,000 | 842 −750 | 92 |
|  | 842 | 92 |  |

Think: 15 times what ones number gives a product closest to 92, without going over? $15 \times 6 = 90$ and $15 \times 7 = 105$, so use 6. Write 6 at the top of the third section, and subtract 90 from 92. The difference 2 is less than 15, so it is the remainder.

|  | 200 | 50 | 6 |
|---|---|---|---|
| 15 | 3,842 −3,000 | 842 −750 | 92 −90 |
|  | 842 | 92 | 2 |

Add the partial quotients, $200 + 50 + 6 = 256$, to get the quotient.

➡ Each shelter will get 256 bottles and there will be 2 bottles left.

---

## Words to Know

**partial quotient:** Numbers that are formed by dividing the value of each digit by the divisor.

**Example:** The partial quotients are in red.

```
              4
             50
            300
      24)8,496
       − 7,200
        1,296
      − 1,200
           96
         − 96
            0
```

**Glossary can be found on pp. 347–350.**

Lesson 10

Guided Instruction

## Understand: How to divide using partial quotients

A publisher shipped 8,496 copies of a new book to stores. The books were shipped in boxes of 24. How many boxes were shipped?

Divide the total number of books by the number of books in each box: 8,496 ÷ 24.

Represent the problem as a long division.

■ ← quotient
divisor → 24)8,496 ← dividend

Think: 24 times what hundreds number gives a product closest to 8,496 without going over?

24 × 300 = 7,200 and 24 × 400 = 9,600, so use 300.

```
      300
24)8,496
  − 7,200
    1,296
```

Write 300 above the division symbol. It is the *first partial quotient*. Write 7,200, which is 24 × 300, under 8,946, and subtract to see how much is left to divide.

Think: 24 times what tens number gives a product closest to 1,296 without going over?

24 × 50 = 1,200 and 24 × 60 = 1,440, so use 50.

```
       50
      300
24)8,496
  − 7,200
    1,296
  − 1,200
       96
```

Write 50, the *second partial quotient*, above 300. Write 1,200 under 1,296, and subtract.

Think: 24 times what ones number gives a product close to 96 without going over?

24 × 4 = 96, so use 4.

```
        4
       50
      300
24)8,496
  − 7,200
    1,296
  − 1,200
       96
  −    96
        0 ← no remainder
```

Write 4, the *third partial quotient*, above 50. Write 96 under 96 and subtract to get 0. The division is complete. There is no remainder.

Add the partial quotients: 300 + 50 + 4 = 354.

▶ 354 boxes of books were shipped.

Unit 2 ■ Focus on Number and Operations in Base Ten  **89**

## Understand: How to divide using partial quotients This presentation asks students to divide using partial quotients.

■ The partial quotients model integrates the skills developed through area models with the symbols and format they will use in the standard division algorithm. This method helps students understand the standard algorithm.

■ Point out that when using a two-digit divisor, the quotient will always begin at least one place to the right of the greatest place value of the dividend. Encourage students to reason why this true. Suggest that students multiply the divisor by 1,000 if they need help justifying their reasoning.

■ Students should be able to mentally add the partial quotients and recognize their sum as the quotient.

■ Encourage students to verbalize the difference between partial quotients and quotients. Partial quotients are the solutions to the division of individual place values. Quotients are the solutions to the division of two whole numbers.

## Support English Language Learners

English language learners may have trouble with the word *partial*. Explain that the word *partial* comes from the word *part*. Write *part*, say it aloud, and have students repeat it. Then ask students to use the word *part* in a sentence. Provide sentence frames, if necessary, such as *I saw the last part of that* _____ or *I ate part of the* _____. Add *-ial* to *part*, say the word aloud, and have students repeat it. Point out that when *-ial* is added to *part*, the *t* changes its sound, Say *part* and *partial* and have students repeat the words. Tell students that *partial* means part of something. Ask them what they think a partial quotient is. Help them conclude that a *partial quotient* is part of the total quotient.

# Guided Instruction

**Connect:** Division methods to the standard division algorithm Use this page to help students apply what they know about division methods and symbols to implement the standard division algorithm.

■ Compare and contrast the standard division algorithm with the previous two methods taught in the lesson.

■ Explain that the first two methods found the quotient by dividing place values and then adding partial quotients. By contrast, the standard division algorithm uses estimation and the place values of the partial quotients to find the quotient.

■ Connect the methods by explaining that writing a 1 in the hundreds place is similar to identifying 100 as a partial quotient; that writing a seven in the tens place is similar to identifying 70 as another partial quotient; and writing a 6 in the ones place is similar to identifying a 6 as the final partial quotient. The sum of partial quotients is 176.

✏ After students write down their answers, ask for volunteers to read their answers aloud. Use the example to show students the connection between the three division strategies.

---

## Guided Instruction

**Connect:** Division methods to the standard division algorithm

> A sports drink company paid participants $32 each to take part in a taste test. They paid $5,632 total. How many people participated in the taste test?

Divide the total amount the company paid by the amount it paid to each person: $5{,}632 \div 32$. Use the standard division algorithm.

Think: You cannot divide 5 by 32. Try 56. What number times 32 will give a product close to 56 without going over? Answer: 1

Write 1 in the hundreds place of the quotient, above the 6. Multiply $1 \times 32$ and write the result, 32, below 56.

Subtract to see that 24 is left, and bring down the digit from the next place to make 243.

$$\begin{array}{r} 1\phantom{,000} \\ 32\overline{)5{,}632} \\ -\underline{32}\phantom{00} \\ 243\phantom{0} \end{array}$$

Think: What number times 32 will give a product close to 243? Answer: 7

Write 7 in the tens place of the quotient, above the 3. Multiply $7 \times 32$ and write the result, 224, below 243.

Subtract to get 19, and bring down the digit from the next place to make 192.

$$\begin{array}{r} 17\phantom{,00} \\ 32\overline{)5{,}632} \\ -\underline{32}\phantom{00} \\ 243\phantom{0} \\ -\underline{224}\phantom{0} \\ 192 \end{array}$$

Think: What number times 32 will give a product close to 192? Answer: 6

Write 6 in the ones place of the quotient, above the 2. Multiply $6 \times 32$ and write the result, 192, below 192.

Subtract. There is nothing left. The quotient is complete.

$$\begin{array}{r} 176 \\ 32\overline{)5{,}632} \\ -\underline{32}\phantom{00} \\ 243\phantom{0} \\ -\underline{224}\phantom{0} \\ 192 \\ -\underline{192} \\ 0 \end{array}$$

➡ 176 people participated in the taste test.

✏ Mel said, "At the start of the division, we are really finding how many times 32 divides into 5,600. That is why the 1 belongs in the hundreds place in the quotient." What do you think Mel means? Possible explanation: The 56 in 5,632 represents 56 hundreds or 5,600. 32 divides into 5,600 one hundred times. We write the 1 in the hundreds place to show this.

---

## Math-to-Finances Connection

**Profit** Explain that profit is the amount of money made by providing a service or a product. Gross profit is the amount of money earned after paying for the items sold. Net profit is the amount of money earned after paying the operating expenses. Operating expenses include things such as salaries, office rental, and utilities.

The gross profit on 48 items is $9,308. Have students divide to find the amount of gross profit made on each item. Encourage students to explain each step as they use estimation and place value with the standard division algorithm. Note that there are several ways to ask the same question: How many times does 48 go into 93? How many groups of 48 are in 93? Ninety-three can be divided into how many groups of 48? No matter how the question is posed, the answer is the same.

Lesson 10

Guided Practice

1. Find 2,101 ÷ 15 by completing the area model.

|     | 100 | 40 |
| --- | --- | --- |
| 15 | 2,101 | 601 |
|     | − 1,500 | − 600 |
|     | 601 | 1 |

Add the partial quotients:

100 + __40__ = __140__.

The remainder is __1__.

2. Complete the steps to divide.

```
        3
       10
      200
 28 )5,970
    − 5,600
       370
    −  280
        90
    −   84
         6
```

Add the partial quotients:

__200__ + 10 + __3__ = __213__.

The remainder is __6__.

5,970 ÷ 28 = __213 R6__

3. Divide using the standard algorithm.

```
         140 R1
   15 )2,101
      − 15
         60
      −  60
         01
```

2,101 ÷ 15 = __140 R1__

### Think • Pair • Share

MP3  4. Compare and contrast the area model method used in exercise 1 and the standard division algorithm method used in exercise 3.
Possible answer: Both methods involve place value understanding, finding partial quotients, and adding the partial quotients to get the final quotient. The area model method helps you to visualize the division. Whereas, in contrast, the standard algorithm method is a more rote approach.

Unit 2 ■ Focus on Number and Operations in Base Ten  **91**

## Mathematical Practices

Mathematical Practice Standards underline the teaching and understanding of all concepts and skills presented. The emphasis of specific practices is noted throughout the guided and independent practice of this lesson.

| MP3 | **Construct viable arguments and critique the reasoning of others.** |
| --- | --- |

**Item 4:** Students compare and contrast two different approaches to solving the same division.

## Observational Assessment

Use page 91 to assess whether students understand how to divide by two-digit numbers. Exercises 1 and 3 are intentionally identical, but use different approaches. A common error is to record the solution to exercise 3 as 14 R1. Ask students to use estimation to check the reasonableness of the solution. Fourteen rounds to 10, and 15 × 10 = 150, which is not close to the dividend, 2,100. Point out that there is one group of 15 in 21, so the first partial quotient, 1, is placed above the 1 in the hundreds place of the dividend. A zero must be written in the ones place of the quotient to signify there are no groups of 15 in 1 one.

### Think•Pair•Share

**Peer Collaboration** Have students work in pairs to compare their explanations by answering these questions:

- *Where do you place the partial quotient for the hundreds, tens, and ones place in each strategy?*

- *What are the advantages and disadvantages of each strategy?*

To summarize, explain that the standard division algorithm is useful to solve division problems quickly, while using an area model is helpful in developing number sense and mental math skills.

### Return to the Essential Question

Reread the Lesson 10 Essential Question on page 88: *How can you use place value strategies to divide whole numbers?*

Ask volunteers to use what they learned in this lesson to answer the question. (Possible responses: An area model lets me visualize the division problem as an area problem with an unknown side length. I can also use estimation and partial quotients to find how many times the divisor will go into each place value. The sum of the partial quotients is the quotient. Lastly, I can use the standard division algorithm to estimate partial quotients, using place value to correctly name the value of the final quotient.)

Unit 2 ■ **Focus on Number and Operations in Base Ten**  **91**

## Concept Application

Students may work independently on these pages in the classroom or at home. They may refer to the first four pages of the lesson to revisit the instruction or to see a worked-out example.

**Common Errors** and **Teaching Tips** may help you support student learning either in the classroom or as a follow-up for work done at home.

## Teaching Tips

### Items 1 and 2

Students may draw a larger rectangle and separate it as they divide, or they may choose to draw the consecutive rectangles as they work. Regardless of their strategy, make sure students understand that each section of the rectangle represents one place value of the quotient. The remainder will not be represented in the rectangles, but rather as the difference of the values in the right-most rectangle.

### Item 4

Provide students with a mnemonic for the steps involved in the standard division algorithm: divide, multiply, subtract, bring down. Some mnemonics used include:

- Dad, Mom, Sister, Brother; and
- Dirty Monkeys Smell Bad.

---

**Lesson 10  Divide Whole Numbers: Use Place Value Strategies**

### Independent Practice

**For exercises 1–2, evaluate the division expressions by using an area model.**

1. $2,020 \div 15$

**Area Model**

|  | 100 | 30 | 4 |
|---|---|---|---|
| 15 | 2,020 | 520 | 70 |
|  | −1,500 | −450 | −60 |
|  | 520 | 70 | 10 |

2. $1,145 \div 35$

**Area Model**

|  | 30 | 2 |
|---|---|---|
| 35 | 1,145 | 95 |
|  | −1,050 | −70 |
|  | 95 | 25 |

Answer 134 R10

Answer 32 R25

3. Find $2,729 \div 22$ by using the partial-quotients method.

```
        4
       20
      100
  22)2,729
   − 2,200
      529
    − 440
       89
     − 88
        1
```

Answer 124 R1

4. Divide $5,648 \div 17$ using the standard division algorithm.

```
        332 R4
  17)5,648
   − 51
      54
    − 51
      38
    − 34
       4
```

Answer 332 R4

---

### Writing About Math

▶ **Write a Descriptive Text** Explain that mnemonics are tools that aid in remembering something. The ABC song is a mnemonic tool. The phrase *i before e, except after c* is a mnemonic spelling rhyme. Sometimes the letters associated with the number on a phone are used to create a mnemonic phone number. For example, 555–CALL represents the phone number 555–2255. Have students write a paragraph listing the steps involved in using the standard division algorithm in a "how-to" format. Then ask students to work in small groups to devise their own mnemonic to help them remember the steps.

Ask groups to share their mnemonic strategies with the class.

MP3 **5.** Adam is dividing 1,640 by 20. He says he can divide 1,640 by 10 and then multiply the answer by 2. Is Adam correct? How would you adjust his strategy? Explain.

No, Adam is not correct. Possible explanation: To divide 1,640 by 20, he can divide 1,640 by 10, and then divide that answer by 2.

MP3 **6.** To divide 1,110 by 10, Aliyah draws the area model below. What is her error? Explain how she can correct her model.

|  | 100 | 1 |
|---|---|---|
| 10 | 1,110 −1,000 | 10 −10 |
|  | 10 | 0 |

Possible answer: Aliyah made a subtraction error in the first section. 1,110 − 1,000 = 110. This error made her neglect that she also needed a second section inserted into the area model to show that 10 × 10 = 100 and 110 − 100 = 10. The correct answer is 111, not 101.

**Choose the correct answer.**

**7.** A roll of industrial wire is 7,776 inches long. It is cut into 36 pieces of the same size. What is the length of each piece of wire?

a. 22 inches

(b.) 216 inches

c. 36 inches

d. 1,296 inches

**8.** Kayla is packing 1,864 books. If 32 books can fit in one box, how many boxes does she need?

a. 55

b. 58

c. 56

(d.) 59

## Common Errors

### Items 8

The quotient for 1,864 ÷ 32 is 58 R8. Some students may simply drop the remainder and choose 58 as the correct answer. Point out that Kayla will need a box for the extra 8 books, so she will need one additional box. The correct answer is, therefore, 59.

## Mathematical Practices

| MP3 | **Construct viable arguments and critique the reasoning of others.** |
|---|---|

**Item 5:** Students critique another student's approach to a problem.

**Item 6:** Students analyze a problem situation and share their reasoning with others.

# Independent Practice

## Common Errors

### Item 14

This problem involves not only the application of a division strategy, but also visualization and reasoning skills. Students may reason that 46 boxes are needed to contain all 1,368 vases. Although that is true, careful reading states that each box will contain 30 vases; therefore, one box cannot contain the remaining 18 vases.

---

## Independent Practice

**Find each quotient. Show your work.**

**9.** 4,750 ÷ 25

**10.** 5,026 ÷ 44

Answer <u>190</u>

Answer <u>114 R10</u>

**11.** 2,889 ÷ 70

**12.** 3,080 ÷ 19

Answer <u>41 R19</u>

Answer <u>162 R2</u>

**Solve the problems.**

**MP1** **13.** A school has 1,235 students that will be divided into 19 groups for sports day. How many students will be in each group? Are there any students who will not be in a group?

▬▬ **Show your work.**
Check students' work: 1,235 ÷ 19 = 65

Answer <u>There will be 65 students in each group, with none left over.</u>

**MP4** **14.** A factory has 1,368 vases to be boxed and shipped. Each box will contain 30 vases. How many boxes can be shipped with 30 vases? If there are vases left over, what is the number?

▬▬ **Show your work.**
Check students' work: 1,368 ÷ 30 = 45 with a remainder of 18

Answer <u>45 boxes can be shipped with 30 vases. There are 18 vases left over.</u>

| Mathematical Practices | |
|---|---|
| **MP1** | **Make sense of problems and persevere in solving them.** |
| **Item 13:** Students analyze and plan a solution to a division word problem. | |
| **MP4** | **Model with mathematics.** |
| **Item 14:** Students relate mathematics to everyday problems and interpret the solution in the context of a situation. | |

MP1 **15.** A chapter in a book has 8,565 words. The chapter is 25 pages long. About how many words are on each page?

[pencil] **Show your work.**
Check students' work: $8,565 \div 25 = 342$ with a remainder of 15

**Answer** There are about 342 words on each page.

MP5 **16.** A bus company has been booked to transport 1,957 passengers from Philadelphia to New York. A bus will seat 50 passengers. How many buses will it take to transport all the passengers?

**Answer** It will take 40 buses to transport all the passengers.

[pencil] **Justify your answer using words, drawings, or numbers.**
$1,957 \div 50 = 39$ with a remainder of 7. Since 7 passengers are left after 39 buses are filled, an extra bus will be needed to transport them. So, 40 buses will be needed in all.

MP8 **17.** A farmer's chickens lay 1,421 eggs a year. The farmer has 120 egg cartons, each of which holds a dozen eggs. Will the farmer need all the egg cartons to package the eggs for the year?

**Answer** No, the farmer will not use all the cartons.

[pencil] **Justify your answer using words, drawings, or numbers.**
$1,421 \div 12 = 118$ with a remainder of 5. The farmer will only need 119 egg cartons, and the 119th carton will not be full.

Unit 2 ■ Focus on Number and Operations in Base Ten **95**

## Teaching Tips

### Item 16 and 17

Explain that these problems involve two steps: (1) applying a division strategy; and (2) interpreting the remainder in the context of the problem.

## Mathematical Practices

| MP1 | **Make sense of problems and persevere in solving them.** |
|---|---|

**Item 15:** Students analyze a problem and plan a solution.

| MP5 | **Use appropriate tools strategically.** |
|---|---|

**Item 16:** Students must decide which solution method to use and then decide how to interpret the result.

| MP8 | **Look for and express regularity in repeated reasoning.** |
|---|---|

**Item 17:** Students obtain fluency using patterns and evaluate the reasonableness of answers.

## OBJECTIVE

Use properties of operations and the relationship between multiplication and division to divide whole numbers.

## ESSENTIAL QUESTION

Explain to students that learning different division strategies gives them more skills for solving and checking division.

## PREREQUISITE SKILLS

Use Item D on page 338 of the Foundational Skills Handbook to review using the Distributive Property to divide.

## FLUENCY PRACTICE

Fluency practice is available at **sadlierconnect.com**.

## Concept Development

### Understand: How to divide using the Distributive Property

■ This presentation shows how to divide using the Distributive Property by breaking apart a multi-digit number into a sum of numbers that can easily be divided by the divisor using place value patterns.

■ The Distributive Property with division is a special case of the Distributive Property. It results from the fact that $(a + b) \div c$ is equivalent to $\frac{1}{c}(a + b)$. Applying the Distributive Property over addition to the latter equation gives $\frac{a}{c} + \frac{b}{c}$, which is $a \div c + b \div c$.

---

**Essential Question:**
How can you use properties of operations to divide whole numbers?

### Guided Instruction

In this lesson you will divide whole numbers using properties of operations and the relationship between multiplication and division.

**Understand: How to divide using the Distributive Property**

> A company has 5,535 boxes of soccer balls to deliver overseas. Before being loaded onto a cargo ship, the boxes are divided equally among 45 shipping containers. How many boxes are in each shipping container?

You have used the Distributive Property to multiply a sum $(a + b)$ by a number $c$. You can also use the Distributive Property to divide a sum $(a + b)$ by a number $c$.

**Remember!**
Distributive Property
$c \times (a + b) = c \times a + c \times b$
$(a + b) \div c = a \div c + b \div c$

Use the Distributive Property to divide 5,535 by 45. First break apart 5,535 into a sum of numbers that can be easily divided by 45.

Find multiples of 45, and use place values of 10, 100, and 1,000 to look for addends of 5,535 that are easy to divide by 45.

Since the greatest place value in 5,535 is thousands, first look for a 4-digit number. Try $45 \times 100$, or 4,500. $5,535 - 4,500 = 1,035$.

> sum = addends
> $5,535 = 4,500 + 1,035$

Next, look for addends of 1,035. Find a number that is easy to divide by 45. Try 900, or $45 \times 20$. $1,035 - 900 = 135$.

> $5,535 = 4,500 + 900 + 135$

Then look for addends of 135. Try 90, or $45 \times 2$. $135 - 90 = 45$. So, you have exactly $45 \times 1$, or 45, as the last addend.

> $5,535 = 4,500 + 900 + 90 + 45$

Now, use the Distributive Property to find the quotient.

$$
\begin{aligned}
5,535 \div 45 &= (4,500 + 900 + 90 + 45) \div 45 \\
&= 4,500 \div 45 + 900 \div 45 + 90 \div 45 + 45 \div 45 \\
&= 100 \quad\quad + 20 \quad\quad + 2 \quad\quad + 1 \\
&= 123
\end{aligned}
$$

➡ There are 123 boxes in each of the 45 shipping containers.

▶ Explain how you can use multiplication to check your answer.
Possible answer: Find the product of $45 \times 123$, which is 5,535.

**96** Unit 2 ■ Focus on Number and Operations in Base Ten

---

## Support English Language Learners

English language learner students may have trouble with phrases that combine adjectives and compound nouns, such as *problem-solving strategy* or *related multiplication*. Write a phrase on the board and say it aloud. Have students repeat your speech. Break down the phrase by defining each word separately. Next, ask students to define each word in their own words. Have students interpret the phrase's meaning based on the definitions of the individual words. Finally, connect students' definitions to the actual definition to provide the meaning of the term.

Lesson 11

## Guided Instruction

**Understand:** How to divide by using the relationship between multiplication and division

> The school band has 1,386 concert tickets to sell. Band members are organized into 11 teams. To sell out the concert, how many tickets must each team sell?

Let $t$ be the number of tickets each team must sell. To find the value of $t$, divide the number of tickets by the number of teams. Write this as a division equation:

$t = 1,386 \div 11$

Use the relationship between multiplication and division to write a related multiplication equation:

$11 \times t = 1,386$

To find the value of $t$, first choose a number for $t$ that you think may be reasonable.

Because $11 \times 100 = 1,100$ and $11 \times 200 = 2,200$ you know that $t$ must be between 100 and 200, and it is closer to 100. Looking at $11 \times t = 1,386$ you know that the ones digit of $t$ must be 6.

Try $t = 136$.

$11 \times 136 = 1,496$

Notice that the product is greater than 1,386. So, try another factor less than 136.

Try $t = 126$.

$11 \times 126 = 1,386$

$t = 126$ is the solution to the multiplication equation.

▶ Each team must sell 126 tickets.

▪▬ · James says that the solution to $y = 322 \div 23$ is $y = 15$. Without doing any calculations, how can you tell that James is incorrect?
Possible answer: For James to be correct $15 \times 23$ would have to equal 322. This is impossible because the ones digit of $15 \times 23$ is 5 because $5 \times 3$ is 15.

Unit 2 ▪ Focus on Number and Operations in Base Ten    **97**

## Understand: How to divide by using the relationship between multiplication and division

▪ This presentation has students divide by writing an equivalent multiplication. Students use the guess-and-check method to arrive at the second factor in the multiplication.

▪ Point out that the given factor, 11, has two digits but the product, 1,386, has four digits. Logically, multiplying 11 by any ten will result in a three-digit product, which is not great enough. Students should recognize the need to begin estimating using hundreds in order to obtain a four-digit product.

▪ Some students may need to practice with simpler examples to help them develop number sense.

✏▭ ▸ Ask students to consider what mental math strategy they can use with this problem. Once they have solved the problem, have students consider how to apply this strategy to other problems, such as multiple-choice addition, subtraction, multiplication, and division problems.

## Math-to-History Connection

**Ancient Mathematics** Explain to students that before the 1600s, people used the scratch method of division, which is also called the galley or batello method. It originated in China two thousand years ago. The Persian mathematician Al-Khwarizmi used it as early as 1,200 years ago.

Using the internet, research this method as a class to show how the digits are scratched out. Explain that it is easier to use this method with a sand abacus than with paper and pencil. Encourage a discussion on how the method used to carry out mathematical operations not only depends on the type of problem, but also on the available tools. For example, many computations today are done with calculators or computers.

**Connect:** **What you know about the properties of operations to check a division answer** Use this page to help students apply what they know about the relationship between multiplication and division and the Distributive Property to check a division answer.

■ Remind students that multiplication can be used to check a division answer because multiplication and division are inverse operations. Help students understand this concept by asking them to describe addition and subtraction as inverse operations.

■ In this presentation, the division has a remainder. Help students see that if they multiply the divisor by the quotient and then add the remainder, they should get the dividend.

■ Encourage students who struggle with determining information from a word problem to underline the necessary information to write a division.

---

**Lesson 11   Divide Whole Numbers: Use Properties of Operations**

## Guided Instruction

**Connect:** **What you know about the properties of operations to check a division answer**

> Lee needs 3,156 yards of red ribbon for her craft store. She buys the ribbon in rolls of 24 yards each. How many rolls does she need to buy?

**Step 1**

Write an expression.

To find the number of rolls she needs to buy, divide the total amount of yards Lee needs by the number of yards in each roll.

$3,156 \div 24$

**Step 2**

Use an area model to divide.

|      | 100 | 30 | 1 |
|------|-----|-----|-----|
| 24   | 3,156 −2,400 | 756 −720 | 36 −24 |
|      | 756 | 36 | 12 |

$3,156 \div 24 = (100 + 30 + 1)\ R12 = 131\ R12$

**Step 3**

Use the Distributive Property to check.

When you multiply 131 by 24 and then add 12, the result should be the 3,156. You can use the Distributive Property to make the multiplication easier.

$$24 \times 131 + 12 = 24 \times (100 + 30 + 1) + 12$$
$$= 2,400 + 720 + 24 \quad + 12$$
$$= 3,156$$

**Step 4**

Interpret the answer.

If Lee buys 131 rolls, she will still need 12 more yards. So, she must buy 132 rolls to have enough.

➡ Lee needs to buy 132 rolls of red ribbon.

**98   Unit 2** ■ Focus on Number and Operations in Base Ten

---

## Math-to-Math Connection

**Ratios and Rates** It is important for students to fully understand the relationship between multiplication and division and how to use this relationship to help them become more accurate in their work. In Grade 6, students are expected to understand and solve ratio and rate problems involving quantities. By possessing a firm grasp on the concepts relating multiplication and division, students will more easily connect ratios and rates.

MORE ONLINE sadlierconnect.com

## Guided Practice

1. Complete the steps to calculate 6,816 ÷ 32.

   Write 6,816 as a sum of numbers that are easy to divide by 32:

   6,816 = 6,400 + 320 + __96__

   Use the Distributive Property.

   6,816 ÷ 32 = (6,400 + 320 + __96__) ÷ 32

   $\qquad$ = 6,400 ÷ 32 + 320 ÷ __32__ + __96__ ÷ __32__

   $\qquad$ = 200 + __10__ + __3__

   $\qquad$ = __213__

2. Complete the steps to solve $n = 3,094 ÷ 17$.

   Write an equivalent multiplication equation: $n \times$ __17__ = __3,094__

   Because 17 × 100 = 1,700 and 17 × 200 = 3,400, the quotient must

   be between 100 and 200, and it must be closer to __200__ since 3,400 is closer to 3,094 than 1,700 is.

   Looking at $n = 3,094 ÷ 17$ the ones digit of $n$ must be __2__.

   Try 172.

   17 × 172 = 2,924. Since the product 2,924 is less than 3,094, try another number greater than 172.

   Try 182.

   17 × 182 = __3,094__

   The solution is $n =$ __182__.

### 👏 Think • Pair • Share

**Explain your reasoning.**

MP7  3. Explain how knowing that 80 × 24 = 1,920 can help you find the quotient of 1,920 ÷ 40.
   Possible explanation: Halve 80 to 40 and double 24 to 48, and then find the product of 40 × 48. If 80 × 24 = 1,920, then 40 × 48 = 1,920. Since multiplication and division are the opposite operations, then it is known that 1,920 ÷ 40 = 48.

## Mathematical Practices

Mathematical Practice Standards underline the teaching and understanding of all concepts and skills presented. The emphasis of specific practices is noted throughout the guided and independent practice of this lesson.

| MP7 | **Look for and make use of structure.** |
| --- | --- |

**Item 3:** Students use the inverse relationship between division and multiplication to help them explain a division strategy.

## Observational Assessment

Use page 99 to assess whether students understand how to use the Distributive Property and the relationship between multiplication and division to solve divisions. Students will apply number sense and the guess-and-check strategy to find partial quotients.

### 👏 Think•Pair•Share

**Peer Collaboration** Have students consider how this problem uses what they already know about multiplication and the relationship that division and multiplication share. Ask students to consider these questions:

- *What other multiplication strategies do you know?*

- *Which of these strategies can you use to solve a division?*

- *Why can you use multiplication strategies to solve a division?*

To summarize, explain that students can apply multiplication strategies like halving and doubling to division problems.

### Return to the Essential Question

Reread the Lesson 11 Essential Question on page 96: *How can you use properties of operations to divide whole numbers?*

Ask volunteers to use what they learned in this lesson to answer this question. (Possible responses: I can use the Distributive Property to solve divisions and to check answers to divisions. I can divide by writing an equivalent multiplication equation with an unknown factor and then using the guess-and-check method or another strategy.)

Invite as many volunteers as possible to express ideas about division strategies in their own words.

# Independent Practice

## Concept Application

Students may work independently on these pages in the classroom or at home. They may refer to the first four pages of the lesson to revisit the instruction or to see a worked-out example.

**Common Errors** and **Teaching Tips** may help you support student learning either in the classroom or as a follow-up for work done at home.

## Common Errors

### Item 3

Students may forget to add the remainder to the product of 18 and 139. Point out that the product, 2502, is exactly 8 less than the dividend. To get the original dividend, students must add the remainder.

## Teaching Tips

### Item 1

Point out to students that the first addend within the parentheses is a multiple of 100 and the second is a multiple of 10. Be sure that students know to proceed from the greatest to the least place value when using the Distributive Property to solve divisions.

---

### Independent Practice

1. Complete the steps to calculate $6{,}594 \div 21$.

   Write 6,594 as a sum of numbers that are easy to divide by 21:

   $6{,}594 = 6{,}300 + 210 + \underline{\ 84\ }$

   Use the Distributive Property.

   $6{,}594 \div 21 = (6{,}300 + 210 + \underline{\ 84\ }) \div 21$

   $\qquad = 6{,}300 \div \underline{\ 21\ } + 210 \div \underline{\ 21\ } + \underline{\ 84\ } \div \underline{\ 21\ }$

   $\qquad = \underline{\ 300\ } + \underline{\ 10\ } + \underline{\ 4\ }$

   $\qquad = \underline{\ 314\ }$

   **Complete the area model to find the quotient of $2{,}510 \div 18$.**

   2.

   | | 100 | 30 | 9 |
   |---|---|---|---|
   | 18 | 2,510 − 1,800 | 710 − 540 | 170 − 162 |
   | | 710 | 170 | 8 |

   $2{,}510 \div 18 = \underline{\ 139\ }$ with a remainder of $\underline{\ 8\ }$

   3. Show how you can check your answer to example 2 using the Distributive Property.

   $18 \times (100 + 30 + 9) + 8 = (18 \times 100) + (18 \times 30) + (18 \times 9) + 8$
   $\qquad\qquad\qquad\qquad\qquad = 1{,}800 + 540 + 162 + 8$
   $\qquad\qquad\qquad\qquad\qquad = 2{,}510$

---

## Writing About Math

▸ **Write a Descriptive Text** Have students compare and contrast the use of area models with the application of the Distributive Property to solve divisions. Ask students to create graphic organizers that identify the properties that are unique to each strategy and the properties that they share. Have students write a few sentences to compare and contrast the two strategies.

Lesson 11

## Independent Practice

**Complete each division.**

4.
$$11\overline{)2{,}145}$$

```
        195
   11 )2,145
      - 11
        104
       - 99
         55
       - 55
          0
```

2,145 ÷ 11 = ___195___

5.
```
        55
   19 )1,056
      - 95
        106
       - 95
         11
```

1,056 ÷ 19 = ___55 R11___

**For exercises 6–7, find each quotient. Show your work.**

6. 3,310 ÷ 13

7. 4,125 ÷ 20

Answer ___254 R8___

Answer ___206 R5___

**For exercises 8–9, choose the correct answer.**

8. The area of a rectangular cornfield is 7,140 square feet. The width of the field is 68 feet. What is the length of the field?

   a. 150 feet

   b. 115 feet

   c. 105 feet

   d. 15 feet

9. Carla spent 2,430 hours at her job last year. She spent about the same number of hours at her job each month. About how many hours did Carla spend at her job each month?

   a. 2,000 hours

   b. 200 hours

   c. 20 hours

   d. 2 hours

## Common Errors

### Item 9

Some students may immediately begin performing a calculation to determine an exact number of hours Carla spent on homework each month. Remind students to carefully read the problem and inform them that they are seeking an estimate.

## Teaching Tips

### Items 4 and 5

Remind students that they can use a mnemonic to remember the steps needed to solve problems using the standard division algorithm.

## Digital Connection

**Online Abacus** Use the Internet to find online long division tools that use two-digit divisors. These online programs provide immediate feedback and can identify specific errors within the algorithm to help students pinpoint their misconceptions in the problem-solving process. These programs also often allow students to use multiplication to check their work. Have partners work together to solve a division, one using the online program and the other using paper and pencil. Ask them to share their division strategies and compare their final answers. Then have them switch places and solve a different division.

## Common Errors

### Item 13

Some students may interpret the remainder incorrectly, stating that it would take the staff 22 or 23 hours to make the sandwiches. Help students see that the answer 22 R30 means that after 22 hours, the staff will still have 30 sandwiches left to make. Because they can make 60 sandwiches in 1 hour, it will take them a half hour to make 30 sandwiches. The total time to make all 1,350 sandwiches is, therefore, $22\frac{1}{2}$ hours.

---

### Lesson 11 Divide Whole Numbers: Use Properties of Operations

#### Independent Practice

**MP3** **10.** Justin's family is going on vacation. They will drive 3,290 miles in 11 days. Justin and his sister, Jackie, use two different ways to estimate how many miles they will drive each day. Whose approach is correct? Explain.

**Justin:** 3,290 rounds to 3,000 and 11 rounds to 10. Then, I can divide.
**Jackie:** 3,290 rounds to 3,300. I know that $11 \times 3 = 33$, $11 \times 30 = 330$, and $11 \times 300 = 3,300$.
Both are correct. Possible explanation: After Justin rounds the numbers and divides 3,000 by 10, he will get 300. Jackie knows that $11 \times 300 = 3300$, so 3,300 divided by 11 is 300. Using different approaches to estimation, they both get the same answer.

**MP3** **11.** Yani divides 1,542 by 19. She writes a multiplication equation for the problem and says the dividend becomes the product. Is Yani correct? Explain.
Yes, Yani is correct. Possible explanation: When dividing 1,542 by 19, the dividend is 1,542. You can write this problem as $19 \times ? = 1,542$, where the product is 1,542.

**Solve the problems.**

**MP1** **12.** A pet store has 1,289 fish. A maximum of 12 fish can fit in a tank. What is the least number of tanks the pet store will need to contain all the fish?

**Show your work.**
$1,289 \div 12 = 107$ with 5 left over. So the pet store will need at least 108 tanks to contain all the fish.

**Answer** The pet store will need at least 108 tanks to contain all the fish.

**MP2** **13.** A caterer is making 1,350 sandwiches for a party. If the catering staff can make 60 sandwiches in an hour, how many hours will it take to make all the sandwiches?

**Show your work.**
$1,350 \div 60 = 22$ with a remainder of 30. If the staff can make 60 sandwiches in an hour, it will take a half hour to make the remaining 30 sandwiches.

**Answer** It will take a total of 22 and one half hours (or 22 hours and 30 minutes) to make all the sandwiches.

---

## Mathematical Practices

| | |
|---|---|
| **MP1** | **Make sense of problems and persevere in solving them.** |
| **Item 12:** Students devise and apply a strategy to solve a division problem. | |
| **MP2** | **Reason abstractly and quantitatively.** |
| **Item 13:** Students solve a division problem and interpret the remainder in the context of a concrete scenario. | |
| **MP3** | **Construct viable arguments and critique the reasoning of others.** |
| **Item 10:** Students evaluate two approaches to solving a division problem. | |
| **Item 11:** Students determine if a division strategy is used correctly. | |

## Independent Practice

MP6 **14.** Volunteers working in 16 teams are filling sandbags to prevent flooding in a beach town. Each sandbag weighs about 35 pounds. If there are 2,900 pounds of sand, how many sandbags can be filled?

**Answer** 82 bags can be filled with 30 pounds of sand left over.

📏 **Justify your answer using words, drawings, or numbers.**
2,900 ÷ 35 = 82 with a remainder of 30.

MP6 **15.** Serena has 1,532 photographs. She has 40 photo albums. Each album holds 36 photographs. Does Serena have enough albums to hold all the photographs?

**Answer** No, Serena needs 3 more albums to hold all the photographs.

📏 **Justify your answer using words, drawings, or numbers.**
1,532 ÷ 36 = 42 with a remainder of 20.

MP6 **16.** A group of 1,058 people are called in for jury duty. A jury is made up of 12 jurors and 2 alternates. How many complete juries can be formed from the jury pool?

**Answer** 75 complete juries can be formed from the jury pool of 1,058 people.

📏 **Justify your answer using words, drawings, or numbers.**
1,058 ÷ 14 = 75 with a remainder of 8.

## Teaching Tips

### Item 14

This problem contains extra information. The fact that 16 teams are filling sandbags is not used in the solution. Encourage students to read the problem carefully before attempting to solve it. Suggest that students underline or circle the relevant information.

### Item 15

Have students break up multi-step word problems. Explain that these problems involve two steps: (1) applying a division strategy; and (2) comparing the quotient to the amount given in the problem. Some students may multiply, rather than divide, to solve this problem. You may want to discuss both methods in class.

### Item 16

Some students may not be familiar with the term *jury duty*. Introduce the basic information about the judicial process needed to understand the context of the problem.

## Mathematical Practices

| MP6 | **Attend to precision.** |
| --- | --- |

**Items 14–16:** Students must justify their answers clearly and precisely, using words, drawings, or numbers.

## OBJECTIVE
Add and subtract decimal numbers.

## ESSENTIAL QUESTION
As a class, describe and discuss some situations where decimal numbers to the hundredths are commonly used, for example, money, percentages, and measurements.

## FLUENCY PRACTICE
Fluency practice is available at **sadlierconnect.com**.

## Concept Development

### Understand: How to add decimals using a number line

■ Students will use concrete models or drawings, such as number lines, hundreds grids, and place-value charts as a strategy for decimal arithmetic.

■ It is important for students to create an accurate number line to be successful with this strategy. Note that the number line given is labeled for every 0.5 and marked for every 0.1, but the numbers being added are given to the hundredth.

### Understand: How to estimate the value of an expression

■ In this presentation, students approximate an answer for an expression involving decimals. Students will need to round to the nearest whole number before adding.

■ Discuss how a quick estimate of the answer can be helpful for checking that an answer is reasonable.

---

**Essential Question:** How do you add and subtract decimal numbers?

### Guided Instruction

In this lesson you will learn how to add and subtract decimal numbers.

**Understand: How to add decimals using a number line**

> Dan rode his bike 1.75 miles from school to the library. Later, he rode 0.75 miles home from the library. How many miles did Dan ride?

To find the total number of miles, add 1.75 + 0.75 using a number line.

- Move along the number line from 0 to 1.75. This represents the 1.75 miles Dan rode from school to the library.

- Add 0.75 to 1.75 by moving along the number line another 0.75. This shows the 0.75 miles Dan rode home.

- The sum is 2.5. This is the total number of miles Dan rode.

1.75 miles + 0.75 miles = 2.5 miles

➡ Dan rode 2.5 miles.

**Understand: How to estimate the value of an expression**

> What is the approximate value of the expression 4.85 + 6 − 3.61?

To find the approximate value of the expression, estimate by rounding each term to the nearest whole number. Then evaluate.

| 4.85 rounds to | | whole number | | 3.61 rounds to | | approximate value of the expression |
|---|---|---|---|---|---|---|
| ↓ | | ↓ | | ↓ | | ↓ |
| 5 | + | 6 | − | 4 | = | 7 |

➡ The approximate value of the expression is 7.

---

## Support English Language Learners

Words such as *approximate, estimate, round,* and *reasonableness* are used in reference to the strategy of estimating. Discuss the meanings of these words and their appropriate use in problem solving. Make a list of different word forms, such as estimate/estimation, round/rounding, approximate/approximation, reasonable/reasonableness. Then have students write sentences with these words, providing support as necessary. Encourage them to use multiple words in the same sentence. For example:

- I can use *estimation* to check the *reasonableness* of my answer.

- I can *round* numbers to *estimate* an answer.

MORE ONLINE sadlierconnect.com

Lesson 12

Guided Instruction

**Understand:** How to subtract decimals using hundreds grids

> Lana had $1.30 to buy a snack. She spent $0.68 on a banana.
> How much money does Lana have left?

Write a subtraction equation and use hundreds grids.

Subtraction equation: $1.30 − $0.68 = ▇

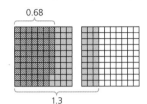

0.68

1.3

**Remember!**
- 1.30 or 1.3 is represented with 1 whole grid and 3 tenths of a grid.
- 0.68 is represented with 6 tenths of a grid and 8 hundredths of a grid.

Shade 1.30. Cross out 0.68 of the shaded part.
The shaded part that is *not crossed out* is the difference.
$1.30 − 0.68 = 0.62$

➡ Lana has $0.62 left.

**Understand:** How to add or subtract decimals using place value

> Evaluate: $3.5 + 1.86$

Line up like place values. Write 3.5 as
3.50 to help you align the digits correctly.

Add the columns from right to left,
as if you were adding whole numbers.
Regroup 13 tenths as 1 one and 3 tenths.

|   | ones | . | tenths | hundredths |
|---|------|---|--------|------------|
|   | 1    |   |        |            |
|   | 3    | . | 5      | 0          |
| + | 1    | . | 8      | 6          |
|   | 5    | . | 3      | 6          |

Write the decimal point in the answer.

➡ The expression $3.5 + 1.86$ has a value of 5.36.

▰▰ Evaluate: $3.5 − 1.86$ using place value. 1.64

Unit 2 ■ Focus on Number and Operations in Base Ten **105**

## Math-to-Real-Word Connection

**Balancing a Checkbook** Lead a class discussion on why it may be important for people to use exact computations, rather than estimations, when balancing their checkbooks. Explain to students how a checkbook works to help you track how much money you currently have in an account. Students should reason that knowing the precise amount of money is important so that you do not spend more money than is currently available.

**Understand:** How to subtract decimals using hundreds grids

■ Students used hundreds grids when they explored place value and when they worked with decimals and fractions. If necessary, have students practice making representations of decimal numbers using hundreds grids prior to introducing addition and subtraction.

■ To model subtraction, shade grids to model the first number and then cross out (take away) part of the model that represents the number being subtracted. The part of the original model that is not crossed out represents the difference.

■ Mention that the hundreds-grid strategy can also be used for addition. To model addition, combine grid models for the two addends. The number represented by the combined models is the sum.

**Understand:** How to add or subtract decimals using place value

■ Call students' attention to the regrouping that occurs in the addition of the tenths place. The sum of 5 tenths and 8 tenths is 13 tenths, which is regrouped as 1 one and 3 tenths. The 1 one is recorded as a 1 at the top of the ones column, and the 3 tenths are recorded by writing a 3 in the tenths place of the sum.

■ Point out that the decimal point is placed in the answer directly underneath the decimal point in the addends.

▰▰ After students have answered this question independently, discuss the solution process. Focus on the idea that the 5 tenths in 3.5 must be regrouped as 4 tenths and 10 hundredths, so that 6 hundredths can be subtracted. Then, the 3 ones in 3.5 must be regrouped as 2 ones and 10 tenths so that 8 tenths can be subtracted.

# Guided Instruction

**Connect:** **What you know about adding and subtracting decimal numbers** Use this page to help students learn to use place value to add and subtract decimal numbers in the same context. The reasonableness of the answer is checked by estimation.

■ Before reading through the given solution, ask students to articulate the order in which the numbers should be added and subtracted in this problem. Note that there are several correct approaches.

■ In Step 2, 4.5 is rewritten as 4.50, so that it has the same number of decimal places as 41.04. This is not necessary, but many students find it helpful if both numbers in an addition or subtraction problem have the same number of decimal places.

■ In Step 3, estimation is used to check the reasonableness of the answer. Ask students what they would do if the estimated answer was not close to the actual answer.

---

## Guided Instruction

**Connect:** **What you know about adding and subtracting decimal numbers**

> May and Will ran a relay race. May ran the first 100 yards in 18.49 seconds (s). Will ran the next 100 yards in 22.55 seconds (s). He lost 4.5 seconds because he tripped on a rock and fell. What would their total running time have been if Will had not fallen?

**Step 1**

Add the actual running times.

|   | tens | ones | . | tenths | hundredths |
|---|------|------|---|--------|------------|
|   | 1    | 1    | . | 1      |            |
| + | 1    | 8    | . | 4      | 9          |
|   | 2    | 2    | . | 5      | 5          |
|   | 4    | 1    | . | 0      | 4          |

**Remember!**
Line up the numbers by place value, and then add the digits from right to left, regrouping when needed.

**Step 2**

Subtract the time Will lost from the actual combined running time.

|   | tens | ones | . | tenths | hundredths |
|---|------|------|---|--------|------------|
|   | 3    | 10   | . | 10     |            |
|   | 4̸    | 1̸    | . | 0̸      | 4          |
| − |      | 4    | . | 5      | 0          |
|   | 3    | 6    | . | 5      | 4          |

**Remember!**
Write 4.5 as 4.50 to help you line up the digits correctly.

**Step 3**

Check the reasonableness of your answer.

Round each running time to the nearest second. ──→ 18.49 rounds down to 18
                                                    22.55 rounds up to 23

Round the time Will fell. ──────────────→ 4.5 rounds up to 5

Add and subtract the rounded times. ────→ 18 + 23 − 5 = 36

The running time of 36.54 s is close to the estimated time of 36 s.

➡ The total time would have been 36.54 s had Will not fallen.

## Math-to-Shopping Connection

**Adding the Total Cost** Adding and subtracting decimal numbers is an important skill in the marketplace, as most costs are given to the nearest cent. Ask students to find prices in a local advertisement for three or four products they may wish to purchase. Then, ask them to find the total cost for the items they have chosen. An extension may be to ask for subtraction due to a coupon or discount. Also, ask students to estimate the cost prior to calculating, in order to check the reasonableness of their answers.

Guided Practice

**Estimate the value of each expression to the nearest whole number.**

1. 6.87 + 3.1

   6.87 rounds up to 7

   3.1 rounds down to _3_

   Estimate: _10_

2. 5.84 − (1.23 + 2.09)

   5.84 rounds up to _6_

   1.23 rounds down to _1_

   2.09 rounds down to _2_

   Estimate: _3_

**Use the hundreds grids to solve each equation.**

3. 1.3 + 0.45 = _1.75_

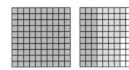

4. 1.85 − 1.22 = _0.63_

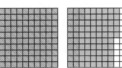

**Use the place-value chart to solve each equation.**

5. 7.81 + 1.75 = _9.56_

| ones | . | tenths | hundredths |
|------|---|--------|------------|
| 1 | | | |
| 7 | . | 8 | 1 |
| +   1 | . | 7 | 5 |
| 9 | . | 5 | 6 |

6. 4.7 − 1.25 = _3.45_

| ones | . | tenths | hundredths |
|------|---|--------|------------|
| | | 6 | 10 |
| 4 | . | 7̶ | 0̶ |
| −   1 | . | 2 | 5 |
| 3 | . | 4 | 5 |

**Think · Pair · Share**

MP1  7. Chris is going shopping for school supplies. He wants to buy a binder for $3.15 and a pack of folders for $1.95. Tax is already included.

   a. Estimate how much Chris will spend on the supplies. _$5_

   b. If Chris has $5, does he have enough to buy the supplies? Explain your reasoning.
   Chris does not have enough money to buy the school supplies. Possible explanation: The supplies cost $5.10, and $5.00 is less than $5.10.

Unit 2 ■ Focus on Number and Operations in Base Ten  **107**

## Mathematical Practices

Mathematical Practice Standards underline the teaching and understanding of all concepts and skills presented. The emphasis of specific practices is noted throughout the guided and independent practice of this lesson.

| MP1 | **Make sense of problems and persevere in solving them.** |
|-----|-----------------------------------------------------------|

**Item 7:** Students plan a solution process, they estimate a total cost, and use a strategy to calculate an exact cost.

## Observational Assessment

Use page 107 to assess whether students are able to correctly round numbers and produce accurate estimates. Also, assess whether students are correctly applying the hundreds grid models to both addition and subtraction. Lastly, assess whether students are correctly regrouping within the place-value charts.

### ☆☆ Think·Pair·Share

**Peer Collaboration**  Have partners share their estimation strategies and their reasoning. Ask students questions such as:

- *Which estimation strategy works best in this situation? Why?*

- *If the estimate and actual amount are the same, how do you decide whether Chris has enough money?*

### Return to the Essential Question

Reread the Lesson 12 Essential Question on page 104: *How do you add and subtract decimal numbers?*

Ask volunteers to use what they learned in this lesson to answer the question. (Possible responses: I can use a hundreds grid to model addition by shading both numbers and giving the total. I can model subtraction by shading the first number, crossing out the second number, and then determining the difference as the part of the hundreds grid that is not crossed out. I can use a place-value chart by lining up the digits by like place value and adding or subtracting from right to left. I can check my answer by rounding each number to the nearest whole number and finding an estimate of the sum or difference.)

Invite volunteers to share ideas about using the strategies presented in this lesson for adding and subtracting decimal numbers.

# Independent Practice

## Concept Application

Students may work independently on these pages in the classroom or at home. They may refer to the first four pages of the lesson to revisit the instruction or to see a worked-out example.

**Common Errors** and **Teaching Tips** may help you support student learning either in the classroom or as a follow-up for work done at home.

## Common Errors

### Item 5

Students may struggle with subtracting the second decimal because it is given to hundredths while the number line is divided into tenths. Remind them that 0.55 is half way between 0.5 and 0.6.

### Item 6

Ensure that students add the first two decimals, then subtract by crossing out.

## Teaching Tips

### Items 1–4

Remind students that one decimal in the expression may round up to the nearest whole number, while another may round down. Each decimal should be analyzed when rounding. Ensure students have a solid grasp on the rules for rounding to the nearest whole number.

---

### Independent Practice

**Complete the steps to estimate each answer to the nearest whole number.**

1. $2.09 + 1.84$

   $\underline{2} + 2$

   $\underline{4}$

2. $48.85 - 3.22$

   $\underline{49} - \underline{3}$

   $\underline{46}$

3. $5.7 + 8.15 + 3.72$

   $\underline{6} + \underline{8} + \underline{4}$

   $\underline{14} + \underline{4}$

   $\underline{18}$

4. $32.2 + (12.91 - 4.75)$

   $\underline{32} + (\underline{13} - \underline{5})$

   $\underline{32} + \underline{8}$

   $\underline{40}$

**Use the model to find the value of the expression.**

5. $1.4 - 0.55$

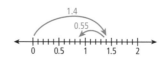

$1.4 - 0.55 = \underline{\quad 0.85 \quad}$

6. $1.3 + 1.5 - 1.14$

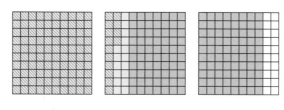

$1.3 + 1.5 - 1.14 = \underline{\quad 1.66 \quad}$

---

## Writing About Math

▶ **Write a Narrative** Ask students to write a paragraph describing a trip around town to run errands at three or four different stores. Provide a starting amount of money for the errands and ask students to describe the reason for each stop, what was purchased, and its cost. Then, ask students to both estimate and calculate how much money is left at the end of the trip. Students should orient the reader by describing the situation necessitating each stop. Encourage the use of transitional phrases to manage the sequence of events.

Ask volunteers to read their paragraphs aloud while the class computes an estimate of the remaining money. Share comparisons of a few volunteers' estimated amounts prior to revealing the calculated amount at the end of the narrative.

Lesson 12

Independent Practice

## Teaching Tips

### Items 7-9
Ensure that students are placing the numbers into the place-value chart correctly by lining up the decimal points and the like place values in each number. Remind students that they can use 0s as place holders if the numbers have a different number of decimal places.

### Items 10-14
Students may need to show work on a separate sheet of paper. Encourage them to use place-value charts, grid paper, or lined paper turned sideways to keep like place values aligned.

**Use the place-value chart to solve each equation.**

7. $3.89 - 2.43 =$ ___1.46___

| ones | . | tenths | hundredths |
|---|---|---|---|
| 3 | . | 8 | 9 |
| − 2 | . | 4 | 3 |
| 1 | . | 4 | 6 |

8. $5.12 + 2.7 + 0.23 =$ ___8.05___

| ones | . | tenths | hundredths |
|---|---|---|---|
| 1 | | | |
| 5 | . | 1 | 2 |
| 2 | . | 7 | 0 |
| + 0 | . | 2 | 3 |
| 8 | . | 0 | 5 |

9. $200.9 + 37.48 + 89 =$ ___327.38___

| hundreds | tens | ones | . | tenths | hundredths |
|---|---|---|---|---|---|
| 1 | 1 | 1 | | | |
| 2 | 0 | 0 | . | 9 | 0 |
| | 3 | 7 | . | 4 | 8 |
| + | 8 | 9 | . | 0 | 0 |
| 3 | 2 | 7 | . | 3 | 8 |

**Evaluate. Show your work.**

10. $11.5 + 7.78$

___19.28___

11. $130.84 - 13.9$

___116.94___

12. $42.2 + 20.85$

___63.05___

13. $3.17 + 109 - 12.95$

___99.22___

14. What is the value of $27.09 + 13.5 - 8.85$?

a. 19.59

b. 21.74

c. 31.74

d. 32.55

## Digital Connection

**Interactive Whiteboard** Choose a quiz-style game that features adding and subtracting decimals to the hundredths. Allow students to work in teams to find the sums and differences, earning points for their team. Allow teams to use the strategies outlined in this lesson when computing the sums and differences.

# Independent Practice

## Common Errors

### Item 16

Students may not line up the like place values, causing an incorrect calculation. Encourage students to use a place-value chart or grid paper to correct this error.

## Teaching Tips

### Item 15

Point out that Renee could have used estimation to check the reasonableness of her answer. Rounding the numbers in the problem to the nearest whole number gives an estimate of 22 − 1, or 21, which is far from Renee's answer of 1.03.

### Items 16–17

These problems require adding three decimals. Be sure students understand that the addition process is the same: line up like place values and then add the columns from right to left, regrouping when necessary. Ensure students are also providing a unit with their answers.

## Independent Practice

**MP3** **15.** Renee says that the value of 21.9 − 1.16 is 1.03. Her work is shown below. What error did Renee make? What is the correct answer?

$$
\begin{array}{r}
2\,1.9 \\
-\,1.16 \\
\hline
1.03
\end{array}
$$

Possible answer: Renee did not line up like place values. She could have written 21.9 with a zero place holder in the hundredths column to help her align the digits correctly. The correct answer is 20.74.

**Solve the problems.**

**MP1** **16.** Gary's backpack weighs 1.2 pounds. His math textbook weighs 3.75 pounds, and his science textbook weighs 2.85 pounds. How much will his backpack weigh with the math and science textbooks in it? Check the reasonableness of your answer.

▸ **Show your work.**

$$
\begin{array}{r}
1\;1 \\
1.20 \\
3.75 \\
+2.85 \\
\hline
7.80
\end{array}
$$

1.2 rounds to 1
3.75 rounds to 4
2.85 rounds to 3

1 + 4 + 3 = 8, which is close to 7.8

**Answer** Gary's backpack will weigh 7.8 pounds.

**MP2** **17.** Steven made punch by mixing 2.8 liters of orange juice, 0.75 liters of pineapple juice, and 1.2 liters of sparkling water. How many liters of punch did Steven make? Check the reasonableness of your answer.

▸ **Show your work.**

$$
\begin{array}{r}
1 \\
2.80 \\
0.75 \\
+1.20 \\
\hline
4.75
\end{array}
$$

2.8 rounds to 3
0.75 rounds to 1
1.2 rounds to 1

3 + 1 + 1 = 5, which is close to 4.75

**Answer** Steven made 4.75 liters of punch.

**110**  Unit 2 ▪ Focus on Number and Operations in Base Ten

## Mathematical Practices

| MP1 | **Make sense of problems and persevere in solving them.** |
| --- | --- |

**Item 16:** Students analyze a word problem and plan a solution pathway. Once they have found the solution, they check its reasonableness by using estimation.

| MP2 | **Reason abstractly and quantitatively.** |
| --- | --- |

**Item 17:** Students make sense of quantities and their relationships in this problem situation.

| MP3 | **Construct viable arguments and critique the reasoning of others.** |
| --- | --- |

**Item 15:** Students analyze the problem solving process given and determine whether or not the solution is correct, identifying any potential errors.

Lesson 12

## Independent Practice

MP1 **18.** The table below shows the cost of fruits at a produce stand. Alberto bought two bananas, a kiwi, and a pound of apples. How much did he spend?

| Fruit | Cost |
|---|---|
| Apples | $2.05 per pound |
| Bananas | $0.39 each |
| Kiwis | $0.50 each |

**Show your work.**

```
  1 2
  0.39      The two bananas are about $1.
  0.39      The apples are about $2.
  0.50      The kiwi is $0.50.
+2.05
 3.33      1 + 2 + 0.50 = 3.50, which is close to 3.33
```

**Answer** Alberto spent $3.33.

MP2 **19.** Radha now pays $45.50 per month for unlimited calls and texts. She can switch to a new wireless company and pay $42.49 per month for unlimited calls plus $3.99 for unlimited texts. Should Radha switch? Explain.

**Show your work.**

```
   1 1        46.48 > 45.50
  42.49
+  3.99
  46.48
```

**Answer** Radha should not change to the new cell phone company because it is more expensive.

MP3 **20.** Tammy's kitten weighed 1.87 pounds when he was a month old. Now he weighs 3.9 pounds. Tammy says her cat gained more than 2 pounds. Is she correct? Explain.

**Show your work.**

```
  8 10
  3.9 0       3.9 rounds up to 4
 -1.8 7       1.87 rounds up to 2
  2.0 3       4 - 2 = 2, which is close to 2.03
```

**Answer** Yes, the kitten gained 2.03 pounds, which is more than 2 pounds.

## Common Errors

### Item 18
Students may not read carefully enough to notice that Alberto bought two bananas. Make sure students carefully identify the amount purchased for each type of fruit.

### Item 19
Ensure students' answers include an explanation of the comparison of the two costs, not just the cost from the new wireless company.

## Teaching Tips

### Item 20
Note that while useful in checking the reasonableness of the solution, estimation does not necessarily help the student answer this particular problem.

| Mathematical Practices | |
|---|---|
| **MP1** | **Make sense of problems and persevere in solving them.** |
| **Item 18:** Students use a chart in planning their solution process. | |
| **MP2** | **Reason abstractly and quantitatively.** |
| **Item 19:** Students reason quantitatively by comparing their solution with the current cost. | |
| **MP3** | **Construct viable arguments and critique the reasoning of others.** |
| **Item 20:** Students agree or disagree with another student's claim and share their reasoning. | |

## OBJECTIVE
**Learn how to multiply decimal numbers.**

## ESSENTIAL QUESTION
Students will learn to multiply decimals by using strategies similar to those they used to multiply whole numbers. Have them share some whole number multiplication strategies they know.

## PREREQUISITE SKILLS
Use Item E on page 339 of the Foundational Skills Handbook to review using place value and partial products to multiply whole numbers.

## FLUENCY PRACTICE
Fluency practice is available at **sadlierconnect.com**.

## Concept Development

### Understand: How to use a model to multiply a decimal by a whole number

■ Point out that the decimal models are similar to the models used to show multiplying whole numbers. You might have students use place-value models to solve 83 × 2. Compare the place-value model and product to the model and product shown on the student page for 0.83 × 2.

✏️ Ask students to estimate a more accurate cost by rounding only the weight. Doubling $1.75 results in $3.50, and $3.50 + $3.50 = $7.00.

---

# Lesson 13 Multiply Decimals to Hundredths

**Essential Question:**
How do you multiply decimal numbers?

## Guided Instruction

In this lesson you will learn how to multiply decimal numbers.

**Understand:** How to use a model to multiply a decimal by a whole number

> Sara has 2 bags of dried fruit. Each bag weighs 0.83 ounce. How many ounces of dried fruit does Sara have in all?

To find the total ounces Sarah has in 2 bags of dried fruit, multiply 0.83 ounce by 2. Use a model.

**1. Model the problem.**

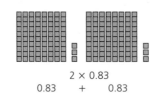

2 × 0.83
0.83   +   0.83

**2. Add the tenths.**

Regroup

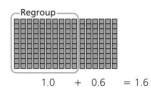

1.0   +   0.6   = 1.6

**3. Add the hundredths.**

0.03 + 0.03 = 0.06

**4. Add the two sums.**

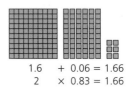

1.6   +  0.06 = 1.66
2     ×  0.83 = 1.66

➡️ Sara has 1.66 ounces of dried fruit.

✏️ A grocery store sells mushrooms for $1.75 per pound. If Cecilia buys 4.2 pounds of mushrooms, about how much will she spend? Use estimation to find the answer. *Hint:* Round each factor to the nearest whole number.
The cost for 4.2 pounds at $1.75 per pound is 4.2 × $1.75. Round 4.2 down to 4. Round $1.75 up to $2. She will spend about 4 × $2 = $8.

---

## Support English Language Learners

Have students practice reading decimals. Explain that decimals can be read in different ways. Use the decimal 1.75 as an example.

1. In math, the decimal is read as "1 and 75 hundredths". The word *and* is used to indicate the decimal point.
2. A more informal way to read the decimal is "1 point 75." The word *point* is used to indicate the decimal point.
3. If the decimal represents money, the decimal is read as "1 dollar and 75 cents."

Have students work in pairs to read the following decimals in three different ways: 1.40, 3.08, and 4.73.

Lesson 13

Guided Instruction

**Understand:** Methods for Multiplying Two Decimals

> Peaches cost $1.30 per pound. How much do 2.8 pounds of peaches cost?

To find the cost, multiply the cost per pound by the number of pounds: $2.8 \times 1.3$.

**Remember!**
$1.30 = 1.3$

Here are two possible methods for finding the product.

**Method 1**

To find $2.8 \times 1.3$, first calculate $28 \times 13$.

$$\begin{array}{r} 2 \\ 13 \\ \times\ 28 \\ \hline 104 \\ +260 \\ \hline 364 \end{array}$$

28 is 10 times as much as 2.8. So, $28 = 10 \times 2.8$.
13 is 10 times as much as 1.3. So, $13 = 10 \times 1.3$.
$28 \times 13$ is $10 \times 10$, or 100 times, as much as $2.8 \times 1.3$.
So, $28 \times 13 = 100 \times 2.8 \times 1.3$.

To find $2.8 \times 1.3$, divide 364 by 100:
$2.8 \times 1.3 = 364 \div 100 = 364 \times \frac{1}{100} = \frac{364}{100} = 3.64$.

**Method 2**

Ignore the decimal points and multiply as you would with whole numbers.

$$\begin{array}{r} 2 \\ 1.3 \\ \times\ 2.8 \\ \hline 104 \\ +260 \\ \hline 364 \end{array}$$

Use estimation to place the decimal point:
$2.8 \times 1.3$ is about $3 \times 1$, or 3. The decimal point should be between the 3 and the 6.

$$\begin{array}{r} 2 \\ 1.3 \\ \times\ 2.8 \\ \hline 104 \\ +260 \\ \hline 3.64 \end{array}$$

▶ 2.8 pounds of peaches cost $3.64.

Unit 2 ■ Focus on Number and Operations in Base Ten  113

**Understand:** Methods for Multiplying Two Decimals

■ In this presentation, students use different methods to multiply two decimal numbers. In both methods, students use the standard algorithm for multiplying whole numbers. In Method 1, students use place value to determine the position of the decimal point in the product. In Method 2, students use estimation.

■ These methods require students to reason about the value of the product. Be sure students can clearly explain their reasoning when using either method.

■ Ask students to use place value to justify why they are able to use 1.3 as a factor instead of 1.30.

## Math-to-Math Connection

**Percents and Discounts** Students will use decimal multiplication extensively in future work with percents. Tell students that percents are used to calculate discounts.

Use an advertisement that shows the original cost of items and the percent of discounts. Have students choose an item and round the cost to the nearest whole dollar. Help students rewrite the percent as a decimal. Have them find the product of the original cost and the percent of discount. Explain that this product represents the amount saved. The difference between the regular price and the amount saved is the sale price. Have students tell the sale price of their items.

# Guided Instruction

**Connect: What you know about multiplying decimals** Use this page to help students strengthen their understanding of multiplying decimals.

■ Remind students first to estimate the product. The cost per pound is about $1 and the amount is close to 4 pounds. The cost is about $4. This estimate will be helpful when determining the reasonableness of the solution.

■ Point out that, unlike decimal addition, the decimal points to not need to be aligned when multiplying. Ask students whether writing 4.2 as 4.20 would change the product. Since the product of any number and 0 equals 0, writing the weight to the hundredths place does not affect the product.

■ Make sure students understand that only the digits to the right of the decimal point are counted when determining the number of decimal places to include in the product. For example, 0.89 only has 2 decimal places. Some students may erroneously count the zero.

✏ After students have found the product using Method 1, ask them how they would find it using Method 2.

---

**Connect: What you know about multiplying decimals**

> Nectarines cost $0.89 per pound. How much do 4.2 pounds of nectarines cost?

To find the cost, multiply the cost per pound by the number of pounds: $4.2 \times 0.89$.

You can use the standard multiplication algorithm.

**Step 1**

Ignore the decimal points and multiply as you would with whole numbers.

$$
\begin{array}{r}
\overset{3}{}\,\overset{3}{} \\
\overset{1}{}\,\overset{1}{} \\
0.89 \\
\times\quad 4.2 \\
\hline
178 \\
+3560 \\
\hline
3738
\end{array}
$$

**Step 2**

Find the total number of decimal places in the two factors.

0.89 has 2 decimal places.
4.2 has 1 decimal place.

There is a total of 3 decimal places.

**Step 3**

Place the decimal point in the product so the number of decimal places equals the total you found in Step 2.

The product has 3 decimal places.

Because the answer is a price, round to the nearest cent to get $3.74.

$$
\begin{array}{r}
\overset{3}{}\,\overset{3}{} \\
\overset{1}{}\,\overset{1}{} \\
0.89 \\
\times\quad 4.2 \\
\hline
178 \\
+3560 \\
\hline
3.738
\end{array}
$$

➡ 4.2 pounds of nectarines cost $3.74.

✏ Find $4.2 \times 0.89$ by first multiplying $42 \times 89$ and then adjusting the product as you did in Method 1 on page 113.
$42 \times 89 = 3{,}738$. Because 42 is 10 times as much as 4.2 and 89 is 100 times as much as 0.89, $42 \times 89$ is $10 \times 100$, or 1,000 times, as much as $4.2 \times 0.89$. So, divide 3,738 by 1,000: $4.2 \times 0.89 = 3{,}738 \div 1{,}000 = 3.738$.

**114**   Unit 2 ■ Focus on Number and Operations in Base Ten

---

## Math-to-Science Connection

**Significant Figures** Scientists use certain rules when working with measurements and decimals. Below is the rule for multiplying with significant figures. Discuss with students how this rule is different than the general rule for multiplying with decimals in math. Stress that the operation is not different, but scientists have agreed upon the rules they use to record the solutions of the operations.

When multiplying numbers, count the number of significant figures. The answer cannot contain more significant figures than the number being multiplied with the least number of significant figures.

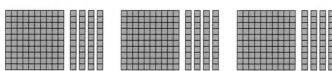

MORE ONLINE sadlierconnect.com

Lesson 13

## Guided Practice

1. Use the model to find $3 \times 1.4$.

$3 \times 1.4 = \underline{4.2}$

**For exercises 2–5, use the given whole number product to find the decimal product.**

2. $73 \times 14 = 1{,}022$, so

   $7.3 \times 1.4 = \underline{10.22}$

3. $7 \times 32 = 224$, so

   $0.7 \times 32 = \underline{22.4}$

4. $25 \times 16 = 400$, so

   $0.25 \times 1.6 = \underline{0.4}$

5. $62 \times 44 = 2{,}728$, so

   $62 \times 0.44 = \underline{27.28}$

**Complete to find each product.**

6.
```
     1.6      __1__ decimal place
   × 0.8      __1__ decimal place
   ------
     1.28     __2__ decimal places
```

7.
```
    21.05     __2__ decimal places
  ×    3.2    __1__ decimal place
  --------
    4 2 1 0
  +6 3 1 5 0
  ---------
  6 7.3 6 0   __3__ decimal places
```

### Think • Pair • Share

**MP6**  8. Explain how the model below shows that $0.4 \times 0.2 = 0.08$.

Possible answer: If the side length of the larger square is 1 unit, then the side lengths of the double-shaded part are 0.4 units and 0.2 units, so the area of this part is $0.4 \times 0.2$ square unit. Each small square has an area of $\frac{1}{100}$, or 0.01, square units, and there are 8 of them in the double shaded part, so that is 0.08 square units. This shows that $0.4 \times 0.2 = 0.08$.

Unit 2 ■ Focus on Number and Operations in Base Ten  **115**

---

## Mathematical Practices

Mathematical Practice Standards underline the teaching and understanding of all concepts and skills presented. The emphasis of specific practices is noted throughout the guided and independent practice of this lesson.

| MP6 | Attend to precision. |
| --- | --- |

**Item 8:** Students carefully formulate a full explanation for modeling decimal multiplication.

---

## Observational Assessment

Use page 115 to assess whether students are able to correctly multiply decimal numbers. Review the strategies in the lesson if students are having difficulty.

### Think•Pair•Share

**Peer Collaboration**  After students have written their explanations, have them work with a partner to discuss their answers. Partners should compare their answers and agree on one explanation to present to the class. Listen for students to discuss these types of questions:

- *What quantity does one square in the model represent?*
- *What quantity does one row or column of the model represent?*
- *What are the length and width of the double-shaded part?*
- *How do the double-shaded squares represent the product?*

### Return to the Essential Question

Reread the Lesson 13 Essential Question on page 112: *How do you multiply decimal numbers?*

Ask volunteers to use what they learned in this lesson to answer this question. (Possible response: I can multiply decimals in the same way I multiply whole numbers and then count the decimal places in the factors and count the same number of decimal places in the product to place the decimal point.)

Allow students with different responses to share with the class.

# Independent Practice

## Concept Application

Students may work independently on these pages in the classroom or at home. They may refer to the first four pages of the lesson to revisit the instruction or to see a worked-out example.

**Common Errors** and **Teaching Tips** may help you support student learning either in the classroom or as a follow-up for work done at home.

## Common Errors

### Item 1

Students may incorrectly interpret the place value model as tens. Remind them that the groups of ten represent tenths. One unit square would be used to represent one hundredth.

## Teaching Tips

### Items 2-3

Students do not have show the division of each tenth into 10 hundredths in their models. They can instead draw a long, skinny rectangle to represent each tenth and a small square to represent each hundredth.

### Items 4-7

Remind students that they can count the decimal places in each factor or use estimation to place the decimal point in the product.

---

### Independent Practice

1. Which expression does the model represent?

   a. 2 × 8     b. 0.2 × 8

   (c.) 2 × 0.8     d. 0.2 × 0.8

**Make a model to find each answer.**

2. 3 × 0.75 = __2.25__
Possible model:

3. 0.7 × 2 = __1.4__
Possible model:

 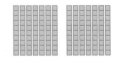

**For exercises 4–7, put the decimal point in the correct place in the product.**

4.
```
      9.2
  ×   3.1
      9 2
  +2 7 6 0
  2 8.5 2
```

5.
```
        2
        2
      0.5 5
  ×   5.5
      2 7 5
  + 2 7 5 0
  3.0 2 5
```

6.
```
      4
      4 6
  ×   0.8
  3 6.8
```

7.
```
    2 5.8
  ×  0.1 1
      2 5 8
  + 2 5 8 0
  2.8 3 8
```

MP2  8. Use estimation to determine which of the following expressions is greater. Explain how you got your answer.
5 × (1.9 + 3.15) and 6.9 × (0.2 + 3.2)
The first expression is greater. Possible explanation: 5 × (2 + 3) or 5 × 5 has a value of 25, and 7 × 3 has a value of 21. 25 > 21.

---

## Writing About Math

⬛➤ **Compare and Contrast** Have students write essays to compare and contrast the methods to multiply two decimals or the methods to multiply whole numbers verses decimal numbers. The first paragraph should focus on the similarities and the second should focus on the differences. Remind students to include examples and clear explanations in their essays.

Lesson 13

Independent Practice

**Evaluate each expression. Show your work.**

**9.** $0.8 \times 0.9$
0.72

**10.** $0.2 \times 0.5$
0.1

**11.** $6.7 \times 2.2$
14.74

**12.** $2.15 \times 0.9$
1.935

**13.** $15.8 \times 10.25$
161.95

**14.** $(9.5 + 12) \times 3.05$
$21.5 \times 3.05$
65.575

**15.** $7 \times [(8 + 2.8) \times 1.5]$
$7 \times (10.8 \times 1.5)$
$7 \times 16.2$
113.4

**16.** $(3.5 + 17.92) \times (21 - 4.5)$
$21.42 \times 16.5$
353.43

**Write an equation for each situation. Let $n$ represent the unknown amount. Then solve.**

**MP4 17.** Dana is skipping down the sidewalk. She jumps over 2.5 sections of sidewalk with each skip. How many sections will she cover after 12 skips?
$2.5 \times 12 = n$
$30 = n$

**Answer:** Dana will cover ____30____ sections in 12 skips.

**MP4 18.** Jodie makes $11.70 an hour working at a clothing store. How much will Jodie earn for working a six and a half hour shift?
$11.70 \times 6.5 = n$
$\$76.05 = n$

**Answer:** Jodie will earn ____$76.05____.

## Common Errors

### Item 18
Some students may neglect to calculate the earnings for the last half of an hour. Other students may not know how to write six and a half hours as a decimal. Be sure that students understand the equation before they solve the problem.

## Teaching Tips

### Items 14–16
Remind students to use the Order of Operations when evaluating each expression.

### Item 17
Some students may use repeated addition to solve this problem, reasoning that one skip covers 2.5 sections, so two skips will cover 5 sections, and 6 times more skips will cover 30 sections. Although the reasoning and solution are correct, remind students that the instructions include writing an equation for the situation.

| Mathematical Practices | | |
|---|---|---|
| **MP2** | **Reason abstractly and quantitatively.** | |
| **Item 8:** Students use properties of operations to estimate and compare decimal products. | | |
| **MP4** | **Model with mathematics.** | |
| **Items 17 and 18:** Students write equations to model real-world situations. | | |

# Independent Practice

## Teaching Tips

### Item 20
Suggest students solve the problem themselves in order to write a justification that includes specific reasoning and examples.

### Items 21-22
Make sure students realize that the cost per tablet depends on the number of tablets manufactured. The more tablets that are made the less the cost per tablet. Remind students to use the correct number of tablets from the first column to find the correct cost to use in their calculations.

### Independent Practice

19. Look back at question 18. Jodie estimated her pay by multiplying 12 by 6.5. Is her estimate more than or less than her actual pay?
    Possible answer: Her estimate is $78, which is $1.95 more than her actual pay of $76.05.

MP3 20. Laura says the product of 5.05 × 20 is 101. Jeremy says Laura's answer is incorrect, because the product must have 2 decimal places. How would you convince Jeremy that Laura's answer is correct?
    To find the product, you multiply 505 × 20. You get 10,100. Then, you place the decimal point to get two decimal places, so you get 101.00. You don't need to put the zeros in the answer because 101.00 equals 101.

**For exercises 21–22, use the information from the table below to answer questions.**

| Cost of manufacturing tablet readers | |
|---|---|
| Number of tablet readers | Cost per tablet reader |
| 1 – 25 | $57.55 |
| 26 – 50 | $52.30 |
| 51 – 100 | $48.18 |

MP5 21. How much will it cost to manufacture 15 tablet readers?

**Show your work.**

$57.55 × 15 = n

```
    $ 57.55
  ×     15
   2 8 7 7 5
   5 7 5 5 0
  $ 8 6 3.25
```

**Answer** The cost of 15 tablet readers will be $863.25.

MP5 22. Is it cheaper to manufacture 48 tablet readers or 52 tablet readers? Explain.
    It is cheaper to manufacture 52 tablet readers than 48.
    48 tablets cost 48 × $52.30 = $2,510.40, and 52 tablets cost 52 × $48.18 = $2,505.36.
    $2,510.40 > $2,505.36

## Mathematical Practices

| MP3 | **Construct viable arguments and critique the reasoning of others.** |
|---|---|

**Item 20:** Students justify a conclusion and respond to the arguments of others.

| MP5 | **Use appropriate tools strategically.** |
|---|---|

**Item 21:** Students use information presented in a table to solve a problem.

**Item 22:** Students use information in a table to compare decimal products.

Lesson 13

Independent Practice

MP6 **23.** Explain why estimating 17.09 × 4.1 and 17.1 × 4.09 by rounding the factors to the nearest whole number will not help you determine which product is greater. Then, find the actual products and compare.

**Answer** Both estimates are 17 × 4, or 68. 17.09 × 4.1 = 70.069, and 17.1 × 4.09 = 69.939, so 17.09 × 4.1 is greater.

MP7 **24.** Explain how you can use the equation given below to find the product of 89.7 × 15.38.

897 × 1,538 = 1,379,586

**Answer** Possible explanation: There are 3 decimal places in the factors. So place a decimal point in 1,379,586 three places from the right to find 89.7 × 15.38. The product is 1,379.586.

MP3 **25.** Ian made the model shown below to represent 0.5 × 0.14 and found that 0.5 × 0.14 = 0.07. Do you agree with Ian's use of the model and his answer? Explain why or why not.

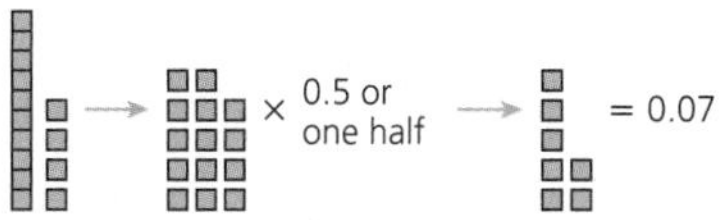

**Answer** Ian's model is correct. Possible explanation: Because 0.5 is a half, 0.5 × 0.14 is half of 14 hundredths, which is 7 hundredths, so 0.5 × 0.14 = 0.07.

Unit 2 ■ Focus on Number and Operations in Base Ten **119**

## Common Errors

### Item 23
Students may reason that since 17.1 is greater than 17.09, the product of 17.1 and 4.09 must also be greater. Remind students to find the actual products to check their reasoning.

## Teaching Tips

### Item 24
Students may use any of the methods presented on pages 113–114 to help them with their explanations.

## Mathematical Practices

| **MP3** | **Construct viable arguments and critique the reasoning of others.** |
|---|---|

**Item 25:** Students interpret another student's multiplication model to determine whether it makes sense.

| **MP6** | **Attend to precision.** |
|---|---|

**Item 23:** Students must write a clear explanation and then do careful calculations.

| **MP7** | **Look for and make use of structure.** |
|---|---|

**Item 24:** Students explain how to use the base 10 structure of the factors to compute a decimal product.

## OBJECTIVE
**Learn methods to divide decimal numbers.**

## ESSENTIAL QUESTION
Students will expand their knowledge of place value to work with decimal division. Explain to students that their understanding of place value is key to understanding how to divide decimals.

## FLUENCY PRACTICE
Fluency practice is available at **sadlierconnect.com**.

## Concept Development

### Understand: How to divide a decimal by a whole number.

■ Students will use decimal models to understand and explain procedures for decimal division. Using decimal models helps students understand the application of the standard division algorithm with a decimal dividend.

■ Note that on this page and page 121, models are given for the dividend. Guide students to use these models for visual support as they read through the solution. If you have place-value models, you might use them to model the steps of the computation.

---

## Lesson 14 Divide Decimals to Hundredths

**Essential Question: How do you divide decimal numbers?**

### Guided Instruction

In this lesson you will learn methods for dividing with decimals.

**Understand: How to divide a decimal by a whole number**

> Evaluate 5.32 ÷ 4.

Use a model to help you visualize the division.

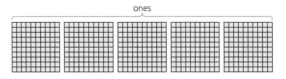
ones     tenths   hundredths

**Step 1**

Divide the 5 ones into 4 equal groups. There will be 1 one in each group with 1 one left over.

$$\begin{array}{r} 1 \\ 4\overline{)5.32} \\ -4 \\ \hline 1 \end{array}$$

**Step 2**

Ungroup the leftover one as 10 tenths, and combine them with the original 3 tenths, making 13 tenths.

Divide the 13 tenths among the 4 groups. There will be 3 tenths in each group with 1 tenth left over.

$$\begin{array}{r} 1 \\ 4\overline{)5.32} \\ -4 \\ \hline 13 \end{array} \longrightarrow \begin{array}{r} 1.3 \\ 4\overline{)5.32} \\ -4 \\ \hline 13 \\ -12 \\ \hline 1 \end{array}$$

**Step 3**

Ungroup the leftover tenth as 10 hundredths and combine them with the original 2 hundredths, making 12 hundredths.

Divide the 12 hundredths among the 4 groups. There will be 3 hundredths in each group.

When you divide 5.32 by 4 each group will have 1 one, 3 tenths, and 3 hundredths.

$$\begin{array}{r} 1.3 \\ 4\overline{)5.32} \\ -4 \\ \hline 13 \\ -12 \\ \hline 12 \end{array} \longrightarrow \begin{array}{r} 1.33 \\ 4\overline{)5.32} \\ -4 \\ \hline 13 \\ -12 \\ \hline 12 \\ -12 \\ \hline 0 \end{array}$$

➡ 5.32 ÷ 4 = 1.33.

---

## Support English Language Learners

Review the terms *tenths* and *hundredths*. Write the words and say them aloud, asking students to repeat them after you. Display decimals with two decimal places and ask students to identify the number of tenths and hundredths in each number. Model identifying the hundredths and the tenths, and make sure that students respond in complete sentences, such as "There are 3 tenths and 2 hundredths in 6.32." This will help you evaluate students' understanding of the concept and will also give students practice in these sometimes-difficult pronunciations.

MORE ONLINE sadlierconnect.com                                    Lesson 14

Guided Instruction

**Understand: How to divide by 0.1 and 0.01**

| Evaluate 4.8 ÷ 0.1 and 4.8 ÷ 0.01. |
|---|

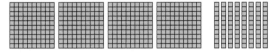

- To evaluate 4.8 ÷ 0.1, find the number of tenths in 4.8.
  There are 10 tenths in each of the ones, so there are 40 tenths in 4.
  There are 8 tenths in 0.8.
  Altogether, there are 48 tenths in 4.8. So, 4.8 ÷ 0.1 = 48.

- To evaluate 4.8 ÷ 0.01, find the number of hundredths in 4.8.
  There are 100 hundredths in each of the ones, so there are 400 hundredths in 4.
  Because 0.8 = 0.80, there are 80 hundredths in 0.8.
  Altogether, there are 480 hundredths in 4.8. So, 4.8 ÷ 0.01 = 480.

Notice that 4.8 ÷ 0.1 = 4.8 × 10 and 4.8 ÷ 0.01 = 4.8 × 100.

➡ 4.8 ÷ 0.1 = 48 and 4.8 ÷ 0.01 = 480.

**Understand: How to relate dividing by a decimal to dividing by a whole number**

| Explain why 4.8 ÷ 0.6 is equivalent to 48 ÷ 6.<br>Explain why 4.8 ÷ 0.06 is equivalent to 480 ÷ 6. |
|---|

➡ 4.8 = 48 tenths and 0.6 = 6 tenths. So, to evaluate 4.8 ÷ 0.6, find the number of groups of 6 tenths in 48 tenths. This is the same as calculating 48 ÷ 6. So, 4.8 ÷ 0.6 = 48 ÷ 6 = 8.

Notice that to get from 4.8 ÷ 0.6 to 48 ÷ 6, you multiply both numbers by 10. The quotient stays the same.

4.8 = 480 hundredths and 0.06 = 6 hundredths. So, to evaluate 4.8 ÷ 0.06, find the number of groups of 6 hundredths in 480 hundredths. This is the same as calculating 480 ÷ 6. So, 4.8 ÷ 0.06 = 480 ÷ 6 = 80.

Notice to get from 4.8 ÷ 0.06 to 480 ÷ 6, you multiply both numbers by 100. The quotient stays the same.

✏ Explain why 0.5 ÷ 0.25 is the same as 50 ÷ 25. Possible answer: 0.5 is 50 hundredths and 0.25 is 25 hundredths. So, 0.5 ÷ 0.25 is the number of groups of 25 hundredths in 50 hundredths, which is the same as 50 ÷ 25.

Unit 2 ■ Focus on Number and Operations in Base Ten    **121**

---

**Math-to-Consumers Connection**

**Vanilla Deal** Often, consumers search for food products that are not only tasty, but are the least expensive per unit. Share the following real-world problem with students. Have them work in pairs to determine which package of vanilla beans would be the least expensive per bean. *When purchasing baking supplies, a baker wants to buy very flavorful and aromatic Madagascar vanilla beans. He chose the package of vanilla beans that are the least cost per bean. Which of these packages did he buy: Package A–7 beans for $7.91; Package B–5 beans for $5.25; or Package C–16 beans for $16.96?* (After dividing, students will see that Package B was the least cost per bean.)

---

**Understand: How to divide by 0.1 and 0.01**

■ This presentation explains how to divide a decimal by one tenth and one hundredth by referring to place value concepts.

■ Explain why 4.8 ÷ 0.1 is the same as 48 ÷ 1 (because 4.8 ÷ 0.1 is the number of groups of 1 tenth in 48 tenths). You may want to review that the place value of a digit is 10 times the value of the digit to its right. Give examples with whole numbers if students struggle with this concept. For example, there are 4 tens or 40 ones in 40.

■ Ask students to explain why 4.8 ÷ 0.01 is the same as 480 ÷ 1 (because 4.8 ÷ 0.01 is the number of groups of 1 hundredth in 480 hundredths). Support students who have difficulty verbalizing their explanations. Breaking apart hundreds models will help students visualize how to rename each digit.

**Understand: How to relate dividing by a decimal to dividing by a whole number**

■ This presentation shows students how to rewrite a decimal division expression as an equivalent whole number division expression.

■ Students will draw upon place value concepts developed in earlier presentations, understanding that 4.8 is equivalent to 48 tenths and 480 hundredths.

■ Some students may need to practice converting decimal numbers into tenths and hundredths before they are ready to create equivalent whole number division expressions.

✏ Have students describe 0.25 as a number of hundredths. Then, have them write 0.5 as 0.50 and then describe 0.50 as a number of hundredths.

**Connect: What you know about place value and dividing decimals** Use this page to help students apply what they know about place value to dividing decimals with the standard division algorithm.

■ Show students how to use arrows with the standard division algorithm to convert problems involving decimal divisors to problems involving whole number divisors. Provide multiple examples that students can use to practice moving a decimal point within the standard division algorithm.

■ In Step 2, have a student explain why multiplying both the dividend and divisor by 10 does not change the quotient.

■ Ask students to describe each step within the algorithm using place value vocabulary and the terms "group" and "ungroup."

■ Encourage students to draw an arrow as they bring down each digit to help keep track of which digits are being used in each step. Remind students that after the first digit of the quotient is placed there must be a number in the quotient above each number in the dividend.

■ Ask students if the quotient is reasonable. Emphasize that it is easy to make a careless mistake when working with decimals and decimal points, so it is important to estimate the quotient and compare the estimate to the actual quotient.

---

**Lesson 14  Divide Decimals to Hundredths**

## Guided Instruction

**Connect: What you know about place value and dividing decimals**

> Kim earned \$43.75 for working a 3.5-hour shift at a bakery. How much did she earn per hour?

**Step 1**

Write an expression for the situation.

Divide the amount Kim earned by the number of hours she worked: $43.75 \div 3.5$.

**Step 2**

Change the problem to an equivalent problem with a whole number divisor.

Multiply both 43.75 and 3.5 by 10 to get $437.5 \div 35$. This does not change the quotient.

> In long division format, move the decimal points in the divisor and dividend the same number of places to get a whole-number divisor.
>
> $3.5\overline{)43.7\,5}$

**Step 3**

Evaluate $437.5 \div 35$.

a.) Divide 43 tens into 35 groups. There is 1 ten in each group, and there are 8 tens left.

b.) Ungroup 8 tens as 80 ones. Bring down the 7 ones making 87 ones.

c.) Divide 87 ones into 35 groups. There are 2 ones in each group with 17 ones left.

d.) Ungroup the 17 ones as 170 tenths and bring down the 5 original tenths to get 175 tenths.

e.) Divide 175 tenths into 35 groups. There are 5 in each group with none left.

Because the answer is a money amount, show the decimal to the hundredths place: $12.5 = 12.50$.

➡ Kim earned \$12.50 per hour.

a.)
$$35\overline{)437.5} \\ \underline{-35} \\ 8$$ (quotient: 1)

b.)
$$35\overline{)437.5} \\ \underline{-35} \\ 87$$ (quotient: 1)

c.)
$$35\overline{)437.5} \\ \underline{-35} \\ 87 \\ \underline{-70} \\ 17$$ (quotient: 12)

d.)
$$35\overline{)437.5} \\ \underline{-35} \\ 87 \\ \underline{-70} \\ 175$$ (quotient: 12)

e.)
$$35\overline{)437.5} \\ \underline{-35} \\ 87 \\ \underline{-70} \\ 175 \\ \underline{-175} \\ 0$$ (quotient: 12.5)

> When the divisor is a whole number, the decimal point in the quotient is placed directly above the decimal point in the dividend.

**122  Unit 2 ■ Focus on Number and Operations in Base Ten**

---

## Math-to-Sports Connection

**Olympic Records** Have students do an Internet search to find Olympic record data. The data should include the distance of the Olympic event and the time it took to complete. Then, students should divide the distance by the time to find the average speed of the athlete. Alternatively, give students the following Olympic data and have them find the average speed of each runner. *Usain Bolt, of Jamaica, sprinted 100 meters in 9.63 seconds. Florence Griffith-Joyner, of the USA, sprinted 100 meters in 10.62 seconds.* Have students solve the divisions up to the thousandths in the quotient, then round the quotient to the nearest hundredth. Bolt sprinted at approximately 10.38 m/sec. Griffith-Joyner sprinted at approximately 9.42 m/sec.

MORE ONLINE ▶ sadlierconnect.com

Lesson 14

## Guided Practice

1. Write the division equation that is modeled below.

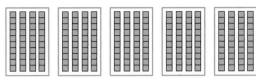

2 ÷ 5 = 0.4 or 2 ÷ 0.4 = 5

2. Complete the statements to find 8 ÷ 0.01.

There are __100__ hundredths in 1.

So, there are __800__ hundredths in 8.

This means that 8 ÷ 0.01 = __800__.

3. Complete the statements to find 2.9 ÷ 0.1.

There are __20__ tenths in 2.

There are __9__ tenths in 0.9.

So, 2.9 ÷ 0.1 = __29__.

**Complete the statements.**

4. 5.4 ÷ 0.6 has the same quotient as 54 ÷ __6__.

5. 36.5 ÷ 0.05 has the same quotient as __3,650__ ÷ 5.

**Rewrite the expression as an equivalent expression with a whole-number divisor.**

6. 9.48 ÷ 2.7

    ___94.8 ÷ 27___

7. 5.8 ÷ 0.65

    ___580 ÷ 65___

### ☗☗ Think • Pair • Share

MP7  8. Find and compare the quotients of 0.4 ÷ 0.02, 4 ÷ 0.2, and 40 ÷ 2.
Explain the relationship among the three expressions.
Possible explanation: 0.4 ÷ 0.02 = 20, 4 ÷ 0.2 = 20, and 40 ÷ 2 = 20.
The quotients are the same. The three problems are equivalent.

Unit 2 ■ Focus on Number and Operations in Base Ten  **123**

## Mathematical Practices

Mathematical Practice Standards underline the teaching and understanding of all concepts and skills presented. The emphasis of specific practices is noted throughout the guided and independent practice of this lesson.

| MP7 | **Look for and make use of structure.** |
| --- | --- |

**Item 8:** Students use place value patterns to determine that three expressions are equivalent.

## Observational Assessment

Use page 123 to assess whether students understand how to relate dividing by a decimal to dividing by a whole number. Have students practice modeling, writing, and verbalizing equivalent decimal and whole number division expressions.

### ☗☗ Think•Pair•Share

**Peer Collaboration** Students can use mental math to find the quotient of 40 ÷ 2. Using that quotient as a base value, have students use place-value models to show 4 ÷ 0.2. Ask students to consider these questions as they work:

- *What basic fact can you use to find the quotient of 40 ÷ 2?*

- *When working with whole numbers, the place-value models represent hundreds, tens, and ones. What do they represent when working with decimals?*

- *What happens when you multiply both the dividend and the divisor by multiples of ten?*

- *How can using multiples of ten be helpful when comparing these three expressions?*

To summarize, explain that since both the dividend and the divisor are multiplied by 10, these expressions are equivalent.

### Return to the Essential Question

Reread the Lesson 14 Essential Question on page 120: *How do you divide decimal numbers?*

Ask volunteers to use what they learned in this lesson to answer this question. (Possible responses: I can use models to divide decimal numbers. I can write equivalent whole number expressions. I can use what I know about place value to apply the division algorithm.)

# Independent Practice

## Concept Application

Students may work independently on these pages in the classroom or at home. They may refer to the first four pages of the lesson to revisit the instruction or to see a worked-out example.

**Common Errors** and **Teaching Tips** may help you support student learning either in the classroom or as a follow-up for work done at home.

## Teaching Tips

### Item 1

There are two possible division equations. Students may write $1.28 \div 4 = 0.32$ to show that when 1.28 is divided into 4 equal groups, there is 0.32 in each group. Or, students may write $1.28 \div 0.32 = 4$ to show that when 1.28 is divided into groups of 0.32, there are 4 groups in all. Have students who wrote different equations explain how they found them.

### Items 3-6

Have students practice drawing the arrow to move the decimal point to the right for both the dividend and the divisor. Ensure students have a firm grasp that the number of places the decimal point moves in the divisor must match the number of places the decimal point moves in the dividend.

---

### Independent Practice

1. Use the model to complete the sentences below and answer the question.

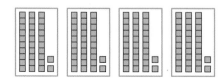

   a. The model shows __1__ ones, __2__ tenths, and __8__ hundredths in all.

   b. There are __4__ groups in all.

   c. Each group has __3__ tenths and __2__ hundredths.

   d. What division equation is modeled above? $\underline{1.28 \div 4 = 0.32}$ or $\underline{1.28 \div 0.32 = 4}$

2. Complete the statements to find $2.39 \div 0.01$.

   There are __200__ hundredths in 2.

   There are __30__ hundredths in 0.3.

   There are __9__ hundredths in 0.09.

   So, $2.39 \div 0.01 = \underline{239}$.

**Complete the statements.**

3. $30 \div 0.5$ has the same quotient as $\underline{300} \div 5$.

4. $2.1 \div 0.42$ has the same quotient as $210 \div \underline{42}$.

**Rewrite the expression as an equivalent expression with a whole-number divisor.**

5. $1.44 \div 1.2$

   $\underline{14.4 \div 12}$

6. $0.49 \div 0.07$

   $\underline{49 \div 7}$

**124**  Unit 2 ■ Focus on Number and Operations in Base Ten

---

## Writing About Math

 · **Report on a Topic**  Present students with the decimal division $78.72 \div 6.4$. Ask them to write a paragraph explaining each step they take to calculate the quotient using the standard division algorithm. Have them use place value vocabulary and the terms "group," "ungroup," and "divide." Emphasize that they can use the sentences found in Step 3 on page 122 as a model. Students should also explain how they know when to stop dividing.

Invite students to present their explanations to the class.

**For exercises 7–12, find each quotient. Show your work.**

7.
```
        9.8
    8)78.4
     −72
      64
     −64
       0
```

8.
```
        10.1
    5)50.5
     −50
      05
     − 5
       0
```

9.
```
        0.2
 1.2.)0.2.4
     −0
      24
     −24
       0
```

10.
```
         8.3
 0.9.)7.4.7
     −72
      27
     −27
       0
```

11.
```
        15
 8.2.)1230
     −82
      410
     −410
        0
```

12.
```
        25
 0.03.)0.75
     − 6
      15
     −15
       0
```

MP1 **13.** Christopher needs to fill 45 cubic feet of his garden with soil. He already has 7.5 cubic feet of soil. If there are 2.5 cubic feet in each bag of soil, then how many bags should he purchase?

a. 2                    (b.) 15

c. 18                   d. 21

**14.** Insert one pair of parentheses in the expression below to make it true.

$2.5 \times 3 + 1.6 \div (1.25 - 0.85) - 2 = 9.5$

Unit 2 ■ Focus on Number and Operations in Base Ten **125**

## Common Errors

### Items 7–12

Students frequently forget to place the decimal point in the quotient. Remind students that, after they have "moved" the decimal points in both numbers to create a whole number divisor, they should position the decimal directly above its position in the dividend.

## Teaching Tips

### Item 14

Suggest that students use the guess-and-check strategy to rule out all possibilities until they arrive at the solution.

## Mathematical Practices

**MP1   Make sense of problems and persevere in solving them.**

**Item 13:** Students solve a two-step word problem involving decimal subtraction and decimal division.

# Independent Practice

## Common Errors

### Item 18

Some students may have difficulty remembering which symbol means greater than and which means less than. Suggest that students always place the wide end of the symbol next to the greater number.

## Teacher Tips

### Item 18

If students get stuck, suggest that they rewrite one or both expressions in each pair so that they have the same divisor. They can then reason that if two problems have the same divisor, the one with the greater dividend has the greater quotient.

## Independent Practice

**MP2** **15.** Write and solve two division equations that include the numbers 2 and 0.8. Write one equation that has a quotient greater than the divisor and the dividend. Write another one that has a quotient less than the divisor and the dividend.
Possible answer: $0.8 \div 0.4 = 2$; 2 is greater than 0.8 and 0.4 $2 \div 2.5 = 0.8$; 0.8 is less than 2 and 2.5

**MP2** **16.** Explain why you can move the decimal point in the divisor to the right, as long as you move the decimal point in the dividend the same number of places to the right.
Possible explanation: When you move the decimal point in the divisor one place to the right, you are multiplying by 10. As long as you multiply both the divisor and dividend by the same factor, the quotient will not change.

**MP2** **17.** Explain how you can determine if $9 \div 0.36$ is greater than or less than $0.9 \div 0.36$ without finding each quotient.
Possible explanation: 9 is greater than 0.9, but both equations are asking how many thirty-sixths are in each number. There will be more thirty-sixths in the greater number.

**18.** Compare the values of each pair of expressions using >, <, or =.

$7 \div 3.5 \;(<)\; 7 \div 0.35$          $7 \div 0.35 \;(>)\; 7 \div 35$

$0.85 \div 0.5 \;(=)\; 8.5 \div 5$          $8.5 \div 5 \;(<)\; 85 \div 5$

**MP4** **19.** Hal is installing a new floor in his office. He uses 352.5 square feet of tile to cover the rectangular floor. The room is 12.5 feet wide. How many feet long is the room?

a. 0.282 feet                    b. 2.82 feet

(c.) 28.2 feet                    d. 282 feet

## Mathematical Practices

| **MP2** | **Reason abstractly and quantitatively.** |
| --- | --- |

**Item 15:** Students use quantitative reasoning to write a division that satisfies the problem.

**Item 16:** Students make sense of quantities to explain the standard algorithm for division.

**Item 17:** Students make sense of quantities and their relationships to compare the values of decimal division expressions.

| **MP4** | **Model with mathematics.** |
| --- | --- |

**Item 19:** Students solve a decimal division problem and interpret the meaning of the quotient in the context of a concrete scenario.

## Independent Practice

**Solve each problem.**

MP6 **20.** The gas tank in Don's car hold 12 gallons of gas. The car can drive for 415.2 miles on one full tank of gas. How many miles per gallon of gas does Don's car get?

**Show your work. Check the reasonableness of your answer.**
415.2 ÷ 12 = 34.6
To check the reasonableness of the answer, round the dividend to the nearest whole number to estimate the quotient, or the miles of gas per gallon Don's car gets. 415 ÷ 12 = 34.5
The estimated 34.5 is close to the actual quotient 34.6.

**Answer** Don's car gets 34.6 miles per gallon of gas.

MP6 **21.** Casey gets paid $2.55 per hour waiting tables. On Friday she earned $72 in tips and made a total of $82.20. How many hours did she work Friday?

**Show your work.**
(82.20 − 72) ÷ 2.55
10.2 ÷ 2.55 = 4

**Answer** Casey worked 4 hours on Friday.

MP3 **22.** Describe two different ways you could explain to a friend that 127.5 ÷ 1.7 cannot have a quotient of 750.

**Answer** Possible answer: If you estimate the answer by rounding each number to the nearest whole number, you get 128 ÷ 2 = 64, and 750 is much larger than 64. Also, multiplication is the inverse of division, and 1.7 × 750 does not equal 127.5.

## Teaching Tips

### Item 21
Remind students to read the entire word problem before beginning any calculations and to break up multi-step word problems into separate steps.

### Item 22
Encourage students to use division and estimation concepts and strategies that they have previously learned, as well as those concepts that are found within this lesson.

## Return to the

Progress Check

Remind students to return to the Progress Check self-assessment, page 37, to check off additional items they have mastered during the unit.

| Mathematical Practices | |
|---|---|
| **MP3** | **Construct viable arguments and critique the reasoning of others.** |

**Item 22:** Students construct two different arguments to explain why a solution to a decimal division problem is incorrect.

| **MP6** | **Attend to precision.** |
|---|---|

**Item 20:** Students must check the reasonableness of their solution to a decimal division problem.

**Item 21:** Students accurately solve a two-step problem by subtracting and dividing decimals.

The Unit 2 Review covers all the standards presented in the unit. Use it to assess your students' mastery of the unit's concepts and skills.

## Depth of Knowledge

The depth of knowledge is a ranking of the content complexity of assessment items based on Webb's Depth of Knowledge (DOK) levels. The levels increase in complexity as shown below.

**Level 1:** Recall and Reproduction
**Level 2:** Basic Skills and Concepts
**Level 3:** Strategic Reasoning and Thinking
**Level 4:** Extended Thinking

| Item | DOK |
|---|---|
| 1-2 | 2 |
| 3 | 1 |
| 4-5 | 2 |
| 6 | 2 |
| 7 | 1 |
| 8 | 1 |
| 9 | 1 |
| 10 | 1 |
| 11 | 2 |
| 12 | 2 |
| 13 | 2 |
| 14 | 2 |
| 15 | 2 |
| 16 | 3 |
| 17 | 2 |
| 18 | 2 |
| 19 | 2 |
| 20 | 2 |
| 21 | 2 |
| 22 | 2 |
| 23 | 2 |
| 24 | 2 |
| 25 | 2 |
| 26 | 2 |
| 27 | 3 |
| 28 | 2 |
| 29 | 4 |

## UNIT 2 Review

**Study the pattern. Complete the sentences to describe the pattern.**

**256,730 25,673 2,567.3 256.73**

1. In each number, the value of 2 is 10 times the value of 2 in the number to its right.

2. In each number, the value of 7 is one tenth the value of 7 in the number to its left.

**Write the expression in exponent form. Determine its value.**

3. ten to the fourth power exponent form: $10^4$ value: 10,000

**For exercises 4–5, choose the correct answer.**

4. $0.67 \times \blacksquare = 67$
   a. $10^1$
   (b.) $10^2$
   c. $10^3$
   d. $10^4$

5. $532.8 \div \blacksquare = 0.5328$
   (a.) $10^3$
   b. $10^4$
   c. $10^5$
   d. $10^6$

6. How many times as great is the value of the digit 8 in 18.43 than the value of the digit 8 in 14.83?
   (a.) 10 times
   b. 100 times
   c. 1,000 times
   d. 10,000 times

**Write each word phrase as a decimal.**

7. four hundred nine thousandths 0.409

8. five hundred twenty-one and six hundred fourteen thousandths 521.614

**Write each decimal in words.**

9. 0.751 seven hundred fifty-one thousandths

10. 39.06 thirty-nine and six hundredths

**Compare. Use place value. Write <, >, or =.**

11. 9.610 (>) 9.609

12. 2.04 (=) 2.040

13. 3.895 (<) 3.985



Copyright © by William H. Sadlier, Inc. All rights reserved.

UNIT 2 Review

**Round each decimal to the ones, tenths, and hundredths places.**

|  | ones | tenths | hundredths |
|---|---|---|---|
| **14.** 0.554 | 1 | 0.6 | 0.55 |
| **15.** 8.497 | 8 | 8.5 | 8.50 |

**Answer the questions.**

**16.** What happens to the digits in 610.24 when you divide by $10^3$?
What is the quotient?

The digits move three places to the right. The quotient is 0.61024.

**17.** How do you write 23.504 in expanded form?

Possible answer: $2 \times 10 + 3 \times 1 + 5 \times \frac{1}{10} + 0 \times \frac{1}{100} + 4 \times \frac{1}{1,000}$

**Find each product. Show your work.**

**18.**
```
    362
  ×  45
  1,810
+14,480
 16,290
```

**19.**
```
    631
  ×  27
  4,417
+12,620
 17,037
```

**20.**
```
   3.45
  × 7.6
  2070
+24150
26.220
```

**Find each quotient. Show your work.**

**21.** 3,647 ÷ 26
```
      140 R7
 26)3,647
    26
    104
    104
     07
      0
     07
```

**22.** 6,095 ÷ 53
```
      115
 53)6,095
    53
    79
    53
    265
    265
      0
```

**23.** 17.28 ÷ 1.2
```
      14.4
 12)172.8
   -12
    52
   -48
    48
   -48
     0
```

**Evaluate each expression.**

**24.** 67.4 + 25.82

93.22

**25.** 260.31 − 43.6

216.71

**26.** 6.15 + 128 + 34.59

168.74

Unit 2 ■ Focus on Number and Operations in Base Ten **129**

This chart correlates the Unit 2 Review items with the lessons in which the concepts and skills are presented.

| Item | Lesson |
|---|---|
| 1 | 4 |
| 2 | 4 |
| 3 | 5 |
| 4 | 5 |
| 5 | 5 |
| 6 | 4 |
| 7 | 6 |
| 8 | 6 |
| 9 | 6 |
| 10 | 6 |
| 11 | 7 |
| 12 | 7 |
| 13 | 7 |
| 14 | 8 |
| 15 | 8 |
| 16 | 5 |
| 17 | 6 |
| 18 | 9 |
| 19 | 9 |
| 20 | 13 |
| 21 | 10 |
| 22 | 10 |
| 23 | 14 |
| 24 | 12 |
| 25 | 12 |
| 26 | 12 |
| 27 | 9 |
| 28 | 10 |
| 29 | 13 |

# Unit 2 Review

## Writing About Math

✏️ Direct students to respond to the Unit 2 Essential Question. (This can also be found on student page 39.)

**Essential Question:**
How can you use place value understanding to perform all operations fluently using whole numbers and decimals?

Possible responses:
- The place to the left of a digit is ten times the value of the place of that digit, and the value of a digit to the right of a digit is one-tenth the value of that digit.
- Use the Distributive Property to perform operations.

### Unit Assessment

- Unit 2 Review, pp. 128–130
- Unit 2 Performance Task (ONLINE)

### Additional Assessment Options

**Optional Purchase:**
- iProgress Monitor (ONLINE)
- Progress Monitor Student Benchmark Assessment Booklet

---

## UNIT 2 Review

**Solve the problems using any strategy.**

**MP3 27.** Cole says there are 2,190 hours in a year. His work is below. What mistake did Cole make? How many hours are in a year?

$$
\begin{array}{r}
{\scriptstyle 1\,1} \\
{\scriptstyle 2\,2} \\
365 \\
\times\ 24 \\
\hline
1{,}460 \\
730 \\
\hline
2{,}190
\end{array}
$$

When Cole multiplied 20 × 365, he forgot to write a zero placeholder in the ones column. 365 × 24 = 8,760. There are 8,760 hours in a year.

**MP4 28.** The business manager for a swim club wants to order tote bags imprinted with the swim club's logo as end-of-the-season gifts for its 2,108 members. The tote bags are sold in bundles of 36. How many bundles must the business manager order?

✏️ **Show your work.**

$$
\begin{array}{r}
58\ R20 \\
36\overline{)2{,}108} \\
\underline{180}\phantom{0} \\
308 \\
\underline{288} \\
20
\end{array}
$$

**Answer** The business manager must order 59 bundles of tote bags.

**MP4 29.** At the grocery store, Sunil buys 5 pounds of chicken breast for $1.59 per pound. He also buys a jar of tomato sauce that costs $3.98. Sunil has a coupon for half off the price of the sauce. He gives the cashier the coupon and a $20 bill. How much change should Sunil receive? Explain how to check the reasonableness of your answer.
Sunil should receive $10.06 in change. Sample check: First, round the cost of the chicken to $1.60: 5 × $1.60 = $8.00. Next, round the cost of the sauce to $4.00, so with the coupon the sauce is about $2.00. Then find the total cost: $8 + $2 = $10. $20 − $10 = $10, so my answer of $10.06 is reasonable.

---

## Mathematical Practices

| MP3 | Construct viable arguments and critique the reasoning of others. |
|-----|------------------------------------------------------------------|

**Item 27:** Students analyze a problem and share their reasoning with others.

| MP4 | Model with mathematics. |
|-----|-------------------------|

**Item 28:** Students relate mathematics to everyday problems.

**Item 29:** Students model a situation using mathematics to solve a real-world problem.

## Progress Check

UNIT 3

Look at how the math concepts and skills you have learned and will learn connect.

It is very important for you to understand the math concepts and skills from the prior grade level so that you will be able to develop an understanding of fractions in this unit and be prepared for next year. To practice your skills, go to sadlierconnect.com.

| GRADE 4 — I Can... | Before Unit 3 | GRADE 5 — Can I ? | After Unit 3 | GRADE 6 — I Will... |
|---|---|---|---|---|
| Add and subtract fractions with like denominators | ☐ | Add and subtract fractions with unlike denominators | ☐ | |
| Add and subtract fractions with like denominators to solve word problems | ☐ | Add and subtract fractions to solve word problems | ☐ | |
| | | Interpret a fraction as division | ☐ | |
| | | Solve problems where fractions are answers to divisions | ☐ | |
| Multiply a unit fraction and a fraction by a whole number | ☐ | Multiply a fraction or whole number by a fraction | ☐ | |
| Interpret a multiplication equation as a comparison | ☐ | Interpret multiplication as scaling (resizing) | ☐ | |
| Multiply fractions by whole numbers to solve problems | ☐ | Multiply fractions and mixed numbers to solve problems | ☐ | |
| Multiply a unit fraction by a whole number | ☐ | Divide unit fractions by whole numbers and whole numbers by unit fractions | ☐ | Divide whole numbers by fractions  Divide fractions by fractions |
| | | Solve problems involving division with unit fractions and whole numbers | ☐ | |

Unit 3 ■ Focus on Number and Operations—Fractions

**Student Page 131**

## Progress Check

Progress Check is a self-assessment tool that students can use to gauge their own progress. Research shows that when students take accountability for their learning, motivation increases.

Before students begin work in Unit 3, have them check any items they know they can do well. Explain that it is fine if they don't check any of the boxes; they will have the opportunity to learn and practice all the standards through the course of the unit.

Let them know that at the end of the unit they will review their checklists to check their progress. After students have completed the last lesson of the unit, before they begin the Unit 3 Review, you will be prompted to have students revisit this page.

## HOME ◆ CONNECT...

The Home Connect feature is a way to keep parents or other adult family members apprised of what their children are learning. The key learning objectives are listed, and some ideas for related activities and discussions are included.

Explain to students that they can share the Home Connect page at home with their families. Let students know there is an activity connected to their classroom learning that they can do with their families.

Encourage students and their parents to share their experiences using the suggestions on the Home Connect. You may wish to invite students to share this work with the class.

## HOME ◆ CONNECT...

Your child will solve real-world problems using the addition, subtraction, multiplication and division of fractions with unlike denominators. Support your child by using the following problem-solving model.

- **Read** Read the problem. Focus on the facts and the questions. Ask: *What facts do you know? What do you need to find out?*
- **Plan** Outline a plan. Plan how to solve the problem. Ask: *What operation will you use? Do you need to use 1 step or 2 steps? Will you draw a picture? How have you solved similar problems?*
- **Solve** Follow your plan to solve the problem. Ask: *Did you answer the question? Did you label your answer?*
- **Check** Test that the solution is reasonable. Ask: *Does your answer make sense? If not, review and revise your plan. How can you solve the problem a different way? Is the answer the same? How can you estimate to check your answer?*

**Conversation Starters:** Using a model or drawing is a method your child will use. Talk about real-world problems that can be organized and solved by using visual supports. For example: determine the area or perimeter of a space in your home with mixed number measures. Ask questions such as: *How can a model of the space help in finding the area or perimeter? What model(s) can we draw?*

### In this unit your child will:

- Add and subtract fractions with unlike denominators.
- Interpret fractions as division.
- Interpret products of fractions.
- Find areas of rectangles.
- Interpret multiplication of fractions as scaling.
- Multiply fractions and mixed numbers.
- Divide unit fractions by whole numbers and whole numbers by unit fractions.

### Ways to Help Your Child

As your child solves more and more complex real-world problems in math, continue to make everyday math part of your daily conversations at home. Talk about the ways you use math for your own work, or in making a recipe or keeping a budget. Involve your child in tasks that require math.

ONLINE
For more Home Connect activities, continue online at sadlierconnect.com

132   Unit 3 ■ Focus on Number and Operations—Fractions

**Student Page 132**

## UNIT PLANNER

| Lesson | Objective |
|---|---|
| **15** Add and Subtract Fractions with Unlike Denominators | Add and subtract fractions with unlike denominators using models and equivalent fractions. |
| **16** Problem Solving: Add and Subtract Fractions | Use the addition and subtraction of fractions to solve real-world problems. |
| **17** Interpret Fractions as Division | Solve problems that involve dividing whole numbers that result in quotients that are fractions or mixed numbers. |
| **18** Interpret Products of Fractions | Multiply a whole number or a fraction by a fraction. |
| **19** Find Areas of Rectangles: Tile and Multiply | Use tiling and multiplication to find the area of a rectangle with fractional side lengths. |
| **20** Interpret Multiplication of Fractions as Scaling | Compare a number and the product of the number and a fraction. |
| **21** Problem Solving: Multiply Fractions and Mixed Numbers | Solve real-world problems by multiplying fractions, mixed numbers, and whole numbers. |
| **22** Divide Unit Fractions by Whole Numbers | Use models and the relationship between multiplication and division to divide unit fractions by whole numbers. |
| **23** Divide Whole Numbers by Unit Fractions | Compute and interpret quotients involving division of whole numbers by unit fractions. |
| **24** Problem Solving: Divide Unit Fractions and Whole Numbers | Use unit fractions and whole numbers in computations, models, and equations to solve real-world problems. |

**Essential Question:** How can you use models and equivalent fractions to perform all operations with fractions or mixed numbers?

UNIT 3

| Essential Question | Words to Know |
|---|---|
| How can you add and subtract fractions with unlike denominators? | unlike denominators common denominator |
| How can you use the addition and subtraction of fractions to solve real-world problems? | |
| How are fractions related to division? | |
| How can you multiply a whole number or a fraction by a fraction? | |
| How do you find the area of rectangles with fractional side lengths? | |
| When you multiply a number by a fraction, how does the product compare to the number? | scaling |
| How can you use the multiplication of fractions, mixed numbers, and whole numbers to solve real-world problems? | |
| How can you divide a unit fraction by a whole number? | |
| How can you divide a whole number by a unit fraction? | |
| How can you use division with unit fractions and whole numbers to solve real-world problems? | |

## Unit Assessment

- Unit 3 Review, *pp. 214–216*
- Unit 3 Performance Task ONLINE

## Additional Assessment Options

- Performance Task 1, *pp. 217–222*
  ALSO ONLINE

**Optional Purchase:**

- iProgress Monitor ONLINE
- Progress Monitor Student Benchmark Assessment Booklet

## ONLINE Digital Resources

- Home Connect Activities
- Unit Performance Tasks
- Additional Practice
- Fluency Practice
- Teacher Resources
- iProgress Monitor (optional purchase)

**Go to SadlierConnect.com to access your Digital Resources.**

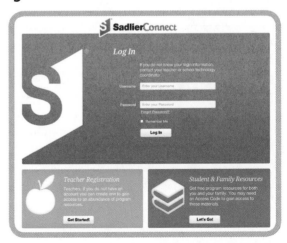

**For more detailed instructions see page T3.**

# LEARNING PROGRESSIONS

This page provides more in-depth detail on the development of math concepts and skills across the grade levels. See also the unit Progress Check page in the Student Edition for a roadmap of the Learning Progressions.

**Grade 4**

- Students interpret multiplication equations as comparisons and write multiplication equations to represent multiplicative comparisons.
- Students add and subtract fractions and mixed numbers with common denominators and solve related word problems.
- Students interpret a fraction *a/b* as a multiple of the unit fraction *1/b*. They understand a multiple of *a/b* as a multiple of *1/b* and apply this understanding to multiply a fraction by a whole number.
- Students solve word problems using multiplication of a fraction by a whole number.

**Grade 5**

- Students apply use of equivalent fractions to add and subtract fractions with unlike denominators and solve related word problems.
- Students interpret a fraction as division of the numerator by the denominator, and solve word problems involving division of whole numbers that lead to answers in the form of fractions or mixed numbers.
- Multiplication with unit fractions is extended to multiplying fractions and whole numbers by fractions. Students relate multiplication of fractions to finding the area of a rectangle with fractional side lengths.
- Interpretation of multiplication as comparison is extended to interpreting multiplication as scaling (resizing), including multiplication by fractional scale factors.
- Students solve real-world problems involving multiplication of fractions and mixed numbers.
- Students perform and interpret division of unit fractions by non-zero whole numbers and division of whole numbers by unit fractions, and solve related real-world problems.

**Grade 6**

- Extension of the four fundamental operations to fractions is completed in Grade 6. Students interpret and find quotients of fractions, and solve word problems involving division of whole numbers by fractions, fractions by whole numbers, and fractions by fractions.

# Focus on Number and Operations–Fractions

**Essential Question:**
How can you use models and equivalent fractions to perform all operations with fractions or mixed numbers?

Unit 3 ■ Focus on Number and Operations—Fractions **133**

## Essential Question:
How can you use models and equivalent fractions to perform all operations with fractions or mixed numbers?

As students become involved with the Essential Question they will model fractions using drawings. They will learn how add and subtract fractions with unlike denominators using equivalent fractions. They will also use models to see what happens when fractions are divided.

## Conversation Starters

Have students discuss the photograph. Ask questions such as: *What do you see when you look at the building? Do you find it interesting, why or why not? How would you describe the building to another person?*

Have students look at a row of shapes on a side of the building. *How many shapes would make one row on the side of the building?* (There are five shapes that make up one row.)

*Are each of the shapes that make up a row the same size?* (Yes the shapes are the same size.)

*One of the shapes is what part of a row?* (One shape would be $\frac{1}{5}$. Two shapes would be $\frac{2}{5}$, three shapes would be $\frac{3}{5}$, and 4 shapes would be $\frac{4}{5}$.)

Look at the shapes that make up the corner of building. *How do these shapes compare with the shapes on the side of the building?* (It seems that two shapes from the side of the building are about the same size as one shape on the corner of the building.)

Let students work in pairs to discuss how fractions can be used to express and compare number differences. Lead them to see that using fractions is a good strategy to use when working with quantities.

## Activity

**Materials:** Paper and pencils for sketching (optional—computer with Internet connection and printer)

Have students sketch the side of a multi-storied office building or have them find one on the Internet and print a copy.

Ask students to describe their buildings. Have them draw a line to partition the building in half. Students will then erase the lines they used to partition their buildings in half and try to find a different way to partition their building into a different number of equal groups.

Lead a class discussion in which students share their work. Some students may have buildings that are several stories tall. Encourage students to use numbers and fractions to explain about partitioning of their buildings.

## OBJECTIVE
Add and subtract fractions with unlike denominators using models and equivalent fractions.

## ESSENTIAL QUESTION
Discuss with students how to find the sum of two fractions with like denominators. Now they will use models and equivalent fractions to add and subtract fractions with unlike denominators.

## FLUENCY PRACTICE
Fluency practice is available at sadlierconnect.com.

## Concept Development

### Understand: How to use a model to subtract fractions with unlike denominators

■ Students subtract fractions with unlike denominators by using fraction strips to rename the first fraction so the second fraction can be subtracted.

■ When discussing that $\frac{3}{4} = \frac{6}{8}$, point out that the numerator and denominator of $\frac{6}{8}$ are twice the numerator and denominator of $\frac{3}{4}$ and that it takes twice as many $\frac{1}{8}$ pieces to build the model.

### Understand: How to use a model to add fractions with unlike denominators

■ Students add fractions with unlike denominators by using fraction strips to rename both fractions so the denominator is the same.

■ Models must be exactly the same length to represent equivalent fractions.

---

# Add and Subtract Fractions with Unlike Denominators

**Essential Question:**
How can you add and subtract fractions with unlike denominators?

**Words to Know:**
unlike denominators
common denominator

## Guided Instruction

In this lesson you will learn how to add and subtract fractions and mixed numbers with unlike denominators.

**Understand:** How to use a model to subtract fractions with unlike denominators

> A one-gallon pitcher was $\frac{3}{4}$ full of juice. Then, Ada drank $\frac{1}{8}$ gallon of the juice in the pitcher. How full was the pitcher after that?

To find the amount of juice left in the pitcher, subtract $\frac{3}{4} - \frac{1}{8}$. You can use fraction strips. Use three $\frac{1}{4}$ pieces to model $\frac{3}{4}$.

To see how you can take away $\frac{1}{8}$ from $\frac{3}{4}$, use $\frac{1}{8}$ pieces to build a fraction equivalent to $\frac{3}{4}$. Notice that $\frac{3}{4} = \frac{6}{8}$.

Now take away one $\frac{1}{8}$. There are five $\frac{1}{8}$ pieces left. So, $\frac{3}{4} - \frac{1}{8} = \frac{6}{8} - \frac{1}{8} = \frac{5}{8}$.

➡ After Ada drank, the pitcher was $\frac{5}{8}$ full.

**Understand:** How to use a model to add fractions with unlike denominators

> Use fraction strips to find $\frac{1}{2} + \frac{1}{3}$.

Combine fraction strips for $\frac{1}{2}$ and $\frac{1}{3}$.
You can see the sum, but you need to find a way to name it.

To name the sum, use same-size pieces to build a strip the same length as the sum. By using $\frac{1}{6}$ pieces, you can build $\frac{1}{2}$ and you can build $\frac{1}{3}$. Notice that $\frac{1}{2} = \frac{3}{6}$ and $\frac{1}{3} = \frac{2}{6}$.

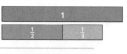

➡ $\frac{1}{2} + \frac{1}{3} = \frac{3}{6} + \frac{2}{6} = \frac{5}{6}$.

---

## Words to Know

**unlike denominators:** the different denominators of two or more fractions

**Example:** In the subtraction expression $\frac{5}{6} - \frac{2}{3}$, the fractions have unlike denominators.

**common denominator:** a shared multiple of the denominators of two or more fractions

**Example:** One common denominator of $\frac{1}{4}$ and $\frac{1}{6}$ is 12. $\frac{1}{4}$ can be written as $\frac{3}{12}$ and $\frac{1}{6}$ can be written as $\frac{2}{12}$.

**Glossary can be found on pp. 347–350.**

Lesson 15

## Guided Instruction

**Understand:** How to add fractions with unlike denominators by using equivalent fractions

> Henry is designing a playground. He plans to cover $\frac{1}{4}$ of the playground with sand and $\frac{3}{10}$ with grass. What fraction of the playground will be covered with sand or grass?

To find the fraction of the playground that will be covered with sand or grass, add: $\frac{1}{4} + \frac{3}{10}$.

$\frac{1}{4}$ and $\frac{3}{10}$ have unlike denominators. This means they are made up of different unit fractions. Before adding, rewrite them as equivalent fractions that have a common denominator or common multiple.

### Method 1

- List the first few multiples of 4 and of 10. Look for a multiple that is on *both* lists.

  Multiples of 4: 4, 8, 12, 16, 20, 24, 28
  Multiples of 10: 10, 20, 30, 40, 50, 60, 70

  20 is on both lists. You can use it as a common denominator of both $\frac{1}{4}$ and $\frac{3}{10}$.

- Rewrite $\frac{1}{4}$ and $\frac{3}{10}$ as equivalent fractions with the denominator 20.

  $\frac{1}{4} = \frac{1 \times 5}{4 \times 5} = \frac{5}{20}$          $\frac{3}{10} = \frac{3 \times 2}{10 \times 2} = \frac{6}{20}$

- Add the fractions: $\frac{1}{4} + \frac{3}{10} = \frac{5}{20} + \frac{6}{20} = \frac{5+6}{20} = \frac{11}{20}$

> To find a fraction equivalent to a given fraction, multiply or divide *both* the numerator *and* the denominator by *the same* number.

### Method 2

- For $\frac{1}{4}$ and $\frac{3}{10}$ you can also use the product of the denominators, $4 \times 10$, or 40, as the common denominator.

  $\frac{1}{4} = \frac{1 \times 10}{4 \times 10} = \frac{10}{40}$          $\frac{3}{10} = \frac{3 \times 4}{10 \times 4} = \frac{12}{40}$

- Add the fractions: $\frac{1}{4} + \frac{3}{10} = \frac{10}{40} + \frac{12}{40} = \frac{10+12}{40} = \frac{22}{40}$

  Simplify $\frac{22}{40}$ by finding an equivalent fraction. $\frac{22}{40} \div \frac{2}{2} = \frac{11}{20}$.

➡ The fraction of the playground that will be covered with sand or grass is $\frac{11}{20}$.

**Understand: How to add fractions with unlike denominators by using equivalent fractions**

■ In this presentation, students will find a common denominator to rewrite fractions as equivalent fractions. Remind students that the goal is to find equivalent fractions with like denominators so they can be easily added or subtracted.

■ For Method 2, show students that an easy way to find a common denominator is to find the product of the denominators. However, this may not produce the least common denominator. Students may need to simplify the sum or difference as a last step.

■ You may want to provide fraction strips as visual support for these concepts.

## Support English Language Learners

Discuss the meaning of *common* in the context of common denominators. Explain that the word *common* can mean *shared*. For example, we may say that two people have a common friend, which means they share the same friend. Next, remind students that a fraction can be written as an equivalent fraction in many ways. Write $\frac{1}{4}$ and the equivalent fractions $\frac{2}{8}, \frac{3}{12}, \frac{4}{16}, \frac{5}{20}$. Then, write $\frac{3}{10}$ and the equivalent fractions $\frac{6}{20}, \frac{9}{30}, \frac{12}{40}, \frac{15}{50}$. Circle the denominator 20 in both lists. Explain that this is a *common denominator* for $\frac{1}{4}$ and $\frac{3}{10}$ because it is a denominator shared by both lists of equivalent fractions.

# Guided Instruction

**Connect: How to add and subtract mixed numbers with unlike denominators** Use this page to help students strengthen and extend their understanding of how to rewrite unlike fractions as equivalent fractions with a common denominator in order to add or subtract them.

■ This presentation explores how to add and subtract mixed numbers with unlike denominators. Tell students that in order to find a common denominator, they only need to work with the fractional part of the mixed number. There is no need to rewrite the mixed number as a fraction.

■ In Step 2, discuss how the common denominator is found. Point out that since 12 is a multiple of both 4 and 12, it can be used as a common denominator. Because the denominator of $4\frac{5}{12}$ already is 12, it is only necessary to rewrite $6\frac{1}{4}$. Multiplying both the numerator and denominator of $\frac{1}{4}$ by 3 gives the equivalent mixed number $6\frac{3}{12}$.

■ Ask students if there is a different way to solve this problem. Some students may see that you can first subtract like fractions: $6\frac{1}{4} - 1\frac{3}{4}$. Then use equivalent fractions to subtract $2\frac{2}{3}$.

---

## Guided Instruction

**Connect: How to add and subtract mixed numbers with unlike denominators**

> Ted had $6\frac{1}{4}$ cups of flour. Then, he used $1\frac{3}{4}$ cups to make a piecrust and $2\frac{2}{3}$ cups to make a loaf of bread. How much flour does Ted have now?

**Step 1**

Add $1\frac{3}{4} + 2\frac{2}{3}$ to find how much flour Ted used.

To add $1\frac{3}{4} + 2\frac{2}{3}$, rewrite the fraction parts as equivalent fractions with a common denominator. You can use 12 as a common denominator.

$$1\frac{3}{4} = 1\frac{3 \times 3}{4 \times 3} = 1\frac{9}{12} \qquad\qquad 2\frac{2}{3} = 2\frac{2 \times 4}{3 \times 4} = 2\frac{8}{12}$$

**Remember!**
You can use the product of the denominators to find the common denominator.

Add the mixed numbers. Add the whole number parts and fraction parts separately.

$$\begin{array}{r} 1\frac{9}{12} \\ + 2\frac{8}{12} \\ \hline 3\frac{17}{12} \end{array}$$

$\frac{17}{12}$ is more than 1 whole, so regroup:

$$3\frac{17}{12} = 3 + \frac{12}{12} + \frac{5}{12} = 3 + 1 + \frac{5}{12} = 4\frac{5}{12}.$$

**Step 2**

Subtract $4\frac{5}{12}$ from $6\frac{1}{4}$ to find how much flour Ted has left.

$$\begin{array}{r} 6\frac{1}{4} \\ - 4\frac{5}{12} \\ \hline \end{array}$$
Rewrite with a common denominator. →
$$\begin{array}{r} 6\frac{3}{12} \\ - 4\frac{5}{12} \\ \hline \end{array}$$
Since $\frac{5}{12} > \frac{3}{12}$, regroup $6\frac{3}{12}$. →
$$\begin{array}{r} 5\frac{15}{12} \\ - 4\frac{5}{12} \\ \hline 1\frac{10}{12} \end{array}$$

$$6 = 5 + \frac{12}{12}. \text{ So,}$$
$$6\frac{3}{12} = 5 + \frac{12}{12} + \frac{3}{12} = 5\frac{15}{12}$$

You can simplify $1\frac{10}{12}$ to get $1\frac{5}{6}$.

➡ Ted has $1\frac{5}{6}$ cups of flour left.

136   Unit 3 ■ Focus on Number and Operations—Fractions

---

## Math-to-Construction Connection

**Carpentry** It is critical for carpenters to be able to measure with precision using fractions, and to accurately add and subtract fractions with like and unlike denominators. If possible, choose an object in the classroom that a carpenter might build, such as the frame around a bulletin board. Divide students into groups of three or four and have each group calculate the total length and width of wood they think a carpenter would need in order to complete the project. Have the groups compare their calculations. If it is not possible to use an object in the classroom, you may wish to provide students with hypothetical measurements for a carpentry project and have them complete the calculations in groups.

---

**MORE ONLINE** sadlierconnect.com

Lesson 15

Guided Practice

**Use the model to help you find the sum or difference.**

1. $\frac{7}{8} - \frac{3}{4}$

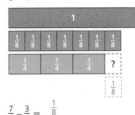

$\frac{7}{8} - \frac{3}{4} = \frac{1}{8}$

2. $\frac{1}{9} + \frac{2}{3}$

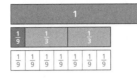

$\frac{1}{9} + \frac{2}{3} = \frac{7}{9}$

**Complete the steps to find each sum or difference.**

3. $\frac{2}{7} + \frac{1}{3}$

$\frac{2}{7} = \frac{6}{21}$

$\frac{1}{3} = \frac{7}{21}$

$\frac{6}{21} + \frac{7}{21} = \frac{6+7}{21} = \frac{13}{21}$

$\frac{2}{7} + \frac{1}{3} = \frac{13}{21}$

4. $1\frac{9}{11} - \frac{1}{3}$

$1\frac{9}{11} = 1\frac{27}{33}$

$\frac{1}{3} = \frac{11}{33}$

$\begin{array}{r} 1\frac{27}{33} \\ - \ \frac{11}{33} \\ \hline 1\frac{16}{33} \end{array}$

**Think • Pair • Share**

MP5  5. Which of the following expressions can the given model represent? Explain your answer.

a. $\frac{1}{5} + \frac{4}{5}$    b. $\frac{1}{12} + \frac{2}{6}$    c. $\frac{2}{24} + \frac{1}{3}$    d. $\frac{1}{12} + \frac{4}{6}$

Possible answer: Both b and c can be represented by this model. The model shows $\frac{1}{12}$ shaded in dark purple. $\frac{1}{12}$ is equivalent to $\frac{2}{24}$. The model also shows an additional $\frac{4}{12}$ shaded in light purple. $\frac{4}{12}$ is equivalent to $\frac{2}{6}$ and $\frac{1}{3}$.

## Mathematical Practices

Mathematical Practice Standards underline the teaching and understanding of all concepts and skills presented. The emphasis of specific practices is noted throughout the guided and independent practice of this lesson.

| MP5 | **Use appropriate tools strategically.** |
| --- | --- |

**Item 5:** Students demonstrate that they are sufficiently familiar with the use of models to analyze their meaning and apply multiple solutions.

## Observational Assessment

Use page 137 to assess whether students are able to add and subtract fractions and mixed numbers with unlike denominators using models and equivalent fractions.

### Think•Pair•Share

**Peer Collaboration** After students select expressions and write their explanations individually, have pairs of students compare their solutions. Ask each pair to develop a final solution together. Then, pairs should share their strategy for arriving at that solution with the rest of the class. While students are sharing with the class, ask:

• *Was the same approach used to find the solution when you were working individually?*

• *Were your solutions the same? Why or why not?*

To summarize, point out that students must consider each solution since it is possible to have multiple equivalent solutions.

### Return to the Essential Question

Reread the Lesson 15 Essential Question on page 134: *How can you add and subtract fractions with unlike denominators?*

Ask volunteers to use what they learned in this lesson to answer this question. (Possible response: To add and subtract fractions with unlike denominators, I can find a common denominator and write equivalent fractions. Then I just add the numerators and keep the same denominator.)

Invite as many volunteers as possible to express ideas about adding and subtracting fractions with unlike denominators in their own words.

## Concept Application

Students may work independently on these pages in the classroom or at home. They may refer to the first four pages of the lesson to revisit the instruction or to see a worked-out example.

**Common Errors** and **Teaching Tips** may help you support student learning either in the classroom or as a follow-up for work done at home.

## Common Errors

### Items 1–2

Some students may not complete the models correctly because they draw unequal parts for $\frac{1}{10}$. Tell them to check their models by verifying that the resulting fractions are equivalent. For example, check that $\frac{4}{5}$ can be rewritten as $\frac{8}{10}$.

## Teaching Tips

### Item 5

Have students read the item carefully. Explain that the word *expressions* is plural, which means that more than one solution is correct.

---

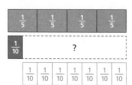

Lesson 15 **Add and Subtract Fractions with Unlike Denominators**

### Independent Practice

**Use the model to help you find the sum or difference.**

1. $\frac{4}{5} - \frac{1}{10}$

| $\frac{1}{5}$ | $\frac{1}{5}$ | $\frac{1}{5}$ | $\frac{1}{5}$ |

| $\frac{1}{10}$ | ? |

| $\frac{1}{10}$ | $\frac{1}{10}$ | $\frac{1}{10}$ | $\frac{1}{10}$ | $\frac{1}{10}$ | $\frac{1}{10}$ | $\frac{1}{10}$ |

$\frac{4}{5} - \frac{1}{10} = \frac{7}{10}$

2. $\frac{2}{5} + \frac{1}{2}$

| $\frac{1}{5}$ | $\frac{1}{5}$ | $\frac{1}{2}$ |

| $\frac{1}{10}$ | $\frac{1}{10}$ | $\frac{1}{10}$ | $\frac{1}{10}$ | $\frac{1}{10}$ | $\frac{1}{10}$ | $\frac{1}{10}$ | $\frac{1}{10}$ | $\frac{1}{10}$ |

$\frac{2}{5} + \frac{1}{2} = \frac{9}{10}$

**Complete the steps to find the sum or difference.**

3. $2\frac{1}{6} + \frac{3}{4}$

$2\frac{1}{6} = 2\frac{2}{12}$

$\frac{3}{4} = \frac{9}{12}$

$2\frac{2}{12} + \frac{9}{12} = 2\frac{11}{12}$

$2\frac{1}{6} + \frac{3}{4} = 2\frac{11}{12}$

4. $1\frac{7}{8} - \frac{2}{3}$

$1\frac{7}{8} = 1\frac{21}{24}$

$\frac{2}{3} = \frac{16}{24}$

$\begin{array}{r} 1\frac{21}{24} \\ - \frac{16}{24} \\ \hline 1\frac{5}{24} \end{array}$

$1\frac{7}{8} - \frac{2}{3} = 1\frac{5}{24}$

5. Which expressions are equivalent to $\frac{5}{18} - \frac{1}{4}$?

a. $\frac{5-1}{18-4}$

b. $\frac{5}{18} - \frac{1}{18}$

(c.) $\frac{10}{36} - \frac{9}{36}$

(d.) $\frac{20}{72} - \frac{18}{72}$

---

## Writing About Math

▸ **Write a Descriptive Text** Provide students with a pair of fractions with different denominators. Ask students to write a paragraph describing how they would find a common denominator and then find the sum of the fractions. Have students use precise vocabulary in order to explain the topic.

Ask volunteers to read their paragraphs aloud. Remind students that there is more than one way to find a common denominator, so the process of finding the common denominator may differ, but the resulting sum should be the same.

Lesson 15

Independent Practice

6. Which expressions are equivalent to $4\frac{2}{7} + 1\frac{3}{4}$?

(a.) $4\frac{16}{56} + 1\frac{42}{56}$      b. $4\frac{10}{36} + 1\frac{27}{36}$

c. $4\frac{2}{28} + 1\frac{3}{28}$      (d.) $4\frac{8}{28} + 1\frac{21}{28}$

**Evaluate each expression. Show your work.**

7. $\frac{1}{3} + \frac{1}{8}$

$\frac{8}{24} + \frac{3}{24}$

$\frac{11}{24}$

8. $\frac{7}{13} - \frac{5}{39}$

$\frac{21}{39} - \frac{5}{39}$

$\frac{16}{39}$

9. $1\frac{5}{9} - \frac{1}{2}$

$1\frac{10}{18} - \frac{9}{18}$

$1\frac{1}{18}$

10. $4\frac{3}{8} + 2\frac{3}{4}$

$4\frac{3}{8} + 2\frac{6}{8}$

$6\frac{9}{8}$

$7\frac{1}{8}$

11. $3 - 1\frac{7}{15}$

$2\frac{15}{15} - 1\frac{7}{15}$

$1\frac{8}{15}$

12. $1\frac{1}{2} - (\frac{1}{6} + \frac{2}{15})$

$1\frac{1}{2} - (\frac{5}{30} + \frac{4}{30})$

$1\frac{1}{2} - \frac{9}{30}$

$1\frac{15}{30} - \frac{9}{30} = 1\frac{6}{30} = 1\frac{1}{5}$

**Solve each problem.**

**MP3** 13. Samantha found the sum of $3\frac{1}{3} + \frac{3}{4}$. Her work is shown below. Is her answer correct? Explain.

$3\frac{1}{3} + \frac{3}{4} = 3\frac{4}{12} + \frac{9}{12} = 3\frac{13}{12}$

Possible response: Samantha's work is correct, but she could rewrite her answer as the equivalent $4\frac{1}{12}$.

**MP3** 14. Manuel says that there is always more than one common denominator for a set of fractions. Do you agree? Explain why or why not.

Possible response: I agree. A common denominator can always be found by finding the product of the denominators. Multiplying a product of the denominators by a whole number can reveal an infinite number of common denominators because there are an infinite number of whole numbers.

Unit 3 ■ Focus on Number and Operations—Fractions **139**

## Common Errors

### Item 11

Because the first number has no fraction part, some students may simply subtract the whole number parts and write $\frac{7}{15}$ as the fraction part of the difference. Ask these students to check their answer using addition or estimation. Then, explain that they must regroup 3 as $2\frac{15}{15}$ before subtracting. Then they can subtract 1 from 2 and $\frac{7}{15}$ from $\frac{15}{15}$.

## Teaching Tips

### Items 7–12

Some students may prefer to write these problems in a vertical format, lining up the whole number parts and the fraction parts, before adding or subtracting. Remind students to write their answers in simplest form.

### Items 8 and 10

Help students see that a denominator of one of the given numbers can be used as a common denominator. So, in both problems, only one of the two numbers needs to be rewritten before adding or subtracting.

## Mathematical Practices

| MP3 | Construct viable arguments and critique the reasoning of others. |
| --- | --- |

**Item 13:** Students analyze another student's work on a fraction addition problem and explain how the sum can be rewritten.

**Item 14:** Students develop an argument to explain how there can be multiple common denominators.

# Independent Practice

## Common Errors

### Items 17–18

Sometimes students will omit steps when solving multi-step word problems. Have students read the entire problem, write an expression using all necessary information, and then solve the problem.

## Teaching Tips

### Items 15–18

Discuss with students the terminology used in word problems to indicate the operations they should use to solve the problem.

---

## Independent Practice

**MP2** **15.** Desiree is driving from Raleigh, North Carolina to Key West, Florida. She drives $\frac{1}{5}$ of the way the first day. She drives $\frac{5}{8}$ of the way the second day. How much of the driving has Desiree completed?

**Show your work.**

$$\frac{1}{5} + \frac{5}{8} = \frac{8}{40} + \frac{25}{40} = \frac{33}{40}$$

**Answer** Desiree has completed $\frac{33}{40}$ of the driving.

**MP1** **16.** Last summer, Ronald grew from $5\frac{7}{12}$ feet tall to $6\frac{1}{8}$ feet tall. How much did Ronald grow last summer?

**Show your work.**

$$6\frac{3}{24} - 5\frac{14}{24} = 5\frac{27}{24} - 5\frac{14}{24} = \frac{13}{24}$$

**Answer** Ronald grew $\frac{13}{24}$ foot last summer.

**MP1** **17.** Sammi makes $4\frac{1}{2}$ cups of granola. She gives $1\frac{1}{2}$ cups to her brother and $\frac{3}{4}$ of a cup to her friend. How much granola does Sammi have left?

**Show your work.**

$$4\frac{1}{2} - (1\frac{1}{2} + \frac{3}{4})$$
$$4\frac{1}{2} - 2\frac{1}{4}$$
$$2\frac{1}{4}$$

**Answer** Sammi has $2\frac{1}{4}$ cups of granola left.

**MP6** **18.** The long-jump record at Tremell High School was $20\frac{3}{4}$ feet in 2000. In 2008, the record was broken by $\frac{1}{8}$ inch. In 2013, it was broken again by an additional $\frac{5}{12}$ inch. What is the new long-jump record?

**Show your work.**

$$20\frac{3}{4} + \frac{1}{8} + \frac{5}{12}$$
$$20\frac{18}{24} + \frac{3}{24} + \frac{10}{24}$$
$$20\frac{31}{24}$$
$$21\frac{7}{24}$$

**Answer** The new record is $21\frac{7}{24}$ feet.

---

## Mathematical Practices

| | |
|---|---|
| **MP1** | **Make sense of problems and persevere in solving them.** |

**Item 16:** Students analyze given information and use relationships to solve the problem.

**Item 17:** Students analyze and solve a multi-step problem.

| | |
|---|---|
| **MP2** | **Reason abstractly and quantitatively.** |

**Item 15:** Students make sense of quantities to solve the problem.

| | |
|---|---|
| **MP6** | **Attend to precision.** |

**Item 18:** Students calculate carefully to solve the problem and express the solution accurately.

---

Lesson 15

## Independent Practice

**MP7** **19.** Complete the equations below.

$$\frac{1}{2} - \frac{1}{4} = \frac{1}{4}$$

$$\frac{1}{5} - \frac{1}{10} = \frac{1}{10}$$

$$\frac{1}{8} - \frac{1}{16} = \frac{1}{16}$$

Describe how the equations are similar. Can you apply the same pattern to find $\frac{1}{30} - \frac{1}{60}$ without determining a common denominator? Explain.
Possible answer: Each equation is a fraction minus half of the fraction. The difference is the same as half of the fraction. You can use the pattern to find $\frac{1}{30} - \frac{1}{60}$, since $\frac{1}{60}$ is half of $\frac{1}{30}$. The answer is $\frac{1}{60}$.

**MP1** **20.** Which expression below has the greater value?

a. $2 - (\frac{4}{5} + \frac{2}{7})$  b. $\frac{2}{7} + \frac{1}{2}$

▬▶ **Show your work.**

$2 - (\frac{4}{5} + \frac{2}{7})$    $\frac{2}{7} + \frac{1}{2}$

$2 - (\frac{28}{35} + \frac{10}{35})$    $\frac{4}{14} + \frac{7}{14}$

$2 - (\frac{38}{35})$    $\frac{11}{14} = \frac{55}{70}$

$2 - 1\frac{3}{35}$

$\frac{32}{35} = \frac{64}{70}$

**Answer** Expression a has the greater value.

**MP4** **21.** Evaluate $\frac{9}{12} - (\frac{1}{2} + \frac{1}{6})$. Draw a model to justify your answer.

▬▶ **Show your work.**

Possible answer:

$\frac{1}{2} + \frac{1}{6}$

$\frac{3}{6} + \frac{1}{6}$

$\frac{4}{6} = \frac{2}{3}$

**Answer** $\frac{9}{12} - (\frac{6}{12} + \frac{2}{12}) = \frac{9}{12} - \frac{8}{12} = \frac{1}{12}$

Unit 3 ■ Focus on Number and Operations—Fractions  **141**

## Common Errors

### Items 20-21
Students may forget to apply the Order of Operations. Remind students to perform any operations in parentheses first.

## Teaching Tips

### Item 19
If students have difficulty finding the pattern, point out that all of the fractions are unit fractions with a numerator of 1. Focus their attention on the denominators. Ask students how they can write an equivalent fraction for the first fraction in each equation.

## Mathematical Practices

| **MP1** | **Make sense of problems and persevere in solving them.** |
|---|---|

**Item 20:** Students analyze and explain correspondence between two expressions to solve the problem.

| **MP4** | **Model with mathematics.** |
|---|---|

**Item 21:** Students use appropriate models to solve the problem and justify their solution.

| **MP7** | **Look for and make use of structure.** |
|---|---|

**Item 19:** Students discern and use a pattern to solve the problem.

## OBJECTIVE
Use the addition and subtraction of fractions to solve real-world problems.

## ESSENTIAL QUESTION
Ask students to share a real-world situation in which adding or subtracting fractions might be necessary.

## PREREQUISITE SKILLS
Use Item F on page 339 of the Foundational Skills Handbook to review writing fractions as mixed numbers and mixed numbers as fractions.

## FLUENCY PRACTICE
Fluency practice is available at **sadlierconnect.com**.

## Concept Development

### Understand: How to use the addition of fractions to solve problems

■ Help students understand that fractions must have a common denominator before they can be added.

■ Some students may suggest adding $\frac{2}{3}$ and $\frac{3}{5}$ by adding the numerators and adding the denominators. Use fraction strips or other models to show why this is incorrect.

■ Ask students why a whole bucket can be represented by the fraction $\frac{15}{15}$. Ask students what is always true about a fraction that represents 1 whole.

---

**Lesson 16**

# Problem Solving: Add and Subtract Fractions

### Guided Instruction

In this lesson you will solve problems using the addition and subtraction of fractions.

**Understand: How to use the addition of fractions to solve problems**

> Ellen is collecting shells for an art project. Each day she collects them in the same size bucket. The first day Ellen collects $\frac{2}{3}$ of a bucket of shells. The second day she collects $\frac{3}{5}$ of a bucket of shells. How many buckets of shells does Ellen have? If she needs 1 full bucket for her project, does Ellen have enough?

To solve the problem, determine whether the total amount of shells Ellen collected over the two days is more or less than 1 full bucket.

Ellen collected $\frac{2}{3}$ bucket the first day and $\frac{3}{5}$ bucket the second day. To find the total for both days, add: $\frac{2}{3} + \frac{3}{5}$.

$\frac{2}{3}$ and $\frac{3}{5}$ have unlike denominators. Before you can add them, you need to rewrite them as equivalent fractions with a common denominator. You can use the product of the denominators 3 × 5, or 15, as the common denominator.

$$\frac{2}{3} = \frac{2 \times 5}{3 \times 5} = \frac{10}{15} \qquad\qquad \frac{3}{5} = \frac{3 \times 3}{5 \times 3} = \frac{9}{15}$$

Now, calculate the sum.

$$\frac{2}{3} + \frac{3}{5} = \frac{10}{15} + \frac{9}{15} = \frac{19}{15}$$

The numerator of $\frac{19}{15}$ is greater than the denominator, so it is greater than 1. It represents more than 1 full bucket. You can rewrite this fraction as a mixed number.

$$\frac{19}{15} = \frac{15}{15} + \frac{4}{15} = 1\frac{4}{15}$$

Ellen has 1 full bucket and $\frac{4}{15}$ of another bucket.

➡ Ellen has $1\frac{4}{15}$ buckets of shells. She has more than 1 bucket full of shells, so she has enough for her art project.

**142** Unit 3 ■ Focus on Number and Operations—Fractions

---

## Support English Language Learners

In this lesson, students will add and subtract fractions. Many students use the word *left* when referring to a direction, such as *Turn left at the end of the hallway.* Some students may struggle with the use of the word *left* to mean *remaining.* Take this opportunity to model this concept with students. Hand three pencils to a student. Then say, *If I take one pencil away, how many pencils are left?* Ask for students to answer the question, and then state the answer: *There are two pencils left.* Ensure that students repeat your language. Have students repeat this modeling until they become comfortable with this use of the term *left.*

## Guided Instruction

**Understand:** How to use the subtraction of fractions to solve problems

Javier rides his bike to visit his friend Abe. Abe's house is $5\frac{1}{2}$ miles away. The first $4\frac{2}{3}$ miles of the trip are on flat land, but the rest is uphill. How many miles of the trip are uphill?

You can make a drawing to help you make sense of the problem.

To find the distance that is uphill, you must subtract: $5\frac{1}{2} - 4\frac{2}{3}$.

Before subtracting, rename the fractions so that they have a common denominator. You can use the product of the denominators $2 \times 3$, or 6, as a common denominator.

$$5\frac{1}{2} = 5\frac{1 \times 3}{2 \times 3} = 5\frac{3}{6} \qquad\qquad 4\frac{2}{3} = 4\frac{2 \times 2}{3 \times 2} = 4\frac{4}{6}$$

Now, calculate the difference.

$$\begin{array}{r} 5\frac{3}{6} \\ -\ 4\frac{4}{6} \\ \hline \end{array} \quad \text{Since } \tfrac{4}{6} > \tfrac{3}{6}, \text{ regroup } 5\tfrac{3}{6}. \longrightarrow \quad \begin{array}{r} 4\frac{9}{6} \\ -\ 4\frac{4}{6} \\ \hline \frac{5}{6} \end{array}$$

**Remember!**
$5\frac{3}{6} = 4 + \frac{6}{6} + \frac{3}{6} = 4\frac{9}{6}$

Use estimation to check that the answer is reasonable. Because $4\frac{2}{3}$ is a little more than $4\frac{1}{2}$, $5\frac{1}{2} - 4\frac{2}{3}$ should be a little less than $5\frac{1}{2} - 4\frac{1}{2}$, which is 1. So, $\frac{5}{6}$ is a reasonable answer.

➡ $\frac{5}{6}$ mile of Javier's trip is uphill.

✏ Suppose Javier walks his bike during the last $\frac{1}{3}$ mile. How many miles does he ride uphill? Show your work.

$\frac{5}{6} - \frac{1}{3} = \frac{5}{6} - \frac{2}{6} = \frac{3}{6} = \frac{1}{2}$ mile. Javier rides only $\frac{1}{2}$ mile uphill.

Unit 3 ▪ Focus on Number and Operations—Fractions **143**

---

## Understand: How to use the subtraction of fractions to solve problems

■ In this presentation, students first determine the necessary operation. Students should understand that they are given the distance of the entire trip and the distance for part of the trip. To find the *rest* of the distance, they must subtract. The drawing may help students understand why subtraction is needed.

■ Using a common denominator of 6, the problem can be rewritten as $5\frac{3}{6} - 4\frac{4}{6}$. Because $\frac{4}{6}$ cannot be subtracted from $\frac{3}{6}$, $5\frac{3}{6}$ must be regrouped as $4\frac{9}{6}$ before subtracting. The steps for regrouping are given in the Remember! box.

■ Discuss the method of checking the answer for reasonableness. The number $4\frac{2}{3}$ is rounded to $4\frac{1}{2}$ because it is easy to subtract this number from $5\frac{1}{2}$. Ask students to suggest other ways of checking the answer. Students may suggest rounding both numbers up to get the estimate $6 - 5$, or 1.

✏ Before answering this question, have students discuss whether they need to add or subtract and how they know which fractions to add or subtract. Have students record their own ideas and then discuss them as a class. Refer students to the diagram at the top of the page. Ask them to redraw the diagram to add the additional information in this problem.

---

## Math-to-Literature Connection

**Put on a Play** Have two students use objects, such as fraction models and containers, to put on a problem-based play. For example, one student could say that he has $\frac{1}{16}$ and $\frac{3}{8}$ in his container. Another student could say that she has $\frac{3}{4}$ in her container. The students could put all the fraction models together in one container and then ask the class what the sum of the fraction models are in the container now. The first person to give a correct total could choose a partner and perform another problem-based play for the class. Repeat this process as time permits.

**Connect: What you know about addition or subtraction of fractions to solve problems** Use this page to help students strengthen their skill in solving word problems involving addition and subtraction of fractions.

■ In Step 1, the situation is represented with a word equation. This strategy is particularly useful for word problems that involve multiple steps. In Step 2, students figure out how to represent each part of the word equation with quantities from the problem and determine what is unknown.

■ This is another opportunity to discuss with students any words that indicate whether to perform addition or subtraction. In this situation *and, give,* and *rest* provide clues.

■ In Step 5, have students explain how they "undo" operations when working backwards.

---

### Guided Instruction

**Connect: What you know about the addition or subtraction of fractions to solve problems**

> Jill and her brother Ray grow tomatoes. Jill picks $3\frac{2}{3}$ pounds and Ray picks $2\frac{1}{2}$ pounds. They give 4 pounds to Uncle Joe and the rest to Uncle Pete. How many pounds of tomatoes do they give to Uncle Pete?

**Step 1**

Make sense of the problem. Write a word equation to represent the situation.

total pounds picked − pounds given to Uncle Joe = pounds given to Uncle Pete

**Step 2**

Rewrite the equation using the information from the problem. The sum in parentheses is the total number of pounds Jill and Ray picked. The number of pounds Uncle Pete gets is not known.

$(3\frac{2}{3} + 2\frac{1}{2}) - 4 = \blacksquare$

**Step 3**

Use the product of the denominators as the common denominator of the mixed numbers.

$3\frac{2}{3} = 3\frac{2 \times 2}{3 \times 2} = 3\frac{4}{6}$        $2\frac{1}{2} = 2\frac{1 \times 3}{2 \times 3} = 2\frac{3}{6}$

**Step 4**

Solve. $(3\frac{4}{6} + 2\frac{3}{6}) - 4 = 5\frac{7}{6} - 4 = 1\frac{7}{6} = 2\frac{1}{6}$

**Remember!**
You can use addition to undo subtraction and use subtraction to undo addition.

**Step 5**

Check your answer by working backward.

First find the sum of $2\frac{1}{6}$ and 4. ⟶ $2\frac{1}{6} + 4 = 6\frac{1}{6}$

Then subtract the amount Jill picked. ⟶ $6\frac{1}{6} - 3\frac{2}{3}$

The difference should be the amount Ray picked, $2\frac{1}{2}$. ⟶ $6\frac{1}{6} - 3\frac{4}{6} = 2\frac{3}{6} = 2\frac{1}{2}$

➡ Uncle Pete will get $2\frac{1}{6}$ pounds of tomatoes.

---

## Math-to-Measurement Connection

**Construction** Many building supplies and tools use fractional measurements. Ask students if they are familiar with any tools or building supplies. Have students find a sales advertisement or list of parts and materials for a hardware store that includes fractional measurements, such as lumber or drill bit sizes. Have students create and solve word problems using these measurements.

Guided Practice

**Tell whether to add or subtract to solve the problem. Draw a diagram or model and solve.**

1. Jack is making a family recipe. He uses $\frac{3}{8}$ teaspoon of curry and $\frac{1}{3}$ teaspoon of rosemary. How much spice does Jack use in all?

**Add or subtract?** _____ add

Possible answer:

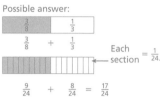

$\frac{3}{8}$  +  $\frac{1}{3}$   Each section $= \frac{1}{24}$.

$\frac{9}{24}$ + $\frac{8}{24}$ = $\frac{17}{24}$

**Answer** Jack uses a $\frac{17}{24}$ teaspoon of spice.

2. Stella had $\frac{7}{8}$ of a bag of popcorn. She gave $\frac{5}{6}$ of the bag to her friends. How much does Stella have left?

**Add or subtract?** _____ subtract

$\frac{7}{8} = \frac{21}{24}$

$\frac{5}{6} = \frac{20}{24}$   ?

$\frac{7}{8} - \frac{5}{6} = \frac{21}{24} - \frac{20}{24} = \frac{1}{24}$

**Answer** Stella has $\frac{1}{24}$ of a bag left.

**Solve the problem. Show your work.**

3. Halley builds a model car for a competition. The maximum car length allowed is $8\frac{3}{4}$ inches. Halley's car measures $6\frac{9}{16}$ inches. How much shorter is her car than the maximum length allowed?

$8\frac{3}{4}$ in. $- 6\frac{9}{16}$ in. $= 8\frac{12}{16}$ in. $- 6\frac{9}{16}$ in. $= 2\frac{3}{16}$ in.

**Answer** Halley's car is $2\frac{3}{16}$ inches shorter than the maximum length.

**👑 Think · Pair · Share**

MP5  4. Show how you can estimate to check each answer in Exercises 1–3. Tell if your answers are reasonable. Hint: Use benchmark fractions.
Possible answer: 1. $\frac{3}{8} + \frac{1}{3}$ is about $\frac{1}{3} + \frac{1}{3} = \frac{2}{3}$. $\frac{2}{3}$ is close to $\frac{17}{24}$.
2. $\frac{7}{8} - \frac{5}{6}$ are both close to 1, so the difference is very small and close to 0.
3. $8\frac{3}{4} - 6\frac{9}{16}$ is about $8\frac{3}{4} - 6\frac{1}{2} = 2\frac{1}{4}$. $2\frac{3}{16}$ is close to $2\frac{1}{4}$.

## Mathematical Practices

Mathematical Practice Standards underline the teaching and understanding of all concepts and skills presented. The emphasis of specific practices is noted throughout the guided and independent practice of this lesson.

**MP5**  **Use appropriate tools strategically.**

**Item 4:** Students use tools, such as benchmark fractions, to check the reasonableness of their answers.

## Observational Assessment

Use page 145 to assess whether students are able to determine which operation is needed to solve a given word problem.

## 👑 Think·Pair·Share

**Peer Collaboration** Have students complete the exercise individually. Then have students pair up and compare their estimations. Ask students if they used the same or different fractions than their partners. Encourage groups to come to an agreement about which estimates work best. As students work, ask questions such as:

• *What are benchmark fractions?*

• *How do you determine which benchmark fraction is best to use?*

• *Can you estimate by rounding to the nearest whole number?*

To summarize, have groups share their estimates with the class. Discuss how they decided on which benchmark fraction to use and which benchmark fractions worked best for each exercise.

## Return to the Essential Question

Reread the Lesson 16 Essential Question on page 142: *How can you use the addition and subtraction of fractions to solve real world problems?*

Ask volunteers to use what they learned in this lesson to answer this question. (Possible responses: I can represent the problem with an equation using what is known and using a symbol for what is unknown. I can write a word equation to represent the situation and replace the quantities with the given whole numbers or fractions.)

Tell students that solving problems with fractions involves the same steps as solving problems with whole numbers. They need to determine what is known and what is unknown, and then choose an operation to solve the problem.

# Independent Practice

## Concept Application

Students may work independently on these pages in the classroom or at home. They may refer to the first four pages of the lesson to revisit the instruction or to see a worked-out example.

**Common Errors** and **Teaching Tips** may help you support student learning either in the classroom or as a follow-up for work done at home.

## Common Errors

### Items 1–5

Some students may add or subtract both the numerators and denominators. Have these students use estimation to check the reasonableness of their answers. Remind students that, before fractions can be added or subtracted, the denominators must be the same.

### Items 1–5

Some students may perform the wrong operation. Ask these students to go back and read the problem and check whether their answer makes sense. For example, in Problem 1, an answer greater than $\frac{7}{8}$ pints is not reasonable because Mr. Nguyen drank some of the water. In Problem 2, an answer less than $\frac{5}{12}$ of the report is not reasonable because Maria wrote more of the report the second week.

## Teaching Tips

### Items 4–5

These problems require using two operations to solve. Encourage students to start by writing a word equation to represent the problem. Then, they can rewrite the equation using the numbers and other information from the problem.

---

## Independent Practice

**Solve the problems. Show your work.**

MP1    **1.** Mr. Nguyen had $\frac{7}{8}$ pint of water in his water bottle. Then, he drank $\frac{2}{3}$ pint. How much water is left in the bottle?

$\frac{5}{24}$ pint of water is left in the water bottle.

MP1    **2.** Maria is writing a book report. The first week she wrote $\frac{5}{12}$ of the report. The next week she wrote $\frac{1}{4}$ of the report. What fraction of the whole report has Maria completed?

Maria has completed $\frac{2}{3}$ of the report.

MP2    **3.** Bella fills her gas tank with $13\frac{1}{2}$ gallons of gas. After driving the car she has $11\frac{4}{5}$ gallons left. How much gas did Bella use?

Bella used $1\frac{7}{10}$ gallons of gas.

MP2    **4.** Teresa has $\frac{3}{4}$ hour to complete a 3-page test. She spends $\frac{1}{3}$ hour on the first page. Teresa spends $\frac{1}{4}$ hour on the second page. How much time is left for the last page?

$\frac{1}{6}$ hour is left for the last page.

MP2    **5.** There were $5\frac{1}{4}$ gallons of water in an aquarium. Then Bruce added $2\frac{2}{3}$ gallons of water. If the aquarium holds 15 gallons, how many more gallons does Bruce need to add to fill the aquarium?

Bruce needs to add $7\frac{1}{12}$ gallons to fill the aquarium.

---

## Writing About Math

**Write an Informative Text** Provide students with a word problem involving both addition and subtraction of fractions. Have students write a detailed explanation of how to solve the problem, using proper vocabulary. Ask them to think about how they would explain the solution to someone who has never added or subtracted fractions to solve problems. Students should also create a visual representation of the problem and all of the work to go along with the explanation.

MORE ONLINE sadlierconnect.com

Lesson 16

## Independent Practice

**Teaching Tips**

**Items 6-7**

Remind students to eliminate answers that clearly do not make sense in the given exercise. Remind students that rounding fractions may be helpful when estimating the answer.

**For exercises 6–7, choose the correct answer.**

6. Penny buys $2\frac{1}{3}$ yards of cloth. She uses $\frac{3}{4}$ yard to make a skirt. Without solving the problem, what is the closest estimate of how much cloth Penny has left?

   a. less than $1\frac{1}{2}$ yards

   (b.) more than $1\frac{1}{2}$ yards

   c. more than 2 yards

   d. more than 3 yards

7. Franco walks $3\frac{1}{3}$ miles from his home to the store. Then he continues walking in the same direction another $1\frac{1}{4}$ miles to his friend's house. Later, Franco walks $2\frac{2}{3}$ miles back toward his home to another friend's house. Without solving the problem, what is the closest estimate of how far Franco is from home?

   (a.) more than 1 mile

   b. more than 2 miles

   c. more than 5 miles

   d. more than 7 miles

MP2 8. Lucia plans to bake a lemon dessert. She has $1\frac{1}{3}$ lemons in her refrigerator. The recipe lists $2\frac{3}{4}$ lemons for the filling and $1\frac{2}{3}$ lemons for the topping. Lucia estimates that if she buys 3 more lemons she will have enough for the recipe. Is Lucia correct? Explain.

Possible answer: No. Lucia needs another $\frac{1}{3}$ lemon ($1\frac{2}{3} - 1\frac{1}{3} = \frac{1}{3}$) for the topping. She must buy enough to have $2\frac{3}{4}$ lemons for the filling, plus the $\frac{1}{3}$ additional for the topping. $2\frac{3}{4} + \frac{1}{3} = 2\frac{9}{12} + \frac{4}{12} = 3\frac{1}{12}$. The addition shows Lucia needs more than 3 more lemons.

MP2 9. Abraham and Kali solve the same problem in two different ways. Choose the approach that you prefer, and explain why you prefer it.

**Abraham:** $(2\frac{3}{8} + 1\frac{1}{2}) - \frac{3}{4}$

$(2\frac{3}{8} + 1\frac{4}{8}) - \frac{3}{4}$

$3\frac{7}{8} - \frac{6}{8}$

$3\frac{1}{8}$

**Kali:** $(2\frac{3}{8} + 1\frac{1}{2}) - \frac{3}{4}$

$(\frac{19}{8} + \frac{12}{8}) - \frac{3}{4}$

$\frac{31}{8} - \frac{6}{8}$

$\frac{25}{8} = 3\frac{1}{8}$

Possible answer. I prefer Abraham's approach because the whole numbers are kept whole and the numerators in the fractions are kept smaller. These numbers make the calculation with more than one operation simpler.

Unit 3 ■ Focus on Number and Operations—Fractions **147**

## Mathematical Practices

| MP1 | Make sense of problems and persevere in solving them. |
|---|---|

**Items 1–2:** Students analyze a problem involving addition and subtraction of fractions and plan a solution. Finally, students check their answers.

| MP2 | Reason abstractly and quantitatively. |
|---|---|

**Items 3–5, 8–9:** Students identify quantities and their relationship to solve a problem.

# Independent Practice

## Teaching Tips

### Items 10-11

Asking students to volunteer information about when they or someone they know have needed to add or subtract fractions in their daily lives may help them to connect the content to their lives. It will also help them to brainstorm possible situations that could be used to model the given equation.

## Independent Practice

**MP4 10.** Write a word problem that can be solved by evaluating $1\frac{3}{4} + 1\frac{2}{3} - 1\frac{1}{2}$.

Sample word problem: Karen spent $1\frac{3}{4}$ hours doing homework yesterday and $1\frac{2}{3}$ hours today. Of this time $1\frac{1}{2}$ hours was spent on math. How much time was spent on other subjects areas?

**MP4 11.** Write a word problem that can be solved by evaluating $6 - 1\frac{5}{6} - 1\frac{4}{9}$.

Sample word problem: Jo bought 6 yards of fabric. She used $1\frac{5}{6}$ yards to make a stuffed bear and $1\frac{4}{9}$ yards to make a stuffed rabbit. How much fabric does Jo have left?

**Solve the problems.**

**MP4 12.** Audrey has $3\frac{1}{3}$ boxes of comic books. Her cousin gives her $2\frac{1}{2}$ boxes. Audrey gives $1\frac{1}{6}$ boxes to her little sister. How many boxes of comic books does she have left? Write an equation and use the number line below.

▭▭ · **Show your work.**

Equation: $(3\frac{1}{3} + 2\frac{1}{2}) - 1\frac{1}{6} = ?$

$3\frac{1}{3} = 3\frac{2}{6}$ $\qquad\qquad$ $2\frac{1}{2} = 2\frac{3}{6}$

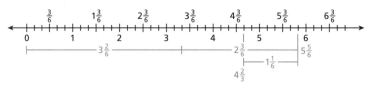

**Answer** Audrey has $4\frac{2}{3}$ boxes left.

**148** Unit 3 ■ Focus on Number and Operations—Fractions

---

| **Mathematical Practices** | |
|---|---|
| **MP4** | **Model with mathematics.** |

**Items 10-11:** Students write a word problem that can be modeled with a given expression involving addition and subtraction of fractions.

**Item 12:** Students model a real-world problem by writing an equation and using a number line.

## Independent Practice

**MP1 13.** Rina has $60 to spend at an amusement park. Her budget is listed below. What fraction of Rina's budget does she spend on food? About what fraction of Rina's budget does she spend on all tickets? What fraction of Rina's budget does she have left?

**Ticket for entry:** $22.00
**Tickets for special rides:** 2 for $8.00 each
**Lunch:** $12.00
**Popcorn:** $3.00
**Ice cream:** $5.00

· **Show your work.**

Food: $\frac{12}{60} + \frac{3}{60} + \frac{5}{60} = \frac{20}{60} = \frac{1}{3}$

Tickets: $\frac{22}{60} + \frac{2 \times 8}{60} = \frac{22}{60} + \frac{16}{60} = \frac{38}{60} = \frac{19}{30} =$ almost $\frac{2}{3}$

Budget left: $\frac{60}{60} - (\frac{1}{3} + \frac{19}{30}) = \frac{60}{60} - (\frac{20}{60} + \frac{38}{60}) = \frac{60}{60} - \frac{58}{60} = \frac{2}{60} = \frac{1}{30}$

Rina spends $\frac{1}{3}$ of her budget on food. She spends $\frac{19}{30}$, or almost $\frac{2}{3}$, of her budget on tickets. Rina has $\frac{1}{30}$ of her budget left.
**Answer** _____

**MP4 14.** Evaluate the expression below. Use the number line provided.

$(5\frac{3}{4} - 3\frac{1}{5}) + 2\frac{3}{10}$

· **Show your work.**

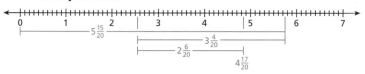

**Answer** $\underline{(5\frac{3}{4} - 3\frac{1}{5}) + 2\frac{3}{10} = 4\frac{17}{20}}$

## Common Errors
### Item 13
Students may not read the word problem carefully and use $8.00 as the cost for tickets rather than multiplying the cost of the ticket by 2. Remind students to read the given information carefully.

## Teaching Tips
### Item 13
Students may prefer to add dollar amounts to find the amount spent on food or tickets and then write the fraction of the budget represented by the result. For example, Rina spent $22 + 2 × $8, or $38 on tickets. This represents $\frac{38}{60}$, or $\frac{19}{30}$ of her $60 budget.

## Mathematical Practices

| **MP1** | **Make sense of problems and persevere in solving them.** |
|---|---|

**Item 13:** Students analyze a multi-step, real-world problem and determine which operations are needed to solve it.

| **MP4** | **Model with mathematics.** |
|---|---|

**Item 14:** Students use a number line to model an expression involving addition and subtract of fractions.

## OBJECTIVE

Solve problems that involve dividing whole numbers that result in quotients that are fractions or mixed numbers.

## ESSENTIAL QUESTION

Many students find division the most difficult of the four operations. Explain to students that thinking of a fraction as the division of the numerator by the denominator may help them make more sense of division.

## FLUENCY PRACTICE

Fluency practice is available at **sadlierconnect.com**.

## Concept Development

### Understand: A fraction as the quotient of whole number division

■ In this presentation, students will use visual fraction models to represent $2 \div 3 = \frac{2}{3}$.

■ $2 \div 3$ is modeled by dividing 2 wholes into three equal groups. One third from each whole goes into each group, so each group gets 2 thirds, or $\frac{2}{3}$.

▸ Up to this point, students have divided whole numbers in which the dividend is greater than the divisor. A common error students might make is to write the division expression as $4 \div 3$. Have students draw a model for the problem as they calculate their answer.

---

# 17 Interpret Fractions as Division

### Guided Instruction

In this lesson you will learn how to solve division problems that result in quotients that are a fraction or mixed number.

**Understand: A fraction as the quotient of whole number division**

> Amy is making raisin bread. She has 2 cups of raisins to divide equally among 3 batches of dough. How many cups should Amy put into each batch?

To find how many cups Amy should put into each batch of dough, divide 2 cups of raisins equally among 3 batches.

Draw a model. Divide each cup into thirds and then put $\frac{1}{3}$ from each cup in each batch of dough. Each batch gets two $\frac{1}{3}$ cups, which is $\frac{2}{3}$ cup.

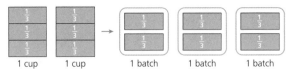

| 1 cup | 1 cup | 1 batch | 1 batch | 1 batch |

This shows that $2 \div 3 = \frac{2}{3}$.

Notice the relationship between the dividend and divisor of the division problem, and the numerator and denominator of the quotient.

$$2 \div 3 = \frac{2}{3}$$

dividend  divisor   numerator / denominator

In fact, you can think of any fraction as the result of dividing its numerator by its denominator.

In general for whole numbers $a$ and $b$, with $b$ not equal to zero, $a \div b = \frac{a}{b}$. ◂ $\frac{a}{b}$ is the result of dividing $a$ into $b$ equal parts or groups.

➡ Amy should put $\frac{2}{3}$ cup of raisins into each batch of dough.

▸ Max has 3 ounces of a solution to pour equally into 4 beakers. How much should he pour into each beaker?
$3 \div 4 = \frac{3}{4}$. Max should pour $\frac{3}{4}$ ounce of the solution into each beaker.

---

## Support English Language Learners

Remind students how to read fractions such as $\frac{4}{5}$. Prepare a list of whole-number denominators from 2–20 and write the fractional words that correspond with each, such as *halves, thirds, fourths,* and so on. Read the words aloud and have students repeat them. Provide an equation such as $4 \div 5 = \frac{4}{5}$ and an accompanying sentence frame *[four] divided by [five] equals [four-fifths].* Point out that the numeral 5 is read differently depending on its use as a numerator or as a denominator. Have students use the sentence frame to practice saying other fractions.

Lesson 17

## Guided Instruction

### Understand: Division problems with mixed-number quotients

> Vick brings 12 bags of granola on a hike to be shared equally among 5 people. How much granola will each person get?

To find how much granola each person will get, divide the 12 bags of granola by 5 people.

**Method 1**

Use what you learned in the previous problem:

$12 \div 5 = \frac{12}{5}$

Rewrite the fraction as a mixed number:

$\frac{12}{5} = \frac{10}{5} + \frac{2}{5} = 2\frac{2}{5}$

**Remember!**

In general for whole numbers $a$ and $b$, with $b$ not equal to zero, $a \div b = \frac{a}{b}$.

**Method 2**

Start by thinking about sharing just 1 bag.

If 5 people share 1 bag, then each person gets $\frac{1}{5}$ bag.

Vick has 12 bags, so each person gets 12 times this much:

$12 \times \frac{1}{5} = \frac{12}{5}$

This is the same as $2\frac{2}{5}$ bag.

**Method 3**

Use long division. Each person gets 2 whole bags, and there are 2 bags left. Each person gets $\frac{1}{5}$ of each of these leftover bags for a total of $\frac{2}{5}$ bag more.

$$\begin{array}{r} 2\ R2 \\ 5\overline{)12} \\ -10 \\ \hline 2 \end{array} \qquad 2\frac{2}{5}$$

➡ Each person will get $2\frac{2}{5}$ bags of granola.

✏ Josh solved this problem: Eleven social studies books are being shipped to a school. One box fits 3 books. How many boxes will the publisher need? Josh said the answer is $\frac{11}{3}$ or $3\frac{2}{3}$. Explain why Josh's answer is not correct.

Possible explanation: 11 social studies books ÷ 3 books per box $= \frac{11}{3} = 3\frac{2}{3}$. The remainder $\frac{2}{3}$ means 2 books of the 11 will not fit into the 3 boxes. Therefore, they must be shipped in an additional box that fits 3 books. The publisher will need 4 boxes in order to ship all 11 books.

Unit 3 ■ Focus on Number and Operations—Fractions **151**

---

### Understand: Division problems with mixed-number quotients

■ This presentation provides three methods for solving divisions of whole numbers with mixed-number quotients.

■ Begin the presentation by asking students whether each person will get more or less than one bag of granola.

■ In Method 1, be sure students understand the relationship between the dividend and divisor in the division expression, and the numerator and denominator in the fractional quotient.

■ Some students may need more than one example to understand the reasoning behind Method 2.

■ Method 3 shows how to use long division to divide the numerator by the denominator. Ask students why the remainder of 2 became a fraction in the solution.

✏ This problem involves interpreting a remainder. Ask students to name the two whole numbers between which the quotient lies. Explain that boxes cannot be divided into units that are less than a whole so Josh needs to round up to four boxes.

---

## Math-to-Social Connection

**Planning a Menu** Tell students that an important part of planning a party is determining how much food will be needed for the guests. Have students work in groups to plan a menu and decide how much food they should buy. They can write expressions for the amounts of food using phrases: 3 pizzas for every 5 people, 1 gallon of punch for every 4 people, and 2 pans of brownies for every 8 people. Once students have planned their menus, have them determine how many people might attend the party and how much of each food item each group member will bring.

# Guided Instruction

**Connect: Solving division problems with quotients that are fractions or mixed numbers** Use this page to help students apply what they know about dividing whole numbers to find quotients that are in the form of mixed numbers.

■ Both Problem A and Problem B are modeled by the same division, 7 ÷ 4, but, because the contexts of the problems are different, the solutions are given in different forms.

■ In Problem A, be sure students understand that the four students will divide the 7 hours equally with no overlap. Only one student will work at a time.

■ If students do not understand that $\frac{3}{4}$ of a dollar is 75¢, have them write $\frac{3}{4}$ as the equivalent fraction $\frac{75}{100}$, which represents 75¢ out of 100¢.

---

## Guided Instruction

**Connect: Solving division problems with quotients that are fractions or mixed numbers**

These word problems are both solved using the same division expression, but the solutions are in different forms. Find the solutions and explain why they are in different forms.

**Problem A**
Four students sign up to work equal amounts of time at a class flower sale. If the sale is 7 hours long, how long must each student work?

**Problem B**
Four friends earned $7 at a carnival stand. If they divide the money equally, how much will each friend get?

**Step 1**

Write a division expression for each problem.

In **Problem A**, 7 hours is divided among 4 students.
In **Problem B**, $7 is divided among 4 friends.

Both problems can be represented by the expression 7 ÷ 4.

**Step 2**

Divide.

$$7 \div 4 = \frac{7}{4} = 1\frac{3}{4}$$

**Remember!**
In general for whole numbers $a$ and $b$, with $b$ not equal to zero, $a \div b = \frac{a}{b}$.

**Step 3**

Interpret the quotient.

For **Problem A**, the answer means that each student must work $1\frac{3}{4}$ hours.

For **Problem B**, the answer means that each friend should receive $1 and $\frac{3}{4}$ of another dollar, which is 75¢.

 For **Problem A**, each student must work $1\frac{3}{4}$ hours. For **Problem B**, each friend will receive $1.75. It makes sense for the first answer to be a mixed number because it is common to talk about fractional parts of an hour. However, money amounts are usually given in dollars and cents, rather than as fractions of dollars.

**152**   Unit 3 ■ Focus on Number and Operations—Fractions

---

## Writing About Math

**Collaborative Writing** Have students work in small groups to write three word problems that involve division with whole numbers. One problem should have a whole number quotient, one problem should have a quotient that is a fraction less than 1, and one problem should have a quotient that is a mixed number. Have students write a justification explaining why the word problems will result in each type of quotient.

Invite groups to present their problems and reasoning to the class. This activity will help students develop the number sense they need for middle school mathematics.

Guided Practice

**Draw a model to represent the division. Give the quotient as a fraction.**

1. $3 \div 4 = \dfrac{3}{4}$
Possible model:

2. $5 \div 1 = \dfrac{5}{1}$ or 5
Possible model:

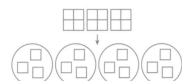

**Solve each equation. Write the quotient as a fraction or mixed number.**

3. $6 \div 11 = \dfrac{6}{11}$

4. $14 \div 4 = \dfrac{14}{4}$ or $3\frac{2}{4}$, or $3\frac{1}{2}$

5. $7 \div 10 = \dfrac{7}{10}$

6. $21 \div 5 = \dfrac{21}{5}$ or $4\frac{1}{5}$

7. $12 \div 7 = 1\frac{5}{7}$

8. $8 \div 15 = \dfrac{8}{15}$

9. $32 \div 4 = \dfrac{8}{1}$

10. $23 \div 11 = 2\frac{1}{11}$

**Think·Pair·Share**

MP3 11. Cassie has a ribbon 6 feet long. She wants to cut it into 12 equal pieces. She calculates that each piece should be 2 feet long. Is Cassie correct? Explain your reasoning.

$12 \div 6 = \dfrac{12}{6} = \dfrac{2}{1} = 2$

Cassie is not correct. Possible explanation: She did not write the division problem correctly. Cassie needs to divide the 6 feet by the 12 pieces: $6 \div 12 = \dfrac{6}{12} = \dfrac{1}{2}$. The pieces will each be $\frac{1}{2}$ foot long.

Unit 3 ■ Focus on Number and Operations—Fractions **153**

## Mathematical Practices

Mathematical Practice Standards underline the teaching and understanding of all concepts and skills presented. The emphasis of specific practices is noted throughout the guided and independent practice of this lesson.

| MP3 | **Construct viable arguments and critique the reasoning of others.** |
|---|---|

**Item 11:** Students critique the work of another student and construct an argument to explain why it is incorrect.

## Observational Assessment

Use page 153 to assess whether students understand how to divide whole numbers and write the quotient as a fraction or a mixed number. Be sure students can write equivalent representations of fractions and mixed numbers.

### Think·Pair·Share

**Peer Collaboration** Ask pairs of students to work together on the problem and present their work for class discussion. Ask questions such as:

- *What mistake did Cassie make?*
- *How do you determine which number is the dividend and which number is the divisor?*
- *How can you use multiplication to check your answer?*

To summarize, explain that the greater number is not always the dividend when solving word problems with division. You must use the context of the problem to determine how to write the correct division equation.

### Return to the Essential Question

Reread the Lesson 17 Essential Question on page 150: *How are fractions related to division?*

Ask volunteers to use what they learned in this lesson to answer the question. (Possible response: When you divide two numbers, you can write the quotient as a fraction. The dividend is used as the numerator and the divisor is used as the denominator.)

Invite as many volunteers as possible to share their answers with the class.

## Concept Application

Students may work independently on these pages in the classroom or at home. They may refer to the first four pages of the lesson to revisit the instruction or to see a worked-out example.

**Common Errors** and **Teaching Tips** may help you support student learning either in the classroom or as a follow-up for work done at home.

## Teaching Tips

### Items 1–4

Suggest that students use the model on page 150 as a guide. In that model, the dividend determines the number of wholes, and the divisor determines how many parts each whole is divided into. One part from each whole is put into each group, and the final size of one group is the quotient.

---

**Lesson 17   Interpret Fractions as Division**

### Independent Practice

**Draw a model to represent the division. Give the quotient as a fraction or mixed number.**

1. $2 \div 7 = \frac{2}{7}$
   Models will vary.

2. $17 \div 3 = \frac{17}{3}$ or $5\frac{2}{3}$

3. $1 \div 4 = \frac{1}{4}$

4. $14 \div 6 = \frac{14}{6}$, or $2\frac{2}{6}$, or $2\frac{1}{3}$

**Solve each equation. Write the quotient as a fraction or mixed number.**

5. $19 \div 4 = 4\frac{3}{4}$

6. $5 \div 21 = \frac{5}{21}$

7. Choose a problem on this page and create a story problem that can be modeled by the problem. Then write the answer to your story problem.
   Sample story problem: Exercise 1: Two pizzas are being split equally among 7 people. How much pizza will each person get? Each person will get $\frac{2}{7}$ of a pizza. If each pizza is sliced into 7 pieces, then each person will get 2 slices.

---

### Digital Connection

**Online Manipulatives** Provide students with two division problems that involve whole numbers: one problem should have a fractional quotient and one problem should have a mixed-number quotient. Have students work with online manipulatives or drawing tools to model each problem. Students should write the division equation to record their work.

Independent Practice

**For exercises 8–11, give each quotient as a fraction or mixed number.**

8. $11 \div 8 = \dfrac{11}{8}$ or $1\dfrac{3}{8}$

9. $7 \div 33 = \dfrac{7}{33}$

10. $9 \div 14 = \dfrac{9}{14}$

11. $45 \div 10 = 4\dfrac{5}{10}$, or $4\dfrac{1}{2}$

**For exercises 12–13, choose the correct answer.**

12. Which expression is represented by the model?

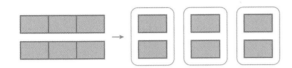

   a. $2 \div 6$

   b. $3 \div 6$

   c. $2 \div 3$

   d. $3 \div 2$

13. Tina has 4 apples to share among 5 people. Which fraction shows how much each person receives?

   a. $\dfrac{5}{30}$

   b. $\dfrac{4}{5}$

   c. $\dfrac{5}{4}$

   d. $\dfrac{30}{4}$

**Solve the problems.**

MP1   14. Fran and 5 friends must share 3 liters of water. How much water will each person get?
Each person will get $\dfrac{3}{6}$ liter of water or $\dfrac{1}{2}$ liter of water.

MP1   15. Dmitri has 16 inches of wire. He wants to bend the wire to make a triangle with 3 equal sides. How long will each side be?
Each side will be $\dfrac{16}{3}$ or $5\dfrac{1}{3}$ inches.

Unit 3 ■ Focus on Number and Operations—Fractions   **155**

## Common Errors

### Items 13-14
Some students may always write the greater number as the dividend. Help students identify key terms such as *divide equally* or *share among* that indicate which number is the divisor.

### Item 14
Some students may calculate $3 \div 5$, rather than $3 \div 6$. Ask these students to read the first sentence of the problem. Point out that *Fran and* 5 friends share the water, so the 3 liters must be divided among 6 people, not 5.

## Teaching Tips

### Items 8-14
Refer students to the methods used on page 151. Encourage them to use at least two different methods when completing these exercises.

| Mathematical Practices | |
|---|---|
| **MP1** | **Make sense of problems and persevere in solving them.** |

**Items 14-15:** Students interpret the meaning of a word problem to identify the dividend and divisor to solve a division problem.

# Independent Practice

## Common Errors

### Item 19

Some students may calculate $2 \div 2$, and state that each person gets one bar. Point out that the problem says that Deanna is dividing the bars among *herself and* 2 friends, so a total of 3 people are sharing the 2 bars.

## Teaching Tips

### Items 16–17

Challenge students to interpret the remainder. For Problem 16, have students determine how many goggles will be not be used. For Problem 17, have students determine how much more wrapping paper is needed.

### Item 17

Some students may solve this problem by using multiplication, calculating $7 \times 18$ to determine how many inches of paper Jose needs for 7 presents and then comparing the product to 120 inches.

---

### Independent Practice

**MP3  16.** Annette buys swim goggles for her swim team at a wholesale store. There are 25 swimmers and the swim goggles are sold in a package of 6. Annette wants to give each swimmer 2 swim goggles, therefore, she buys 9 packages. Is Annette correct? Explain.

Yes, Annette is correct. Possible explanation: If Annette buys 9 packages she will have $6 \times 9 = 54$ swim goggles. She needs to divide 54 swim goggles among 25 swimmers: $\frac{54}{25} = 2\frac{4}{25}$. This means Annette has enough to give each of the swimmers 2 swim goggles.

**MP3  17.** Jose has a 120-inch roll of wrapping paper. He needs an 18-inch piece to wrap each present. Does Jose have enough to wrap 7 presents? Explain.

Jose does not have enough paper for 7 presents. Possible explanation: $\frac{120}{18} = 6\frac{12}{18}$, so he only has enough paper for 6 presents.

**MP1  18.** Allen has 13 carrots. He wants to put an equal amount of carrots into 5 sandwich sized bags. How much should Allen put into each bag?

**Show your work.**

$$\frac{13}{5} = 2\frac{3}{5}$$

**Answer** Allen should put $2\frac{2}{5}$ carrots into each bag.

**MP2  19.** Deanna has 2 nutrition bars that she wants to share among herself and 2 other friends. How can Deanna divide the nutrition bars into equal portions?

**Show your work.**

$$2 \div 3 = \frac{2}{3}$$

**Answer** Deanna can divide the nutrition bars into thirds. Each person will get $\frac{2}{3}$ of a bar.

**156**   Unit 3 ■ Focus on Number and Operations—Fractions

---

## Mathematical Practices

| | |
|---|---|
| **MP1** | **Make sense of problems and persevere in solving them.** |

**Item 18:** Students apply their understanding of fractions and whole number quotients to solve a word problem.

| | |
|---|---|
| **MP2** | **Reason abstractly and quantitatively.** |

**Item 19:** Students solve a division problem and interpret the solution.

| | |
|---|---|
| **MP3** | **Construct viable arguments and critique the reasoning of others.** |

**Item 16:** Students analyze another student's solution to a word problem and explain why the solution is correct.

**Item 17:** Students explain why a solution to a division problem is incorrect.

---

**MORE ONLINE** sadlierconnect.com

Lesson 17

## Independent Practice

MP1 **20.** Greg completes his drills for football training camp in 75 minutes. He needs to record the time in hours. How many hours did Greg engage in drills? (Remember: There are 60 minutes in one hour.)

▭ **Show your work.**

If there are 60 minutes in an hour, then Greg engaged in drills for $\frac{75}{60}$ hours; $\frac{75}{60} = 1\frac{15}{60}$ or $1\frac{1}{4}$.

**Answer** Greg engaged in drills for $1\frac{1}{4}$ hours or 1 hour and 15 minutes.

MP6 **21.** Darren and his 2 sisters want to equally share 17 tokens at an arcade. How many tokens will each of them get?

▭ **Show your work.**

$17 \div 3 = \frac{17}{3} = 5\frac{2}{3}$. So each person can get 5 tokens and 2 tokens are left over.

**Answer** Each person will get 5 tokens.

MP1 **22.** Mr. Fried plans to give fruit flies to 6 groups of lab students for an experiment. He wants to give the same number of flies to each group. He has different size bottles. How can Mr. Fried give each group the same number of fruit flies without opening the bottles?

2 large bottles: 12 fruit flies in each bottle
10 medium bottles: 8 fruit flies in each bottle
14 small bottles: 2 fruit flies in each bottle

▭ **Show your work.**

There are 132 fruit flies to share. $(12 \times 2) + (8 \times 10) + (2 \times 14) = 132$. The 6 groups get 22 fruit flies each: $\frac{132}{6} = 22$. Two groups get a set of 1 large, 1 medium, and 1 small bottle $(12 + 8 + 2 = 22)$. Four groups get 2 medium and 3 small bottles $(8 \times 2) + (2 \times 3) = 22$.

**Answer** Two groups get a set of 1 large, 1 medium, and 1 small bottle. Four groups get 2 medium and 3 small bottles.

## Common Errors

### Item 21

Some students may use the numbers they see in the problem and divide by 2. Remind students to read the problem carefully to determine how many people will be sharing the tokens.

## Teaching Tips

### Item 20

The quotient can be written as $1\frac{1}{4}$ hour or 1 hour and 15 minutes. Students may need assistance in recalling that there are four 15-minute intervals in 1 hour.

### Item 22

Some students may have difficulty approaching multistep problems. Encourage students to underline key information, write a word equation, or draw a model to solve word problems that they find challenging.

## Mathematical Practices

| MP1 | **Make sense of problems and persevere in solving them.** |
|---|---|

**Item 20:** Students must interpret a division word problem involving a mixed-number quotient.

**Item 22:** Students must make sense of a complex word problem and then devise and carryout a plan to find the solution.

| MP6 | **Attend to precision.** |
|---|---|

**Item 21:** Students must solve a division problem with a mixed-number quotient and interpret the meaning of the remainder.

## OBJECTIVE
**Multiply a whole number or a fraction by a fraction.**

## ESSENTIAL QUESTION
In Grade 4, students multiplied a fraction by a whole number. Present the problem $3 \times \frac{2}{5}$ and discuss how to solve it. Tell students that in this lesson, they will extend their understanding of multiplication with fractions to multiplying a whole number by a fraction and multiplying two fractions.

## FLUENCY PRACTICE
Fluency practice is available at **sadlierconnect.com**.

## Concept Development

**Understand:** How to multiply a whole number by a unit fraction when the whole number is divisible by the denominator

■ This presentation models $\frac{1}{4} \times 20$ by partitioning 20 objects into 4 equal groups and shading one group—that is, by shading $\frac{1}{4}$ *of* the 20 objects. Be sure students understand that $\frac{1}{4}$ of 20 and $\frac{1}{4} \times 20$ have the same meaning.

**Understand:** How to multiply a whole number by a non-unit fraction when the whole number is divisible by the denominator

■ Discuss the idea that $\frac{3}{4} \times 20$ is equivalent to $3 \times \frac{1}{4} \times 20$, which is $3 \times (\frac{1}{4} \times 20)$. So, to calculate $\frac{3}{4} \times 20$, you can find $\frac{1}{4} \times 20$ and then multiply the result by 3.

---

### Lesson 18 — Interpret Products of Fractions

**Essential Question:** How can you multiply a whole number or a fraction by a fraction?

**Guided Instruction**

In this lesson you will find the product of a fraction and a whole number and of two fractions.

**Understand: How to multiply a whole number by a unit fraction when the whole number is divisible by the denominator**

> Jorge has 20 autographed baseballs. One-quarter of them are autographed by pitchers. How many of Jorge's baseballs are autographed by pitchers?

To find how many of the baseballs are autographed by pitchers, find $\frac{1}{4}$ of 20, which is the same as $\frac{1}{4} \times 20$.

Draw a model. Use 20 circles to represent the baseballs. Divide the circles into four equal groups. Shade 1 of the 4 groups to show $\frac{1}{4}$ of 20.

There are 5 circles shaded.

$$\frac{1}{4} \times 20 = \frac{1}{4} \text{ of } 20$$
$$= 20 \div 4$$
$$= 5$$

➡ 5 of Jorge's baseballs are autographed by pitchers.

**Understand: How to multiply a whole number by a non-unit fraction when the whole number is divisible by the denominator**

> Of Jorge's 20 baseballs, $\frac{3}{4}$ are autographed by American League players. How many of Jorge's baseballs are autographed by American League players?

Find $\frac{3}{4}$ of 20, which is the same as $\frac{3}{4} \times 20$.

Draw 20 circles and divide them into 4 equal groups. Shade 3 of the groups to represent $\frac{3}{4}$ of 20.

There are 15 circles shaded.

$$\frac{3}{4} \times 20 = (3 \times \frac{1}{4}) \times 20$$
$$= 3 \times (\frac{1}{4} \times 20)$$
$$= 3 \times 5$$
$$= 15$$

➡ 15 of Jorge's baseballs are autographed by American League players.

**158** Unit 3 ■ Focus on Number and Operations—Fractions

---

## Support English Language Learners

In the presentation on page 158, both problems involve a whole number that is *divisible* by the denominator of the fraction. Write *divisible* on the board and underline the first four letters. Ask students to think of another word that begins this way. Write the word *divide* and underline the first four letters. Explain that *divisible* comes from the word *divide*. Tell students that a number is divisible by a whole number *n* if the number can be divided into *n* equal parts with no remainder.

Have students draw models to show how 10 is divisible by 2, but not divisible by 3. Ask students for other examples. Then have students define *divisible* in their own words using mathematical terms such as *whole numbers, divide, quotient,* and *remainder.*

Lesson 18

## Guided Instruction

**Understand: How to multiply a whole number by any unit fraction**

> Zoe bought 2 pounds of seaweed salad. She and her sister ate $\frac{1}{5}$ of it with their lunch. How much seaweed salad did Zoe and her sister eat with lunch?

To determine how much they ate, find $\frac{1}{5}$ of 2, which is the same as $\frac{1}{5} \times 2$.

Draw a model.

Each bar represents 1 whole pound. To find $\frac{1}{5} \times 2$ pounds, find $\frac{1}{5}$ of each pound and add.

$\frac{1}{5} \times 2 = \frac{1}{5}$ of 2
$= \frac{1}{5} + \frac{1}{5}$
$= \frac{2}{5}$

➡ Zoe and her sister ate $\frac{2}{5}$ pound of seaweed salad.

**Understand: How to multiply a whole number by any non-unit fraction**

> Zoe also bought 3 pounds of bean salad. Her family ate $\frac{4}{5}$ of it with their dinner. How much bean salad did Zoe's family eat?

Find $\frac{4}{5}$ of 3, which is the same as $\frac{4}{5} \times 3$.

Draw a model.

Each bar represents 1 whole pound. To find $\frac{4}{5} \times 3$ pounds, find $\frac{4}{5}$ of each pound and add.

$\frac{4}{5} \times 3 = \frac{4}{5}$ of 3
$= \frac{4}{5} + \frac{4}{5} + \frac{4}{5}$
$= \frac{12}{5}$

➡ Zoe's family ate $\frac{12}{5}$ pounds, or $2\frac{2}{5}$ pounds of bean salad.

▪ If $\frac{a}{b}$ is a fraction and $q$ is a whole number greater than 1, then $\frac{a}{b} \times q = \frac{a \times q}{b}$. Show that this general principle works for the four problems you have seen so far in this lesson.

First problem: $\frac{1}{4} \times 20 = \frac{1 \times 20}{4} = \frac{20}{4} = 5$.

Second problem: $\frac{3}{4} \times 20 = \frac{3 \times 20}{4} = \frac{60}{4} = 15$.

Third problem: $\frac{1}{5} \times 2 = \frac{1 \times 2}{5} = \frac{2}{5}$.      Fourth problem: $\frac{4}{5} \times 3 = \frac{4 \times 3}{5} = \frac{12}{5} = 2\frac{2}{5}$.

Unit 3 ▪ Focus on Number and Operations—Fractions   **159**

## Math-to-Transportation Connection

**Gas Mileage**  Ask students if they have seen the fuel gauge on an automobile. Explain that automobiles and other vehicles have gauges that show the driver what fraction of the tank is filled with fuel. Using this gauge, drivers can compute how far they can travel.

Tell students that a certain model of car has a tank that holds 15 gallons of fuel. The car can travel an average of 25 miles on 1 gallon of gas. Show students how to calculate how far the car can travel on $\frac{1}{3}$ tank of fuel. First, calculate the number of gallons in the tank by multiplying 15 gallons by $\frac{1}{3}$ of a tank. Then multiply the product by 25 miles per gallon to find how many miles the car can travel. Have students create their own problems and have a partner solve them.

**Understand:** **How to multiply a whole number by any unit fraction**

▪ To multiply a whole number by a fraction in cases where the whole number is not divisible by the denominator, students must use a different modeling strategy. In this presentation, a bar model is used. Each bar represents 1 whole.

▪ To model $\frac{1}{5} \times 2$, each of the two bars is divided into 5 equal parts. One fifth of each bar is shaded and then the 2 fifths are combined to get the final product. So, to find $\frac{1}{5} \times 2$, or $\frac{1}{5}$ of 2, find $\frac{1}{5}$ of each whole and add.

▪ A common misconception is that multiplication always results in a greater number. Using models helps students conceptualize that multiplying by a fraction less than 1, results in a lesser number. If students struggle with this concept, provide additional practice by using this drawing and shading strategy with other multiplications.

**Understand:** **How to multiply a whole number by any non-unit fraction**

▪ In this presentation, students use the strategy from the previous problem to multiply a whole number by a non-unit fraction.

▪ To model $\frac{4}{5} \times 3$, 4 fifths of each of the three bars is shaded, and then the 3 groups of 4 fifths are combined to get the final product. So, to find $\frac{4}{5} \times 3$, or $\frac{4}{5}$ of 3, find $\frac{4}{5}$ of each whole and add. So, $\frac{4}{5} \times 3 = \frac{4}{5} + \frac{4}{5} + \frac{4}{5}$, which is $\frac{12}{5}$.

✏ ▪ Remind students that a letter is sometimes used to represent an unknown number.  Students may need help identifying the values of *a*, *b*, and *q* in each of the examples. State, or have a student state, the general principle in words: The product of a fraction and a whole number is the product of the numerator and the whole number over the denominator.

Unit 3 ▪ Focus on Number and Operations—Fractions   **159**

# Guided Instruction

**Connect: What you know about multiplying by a fraction to multiply two fractions** Use this page to help students apply what they know about multiplying a fraction by a whole number to multiplying two fractions.

■ This presentation builds on students' understanding of partitioning a number line from Grade 4 to multiply two fractions.

■ Remind students that × means "of." The first problem models $\frac{1}{3}$ of $\frac{1}{4}$. The second models $\frac{2}{3}$ of $\frac{3}{4}$.

■ Be sure students understand that dividing each fourth into three parts, or thirds, creates twelfths.

■ In the model for $\frac{2}{3} \times \frac{3}{4}$, 3 fourths are highlighted and then $\frac{2}{3}$ *of each* fourth is circled. This is 3 groups of 2 twelfths. The 3 groups are combined to get a product of 6 twelfths, or $\frac{6}{12}$.

■ Point out that, for both problems, the product of the denominators, 3 × 4, or 12, is the total number of intervals in one whole of the final model. The product of the numerators is the number of circled intervals. So, the product of the fractions is the product of the numerators over the product of the denominators.

✎ ▸ State, or have a student state, the general principle in words: The product of two fractions is the product of the numerators over the product of the denominators. Point out that this principle can also be used to multiply a whole number by a fraction if the whole number is rewritten as a fraction with a denominator of 1.

---

## Guided Instruction

**Connect:** What you know about multiplying by a fraction to multiply two fractions

Evaluate $\frac{1}{3} \times \frac{1}{4}$ and $\frac{2}{3} \times \frac{3}{4}$.

**Step 1**

Use a number line to find $\frac{1}{3} \times \frac{1}{4}$.

Divide the interval from 0 to 1 into fourths, and highlight $\frac{1}{4}$.

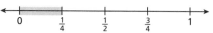

To find $\frac{1}{3} \times \frac{1}{4}$, or $\frac{1}{3}$ of $\frac{1}{4}$, divide each fourth into three equal intervals. This makes twelfths. Circle $\frac{1}{3}$ of the highlighted $\frac{1}{4}$. This interval represents $\frac{1}{12}$.

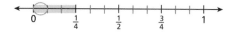

**Step 2**

Use a number line to find $\frac{2}{3} \times \frac{3}{4}$.

Divide the interval from 0 to 1 into fourths, and highlight $\frac{3}{4}$.

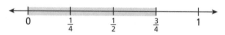

To find $\frac{2}{3} \times \frac{3}{4}$, or $\frac{2}{3}$ of $\frac{3}{4}$, divide each fourth into three equal parts. This makes twelfths. Then circle $\frac{2}{3}$ of each of the 3 highlighted fourths.

The total amount circled is $\frac{2}{12} + \frac{2}{12} + \frac{2}{12} = \frac{6}{12}$.

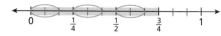

▶ $\frac{1}{3} \times \frac{1}{4} = \frac{1}{12}$ and $\frac{2}{3} \times \frac{3}{4} = \frac{6}{12}$

✎ ▸ If $\frac{a}{b}$ and $\frac{c}{d}$ are any two fractions, with $b$, $d$ not zero, then $\frac{a}{b} \times \frac{c}{d} = \frac{a \times c}{b \times d}$. Show that this general principle works for the two expressions on this page.   First expression: $\frac{1}{3} \times \frac{1}{4} = \frac{1 \times 1}{3 \times 4} = \frac{1}{12}$.
Second expression: $\frac{2}{3} \times \frac{3}{4} = \frac{2 \times 4}{3 \times 4} = \frac{6}{12}$.

**160**   Unit 3 ■ Focus on Number and Operations—Fractions

---

## Writing About Math

✎ ▸ **Collaborative Writing** Divide the class into six groups. Assign one of problems presented on pages 158–160 to each group. Instruct each group to prepare a written outline of how they will "teach" the class to solve the problem they have been assigned. Students should include a model in their explanation. Students should also demonstrate the general principles $\frac{a}{b} \times q = \frac{a \times q}{b}$ and $\frac{a}{b} \times \frac{c}{d} = \frac{a \times c}{b \times d}$ for their problem. Students should determine the role of each person in the group and decide what part of the demonstration each student will present.

**Use the model to find each product.**

1. $\frac{1}{6} \times 24$

24 is divided into 6 groups of __4__.

$\frac{1}{6} \times 24 = $ __4__

2. $\frac{1}{4} \times \frac{1}{2}$

```
←——|——|——|——|——|——|——|——|——→
   0        1/2         1
```

$\frac{1}{2}$ is highlighted.

Each half is divided into __4__ intervals.

The circled interval represents $\frac{1}{8}$.

$\frac{1}{4} \times \frac{1}{2} = \frac{1}{8}$

**Find each product.**

3. $\frac{4}{5} \times \frac{3}{8}$

$\frac{4 \times 3}{5 \times 8}$

$\frac{12}{40}$

4. $\frac{2}{5} \times 12$

$\frac{2 \times 12}{5}$

$\frac{24}{5}$

$4\frac{4}{5}$

### ☝☝ Think • Pair • Share

MP3  5. Write a story problem for the equation $\frac{5}{6} \times \frac{2}{5} = $ ▇. What is the answer to your problem? Then ask a classmate to solve the equation two ways and interpret the product.
Sample story problem: Cassie walked $\frac{2}{5}$ mile. Asha walked $\frac{5}{6}$ of Cassie's distance. What fraction of a mile did Asha walk? Asha walked $\frac{1}{3}$ mile. The product is the number of miles Asha walked. Students can solve the problem using a model and by multiplying numerators and denominators.

## Mathematical Practices

Mathematical Practice Standards underline the teaching and understanding of all concepts and skills presented. The emphasis of specific practices is noted throughout the guided and independent practice of this lesson.

| MP3 | **Construct viable arguments and critique the reasoning of others.** |
| --- | --- |

**Item 5:** Students write and solve word problems requiring the multiplication of two fractions and then determine whether a classmate has correctly interpreted the product and justified their conclusions.

## Observational Assessment

Use page 161 to assess whether students understand how to multiply a whole number or a fraction by a fraction. Be sure that students understand how the models represent the factors and products. As the amount of scaffolding drops off, students should be able to multiply two fractions by multiplying the numerators and multiplying the denominators.

### ☝☝ Think•Pair•Share

**Peer Collaboration** Before writing their problems, have students review the word problems presented in the lesson up to this point. Once pairs have solved their partners' problem, have them share their word problems with the class. During their presentation, ask questions such as:

- *Which two methods did you use to multiply the fractions?*

- *How does your problem represent multiplication?*

To summarize, choose one of the word problems created by a student. Draw a model for the multiplication and find the product. Show that the product represented by the model is the same as the product of the numerators over the product of the denominators.

### Return to the Essential Question

Reread the Lesson 18 Essential Question on page 158: *How can you multiply a whole number or a fraction by a fraction?*

Ask volunteers to use what they learned in this lesson to answer the question. (Possible responses: I can multiply fractions by using models or by multiplying numerators and multiplying the denominators.)

# Independent Practice

## Concept Application

Students may work independently on these pages in the classroom or at home. They may refer to the first four pages of the lesson to revisit the instruction or to see a worked-out example.

**Common Errors** and **Teaching Tips** may help you support student learning either in the classroom or as a follow-up for work done at home.

## Common Errors

### Items 3 and 5

When multiplying by a whole number by a fraction, students may multiply the denominator of the fraction by the whole number. Suggest that these students write the whole number as a fraction with a denominator of 1 and then multiply numerators and denominators.

## Teaching Tips

### Item 1

Ask students if the whole number is divisible by the denominator. If so, what does that tell them about the product? Students should explain that the product will be a whole number.

### Independent Practice

**Use the model to find each product.**

1. $\frac{3}{5} \times 10$

$\frac{3}{5} \times 10 = \underline{\phantom{0}6\phantom{0}}$

2. $\frac{5}{6} \times \frac{2}{3}$

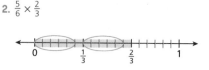

$\frac{5}{6} \times \frac{2}{3} = \underline{\frac{10}{18}}$

**Draw a model to find each product.**

3. $\frac{2}{3} \times 9$

Models will vary.

$\frac{2}{3} \times 9 = \underline{\phantom{0}6\phantom{0}}$

4. $\frac{3}{5} \times \frac{6}{7}$

Models will vary.

$\frac{3}{5} \times \frac{6}{7} = \underline{\frac{18}{35}}$

**Solve each equation. Show your work.**

5. $\frac{1}{4} \times 44 = \underline{\phantom{0}11\phantom{0}}$

6. $\frac{1}{5} \times \frac{2}{3} = \underline{\frac{2}{15}}$

## Digital Connection

**Random Number Generator** Use a search engine to find a random number generator Web site. Assign parameters for the random number generator to select four different numbers from 1 to 10. Have students create two fractions from the four numbers and then multiply the fractions. Remind students that a whole number, such as 2, can be written as $\frac{2}{1}$. Then have students create three more pairs of fractions and three more multiplication problems using the same four numbers. (If two or more of the integers are the same, it will not be possible to create four unique equations.)

## Independent Practice

7. $\frac{1}{6} \times \frac{4}{5} = \underline{\frac{4}{30}}$ or $\frac{2}{15}$

8. $\frac{2}{3} \times 20 = \underline{\frac{40}{3}}$ or $13\frac{1}{3}$

9. $\frac{1}{4} \times 9 = \underline{\frac{9}{4}}$ or $2\frac{1}{4}$

10. $\frac{5}{6} \times \frac{3}{4} = \underline{\frac{15}{24}}$ or $\frac{5}{8}$

11. $\frac{1}{5} \times \frac{2}{3} = \underline{\frac{2}{15}}$

12. $\frac{5}{9} \times \frac{2}{5} = \underline{\frac{10}{45}}$ or $\frac{2}{9}$

**Choose the correct answer.**

13. Mel has a $\frac{1}{2}$ gallon of milk in the refrigerator. He drinks $\frac{1}{4}$ of the milk. How much milk does Mel drink?

    **a.** $\frac{1}{8}$ gallon           **b.** $\frac{1}{6}$ gallon

    **c.** $\frac{1}{4}$ gallon           **d.** $\frac{3}{4}$ gallon

Unit 3 ■ Focus on Number and Operations—Fractions  **163**

## Teaching Tips

### Items 7-12

Ask students to predict whether the product of each exercise will be greater than 1 or less than 1. After students complete the exercises, they should compare their answers to their predictions. Have students analyze any inaccurate predictions by determining whether the size of the factors has any effect on the size of the product.

### Item 13

If students are struggling, have them draw a model to represent a carton of milk so that they can visualize the operation. Also, remind students that $\frac{1}{4}$ of $\frac{1}{2}$ is the same as $\frac{1}{4} \times \frac{1}{2}$.

## Math-to-Nutrition Connection

**Nutrition Labels** Ask students if they have ever read the Nutrition Facts on a food item. Explain that food manufacturers are required to display nutritional information on the packaging. The nutrition information includes a serving size and the number of servings per container.

Provide different food labels that have serving sizes that are fractional amounts, such as $\frac{1}{2}$ cup. Have students calculate the amount of the food in the entire container by multiplying the serving size by the number of servings per container.

## Teaching Tips

### Item 15

Tell students that a whole number can represent one item like an 18-gallon barrel, or it can represent a number of items like 18 marbles. Since the whole number is not divisible by the denominator, using the whole to represent a number of items is not useful in this problem.

**Independent Practice**

MP3  **14.** Amy multiplies $\frac{4}{5}$ and $\frac{2}{3}$ and says that the product is $\frac{6}{15}$. Identify the error Amy made and then find the correct answer.
Possible answer: Amy added the numerators, instead of multiplying them.
The product of $\frac{4}{5} \times \frac{2}{3}$ is $\frac{8}{15}$.

MP4  **15.** Create a story problem for the expression below. Then find the answer to your problem.

$$\frac{3}{4} \times 18$$

Sample story problem: Rupert's dog weighs 18 pounds. Jasmine's dog is $\frac{3}{4}$ the weight of Rupert's dog. How much does Jasmine's dog weigh? Jasmine's dog weighs $13\frac{1}{2}$ pounds.

**Solve the problems.**

MP1  **16.** A recipe calls for 6 cups of flour. Gunnar is only making $\frac{1}{4}$ of the recipe. How much flour does he need?

▶ **Show your work.**

$$\frac{1}{4} \times 6 = \frac{6}{4} = 1\frac{2}{4} = 1\frac{1}{2}$$

**Answer** Gunnar needs $1\frac{1}{2}$ cups of flour.

MP1  **17.** Sarah is $\frac{3}{4}$ as old as Richardo. Richardo is 16 years old. How old is Sarah?

▶ **Show your work.**

$$\frac{3}{4} \times 16 = \frac{48}{4} = 12$$

**Answer** Sarah is 12 years old.

## Mathematical Practices

| MP1 | **Make sense of problems and persevere in solving them.** |
|---|---|

**Items 16–17:** Students interpret a real-world problem, analyze the given information, and solve.

| MP3 | **Construct viable arguments and critique the reasoning of others.** |
|---|---|

**Item 14:** Students identify an error a student made when multiplying a fraction by a fraction.

| MP4 | **Model with mathematics.** |
|---|---|

**Item 15:** Students write a word problem that can be modeled by a given multiplication expression.

**MORE ONLINE** sadlierconnect.com

## Independent Practice

MP1 **18.** Jacob lives $\frac{3}{10}$ mile from school. Mia lives $\frac{2}{3}$ as far from school as Jacob. How far does Mia live from school?

✎ **Show your work.**

$\frac{2}{3} \times \frac{3}{10} = \frac{2 \times 3}{3 \times 10} = \frac{6}{30}$, or $\frac{1}{5}$

**Answer** Mia lives $\frac{1}{5}$ mile from school.

MP7 **19.** An apple weighs $\frac{9}{16}$ pound. A smaller apple is only $\frac{4}{5}$ as heavy. What is the weight of the smaller apple?

✎ **Show your work.**

$\frac{4}{5} \times \frac{9}{16} = \frac{4 \times 9}{5 \times 16} = \frac{36}{80}$ or $\frac{9}{20}$

**Answer** The smaller apple weighs $\frac{36}{80}$ pound, or $\frac{9}{20}$ pound.

MP4 **20.** Wylie is tiling a closet. Each tile is $\frac{3}{4}$ foot by $\frac{2}{3}$ foot. The closet floor is 6 square feet. How many tiles does Wylie need to cover the closet floor?

✎ **Show your work.**

Area of one tile: $\frac{3}{4} \times \frac{2}{3} = \frac{3 \times 2}{4 \times 3} = \frac{6}{12}$ or $\frac{1}{2}$ square foot
If one tile is $\frac{1}{2}$ square foot, then 2 tiles are 1 square foot.
So it will take 12 tiles to cover 6 square feet.

**Answer** Wylie needs 12 tiles to cover the floor.

## Teaching Tips

### Items 18-20
Remind students that they can multiply the factors in either order due to the Commutative Property.

### Item 20
Be sure that students know that they can find the area of each tile by multiplying its length by its width.

### Mathematical Practices

| MP1 | **Make sense of problems and persevere in solving them.** |
|---|---|

**Item 18:** Students interpret a real-world problem, analyze the given information, and solve.

| MP4 | **Model with mathematics.** |
|---|---|

**Item 20:** Students use mathematical expressions or visual models to solve a multi-step word problem.

| MP7 | **Look for and make use of structure.** |
|---|---|

**Item 19:** Students understand weight relationships to interpret a real-world problem and find the solution.

## OBJECTIVE
**Use tiling and multiplication to find the area of a rectangle with fractional side lengths.**

## ESSENTIAL QUESTION
Ask a volunteer to explain how to find the area of a rectangle with whole number side lengths. Point out that they will now be working with fractional side lengths as they make connections between area and fraction multiplication.

## FLUENCY PRACTICE
Fluency practice is available at **sadlierconnect.com**.

## Concept Development

### Understand: How to find the area of a rectangle with unit-fraction side lengths

■ Remind students that a unit fraction has a numerator of 1.

■ Be sure students understand the model. The denominator of each fraction is used to divide the model into rows and columns.

### Understand: How to find the area of a rectangle with fractional side lengths

■ Have students add a fourth column and a third row to the drawing so that they can see that the unit square is partitioned into 12 equal parts, and 6 of those parts are shaded.

---

**Essential Question:** How do you find the area of rectangles with fractional side lengths?

## Guided Instruction

In this lesson you will learn how to use tiling and multiplication to find the area of rectangles with fractional side lengths.

**Understand: How to find the area of a rectangle with unit-fraction side lengths**

> Find the area of a rectangle with side lengths of $\frac{1}{3}$ unit and $\frac{1}{4}$ unit.

The model at the right shows that $3 \times 4$, or 12, $\frac{1}{3}$-unit by $\frac{1}{4}$-unit rectangles fit inside a unit square.

The area of the unit square is 1 square unit. So, the $\frac{1}{3}$-unit by $\frac{1}{4}$-unit rectangle has an area of $\frac{1}{12}$ square unit, or (unit)$^2$.

➡ The area of a rectangle with side lengths of $\frac{1}{3}$ unit and $\frac{1}{4}$ unit is $\frac{1}{12}$ square unit, or (unit)$^2$.

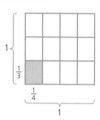

**Understand: How to find the area of a rectangle with fractional side lengths**

> A rectangular field has side lengths of $\frac{2}{3}$ mile and $\frac{3}{4}$ mile. What is the area of the field?

The model at the right shows that a $\frac{2}{3}$-mi by $\frac{3}{4}$-mi rectangle can be tiled with $\frac{1}{3}$-mi by $\frac{1}{4}$-mi rectangles. From the previous problem, you know that each small rectangle has an area of $\frac{1}{12}$ mi$^2$. There are $2 \times 3$, or 6 of these *unit-fraction rectangles* inside the larger rectangle.

So, the area of the field is $6 \times \frac{1}{12} = \frac{6}{1} \times \frac{1}{12}$, or $\frac{6}{12}$ mi$^2$, which is the same as $\frac{1}{2}$ mi$^2$.

Notice that you get the same result if you multiply the side lengths.

$\frac{2}{3} \times \frac{3}{4} = \frac{2 \times 3}{3 \times 4} = \frac{6}{12} = \frac{1}{2}$

➡ The area of the field is $\frac{6}{12}$ mi$^2$, or $\frac{1}{2}$ mi$^2$.

**166** Unit 3 ■ Focus on Number and Operations—Fractions

---

## Support English Language Learners

English language learners may not know the definition of *tiling*. First have students identify the base word *tile*. Ask students to read through the example on page 166 to try to determine its meaning from the context of the example. Some students may relate the rectangles in the models to tiles that are used in flooring. Explain to students that some words can be used as a noun and a verb with similar meanings. For example, to *tile* a floor, you position *tiles* on a floor or to *graph* a point, you plot a point on a *graph*.

MORE ONLINE  sadlierconnect.com

Lesson 19

Guided Instruction

## Understand: How to find the area of a rectangle with mixed-number side lengths

> Madeline made a banner to advertise the school carnival. The banner is $2\frac{1}{3}$ yards wide and $1\frac{1}{2}$ yards tall. What is the area of the banner?

Make a model or drawing of the banner. Divide it into rectangles with unit-fraction side lengths. Each unit-fraction rectangle has an area of $\frac{1}{2} \times \frac{1}{3}$ or $\frac{1}{6}$ yd².

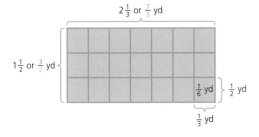

You can tile the banner with $3 \times 7$, or 21 unit-fraction rectangles. So the area of the banner in square yards is

$21 \times \frac{1}{6} = \frac{21}{1} \times \frac{1}{6} = \frac{21}{6} = \frac{7}{2} = 3\frac{1}{2}$.

Notice that you get the same result if you multiply the side lengths.

$2\frac{1}{3} \times 1\frac{1}{2} = \frac{7}{3} \times \frac{3}{2}$  → Rewrite the mixed numbers as fractions.

$= \frac{7 \times 3}{3 \times 2}$  → Multiply the fractions.

$= \frac{21}{6} = \frac{7}{2} = 3\frac{1}{2}$

In general, you can find the area of a rectangle with fractional or mixed number side lengths by multiplying the side lengths, just as you do for rectangles with whole number side lengths.

➡ The area of the banner is $3\frac{1}{2}$ yd².

Unit 3 ■ Focus on Number and Operations—Fractions  **167**

## Understand: How to find the area of a rectangle with mixed-number side lengths

■ Expect that students can represent fraction products as rectangular areas. The model in this problem represents the product $2\frac{1}{3} \times 1\frac{1}{2}$.

■ Point out to students that they can count squares to find the area, just as they did with area models for whole numbers. This model shows 21 squares that are each $\frac{1}{6}$ yd², so the area is $\frac{21}{6}$ yd² or $3\frac{1}{2}$ yd².

■ Remind students that mixed numbers should be converted to fractions before multiplying. Use this opportunity to review the process for converting mixed numbers to fractions, and back to mixed numbers.

## Math-to-Real-World Connection

**Construction** In this lesson, students are using the word *tiling* to refer to the unit-fraction tiles that cover a rectangular area. Point out to students that tiling has real-world application and can be seen in many venues. Find an area on the school ground that is tiled and point out to students the same-size tiles that cover the area. Have students identify the floor as a whole that has been divided into equal sections. Have students describe other tiled areas in their own homes, supermarkets, or malls.

# Guided Instruction

**Connect: How to find the area of rectangles with fractional side lengths** Use this page to help students strengthen their understanding of how to use multiplication to determine the area of a rectangle.

■ Ask students to describe a plan to solve the problem before reviewing the solution. After reviewing the solution, have students compare their plan to the steps listed in the presentation.

■ During Step 2, ask students if they can immediately tell which rectangle has the greater area. Invite students to explain why they can or cannot tell which is greater. Remind students that to compare two fractions, it is sometimes helpful to rewrite them as equivalent fractions with a common denominator. When the denominators are the same, the fraction with the greater numerator is greater.

▸ Students extend their understanding of area models showing whole number multiplication to models showing fraction multiplication. Ask students to work in pairs to share their models and explanations. As you monitor pairs, listen for explanations that make the connection that the lengths of the sides of the rectangle are factors in the multiplication problem.

## Guided Instruction

**Connect: How to find the area of rectangles with fractional side lengths**

**Rectangle A** has side lengths of $\frac{3}{4}$ yard and $\frac{3}{5}$ yard. **Rectangle B** has side lengths of $\frac{2}{5}$ yard and $\frac{1}{2}$ yard. Which rectangle has the greater area?

**Step 1**

Write multiplication expressions to represent the areas.

Area of **Rectangle A**: $\frac{3}{4} \times \frac{3}{5}$

Area of **Rectangle B**: $\frac{2}{5} \times \frac{1}{2}$

**Remember!**
The area of a rectangle is *length × width*.

**Step 2**

Multiply the fractions to determine the areas.

| Rectangle A | Rectangle B |
|---|---|
| $\frac{3}{4} \times \frac{3}{5} = \frac{9}{20}$ | $\frac{2}{5} \times \frac{1}{2} = \frac{2}{10}$ |

**Step 3**

Compare the areas of **Rectangle A** and **Rectangle B**.

**Rectangle A** $= \frac{9}{20}$ yd².

**Rectangle B** $= \frac{2}{10}$, or $\frac{4}{20}$ yd².

Write an equivalent fraction for $\frac{2}{10}$ with a denominator of 20. $\frac{2}{10} = \frac{2 \times 2}{10 \times 2} = \frac{4}{20}$

$\frac{9}{20} \quad > \quad \frac{4}{20}$

Then compare the numerators.    **Rectangle A > Rectangle B**

➡ **Rectangle A** has the greater area.

▸ Draw a model to represent a $\frac{3}{4}$ by $\frac{3}{5}$ rectangle. Then explain how your model shows that $\frac{3}{4} \times \frac{3}{5} = \frac{9}{20}$.
Possible answer: One side of the model is divided into fourths. The other is divided into fifths. Each of the 9 unit rectangles has area $\frac{1}{20}$ square unit, so the area of the whole rectangle is $\frac{9}{20}$ square unit.

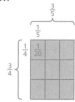

## Writing About Math

▸ **Write a Narrative Problem** Ask students to write an original word problem whose solution requires finding the area of a rectangle with fractional side lengths. Remind students to use appropriate units in their problem. Encourage students to make the problem as engaging and interesting as possible. Then have students use the same fractional side lengths to write a second problem with a different situation. Remind students that the area of rectangles with the same side lengths will have the same area.

Ask students to trade their word problems with a partner and solve them. Have students use a unit-rectangle tile model to solve the first problem and multiplication to solve the second problem. Ensure that the areas match for both problems.

## Guided Practice

**Complete the statements.**

1. The unit square at the right is tiled with unit-fraction rectangles.

   The side lengths of each unit-fraction rectangle are $\frac{1}{3}$ unit and $\frac{1}{6}$ unit.

   There are __18__ unit-fraction rectangles in the unit square.

   Each unit-fraction rectangle has an area of $\frac{1}{18}$ square unit.

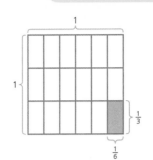

2. The rectangle shown at the right has side lengths $\frac{2}{3}$ unit and $\frac{5}{6}$ unit.

   This rectangle is tiled with $2 \times \underline{5}$ or $\underline{10}$ unit-fraction rectangles.

   From exercise 1, you know that each unit-fraction rectangle, $\frac{1}{3} \times \frac{1}{6}$, has an area of $\frac{1}{18}$ square unit.

   So, the area of this rectangle in square units is:

   $\underline{10} \times \frac{1}{18} = \frac{10}{18}$. or $\frac{5}{9}$

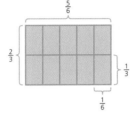

3. For the rectangle in exercise 2, show that you get the same area if you multiply the side lengths.

   $\frac{2}{3} \times \frac{5}{6} = \frac{2 \times 5}{3 \times 6} = \frac{10}{18}$

### ♔ Think · Pair · Share

MP7 4. Explain two different ways you can find the area of a rectangle with a width of $\frac{2}{7}$ unit and a length of $\frac{3}{4}$ unit.

   Possible answer: You can draw a $\frac{2}{7}$ by $\frac{3}{4}$ rectangle and tile it with rectangles with side lengths of $\frac{1}{7}$ and $\frac{1}{4}$. Multiply the number of these unit-fraction rectangles by $\frac{1}{28}$, which is the area of each one. Or, you can just multiply the fractions $\frac{2}{7}$ and $\frac{3}{4}$.

Unit 3 ■ Focus on Number and Operations—Fractions    **169**

---

## Mathematical Practices

Mathematical Practice Standards underline the teaching and understanding of all concepts and skills presented. The emphasis of specific practices is noted throughout the guided and independent practice of this lesson.

| MP7 | **Look for and make use of structure.** |
| --- | --- |

**Item 4:** Students identify more than one way to use structure to determine the area of the rectangle.

---

## Observational Assessment

Use page 169 to assess whether students are able to determine the area of a rectangle with fractional side lengths by tiling and by multiplication. Be sure that students are able to identify the size of each unit-fraction rectangle by using the model and by using multiplication.

### ♔ Think·Pair·Share

**Peer Collaboration** Have students work in small groups to share their different ways of finding the area. Tell students to determine the area using the methods they chose. After students complete their work, ask students to share their answers with the class. Ask questions such as:

• *When would it be most helpful to use a model?*

• *When would you choose to multiply side lengths?*

• *Did you get the same area with both methods?*

To summarize, be sure students understand that tiling with unit-fraction rectangles or multiplying fractions both produce the same total area. Point out that tiling shows the reason why fraction multiplication works.

### Return to the Essential Question

Reread the Lesson 19 Essential Question on page 166: *How do you find the area of rectangles with fractional side lengths?*

Ask volunteers to use what they learned in this lesson to answer this question. (Possible response: I can use a model to determine how many unit-fraction rectangles will tile the total area or I can use fraction multiplication to multiply the side lengths to find the total area.)

Invite as many volunteers as possible to express ideas about finding the area of rectangles with fractional side lengths in their own words.

# Independent Practice

## Concept Application

Students may work independently on these pages in the classroom or at home. They may refer to the first four pages of the lesson to revisit the instruction or to see a worked-out example.

**Common Errors** and **Teaching Tips** may help you support student learning either in the classroom or as a follow-up for work done at home.

## Common Errors

### Item 4

Students who do not read carefully may attempt to multiply the two fractions in the problem as fractional side lengths. Help students see the problem as a unknown factor problem by reviewing the formula for the area of a rectangle: *length × width = area.* Point out that the missing value in that formula is the width.

## Teaching Tips

### Items 1–2

In exercise 1, students are determining the area of the $\frac{1}{5} \times \frac{1}{5}$ unit-fraction rectangle (the shaded part). Point out that, in this case, the unit fraction rectangle is a square. In exercise 2, students are determining the area of the entire model (not just the shaded part). Be sure students see this distinction.

## Independent Practice

**Complete the statements.**

1. The unit square at the right is tiled with unit-fraction rectangles.

   The side lengths of each unit-fraction rectangle are $\frac{1}{5}$ and $\underline{\frac{1}{5}}$.

   There are $\underline{25}$ unit-fraction rectangles in the unit square.

   Each unit-fraction rectangle has an area of $\underline{\frac{1}{25}}$ square unit.

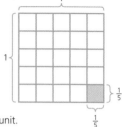

2. The rectangle shown here has side lengths $\underline{\frac{4}{5}}$ unit by $\underline{\frac{3}{5}}$ unit.

   This rectangle is tiled with $\underline{4} \times \underline{3}$ or $\underline{12}$, unit-fraction rectangles.

   From exercise 1, you know that each unit-fraction rectangle, $\frac{1}{5} \times \underline{\frac{1}{5}}$, has an area of $\underline{\frac{1}{25}}$ square unit.

   So, the area of this rectangle in square units is:

   $\underline{12} \times \frac{1}{25} = \underline{\frac{12}{25}}$.

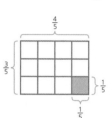

3. For the rectangle in exercise 2, show that you get the same area if you multiply the side lengths.

   $\frac{3}{5} \times \frac{4}{5} = \frac{3 \times 4}{5 \times 5} = \frac{12}{25}$

MP2  4. A rectangle has an area of $\frac{5}{18}$ square meter and a length of $\frac{5}{6}$ meter. What is its width? Explain your answer.
   The width is $\frac{1}{3}$ meter. Possible answer: I thought about the problem as a multiplication equation with a missing factor. I looked at the numerators and thought, "What number times 5 is 5?" The answer is 1. I looked at the denominators and thought, "What number times 6 is 18?" The answer is 3. So the missing side is $\frac{1}{3}$ meter.

## Mathematical Practices

| MP2 | **Reason abstractly and quantitatively.** |
| --- | --- |

**Item 4:** Students analyze the relationship between the quantity for area and the quantity for length to determine the quantity for width.

MORE ONLINE sadlierconnect.com

Lesson 19

## Independent Practice

**Find the area of each figure. Show your work.**

5.

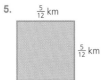

$\frac{5}{12}$ km

$\frac{5}{12}$ km

Area: _____ $\frac{25}{144}$ km²

6.

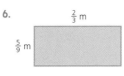

$\frac{2}{3}$ m

$\frac{5}{9}$ m

Area: _____ $\frac{10}{27}$ m²

7. A square with side lengths of $\frac{7}{9}$ inches.

Area: _____ $\frac{49}{81}$ in.²

8. A rectangle with a width of $\frac{1}{2}$ cm and length of 10 cm.

Area: _____ 5 cm²

9. A rectangle with a length of $\frac{1}{5}$ yd and width of $\frac{2}{3}$ yd.

Area: _____ $\frac{2}{15}$ yd²

10. A rectangle with a length of $\frac{2}{3}$ ft and width of $\frac{1}{2}$ ft.

Area: _____ $\frac{2}{6}$, or $\frac{1}{3}$ ft²

**For exercises 11–12, choose the correct answer.**

11. A private beach is $\frac{6}{7}$ mile in length and $\frac{1}{4}$ mile in width. What is the area of the beach?

   a. $\frac{3}{14}$ mi²

   b. $\frac{7}{11}$ mi²

   c. $\frac{1}{28}$ mi²

   d. $\frac{28}{6}$ mi²

## Common Errors

### Items 5–10
If students do not include units or include incorrect units, then remind them that when they multiply side lengths, they are also multiplying units.

### Item 11
Remind students to simplify the fraction, if necessary. Students who rely simply on multiplying the denominators to find the answer will choose incorrectly.

## Teaching Tips

### Items 5–6
If students have difficulty determining the multiplication necessary to calculate the area of each square, remind them that they can draw lines to divide the areas into unit-fraction rectangles. Allow students to use a separate sheet of paper if they need to make larger models.

## Digital Connection

**Tables** Use a spreadsheet program or a word processing program to create a unit-fraction multiplication chart, similar to a whole number multiplication chart. List unit fractions from $\frac{1}{2}$ through $\frac{1}{10}$ across the top row and down the right column of the spreadsheet. Fill-in the resulting unit fraction products throughout the chart and use it to make connections to a whole number multiplication chart. Point out that the whole number products are the same as the denominators in fraction multiplication. Remind students that knowing their multiplication facts helps them quickly find the answer to unit fraction multiplication problems.

# Independent Practice

## Teaching Tips

### Item 13

If students have difficulty answering the problem, ask them to draw several examples and determine the area of each example. Ask students if any of their examples are greater than 1 square unit. Then ask students if they can think of any way to create a rectangle with fractional side lengths less than 1 that has an area greater than 1 square unit.

### Item 14

Remind students that this problem does not ask them to calculate the answer. Explain that they should describe the process in such a way that someone else could solve the problem.

---

Lesson 19  Find Areas of Rectangles: Tile and Multiply

### Independent Practice

12. What is the area of a rectangle with a width of $\frac{1}{3}$ yd and a length of $\frac{9}{10}$ yd?

   **a.** $\frac{9}{30}$ yd² ⊙

   **b.** $\frac{30}{9}$ yd²

   **c.** $\frac{10}{13}$ yd²

   **d.** $\frac{27}{10}$ yd²

**MP3** 13. If both sides of a rectangle are less than 1 unit long, will the area of that rectangle be less than or greater than 1 square unit? Explain your reasoning.
   The area will be less than 1 square unit. Possible response: If both sides are shorter than 1 unit, then the rectangle will fit inside of a unit square. So, its area must be less than the area of a unit square.

**MP7** 14. Without calculating the answer, explain how to find the area of the figure below.

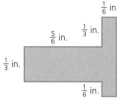

$\frac{1}{6}$ in.

$\frac{1}{3}$ in.

$\frac{5}{6}$ in.

$\frac{1}{3}$ in.

$\frac{1}{6}$ in.

Possible answer: The figure can be divided into three rectangles: $\frac{1}{3}$ in. by 1 in., $\frac{1}{3}$ in. by $\frac{1}{6}$ in., and $\frac{1}{6}$ in. by $\frac{1}{6}$ in. Find the area of each of these smaller rectangles and then add their areas.

**Solve the problems.**

**MP1** 15. Ben has an herb garden in his backyard. The garden is a square. Each side measures $\frac{5}{6}$ foot. What is the area of Ben's herb garden?

   ▭ **Show your work.**

   $\frac{5}{6} \times \frac{5}{6} = \frac{25}{36}$

   **Answer** _The area of Ben's herb garden is $\frac{25}{36}$ ft²._

172  Unit 3 ▪ Focus on Number and Operations—Fractions

---

| Mathematical Practices | |
|---|---|
| **MP1** | **Make sense of problems and persevere in solving them.** |
| **Item 15:** Students determine needed problem information to solve. | |
| **MP3** | **Construct viable arguments and critique the reasoning of others.** |
| **Item 13:** Students must construct an argument for a generalization and explain their reasoning. | |
| **MP7** | **Look for and make use of structure.** |
| **Item 14:** Students look at smaller parts of the whole and combine them to plan a solution. | |

Lesson 19

## Independent Practice

MP1 16. The ancient Egyptians used the expression $\frac{1}{4} \times (a + c) \times (b + d)$ to find the area of four-sided figures. With a rectangle, $a$ and $c$ are the width and $b$ and $d$ are the length. Find the area of the rectangle shown below using the expression $\frac{1}{4} \times (a + c) \times (b + d)$. Also, find the area of the rectangle by multiplying the length by the width. Compare your answers.

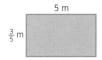

5 m

$\frac{3}{5}$ m

**Show your work.**

$\frac{1}{4} \times (a + c) \times (b + d) = \frac{1}{4} \times (5 + 5) \times (\frac{3}{5} + \frac{3}{5})$

$= \frac{1}{4} \times (\frac{10}{1}) \times (\frac{6}{5}) = \frac{60}{20} = 3 \text{ m}^2;$

length $\times$ width $= \frac{5}{1}$ m $\times \frac{3}{5}$ m $= \frac{15}{5} = 3 \text{ m}^2$

**Answer** The answers are the same. The area of the rectangle is 3 m².

MP1 17. Find the area of the shaded region below.

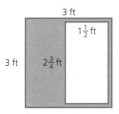

3 ft

$1\frac{1}{2}$ ft

3 ft

$2\frac{3}{4}$ ft

**Show your work.**

Area of nonshaded region: $2\frac{3}{4}$ ft $\times 1\frac{1}{2}$ ft $= \frac{11}{4}$ ft $\times \frac{3}{2}$ ft $= \frac{33}{8}$, or $4\frac{1}{8}$ ft².

area of shaded region − area of nonshaded region

$9$ ft² $- 4\frac{1}{8}$ ft² $= 4\frac{7}{8}$ ft².

**Answer** The area of the shaded region is $4\frac{7}{8}$ ft².

## Mathematical Practices

| **MP1** | **Make sense of problems and persevere in solving them.** |
|---|---|

**Item 16:** Students analyze a different solution process and use their own process to check its validity.

**Item 17:** Students relate a more complex problem to similar problems that they have already solved.

---

## Common Errors

### Item 17

Students may be tempted to solve this problem the same way they solved exercise 14 on the previous page. This leads to computational errors as students try to break the shaded area into smaller rectangles without enough information to do so. Suggest that students visualize the figure as a 3 feet by 3 feet sheet of paper with a rectangular hole cut out. Ask students how finding the area of the original paper and the area of the hole can help them find the area that is left.

## Teaching Tips

### Item 16

If time permits, challenge students to explain why this formula works. Compare it to the formula *length × width = area*. Have students use graph paper to draw a rectangle with a width of $\frac{3}{5}$ m and a length of 5 m. Then have students extend each width and length to show $a + c$ and $b + d$, resulting in a rectangle with a width of $\frac{6}{5}$ m and a length of 10 m. Students will see that the area of new rectangle is four times greater than the area of the original rectangle. Therefore, to find the area of the original rectangle, Egyptians multiplied the greater area by $\frac{1}{4}$, which is equivalent to dividing by 4.

## OBJECTIVE
**Compare a number and the product of the number and a fraction.**

## ESSENTIAL QUESTION
In this lesson, students will explore the relationship between a factor and the product of the factor and a fraction. They will also learn to view multiplying fractions as scaling.

## PREREQUISITE SKILLS
Use Item G on page 340 of the Foundational Skills Handbook to review multiplying using repeated addition.

## FLUENCY PRACTICE
Fluency practice is available at **sadlierconnect.com**.

## Concept Development

### Understand: Comparing factors and products

■ Explain that when multiplying a whole-number factor by a fraction less than 1, the product is less than the whole number factor.

---

**Essential Question:**
When you multiply a number by a fraction, how does the product compare to the number?

Words to Know:
scaling

### Guided Instruction

In this lesson you will understand how multiplying by fractions less than or greater than 1 affects the size of products.

**Understand: Comparing factors and products**

> Eli has 12 baseball cards. Marcos has $\frac{5}{4}$ as many cards as Eli. Lynne has $\frac{3}{4}$ as many cards as Eli. Without any computation, determine who has fewer cards than Eli and who has more cards than Eli.

To find who has fewer and more cards than Eli, you can use a model to visualize the numbers of baseball cards and make comparisons.

Eli has 12 baseball cards. Marcos has $\frac{5}{4}$ as many cards as Eli. Write an expression to show how many cards Marcos has. Notice the factor $\frac{5}{4}$ is $1\frac{1}{4}$, which is *greater than* 1 whole.　　Expression: $\frac{5}{4} \times 12$

Eli has 12 baseball cards. Lynne has $\frac{3}{4}$ as many cards as Eli. Write an expression to show how many cards Lynne has. Notice the factor $\frac{3}{4}$ is *less than* 1 whole.　　Expression: $\frac{3}{4} \times 12$

Draw a 3 by 4 model to represent Eli's 12 baseball cards.

Marcos has $\frac{5}{4} \times 12$ cards. You can see from the model that the product of $\frac{5}{4} \times 12$ is *greater than* 12.

Lynne has $\frac{3}{4} \times 12$ cards. You can see from the model that product of $\frac{3}{4} \times 12$ is *less than* 12.

$\frac{5}{4} \times 12$

$\frac{3}{4} \times 12$

➡ Lynne has fewer cards than Eli. Marcos has more cards than Eli.

---

## Words to Know

**scaling:** resizing a number by using multiplication

**Glossary can be found on pp. 347–350.**

Lesson 20

Guided Instruction

## Connect: Multiplying fractions as scaling

When you multiply a number by a fraction, you are scaling, or resizing, that number. The size of the fraction determines whether the product will be less than, greater than, or equal to the original number.

- When you multiply a number by a fraction *less than* 1, the product is *less than* that number.

- When you multiply a number by a fraction *greater than* 1, the product is *greater than* that number.

- When you multiply a number by a fraction *equivalent* to 1, the product is *equal* to that number.

> **Remember!**
> The Identity Property of Multiplication: for any number $a$, $1 \times a = a \times 1 = a$.

> Omar walks $\frac{3}{5}$ mile. Nate walks $\frac{4}{5}$ as far as Omar. Chris walks $\frac{4}{3}$ as far as Omar. Jen walks $\frac{4}{4}$ as far as Omar. Who walks a greater number of miles than Omar? Who walks fewer miles than Omar? Who walks the same number of miles as Omar? Find these answers without computing.

Write an expression to show how far Nate walks.
You are multiplying $\frac{3}{5}$ by a fraction that is *less than* 1.
The product will be *less than* $\frac{3}{5}$.

$\frac{4}{5} \times \frac{3}{5}$ | $\frac{4}{5} < 1$

$\frac{4}{5} \times \frac{3}{5} < \frac{3}{5}$

Write an expression to show how far Chris walks.
You are multiplying $\frac{3}{5}$ by a fraction that is *greater than* 1.
The product will be *greater than* $\frac{3}{5}$.

$\frac{4}{3} \times \frac{3}{5}$ | $\frac{4}{3} > 1$

$\frac{4}{3} \times \frac{3}{5} > \frac{3}{5}$

Write an expression to show how far Jen walks.
You are multiplying $\frac{3}{5}$ by 1.
The product will be *equal to* $\frac{3}{5}$.

$\frac{4}{4} \times \frac{3}{5}$ | $\frac{4}{4} = 1$

$\frac{4}{4} \times \frac{3}{5} = \frac{3}{5}$

➡ Chris walks a greater number of miles than Omar. Nate walks fewer miles than Omar. And Jen walks the same number of miles as Omar.

✏ Without any computation, explain why $2 \times 3$ is greater than 3, and $\frac{1}{2} \times 3$ is less than 3.
Possible answer: $2 \times 3$ is greater than 3 because 3 is doubled when it is multiplied by 2, and $3 + 3 > 3$. $\frac{1}{2} \times 3$ is less than 3 because 3 is half of 3 when multiplied by $\frac{1}{2}$, and $3 \div 2 < 3$.

**Unit 3 ■ Focus on Number and Operations—Fractions** 175

## Connect: Multiplying fractions as scaling

■ In this presentation, students understand multiplying as scaling. Begin by defining the term *scaling*. Review the rules in the bulleted list at the top of the page as a class. Have students commit these rules to memory. Use the presentation to show students that when they multiply a number by fraction, they are resizing or scaling it.

■ Students should see that Omar's distance is the common thread of the problem. The distance for each of the other walkers can be found by multiplying Omar's distance by a fraction.

■ Before comparing Omar and Jen's distances, review the Identity Product of Multiplication.

■ Some students may want to compute the actual products to verify that the rules really do work.

✏ Show students that 2 can be expressed as a fraction that is greater than 1, such as $\frac{2}{1}$, $\frac{4}{2}$, or $\frac{10}{5}$.

## Support English Language Learners

The term *scale* has many different meanings. English language learners may know the word *scale* as an instrument used to measure weight. Some students may recognize fish as having scales. Write the word *scale* on the board. Say the word aloud and have the class repeat it back. In different circles around the word, write different definitions of the word *scale* as the class provides them. Encourage students to say sentences using the different contexts of the word. Then explain that in this lesson, the word *scale* will be used as a verb, meaning to make something bigger or smaller.

# Guided Practice

## Observational Assessment

Use pages 176–177 to assess whether students understand the connection between multiplying by a fraction and scaling. Be sure that students understand that 1 can be represented by fractions like $\frac{6}{6}$.

### Guided Practice

**For exercises 1–4, use the models to determine whether the product is *less than*, *greater than*, or *equal to* the second factor.**

1. $\frac{3}{5} \times 10$

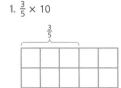

The product is ___less than___ 10.

2. $\frac{7}{4} \times 16$

The product is ___greater than___ 16.

3. $\frac{6}{6} \times \frac{2}{3}$

The product is ___equal to___ $\frac{2}{3}$.

4. $\frac{3}{2} \times \frac{3}{4}$

The product is ___greater than___ $\frac{3}{4}$.

**For exercises 5–8, complete the statements to determine whether each product is *less than*, *greater than*, or *equal to* the second factor.**

5. $\frac{6}{7} \times 64$

$\frac{6}{7}$ is ___less than___ 1.

So, the product is ___less than___ 64.

6. $\frac{7}{5} \times \frac{4}{13}$

$\frac{7}{5}$ is ___greater than___ 1.

So, the product is ___greater than___ $\frac{4}{13}$.

7. $\frac{12}{12} \times \frac{8}{11}$

$\frac{12}{12}$ is ___equal to___ 1.

So, the product is ___equal to___ $\frac{8}{11}$.

8. $\frac{9}{15} \times 112$

$\frac{9}{15}$ is ___less than___ 1.

So, the product is ___less than___ 112.

## Math-to-Geography Connection

**Drawing a Map**  A cartographer is a person who makes maps. Show students maps of subway systems, roads and highways, or geographical areas. Explain that cartographers must measure and analyze geographic information to create maps. They represent large areas by multiplying actual distances between two points by a fraction less than 1, called a scale.

Have students draw a map of the classroom. Assign groups the task of measuring the actual distances. Then, use the guess-and-check strategy to find a scale of the real distance that they can use to represent a map of the classroom on a sheet of paper.

Invite students to present their maps to the class.

Lesson 20

### Guided Practice

Tell whether the product of each expression is *less than*, *greater than*, or *equal to* the second factor.

9. $\frac{1}{4} \times 109$

_less than_

10. $\frac{5}{3} \times \frac{2}{7}$

_greater than_

11. $\frac{9}{9} \times 312$

_equal to_

12. $\frac{3}{4} \times \frac{5}{9}$

_less than_

Complete each comparison with >, <, or =.

13. $\frac{1}{2} \times 87 \underline{<} 87$

14. $\frac{5}{5} \times \frac{4}{20} \underline{=} \frac{4}{20}$

15. $\frac{11}{12} \times \frac{8}{11} \underline{<} \frac{8}{11}$

16. $\frac{8}{7} \times \frac{10}{13} \underline{>} \frac{10}{13}$

17. $\frac{2}{2} \times 55 \underline{=} 55$

18. $\frac{9}{13} \times \frac{13}{9} \underline{<} \frac{13}{9}$

#### ☖ Think • Pair • Share

MP6  19. Complete the table below. Then ask a classmate to draw a model for each of your examples and verify your responses. Check students' models.

| If a number is multiplied by . . . | then the product is . . . | Example: |
|---|---|---|
| a fraction less than 1, | less than the number. | $\frac{1}{3} \times \frac{1}{2} = \frac{1}{6}$ |
| a fraction greater than 1, | greater than the number. | $\frac{5}{4} \times 8 = 10$ |
| a fraction equal to 1, | equal to the number. | $\frac{6}{6} \times \frac{1}{5} = \frac{1}{5}$ |

Unit 3 ▪ Focus on Number and Operations—Fractions  **177**

#### ☖ Think•Pair•Share

**Peer Collaboration**  Give time for each student to complete the table. Then break the class up into student pairs. Have partners exchange their tables and have each partner model each example in the chart. As student pairs are drawing models, ask:

- *Did you and your partner reach the same conclusion for multiplying a fraction less than 1? Did you and your partner reach the same conclusion for multiplying a fraction greater than 1?*

- *How will you model a fraction that is equal to 1?*

To summarize, explain that the product of a fraction and a whole number will either be greater than, less than, or equal to the whole number product depending on whether the fraction is less than 1, greater than 1, or equal to 1.

#### Return to the Essential Question

Reread the Lesson 20 Essential Question on page 174: *When you multiply a number by a fraction, how does the product compare to the number?*

Ask volunteers to use what they learned in this lesson to answer this question. (Possible responses: The product is smaller than the number if the fraction is less than 1. The product is larger than the number if the fraction is greater than 1. The product is the same size as the number if the fraction is equivalent to 1.)

Invite as many volunteers as possible to express ideas about multiplying a number by a fraction in their own words.

### Mathematical Practices

Mathematical Practice Standards underline the teaching and understanding of all concepts and skills presented. The emphasis of specific practices is noted throughout the guided and independent practice of this lesson.

| MP6 | **Attend to precision.** |
|---|---|

**Item 19:** Students use mathematical language to carefully complete a table comparing the size of a number and the product of that number and a fraction.

## Concept Application

Students may work independently on these pages in the classroom or at home. They may refer to the first four pages of the lesson to revisit the instruction or to see a worked-out example.

**Common Errors** and **Teaching Tips** may help you support student learning either in the classroom or as a follow-up for work done at home.

## Teaching Tips

### Items 3–4

Direct students' attention to the first fraction in the expression. Ask students how they identify if a fraction is *greater than* or *less than* 1.

### Item 7

Encourage students to use what they know about comparing factors and products to determine which statement is true, rather than multiplying to find the product and then comparing the product to the fraction or whole number on the other side of the inequality symbol.

---

**Lesson 20** Interpret Multiplication of Fractions as Scaling

### Independent Practice

**For exercises 1–2, use the models to determine whether each product is *less than*, *greater than*, or *equal to* the second factor.**

1. $\frac{7}{6} \times \frac{2}{3}$

$\frac{7}{6}$

The product is <u>greater than</u> $\frac{2}{3}$.

2. $\frac{1}{2} \times 8$

$\frac{1}{2}$

The product is <u>less than</u> 8.

**For exercises 3–6, write *less than*, *greater than*, or *equal to*.**

3. $\frac{9}{5} \times 41$

$\frac{9}{5}$ is <u>greater than</u> 1.

So, the product is <u>greater than</u> 41.

4. $\frac{5}{7} \times \frac{3}{8}$

$\frac{5}{7}$ is <u>less than</u> 1.

So, the product is <u>less than</u> $\frac{3}{8}$.

5. $\frac{7}{17} \times \frac{6}{7}$

$\frac{7}{17}$ is <u>less than</u> 1.

So, the product is <u>less than</u> $\frac{6}{7}$.

6. $\frac{7}{7} \times \frac{4}{5}$

$\frac{7}{7}$ is <u>equal to</u> 1.

So, the product is <u>equal to</u> $\frac{4}{5}$.

**For exercises 7–8, choose the correct answer.**

7. Which of the following is true?

a. $\frac{1}{7} \times 24 > 24$

b. $\frac{5}{4} \times \frac{4}{5} > \frac{4}{5}$

c. $\frac{4}{4} \times \frac{3}{8} < \frac{3}{8}$

d. $\frac{3}{4} \times \frac{1}{2} > \frac{1}{2}$

---

## Writing About Math

▸ **Writing an Opinion** Show students three images of objects in the real world, such as photos, paintings, diagrams, or maps. Ask students to write a paragraph explaining which of the images uses the smallest scale to represent the real-world object.

Invite students to read their paragraphs to the class.

**Independent Practice**

8. Franklin reads 6 pages in his textbook. Ann reads $\frac{1}{2}$ as many pages as Franklin. Billy reads $\frac{5}{3}$ as many pages as Franklin. Danny reads $\frac{4}{4}$ as many pages as Franklin. Which statement is correct?

    (a.) Ann reads fewer pages than Franklin.

    b. Danny reads more pages than Franklin.

    c. Billy reads the same number of pages as Franklin.

    d. Franklin reads the greatest number of pages.

**Tell whether each product is *less than*, *greater than*, or *equal to* the second factor.**

9. $\frac{8}{9} \times 212$             10. $\frac{5}{5} \times \frac{7}{5}$

    ___less than___               ___equal to___

**Complete each comparison with >, <, or =.**

11. $\frac{4}{7} \times \frac{19}{4}$ ___<___ $\frac{19}{4}$        12. $\frac{3}{11} \times 33$ ___≤___ $33$

13. $\frac{9}{9} \times \frac{5}{12}$ ___=___ $\frac{5}{12}$        14. $\frac{7}{8} \times \frac{2}{3}$ ___<___ $\frac{2}{3}$

15. $\frac{4}{3} \times 450$ ___>___ $450$        16. $\frac{8}{8} \times \frac{13}{9}$ ___=___ $\frac{13}{9}$

**Write a fraction that makes each comparison true.** Specific fractions will vary, but the criteria for its value are given below each exercise.

17. ___ $\times 506 < 506$        18. ___ $\times \frac{5}{19} = \frac{5}{19}$
    any fraction less than 1        any fraction equal to 1

19. ___ $\times \frac{12}{13} > \frac{12}{13}$        20. ___ $\times \frac{6}{5} < \frac{6}{5}$
    any fraction greater than 1      any fraction less than 1

## Teaching Tips

### Item 8
Suggest that students make a list or a table to help them solve this problem.

### Items 11–16
Students with dyslexia and other visual processing disorders may confuse the *greater than* and *less than* symbols. Provide them with a method of differentiating between them, such as telling them that the point always points to the lesser quantity.

### Items 17–20
Be sure students understand that there are many possible answers for each of these items.

## Digital Connection

**Online Research** Explain to students that it is not always possible to tell how large an object is in a photograph. Photographers often place a coin or another object in the photo so that the viewer can determine the size of the object. Have students search for photos of insects with coins, rulers, or other reference objects. Ask students to estimate the size of the insects in real life.

# Independent Practice

## Common Errors

### Item 25

Some students may try to incorporate the number of servings, 6, into their solution. This number is extra information and is not used in the solution. Ask students to read the problem carefully and think about what information is necessary. Suggest that they cross out any information they do not need.

## Teaching Tips

### Items 21–25

Some students are easily overwhelmed by pages that present a large number of exercises or word problems. Suggest that they use a blank sheet of paper to cover the problems that they are not working on. This practice will help them focus on one problem at a time.

## Independent Practice

**Answer each question without multiplying.**

MP3  **21.** Ari says that the product of $\frac{1}{18} \times 18$ is equal to 18. Is he correct? Explain your answer.

Ari is not correct. Possible explanation: Since $\frac{1}{18}$ is less than 1, the product will be less than 18.

MP3  **22.** Marcy did this problem for her homework.

$$\frac{1}{2} \times 6 = 3$$

Her brother says that she is wrong because when you multiply, the product is always greater than either factor. In your own words, explain to Marcy's brother why her answer is correct.

Possible answer: When you multiply a number by a fraction that is less than 1, the product is less than that number. In this case half of 6 is 3, or 3 is half of 6.

MP2  **23.** A chef is making dinner for 12 people. She plans to use $\frac{1}{4}$ pound of turkey for each person. Will she need more than or less than 12 pounds of turkey? Explain your reasoning.

The chef will need less than 12 pounds of turkey. Possible explanation: When you multiply a whole number by a fraction less than 1, the answer is less than the whole number.

MP2  **24.** Mr. Amon's classroom has 30 desks. Ms. Wu's classroom has $\frac{4}{3}$ as many desks as Mr. Amon's classroom. Are there more than 30 desks, fewer than 30 desks, or exactly 30 desks in Ms. Wu's classroom? Explain your reasoning.

There are more than 30 desks in Ms. Wu's classroom. Possible explanation: $\frac{4}{3}$ is greater than 1 and when you multiply a number by a fraction greater than 1, the product is greater than that number.

MP2  **25.** Grace is making soup for friends. The recipe calls for 5 cups of broth for 6 servings. Grace wants to make $\frac{1}{4}$ the number of servings. Does she need to use the amount of broth the recipe calls for, use less broth, or use more broth? Explain your reasoning.

Grace needs to use less broth. Possible explanation: She is multiplying 5 by $\frac{1}{4}$. Because $\frac{1}{4}$ is less than 1, the product will be less than 5.

## Mathematical Practices

| | |
|---|---|
| **MP2** | **Reason abstractly and quantitatively.** |

**Items 23–24:** Students interpret a real-world problem using their knowledge of multiplying fractions.

**Item 25:** Students compare the product's value to the factor multiplied by a fraction less than 1.

| | |
|---|---|
| **MP3** | **Construct viable arguments and critique the reasoning of others.** |

**Item 21:** Students analyze a student's work and identifies the error.

**Item 22:** Students construct an argument to explain why a student is incorrect.

Lesson 20

Independent Practice

**Teaching Tips**

**Items 27–28**
Some students may have trouble grasping the idea that a product may be smaller than its factors. Encourage these students to justify their answers by drawing. This will help them visualize the process of multiplying by fractions smaller than 1.

**Solve the problems.**

MP7  **26.** Kayla ran $\frac{9}{10}$ mile yesterday. Today, she ran $\frac{8}{9}$ the distance she ran yesterday. On which day did Kayla run more miles? Explain your reasoning.

Kayla ran more yesterday. Possible explanation: The product of $\frac{9}{10}$ and $\frac{8}{9}$ will be less than $\frac{9}{10}$ because $\frac{8}{9}$ is less than 1.

MP4  **27.** Marta has $\frac{2}{3}$ yard of ribbon. Julian has a ribbon that is $\frac{1}{2}$ as long as Marta's ribbon. Is Julian's ribbon longer or shorter than $\frac{2}{3}$ yard?

**Answer** Julian's ribbon is shorter than $\frac{2}{3}$ yard.

▸ **Justify your answer with a model, drawings, or numbers.**

Possible justification:

| 1 yard of ribbon | | | |
|---|---|---|---|
| Marta's ribbon | | $\frac{2}{3}$ yard | |
| Julian's ribbon | $\frac{1}{2}$ of $\frac{2}{3}$ yard | | |

MP1  **28.** Matt is 60 inches tall. Jeff is $\frac{13}{12}$ as tall as Matt. Which statement is true?

**a.** Matt and Jeff are the same height.

**b.** Matt is taller than Jeff.

**c.** Jeff is taller than Matt.

**Answer** Statement C is true.

▸ **Justify your answer with a model, drawings, or numbers.**
Possible justification:

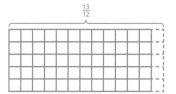

$\frac{13}{12}$

Unit 3 ■ Focus on Number and Operations—Fractions  **181**

## Mathematical Practices

| MP1 | **Make sense of problems and persevere in solving them.** |
|---|---|

**Item 28:** Students evaluate statements that compare the value of a product and one of its factors.

| MP4 | **Model with mathematics.** |
|---|---|

**Item 27:** Students justify their comparison of a product to a factor using a drawing, a model, or expressions.

| MP7 | **Look for and make use of structure.** |
|---|---|

**Item 26:** Students apply the patterns they have observed in previous examples of multiplying by a fraction to solve a problem.

## OBJECTIVE
Solve real world problems by multiplying fractions, mixed numbers, and whole numbers.

## ESSENTIAL QUESTION
Students will use drawings, models, and equations to represent word problems as they continue to build their problem-solving skills.

## PREREQUISITE SKILLS
Use Item H on page 340 of the Foundational Skills Handbook to review multiplying a fraction by a whole number.

## FLUENCY PRACTICE
Fluency practice is available at **sadlierconnect.com**.

## Concept Development

### Understand: How to use a drawing to multiply a whole number by a fraction

■ It is important for students to always identify what information is given in the problem and what they need to find. This problem has "hidden" information that is not directly given to the students. Point out to students that they are asked to answer a question about pies that are *not* apple, but they are not given any information about those pies.

■ Discuss with students ways they can find the number of pies that are not apple. Some students will reason intuitively that if $\frac{1}{3}$ of the pies are apple, then $\frac{2}{3}$ of them are *not* apple.

✏ Ask students to explain the meaning of the expression and have students share their drawings.

---

**Lesson 21**

## Problem Solving: Multiply Fractions and Mixed Numbers

**Essential Question:** How can you use the multiplication of fractions, mixed numbers, and whole numbers to solve real world problems?

### Guided Instruction

In this lesson you will solve word problems using the multiplication of fractions, mixed numbers, and whole numbers.

**Understand: How to use a drawing to multiply a whole number by a fraction**

> On a typical day, Stan's Restaurant sells 9 homemade pies. If $\frac{1}{3}$ of the homemade pies sold are apple, how many apple pies are sold each day? How many are not apple?

To find how many homemade pies are apple, find $\frac{1}{3}$ of 9, or $\frac{1}{3} \times 9$. Use a drawing to represent the situation.

Draw 9 pies. Separate the 9 pies into thirds. $\frac{1}{3}$ are apple pies. The rest are *not* apple pies.

$\frac{1}{3}$ of the homemade pies sold are apple

$\frac{2}{3}$ of the homemade pies sold are *not* apple

The drawing shows that 3 pies are apple and 6 pies are *not* apple.

You can also find the answers by multiplying.

$\frac{1}{3} \times 9 = \frac{9}{3} = 3$. Three homemade pies are apple.

To find how many homemade pies are *not* apple, multiply 9 by $\frac{2}{3}$.

$\frac{2}{3} \times 9 = \frac{18}{3} = 6$. Six homemade pies are *not* apple.

▷ On a typical day, Stan's Restaurant sells 3 apple pies and 6 pies that are not apple.

✏ Use a drawing to represent and evaluate $\frac{3}{4} \times 8$.

$$\frac{3}{4} \times 8 = 6$$

---

## Support English Language Learners

Review some of the mathematical terms seen throughout this lesson, such as area, equation, expression, and equivalent. Write the terms on the board and say them aloud with students. Allow students to share their understanding of what each term means, reinforcing their usage and meanings as needed to increase comprehension levels. Give students additional support as they provide models and examples of the terms.

Lesson 21

Guided Instruction

**Understand:** How to find the area of a rectangle with mixed-number side lengths.

> Ted is making a wall tapestry that is $3\frac{1}{2}$ feet by $4\frac{2}{5}$ feet. What is the area of the tapestry?

**Method 1**

Make a drawing and use logical reasoning.

The width is $3\frac{1}{2}$ feet, and the length is $4\frac{2}{5}$ feet.

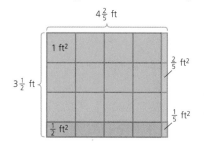

$4\frac{2}{5}$ ft

1 ft²    $\frac{2}{5}$ ft²

$3\frac{1}{2}$ ft    $\frac{1}{5}$ ft²

$\frac{1}{2}$ ft²

There are 12 squares that each represent 1 square foot.

There are 3 rectangles that each represent $\frac{2}{5}$ square foot.

There are 4 rectangles that each represent $1 \times \frac{1}{2}$, or $\frac{1}{2}$ square foot.

There is one rectangle that represents $\frac{2}{5} \times \frac{1}{2}$, or $\frac{1}{5}$ square foot.

$12 \text{ ft}^2 + \frac{6}{5} \text{ ft}^2 + \frac{4}{2} \text{ ft}^2 + \frac{1}{5} \text{ ft}^2 = 15\frac{2}{5} \text{ ft.}^2$

**Method 2**

Use the area formula for a rectangle to write an equation. Then, solve the equation.

| | |
|---|---|
| $A = \ell \times w$ | The area formula. |
| $A = 4\frac{2}{5} \times 3\frac{1}{2}$ | Substitute the length and width values. |
| $A = \frac{22}{5} \times \frac{7}{2}$ | Rewrite the mixed numbers as fractions. |
| $A = \frac{154}{10}$ | Multiply. |
| $A = 15\frac{4}{10} = 15\frac{2}{5}$ | Write the answer as a mixed number. |

➡ The area of the wall tapestry is $15\frac{2}{5}$ square feet.

## Math-to-Math Connection

**Arithmetic and Geometry** An important concept in geometry is being able to find the area of various figures. The side lengths of these figures may be whole numbers, fractions, mixed numbers, variables, or expressions. Creating and utilizing visual models will benefit students as they learn to apply strategies to find the areas of increasingly complex figures in geometry.

**Understand:** How to find the area of a rectangle with mixed-number side lengths.

■ In Method 1, the diagram represents the whole tapestry. The length and width of each red rectangle are 1 ft, so the area of each is 1 ft². The width of each blue rectangle is $\frac{2}{5}$ ft and the length is 1 ft, so the area of each is $\frac{2}{5} \times 1$, or $\frac{2}{5}$ ft². The length of each purple rectangle is $\frac{1}{2}$ ft and the width is 1 ft, so the area of each is $\frac{1}{2} \times 1$, or $\frac{1}{2}$ ft². The length of each green rectangle is $\frac{1}{2}$ ft and the width is $\frac{2}{5}$ ft, so the area is $\frac{1}{2} \times \frac{2}{5}$, or $\frac{1}{5}$ ft².

■ Some students may be able to better visualize the fractional parts if the original drawing shows five whole columns and 4 whole rows. Model dividing the last column into fifths, and then discuss why $\frac{2}{5}$ are needed and the other $\frac{3}{5}$ are discarded. Repeat the same process with the bottom row, dividing it in half and discarding the unneeded part.

■ Show students the fractions $\frac{6}{5}$ and $\frac{4}{2}$ and can be rewritten as $1\frac{1}{5}$ and 2, respectively, in the equation: $12 + \frac{6}{5} + \frac{4}{2} + \frac{1}{5} = 12 + 1\frac{1}{5} + 2 + \frac{1}{5} = 15\frac{2}{5}$. Have students discuss how to use the Commutative Property of Addition to add these numbers using mental math.

■ In Method 2, some students may need additional support writing mixed numbers as improper fractions. Ask students to write 4 as a fraction, and then ask them to rewrite it as an equivalent fraction with a denominator of 5. Once the fractions have common denominators, the improper fraction $\frac{20}{5}$ can be added to $\frac{2}{5}$.

# Guided Instruction

**Connect: What you know about multiplication with fractions, mixed numbers, and whole numbers to solve problems** Use this page to help students strengthen their problem-solving strategies involving word problems.

■ After reading the problem, ask students how many of them think they could solve the problem on their own. This type of word problem can be very challenging for students, and many will not know how to approach the solution. Explain that breaking a problem into parts and solving it step-by-step is a strategy that they can apply when independently solving many real-world problems.

■ Review the key information in Step 1. Suggest students define a variable for each type of tree: $m$ = maple, $k$ = oak, and $p$ = pine. Model how to rewrite the key information as equations: $m = 30$, $k = \frac{3}{4} \times m$, and $p = 1\frac{4}{5} \times k$. Using these equations, students can substitute the equation for $k$ into the equation for $p$, as shown in Step 2.

■ In Step 4, point out that the factors are not rounded to the nearest whole number, but to numbers that are easy to compute with mentally. Suggest that students carefully consider the numbers involved when making an estimate, rather than automatically rounding to the nearest whole number.

## Guided Instruction

**Connect: What you know about multiplication with fractions, mixed numbers, and whole numbers to solve problems**

In Doug's backyard, an oak tree is $\frac{3}{4}$ as tall as a maple tree. A pine tree is $1\frac{4}{5}$ times as tall as the oak tree. The maple tree is 30 feet tall. What is the height of the pine tree?

**Step 1**

Identify the key information: The maple tree is 30 feet tall.
The oak tree is $\frac{3}{4}$ as tall as the maple tree.
The pine tree is $1\frac{4}{5}$ times as tall as the oak tree.

**Step 2**

Write an equation for the situation. Use $p$ to represent the height of the pine tree.

height of maple tree

$$p = 1\frac{4}{5} \times \frac{3}{4} \times 30$$

height of oak tree

**Step 3**

Solve the equation.

$p = 1\frac{4}{5} \times \frac{3}{4} \times 30$

$p = \frac{9}{5} \times \frac{3}{4} \times \frac{30}{1}$    Write the mixed and whole numbers as fractions.

$p = \frac{9 \times 3 \times 30}{5 \times 4 \times 1}$    Multiply numerators and multiply denominators

$p = \frac{810}{20} = 40\frac{10}{20} = 40\frac{1}{2}$    Simplify.

**Step 4**

Estimate to check the reasonableness of your answer.

$\frac{3}{4}$ of 30 is a little more than $\frac{3}{4}$ of 28 which is 21.

$1\frac{4}{5}$ is close to 2, and $2 \times 21 = 42$

42 is close to $40\frac{1}{2}$, so $40\frac{1}{2}$ is a reasonable answer.

➡ The height of the pine tree is $40\frac{1}{2}$ feet.

## Math-to-Real-World Connection

**Stamp Collecting** Philately, or the study of postage stamps and their use, includes stamp collecting. It is a popular hobby, attracting about 20 million participants in the United States alone. People have been collecting stamps since Great Britain issued the first adhesive postage stamp in 1840. Stamps come in all sizes. They are printed in sheets that contain many copies of one or more stamps. One stamp measures $\frac{7}{8}$ inches long and $1\frac{1}{3}$ inches wide. It is printed on a sheet that is 20 stamps long and 8 stamps wide. Have students draw a model and write an equation to find the length and width in inches of one sheet of stamps.

Lesson 21

Guided Practice

**Use the given drawing or model to solve each problem.**

1. Christine is paid $12 an hour to stock shelves at a grocery store. Jon gets paid $\frac{5}{6}$ as much as Christine to bag groceries. How much does Jon get paid per hour? 12 circles represent $12. Separate the twelve $1 into sixths. This is six groups of $2. Since Jon gets paid $\frac{5}{6}$ as much, only consider 5 of the 6 groups, which is 5 × $2, or $10. Check: $\frac{5}{6} \times 12 = \frac{60}{6}$, or 10.

10
Jon gets paid $10 an hour.

2. Ross's gray pet mouse is $5\frac{5}{8}$ inches long. His white mouse is $1\frac{1}{2}$ times as long as his gray mouse. How long is the white mouse? Although this problem does not involve finding an area, an area model can be used. Find the area of each small rectangle. Add those areas together. Express the answer in inches.
$5 \text{ in.}^2 + \frac{5}{2} \text{ in.}^2 + \frac{5}{16} \text{ in.}^2 + \frac{5}{8} \text{ in.}^2 = 8\frac{7}{16} \text{ in.}^2$
The white mouse is $8\frac{7}{16}$ inches long.

$5\frac{5}{8}$ in.

| | 1 in.² | 1 in.² | 1 in.² | 1 in.² | 1 in.² | — $\frac{5}{8}$ in.² |
|---|---|---|---|---|---|---|
| $1\frac{1}{2}$ in. | $\frac{1}{2}$ in.² | $\frac{1}{2}$ in.² | $\frac{1}{2}$ in.² | $\frac{1}{2}$ in.² | $\frac{1}{2}$ in.² | — $\frac{5}{16}$ in.² |

**Solve. Show your work.**

3. $8 \times \frac{5}{6} \times 1\frac{3}{5} = \frac{8}{1} \times \frac{5}{6} \times \frac{8}{5} = \frac{320}{30} = \frac{32}{3} = 10\frac{2}{3}$

4. A produce company is filling an order of vegetables for a local restaurant. The restaurant ordered $3\frac{3}{4}$ small crates of onions. Each crate of onions weighs $4\frac{1}{2}$ pounds.

   a. Write an expression to represent the total weight of the restaurant's order. $3\frac{3}{4} \times 4\frac{1}{2}$

   b. How many pounds of onions did the restaurant order? $16\frac{7}{8}$

   c. If each pound of vegetables costs $2, how much did the restaurant spend? Write your answer as a mixed number and a decimal. $\$33\frac{3}{4}$ or $33.75

**Think·Pair·Share**

MP1 5. Write a story problem that represents the expression $\frac{5}{6} \times 7$.
Sample problem: Rhonda went to a 7 mile trail to jog. She jogged $\frac{5}{6}$ of the way before walking the rest of the way. How far did she jog?

## Observational Assessment

Use page 185 to assess students' ability to solve word problems that require multiplying fractions to solve. Note students who have difficulty writing expressions based on the context of the problems.

### Think·Pair·Share

**Peer Collaboration** After students have written their story problems, have them form small groups and share their work. Students should write an expression for each group member's story problem to make sure the problem matches the given expression. Encourage groups to discuss questions such as these:

- *How are $\frac{5}{6}$ and 7 represented in your story problem?*

- *How is multiplication represented in your story problem?*

- *Does your story problem include a question that represents the product of $\frac{5}{6}$ and 7?*

### Return to the Essential Question

Reread the Lesson 21 Essential Question on page 182: *How can you use the multiplication of fractions, mixed numbers, and whole numbers to solve real world problems?*

Ask volunteers to use what they learned in this lesson to answer this question. (Possible response: I can use a drawing or an equation to represent the problem. I can rewrite mixed numbers as improper fractions to make them easier to multiply.)

## Mathematical Practices

Mathematical Practice Standards underline the teaching and understanding of all concepts and skills presented. The emphasis of specific practices is noted throughout the guided and independent practice of this lesson.

| MP1 | **Make sense of problems and persevere in solving them.** |
|---|---|

**Item 5:** Students write a story problem to represent an expression.

# Independent Practice

## Concept Application

Students may work independently on these pages in the classroom or at home. They may refer to the first four pages of the lesson to revisit the instruction or to see a worked-out example.

**Common Errors** and **Teaching Tips** may help you support student learning either in the classroom or as a follow-up for work done at home.

## Common Errors

### Item 1

Students may assume the product of 10 and $\frac{2}{5}$ is the sale price. Point out that $\frac{2}{5}$ is the fractional amount *off*, so the product is the amount subtracted from the original price.

### Item 3

Students may try to separate the 16 pieces of fruit into three equal groups. Point out that there are different fractional parts represented in the same whole.

## Teaching Tips

### Items 3–4

If students struggle to determine how to model the problems, suggest that they look back at the models used in this and earlier lessons.

---

### Independent Practice

**Use the given model to solve each problem.**

1. The original price of a comic book is $10, but it is on sale for $\frac{2}{5}$ off the original price. What is the sale price of the comic book?

6

The sale price of the comic book is $6.

10 circles represent $10. Separate the ten $1 into fifths. This is five groups of $2. Since the comic is on sale for $\frac{2}{5}$ off the original price, only consider 3 of the 5 groups, which is $3 \times \$2$, or $6. Check: $\frac{2}{5} \times 10 = \frac{20}{5} = 4$, and $10 - 4 = 6$.

2. A photograph is $3\frac{1}{2}$ inches by $4\frac{1}{2}$ inches. Find the area of the photograph.

Find the area of each smaller rectangle inside the larger rectangle. Then add those areas together.

$12 \text{ in.}^2 + 3 \text{ in.}^2 + \frac{1}{2} \text{ in.}^2 + \frac{1}{4} \text{ in.}^2$
$= 12 \text{ in.}^2 + 3 \text{ in.}^2 + \frac{2}{4} \text{ in.}^2 + \frac{1}{4} \text{ in.}^2$
$= 15 \text{ in.}^2 + \frac{3}{4} \text{ in.}^2$
$= 15\frac{3}{4} \text{ in.}^2$

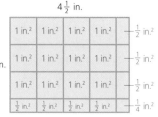

$4\frac{1}{2}$ in.

$3\frac{1}{2}$ in.

The area of the photograph is $15\frac{3}{4}$ square inches.

**Make a model to represent each problem and solve.**

3. A basket contains 16 pieces of fruit. $\frac{1}{4}$ are bananas, $\frac{1}{2}$ are apples, and the rest are oranges. How many oranges are there?

There are 4 oranges in the basket of fruit.

4. Cheng made a batch of her famous seafood gumbo. She made $5\frac{1}{2}$ servings of $1\frac{2}{3}$ cups. How many cups of gumbo did Cheng make?

$5\frac{1}{2}$

$1\frac{2}{3}$

She made $9\frac{1}{6}$ cups of seafood gumbo.

---

## Writing About Math

▸ **Write an Informative Text** Ask students to write a paragraph that explains how to create a visual model to represent multiplying fractions, mixed numbers, and whole numbers to solve real-world problems. Students should assume that their audience is not familiar with this process and all details are important. Be sure that students include examples from their text to support their writing.

Ask students to share their writing with a peer to determine if they have missed any details that would be important in the modeling process. Have students return the papers and revise.

Lesson 21

Independent Practice

**Evaluate each expression. Show your work.**

5. $8\frac{1}{2} \times 1\frac{1}{2}$

$\frac{17}{2} \times \frac{3}{2}$

$\frac{51}{4}$

$12\frac{3}{4}$

$\underline{12\frac{3}{4}}$

6. $\frac{2}{9} \times 2 \times 3\frac{7}{12}$

$\frac{2}{9} \times 2 \times \frac{43}{12}$

$\frac{172}{108}$

$1\frac{64}{108}$

$1\frac{16}{27}$

$\underline{1\frac{16}{27}}$

7. $\frac{8}{11} \times \frac{9}{12} \times 6$

$\frac{432}{132}$

$3\frac{36}{132}$

$3\frac{9}{33} = 3\frac{3}{11}$

$\underline{3\frac{3}{11}}$

8. $2\frac{2}{3} \times (\frac{9}{10} + \frac{4}{5})$

$2\frac{2}{3} \times (\frac{9}{10} + \frac{8}{10})$

$2\frac{2}{3} \times 1\frac{7}{10}$

$\frac{8}{3} \times \frac{17}{10}$

$\frac{136}{30}$

$4\frac{16}{30} = 4\frac{8}{15}$

$\underline{4\frac{8}{15}}$

**Solve the problems.**

MP1 9. Louis has 20 rocks in his rock collection. $\frac{3}{10}$ of the rocks are sedimentary, and $\frac{2}{5}$ of the rocks are metamorphic. The rest of the rocks are igneous. How many igneous rocks does Louis have in his collection?

**Show your work.** $\frac{3}{10}$ sedimentary $\times$ 20 total rocks =
6 sedimentary rocks; $\frac{2}{5}$ metamorphic $\times$ 20 total rocks = 8 metamorphic rocks.
20 total rocks − (6 sedimentary rocks + 8 metamorphic rocks) = 6 igneous rocks.

**Answer** Louis has 6 igneous rocks in his collection.

MP1 10. Every weekday, Nelly runs $3\frac{1}{2}$ laps around her school track, which is $\frac{3}{5}$ of a mile long. How far does she run in a week?

**Show your work.**
$3\frac{1}{2} \times \frac{3}{5} \times 5$

**Answer** Nelly runs $10\frac{1}{2}$ miles in a week.

## Mathematical Practices

| MP1 | Make sense of problems and persevere in solving them. |
|---|---|

**Item 9:** Students analyze and plan a solution to a real-world problem.

**Item 10:** Students relate a verbal description to an equation to find a solution.

## Common Errors

### Items 5-8

Students may multiply the whole numbers together and then multiply the fractions together to get the product. Remind students that a mixed number is the sum of its whole number part and its fraction part. So, for example, $8\frac{1}{2} \times 1\frac{1}{2}$, is equivalent to $(8 + \frac{1}{2})(1 + \frac{1}{2})$. This product cannot be found simply by multiplying 8 by 1 and $\frac{1}{2}$ by $\frac{1}{2}$. Rather, the Distributive Property must be used twice. You might demonstrate the steps of doing this to show that the product is actually $8 \times 1 + \frac{1}{2} \times 1 + 8 \times \frac{1}{2} + \frac{1}{2} \times \frac{1}{2}$. This will help students see that it is much easier to rewrite the mixed numbers as fractions before multiplying!

### Item 10

Some students may calculate $3\frac{1}{2} \times \frac{3}{5} \times 7$ because there are 7 days in a week. Point out that the first sentence says that Nelly runs on "weekdays." Remind students that the weekdays are the five days from Monday through Friday.

## Teaching Tips

### Items 6 -7

Suggest that students rewrite the whole numbers as fractions to reduce the risk of multiplication errors.

### Item 8

Remind students to utilize their previous skills in adding fractions with unlike denominators in order evaluate the expression.

# Independent Practice

## Common Errors

### Item 13

Students may give their answers to Parts **a** and **b** as mixed numbers, rather than in dollars and cents. Remind students to write the fractional part as an equivalent fraction with a denominator of 100. Since there are 100 pennies in one dollar, each numerator is now equal to the number of pennies in one dollar.

## Teaching Tips

### Item 12

Remind students to include the proper unit with their answers. Area is always written in square units.

---

### Independent Practice

MP3 **11.** Walter says that $2\frac{2}{3} \times 5\frac{1}{7}$ is equivalent to $2 \times 5 + \frac{2}{3} \times \frac{1}{7}$. Explain why Walter is not correct.

Possible answer: $2\frac{2}{3} \times 5\frac{1}{7}$ is equal to $(2 + \frac{2}{3}) \times (5 + \frac{1}{7})$. To find the product of two sums, you have to use the distributive property twice. When you do this, you get $2 \times 5 + 2 \times \frac{1}{7} + \frac{2}{3} \times 5 + \frac{2}{3} \times \frac{1}{7}$. Walter's expression does not include all of these addends.

MP2 **12.** A 1 dollar bill is about $6\frac{1}{10}$ inches in length and $2\frac{3}{5}$ inches in width. If you place two 1 dollar bills side by side, what is the area of the rectangle formed by the bills?

**Show your work.**

$2 \times 6\frac{1}{10} \times 2\frac{3}{5}$

$2 \times \frac{61}{10} \times \frac{13}{5}$

$\frac{1586}{50}$

$31\frac{36}{50} = 31\frac{18}{25}$

**Answer** <u>The area formed by the two one-dollar bills is $31\frac{18}{25}$ square inches.</u>

MP2 **13.** Jerry is shipping his bike, which weighs $34\frac{4}{5}$ pounds.

**a.** To calculate the shipping charge in dollars, Shipping Company A will multiply the weight of his bike by $2\frac{1}{5}$. How much will Shipping Company A charge Jerry? Show your work.

Shipping Company A: $2\frac{1}{5} \times 34\frac{4}{5} = \frac{11}{5} \times \frac{174}{5} = 76\frac{14}{25}$

Shipping Company A will charge Jerry $76.56.

**b.** Shipping Company B will multiply the weight of the bike by 3 and then subtract $15. How much will Shipping Company B charge Jerry? Show your work.

Shipping Company B: $3 \times 34\frac{4}{5} = 104\frac{2}{5}$; $104\frac{2}{5} - 15 = 89\frac{2}{5}$

Shipping Company B will charge Jerry $89.40.

**c.** Which company will charge Jerry less?

Shipping Company A will charge Jerry less.

---

## Mathematical Practices

| MP2 | **Reason abstractly and quantitatively.** |
| --- | --- |

**Item 12:** Students represent a real-word problem using symbols, use mathematics to find the solution, and then interpret the solution in the context of the problem.

**Item 13:** Students make sense of quantities and their relationships in a complex problem situation.

| MP3 | **Construct viable arguments and critique the reasoning of others.** |
| --- | --- |

**Item 11:** Students construct an argument to explain why another student's work is incorrect.

---

Lesson 21

Independent Practice

MP3 **14.** Samuel says that $7 \times (\frac{1}{2} \times 2\frac{3}{4})$ is equivalent to $(7 \times \frac{1}{2}) \times 2\frac{3}{4}$. Do you agree with Samuel?

▸ **Show your work.**

$7 \times (\frac{1}{2} \times 2\frac{3}{4}) = 9\frac{5}{8}$

$(7 \times \frac{1}{2}) \times 2\frac{3}{4} = 9\frac{5}{8}$

**Answer** I agree with Samuel. Multiplication is associative, so the way the factors are grouped doesn't matter. Both expressions are equivalent to $9\frac{5}{8}$.

MP2 **15.** The area model below represents $1 \times 1$. Use the model to explain why the product of two mixed numbers will always be greater than one.

**Answer** Possible answer: You can model the product with a rectangle whose side lengths are greater than 1. Because the side lengths of the square are 1 unit, the square will fit inside the rectangle. Therefore, the area of the rectangle is greater than the area of the square, which is 1 square unit.

MP3 **16.** Lucia and Julia evaluated the expression $2\frac{2}{3} \times 1\frac{4}{5}$ two different ways. Lucia wanted to multiply using decimals, so she evaluated $2.67 \times 1.8$. Julia wanted to multiply using equivalent fractions, so she evaluated $\frac{8}{3} \times \frac{9}{5}$. If both girls multiplied correctly, whose answer is accurate? Explain your answer.

▸ **Show your work.**

$2\frac{2}{3}$ is exactly $\frac{8}{3}$. 2.67 is $2\frac{2}{3}$ rounded to the nearest hundredth.

**Answer** Possible answer: Julia's answer is the most accurate because there was no approximation of either factor to arrive at the product.

## Teaching Tips

### Item 15
Ask students to discuss the validity of the statement in terms of scaling. Multiplying two mixed numbers is multiplying a number greater than 1 by a fraction greater than 1, so the product will be greater than the original number (which is greater than 1).

### Item 16
Discuss how working with fractions rather than decimals may be better in situations where the answer needs to be precise.

## Mathematical Practices

| MP2 | Reason abstractly and quantitatively. |
|---|---|

**Item 15:** Students reason abstractly and quantitatively to explain why the product of two mixed numbers must be greater than one.

| MP3 | Construct viable arguments and critique the reasoning of others. |
|---|---|

**Item 14:** Students share their reasoning with others.

**Item 16:** Students analyze a problem situation and explain the most accurate approach.

## OBJECTIVE

**Use models and the relationship between multiplication and division to divide unit fractions by whole numbers.**

## ESSENTIAL QUESTION

Tell students that, in this lesson, they will use models such as rectangles, number lines, and fraction strips to represent the division of a unit fraction by a whole number. Remind students that a unit fraction is a fraction with a numerator of 1.

## FLUENCY PRACTICE

Fluency practice is available at **sadlierconnect.com**.

## Concept Development

### Understand: How to use a model to divide a unit fraction by a whole number

■ Expect students to be able to divide a unit fraction by a whole number and a whole number by a unit fraction. General fraction division is covered in Grade 6.

■ Remind students that 0 is a whole number, but that division by 0 is not defined. Therefore, only non-zero whole numbers can be used when dividing a quantity by a whole number. Throughout this lesson, when the term *whole number* is used, it implies a *non-zero whole number.*

■ Be sure students understand that the denominator of a unit fraction represents *equal* parts and the importance of that definition when making models of fractions.

---

**Lesson 22 — Divide Unit Fractions by Whole Numbers**

Essential Question:
How can you divide a unit fraction by a whole number?

### Guided Instruction

In this lesson you will divide unit fractions by whole numbers.

**Understand: How to use a model to divide a unit fraction by a whole number**

> Jake is planting a vegetable garden. He plans to divide the garden into four equal sections and use $\frac{1}{4}$ for peppers. He will use the other three sections for zucchini, lettuce, and kale. Jake divides the area for peppers into 3 equal parts to plant bell peppers, jalapeño peppers, and pimento peppers. What fraction of the entire garden will be used to plant bell peppers?

To find what fraction of the entire garden will be used to plant bell peppers, divide $\frac{1}{4}$, the fraction of the garden used to plant peppers, by the 3 types of peppers: $\frac{1}{4} \div 3$.

**Remember!**
A unit fraction has 1 in the numerator. Some examples are $\frac{1}{4}$, $\frac{1}{10}$, and $\frac{1}{16}$.

Use a model or drawing to represent the problem. First, draw the four equal sections of the garden.

| peppers | zucchini | lettuce | kale |
|---------|----------|---------|------|
| $\frac{1}{4}$ | $\frac{1}{4}$ | $\frac{1}{4}$ | $\frac{1}{4}$ |

Divide each of the 4 sections into 3 equal parts. Shade the part of the garden used to plant bell peppers.

| peppers | zucchini | lettuce | kale |
|---------|----------|---------|------|
| $\frac{1}{12}$ bell | | | |
| jalapeño | | | |
| pimento | | | |

One part is shaded, and there are 12 parts in all. So, $\frac{1}{4} \div 3 = \frac{1}{12}$.

➜ $\frac{1}{12}$ of the garden will be used to plant bell peppers.

---

## Support English Language Learners

It may be helpful to review fraction terminology with English language learners by reviewing what constitutes a *unit fraction.* They may benefit from a reminder of *numerator* and *denominator* as well. Write a few examples of fractions on the board, with at least one being a unit fraction. Provide a sentence for students to repeat to you as you point to each fraction: *This fraction is/is not a unit fraction because it does/does not have* 1 *in the numerator.*

Remind students that when written as a fraction, a whole number always has 1 in the denominator and a unit fraction always has 1 in the numerator.

Lesson 22

Guided Instruction

**Understand:** How to use a number line or fraction strips to divide a unit fraction by a whole number

> Max had a strip of wood that was $\frac{1}{2}$ yard long. He cut the strip into 4 pieces of equal length to use as the sides of a picture frame. How long was each of the four pieces?

To find the length of each piece, divide $\frac{1}{2}$ yard into 4 equal parts: $\frac{1}{2} \div 4$.
You can solve this using a number line or fraction strips.

**Method 1** Use a number line.
Draw a number line divided into intervals of $\frac{1}{2}$ yard.
Divide each $\frac{1}{2}$-yard interval into four equal intervals.
Each smaller interval is $\frac{1}{8}$ yard.

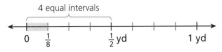

**Method 2** Use fraction strips.
Use two $\frac{1}{2}$ strips to represent 1 yard.
Find the fraction strips that can be used to evenly divide $\frac{1}{2}$ into 4 equal parts.
Four $\frac{1}{8}$ strips will divide $\frac{1}{2}$ into 4 equal parts.

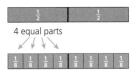

➡ Each piece will be $\frac{1}{8}$ yard long.

✏ Ryan said, "To divide a unit fraction by a whole number, you just multiply the denominator by the whole number." Show that Ryan's conclusion works for the two problems you have seen in this lesson.

$\frac{1}{4} \div 3 = \frac{1}{4 \times 3} = \frac{1}{12}$ and $\frac{1}{2} \div 4 = \frac{1}{2 \times 4} = \frac{1}{8}$

Unit 3 ■ Focus on Number and Operations—Fractions **191**

**Understand:** How to use a number line or fraction strips to divide a unit fraction by a whole number

■ Have students use quantitative reasoning to determine the relationship of the quotient to the fraction in $\frac{1}{2} \div 4$. They should deduce that the quotient will be less than $\frac{1}{2}$ because $\frac{1}{2}$ is being divided into 4 parts.

■ After completing the example by using the two methods provided, challenge students to make a rectangular model to represent the problem.

■ Ask students for ways to justify that the answer, $\frac{1}{8}$ yard, is correct. If they have difficulty, guide them to remember how multiplication can be used to check the answer to a division problem.

✏ After students have shown that Ryan's conclusion is true, have them explain why they think Ryan's method works.

## Math-to-Math Connection

**Geometry** Students have used area models when multiplying. Students may also have realized that the shaded area of an area model can also represent a division fact.

Area models can also be extended to illustrate the division of a unit fraction by a whole number. For example, draw an area model that represents $\frac{1}{8} \times 4$. Ask students how the drawing illustrates the meaning of $\frac{1}{8} \times 4 = \frac{1}{2}$. Then ask how the model could be used to show the meaning of $\frac{1}{2} \div 4 = \frac{1}{8}$.

| | 1 | 2 | 3 | 4 |
|---|---|---|---|---|
| $\frac{1}{8}$ | | | | |

$\frac{1}{8} \times 4 = \frac{1}{8} + \frac{1}{8} + \frac{1}{8} + \frac{1}{8} = \frac{4}{8}$

**Connect:** Dividing a unit fraction by a whole number by relating division to multiplication Use this page to help students understand how they can use the relationship of multiplication and division to divide a unit fraction by a whole number.

■ Some students may benefit from a review on how to multiply fractions before the presentation.

■ Rectangular models may be helpful in reinforcing the concept that dividing by a whole number, such as 3, is the same as multiplying by a unit fraction with the whole number in the denominator, in this case $\frac{1}{3}$.

■ Compare the division method used here to Ryan's method from the bottom of page 191. This method multiplies the unit fraction by a unit fraction with the whole number in the denominator. Ryan's method multiplies the denominator of the unit fraction by the whole number. In both methods, the numerator of the product is 1, and the denominator is the product of the whole number and the denominator of the unit fraction.

✏️ Students should explain how the inverse relationship between multiplication and division can be used to check the answer.

---

## Guided Instruction

**Connect:** Dividing a unit fraction by a whole number by relating division to multiplication

> The May family plans to use $\frac{1}{5}$ of their monthly budget for recreation. Mrs. May further divides the recreation funds into 3 parts that are equal in dollars. One part is going to be used for family day trips. What fraction of the family's budget is going toward day trips?

To find what fraction of the family's budget is going toward day trips, divide the $\frac{1}{5}$ family recreation budget by 3. To solve, use what you know about the relationship between multiplication and division.

**Step 1**

Write a division expression to represent the problem. Mrs. May divides $\frac{1}{5}$ of the family's monthly recreation funds by 3.

$$\frac{1}{5} \div 3$$

**Remember!**
Dividing a number by 3 means finding $\frac{1}{3}$ of the number. So, it is the same as multiplying the number by $\frac{1}{3}$.

**Step 2**

Rewrite the division expression as a multiplication expression.

$$\frac{1}{5} \div 3 = \frac{1}{3} \times \frac{1}{5}$$

**Step 3**

Multiply the fractions.

$$\frac{1}{3} \times \frac{1}{5} = \frac{1}{15}$$

➡ The May family will spend $\frac{1}{15}$ of their entire recreation budget on day trips.

✏️ How can you check the answer to this problem?
Possible response: I can multiply: $\frac{1}{15} \times 3 = \frac{3}{15} = \frac{1}{5}$. The monthly recreation budget is $\frac{1}{5}$. The answer to the problem is correct.

---

## Math-to-Physical Education Connection

**Square Dancing** Though there are lots of types of dance that are taught in physical education, square dancing consists of eight dancers that form a square. Have students write a paragraph about square dancing. Have them research information about square dancing ensuring that they discover that traditional western square dance squares consist of four couples, or eight people. Next, have them determine how they can use unit fractions to divide the class to create square dance squares. Ensure they use language such as *To create square dance squares, we have to divide the class into eighths.* Have students write the division equation to support their paragraph. For an extra challenge, ask them how they can create squares that consist of other classes in their school, or even the entire school.

## Guided Practice

1. Use the model and steps a–c below to find the quotient of $\frac{1}{5} \div 3$.

 a. The rectangle is divided into __5__ equal parts. Each part is $\frac{1}{5}$ of the whole.

 b. Draw __two__ horizontal lines to divide the rectangle into 3 equal parts. Shade $\frac{1}{15}$.

 c. What is $\frac{1}{5}$ divided by 3? __$\frac{1}{15}$__

2. Use the number line and steps a–c below to find the quotient of $\frac{1}{4} \div 2$.

 a. To start, the number line is divided into intervals of __$\frac{1}{4}$__.

 b. Divide each $\frac{1}{4}$ into __2__ equal intervals. Each smaller interval represents __$\frac{1}{8}$__.

 c. What is $\frac{1}{4}$ divided by 2? __$\frac{1}{8}$__

**For exercises 3–4, use the fraction strips.**

3. Look at the top fraction strip. What fraction of the whole strip does the green rectangle show? __$\frac{1}{3}$__

4. Look at the bottom fraction strip. Into how many equal parts is the green rectangle partitioned? __4__ What fraction of the whole fraction strip does one of these parts show? __$\frac{1}{12}$__

### ☝☝ Think·Pair·Share

MP4 5. What division equation does the model used for exercises 3 and 4 represent? Explain how the model shows the quotient.
Possible answer: The model shows $\frac{1}{3} \div 4 = n$. One part of the bottom fraction strip is $\frac{1}{12}$. So, $\frac{1}{3} \div 4 = \frac{1}{4} \times \frac{1}{3} = \frac{1}{12}$.

Unit 3 ▪ Focus on Number and Operations—Fractions **193**

---

## Observational Assessment

Use page 193 to assess whether students are able to divide a unit fraction by a whole number. The models presented earlier in the lesson—rectangular grids, number lines, and fraction strips—are used in the exercises on this page. Even though students may be able to solve the problems without completing each step or using the models, ask them to use the steps and models to help solidify their understanding.

### ☝☝ Think·Pair·Share

**Peer Collaboration** Separate students into groups of four. Each group should work together to write the division equation. Assign each of the following tasks to one member of each group.

1. Identify the unit fraction being divided.
2. Identify the divisor.
3. Write the quotient.
4. Write the equation.

At each step, the person should refer to the fraction strip model to justify his or her answer. The group should agree on the answer to each step before moving to the next step. After all groups have finished, ask:

- *How does the model help you find the quotient?*

- *What other models could you use to represent this division equation?*

- *What multiplication equation does the model represent?*

### Return to the Essential Question

Reread the Lesson 22 Essential Question on page 190: *How can you divide a unit fraction by a whole number?*

Ask volunteers to use what they learned in this lesson to answer this question. (Possible response: I can use a model to represent the unit fraction and then divide it into parts to show the division by a whole number. I can multiply the unit fraction by a fraction with 1 in the numerator and the whole number in the denominator.)

---

## Mathematical Practices

Mathematical Practice Standards underline the teaching and understanding of all concepts and skills presented. The emphasis of specific practices is noted throughout the guided and independent practice of this lesson.

| MP4 | **Model with mathematics.** |
| --- | --- |

**Item 5:** Students use fraction strip models to explain the division of a unit fraction by a whole number.

# Independent Practice

## Concept Application

Students may work independently on these pages in the classroom or at home. They may refer to the first four pages of the lesson to revisit the instruction or to see a worked-out example.

**Common Errors** and **Teaching Tips** may help you support student learning either in the classroom or as a follow-up for work done at home.

## Teaching Tips

### Items 1–2

To complete these items, students can refer to the models on page 190. Point out that the labels $\frac{1}{4}$ and $\frac{1}{6}$ represent the columns.

### Items 3–5

Students can refer to the number lines on page 191 to help them complete these items.

### Item 6

Students may want to refer to the steps in exercises 3–5 to create the model.

## Independent Practice

**For exercises 1–2, use the models to answer the questions below.**

1. $\frac{1}{4}$

a. The vertical lines divide the rectangle into __fourths__. Each column is what fraction of the whole rectangle? $\underline{\frac{1}{4}}$

b. The horizontal lines divide the rectangle into how many equal parts? __4__

c. $\frac{1}{4} \div 4 = \underline{\frac{1}{16}}$

2. $\frac{1}{6}$

a. The vertical lines divide the rectangle into __sixths__. Each column is what fraction of the whole rectangle? $\underline{\frac{1}{6}}$

b. The horizontal lines divide the rectangle into how many equal parts? __3__

c. $\frac{1}{6} \div 3 = \underline{\frac{1}{18}}$

**For exercises 3–5, use the number lines below.**

3. The top number line is divided into __4__ equal parts. What fraction of the number line is one of these parts? $\underline{\frac{1}{4}}$

4. The bottom number line shows $\frac{1}{4}$ divided into __3__ equal parts. What fraction of the number line is one of these parts? $\underline{\frac{1}{12}}$

5. Write the division equation represented by the bottom number line. $\underline{\frac{1}{4} \div 3 = \frac{1}{12}}$

6. Draw a number line model to show $\frac{1}{8}$ divided by 2.

## Writing About Math

▸ **Write an Explanatory Text** Have students pretend they need to teach dividing a unit fraction by a whole number to a person who is not in the class. Ask them to write a paragraph that explains the concept clearly. The text should include the following items.

- One sentence to introduce the concept

- An example with a drawing/model to develop the concept

- A story context that illustrates the concept

Be sure students use precise language and vocabulary in their paragraphs.

MORE ONLINE sadlierconnect.com                                    Lesson 22

### Independent Practice

**To complete exercises 7–9, use the fraction strips below.**

2 equal parts

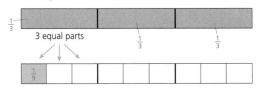

7. The top strip is divided into __5__ equal parts. What fraction of the strip
   is one of these parts? __$\frac{1}{5}$__

8. The bottom strip shows $\frac{1}{5}$ being divided into __2__ equal parts. What
   fraction of the strip is one of these parts? __$\frac{1}{10}$__

9. Write the division equation shown by the model. __$\frac{1}{5} \div 2 = \frac{1}{10}$__

10. Divide $\frac{1}{3}$ by 3. Use the fraction strips below to show the division.

**For exercises 11–14, use what you know about the relationship
between multiplication and division to complete these problems.**

11. $\frac{1}{12} \times 6 = \frac{1}{2}$

    So, this division equation is true:

    $\frac{1}{2} \div 6 = \underline{\frac{1}{12}}$.

12. $\frac{1}{10} \times 2 = \frac{1}{5}$

    So, this division equation is true:

    $\frac{1}{5} \div 2 = \underline{\frac{1}{10}}$.

13. Dividing by 4 is the same as
    multiplying by $\frac{1}{4}$. So, these equations
    show the same situation:

    $\frac{1}{5} \div 4 = \underline{\frac{1}{20}}$ and $\frac{1}{4} \times \frac{1}{5} = \underline{\frac{1}{20}}$.

14. Dividing by 8 is the same as
    multiplying by $\frac{1}{8}$. So, these equations
    show the same situation:

    $\frac{1}{3} \div 8 = \underline{\frac{1}{24}}$ and $\frac{1}{8} \times \frac{1}{3} = \underline{\frac{1}{24}}$.

Unit 3 ■ Focus on Number and Operations—Fractions **195**

## Common Errors

### Item 10

In the second model, students may not
consider the whole rectangle, when
determining the quotient. For example,
students may only consider one of
the 3 parts in the second step and
determine that the quotient is $\frac{1}{3}$. Tell
students to count all of the parts in the
second model to correctly determine the
denominator of the quotient.

## Teaching Tips

### Items 7–9

Students should refer to the fraction
strips on page 191 to help them
complete these items.

### Item 10

Students may want to refer to the steps
in exercises 7–9 to create the model.

## Digital Connection

**Use Drawing Software** Students may use simple drawing software or
applications to create rectangular models, number lines, or fraction strips
to represent the concept of dividing a unit fraction by a whole number.
If this is not available, the Table menu in word processing software
could also be used to create the rectangular models and fraction strips.
Students should use shading and labels to denote the unit fraction and
partitions for the whole number divisor. Encourage students to create
shaded fraction strips for use in the classroom.

## Teaching Tips

### Item 15

Remind students that when answering a multiple choice question it is often helpful to use quantitative reasoning to eliminate incorrect choices. In this item, ask students whether the quotient of a unit fraction divided by a whole number is greater than, equal to, or less than the unit fraction. They can use this reasoning to eliminate 2 of the 4 choices.

### Item 16

Some students may not know how to approach a problem where a completed model is already provided. Have them list the steps they use to find a quotient using a number line. As they write each step, they can identify how it was used in this problem to lead them to the division equation.

### Item 17

It may be helpful for students to use an actual meter stick when solving this problem.

### Item 18

Some students may find it helpful to cut out a paper rectangle to represent the pizza. They can fold it in half to represent the half of the pizza being shared. Then they can fold this into thirds by folding each side into the middle to create 3 equal parts. Before unfolding, they should shade one part to indicate the piece each person will get. Have them unfold the paper to see what fraction of the whole pizza each person will get.

---

**Choose the correct answer.**

15. Sam has $\frac{1}{7}$ meter of rope. He divides it into 2 equal parts. What fraction of a meter is each part of the rope?

   (a.) $\frac{1}{14}$ meter

   b. $\frac{1}{7}$ meter

   c. $\frac{14}{7}$ meter

   d. $\frac{2}{7}$ meter

**Solve the problems.**

MP4 16. The figure is part of a number line model. Explain how the model represents a division equation.
Possible answer: The light yellow rectangle shows $\frac{1}{3}$. This is divided into 4 equal parts. So, $\frac{1}{3} \div 4 = \frac{1}{12}$.

MP3 17. Tricia used a meter stick to help her divide $\frac{1}{4}$ by 5. Explain how she could have done this and give the answer as a fraction of a meter.
Possible answer: $\frac{1}{4}$ of a meter is 25 cm. She divided 25 cm into 5 equal parts and got 5 cm. 5 cm is $\frac{1}{20}$ of a meter because $\frac{5}{100} = \frac{1}{20}$. So, she found that $\frac{1}{4} \div 5$ equals $\frac{1}{20}$.

MP4 18. Three people have $\frac{1}{2}$ of a pizza to share equally. What fraction of a whole pizza will each person get?

   **Show your work. Include a model in your answer and explain the steps you use.**
   Possible answer: First I divided a rectangle into 2 parts to show $\frac{1}{2}$. Then I used horizontal lines to divide $\frac{1}{2}$ into 3 parts. Each person gets $\frac{1}{6}$. I could have made a circle for the model, but the rectangle was easier to draw.

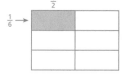

   **Answer** Each person will get $\frac{1}{6}$ of a pizza.

196   Unit 3 ■ Focus on Number and Operations—Fractions

---

## Mathematical Practices

| MP3 | **Construct viable arguments and critique the reasoning of others.** |
|---|---|

**Item 17:** Students analyze a problem situation and explain how using a meter stick helped solve the problem.

| MP4 | **Model with mathematics.** |
|---|---|

**Item 16:** Students explain how a given number line model represents a division equation.

**Item 18:** Students create a model to represent an everyday situation involving division.

Lesson 22

## Independent Practice

MP2 **19.** Vincent has $\frac{1}{3}$ pound of cherries. Create two story situations about Vincent's cherries, one that represents $\frac{1}{3} \div 4$ and another that represent $4 \times \frac{1}{3}$. Include the answers to the problems in your stories.

Possible answer for $\frac{1}{3} \div 4$: Vincent shares the cherries equally with 3 friends. Each person gets $\frac{1}{12}$ of a pound because $\frac{1}{3} \div 4 = \frac{1}{12}$.

Possible answer for $4 \times \frac{1}{3}$: Vincent needs 4 times as many cherries for a recipe. So, he will need $1\frac{1}{3}$ pounds because $4 \times \frac{1}{3} = \frac{4}{3} = 1\frac{1}{3}$.

MP2 **20.** Use your stories from exercise 19 to compare dividing a fraction by 4 with multiplying that fraction by 4. How do the answers compare to the original fractions?

· **Justify your answer using words, drawings, or numbers.**

Possible answer: If you divide a fraction by 4, the answer is less than the original fraction. If you multiply by 4, the answer is greater than the original fraction.

MP2 **21.** Show that $\frac{1}{2} \div 5$ and $\frac{1}{5} \div 2$ result in the same quotient by renaming the fractions in both expressions as decimals.

· **Justify your answer using words, drawings, or numbers.**

Possible answer: $\frac{1}{2} = 0.5$, so $\frac{1}{2} \div 5 = 0.5 \div 5 = 0.1$. $\frac{1}{5} = 0.2$, so $\frac{1}{5} \div 2 = 0.2 \div 2 = 0.1$. Both expressions have a value of 0.1, which is same as $\frac{1}{10}$.

## Teaching Tips

### Item 19

Students should be able to create a story context for problems involving multiplication and division with whole numbers and unit fractions. Students should use quantitative reasoning to determine whether the answers to their problems will be greater than or less than the whole number before actually multiplying or dividing.

### Item 20

After students have answered this question, ask a few volunteers to share their answers. Discuss how writing the expressions in a story context helped them to think more deeply about the difference between the multiplication expression and the division expression.

### Item 21

Have students discuss why it was or wasn't helpful to rename the fractions as decimals before evaluating each expression.

## Mathematical Practices

| MP2 | **Reason abstractly and quantitatively.** |
| --- | --- |

**Item 19:** Students add context to a division and a multiplication by writing story situations to represent them.

**Item 20:** Students attend to the meaning of quantities and operations to understand how dividing a fraction by a whole number compares to multiplying the fraction by the whole number.

**Item 21:** Students rename fractions as decimals to compare two division problems. They justify their conclusions with words, drawings, or numbers.

## OBJECTIVE
Compute and interpret quotients involving division of whole numbers by unit fractions.

## ESSENTIAL QUESTION
Introduce the topic of division of a whole number by a unit fraction by describing a situation where this would be needed. For example, "You have 3 pies, each pie is cut into sixths, how many pieces of pie do you have?" Anticipate that most students will use multiplication to quickly give the answer, but convey that this lesson will ask them to think in a new way about this type of situation.

## FLUENCY PRACTICE
Fluency practice is available at **sadlierconnect.com**.

## Concept Development

### Understand: How to use a model to show division of whole numbers by unit fractions

■ Students may think of this as multiplication (5 × 8 = 40), but ask them to think about how the situation can also be modeled by a division expression that includes a unit fraction.

■ Point out that this problem is an equal-groups division situation in which the number of groups is unknown. The solution is the number of groups of $\frac{1}{8}$ in 5.

### Understand: How to use a number line to divide whole numbers by unit fractions

■ Students may need assistance to see how this problem can be modeled with division. Point out that the problem requires finding the number of groups of $\frac{1}{4}$ in 3, which is $3 \div \frac{1}{4}$.

---

### Lesson 23 — Divide Whole Numbers by Unit Fractions

**Essential Question:** How can you divide a whole number by a unit fraction?

#### Guided Instruction

In this lesson you will divide whole numbers by unit fractions.

**Understand: How to use a model to show division of whole numbers by unit fractions**

> Katie ordered 5 pizzas. Each pizza is cut into eighths. How many pieces of pizza does Katie have?

To find how many pieces of pizza Katie has, use a model and division.

Draw 5 circles to represent the pizzas. Then divide each circle into eighths.

5 pizzas divided into eighths make 40 pieces of pizza. That is, $5 \div \frac{1}{8} = 40$.

➡ Katie has 40 pieces of pizza.

**Understand: How to use a number line to divide whole numbers by unit fractions**

> Jessica uses $\frac{1}{4}$ yard of ribbon to trim a baby bib. How many bibs can she trim with 3 yards of ribbon?

To find how many bibs Jessica can trim, divide 3 yards by $\frac{1}{4}$ yard. That is, find $3 \div \frac{1}{4}$.

Draw a number line from 0–3 to show 3 yards of ribbon. Divide each yard into fourths.

There are 4 fourths in each yard, so there are 12 fourths in 3 yards. That is, $3 \div \frac{1}{4} = 12$.

4 equal parts

➡ Jessica can trim 12 baby bibs with 3 yards of ribbon.

---

## Support English Language Learners

This lesson provides an opportunity to review mathematical terms that students have encountered while working with unit fractions. Some English language learners may struggle with the word *unit fraction*. Provide an opportunity to explore the meaning of the word *unit* as a class. Write a unit fraction on the board and say the name. Then have students repeat the name of the unit fraction as a class. Relate to students that it is called a unit fraction because it is one part when the whole is divided equally. Have students come to the board and write unit fractions on the board. Give students the whole and how many parts the whole is divided into. Have the student write the unit fraction on the board while other students write unit fractions on paper.

Lesson 23

Guided Instruction

**Understand:** How to divide whole numbers by unit fractions using the relationship between division and multiplication

> One quart of milk is equivalent to $\frac{1}{4}$ gallon. How many quarts are there in 7 gallons?

Finding the number of quarts in 7 gallons is the same as finding the number of $\frac{1}{4}$ gallon in 7 gallons. So, divide 7 by $\frac{1}{4}$.

The two solution methods below both use multiplication to solve $7 \div \frac{1}{4}$.

**Method 1** Think about the number of fourths in each whole.
There are 4 fourths in 1 whole.
So, to find the number of fourths in 7 wholes, multiply 4 by 7.

$7 \div \frac{1}{4} = 7 \times 4 = 28$

**Method 2** Write a division equation as an equivalent multiplication equation.
If $q$ equals the number of quarts in 7 gallons, then

$q = 7 \div \frac{1}{4}$.

Rewrite this as an equivalent multiplication equation with an unknown factor.

$q \times \frac{1}{4} = 7$

Because $28 \times \frac{1}{4} = \frac{28}{4} = 7$, $q = 28$.

➡ There are 28 quarts of milk in 7 gallons.

✏ Explain why $6 \div \frac{1}{5} = 6 \times 5$. Draw a model to justify your answer.
Possible explanation: Evaluating $6 \div \frac{1}{5}$ means finding the number of $\frac{1}{5}$s, or fifths, in 6. There are 5 fifths in 1, so there are $6 \times 5$ fifths in 6. The model shows that there are 30 fifths in 6.
Possible model:

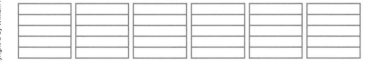

Unit 3 ▪ Focus on Number and Operations—Fractions  **199**

---

**Understand: How to divide whole numbers by unit fractions using the relationship between division and multiplication**

■ Method 1 helps students see why dividing a whole number by a unit fraction is the same as finding the product of the whole number and the denominator of the unit fraction.

■ In general, to find $w \div \frac{1}{n}$, where $w$ is a whole number, reason that there are $n$ $n$ths in each whole, so there are $w \times n$ $n$ths in $w$ wholes.

■ Method 2 uses the inverse relationship between division and multiplication. It solves $7 \div \frac{1}{4} = q$ by rewriting it as $q \times \frac{1}{4} = 7$.

✏ Along with the model, students should write a sentence or two explaining how they created the model and how it shows that $6 \div \frac{1}{5} = 6 \times 5$. Ask a few volunteers to share their models and explanations.

---

## Math-to-Social Studies Connection

**Map Scales** Students could apply the concept of division by unit fractions to reading distances on a map of a small area. For example, the scale on a map of a local park may show that $\frac{1}{4}$ inch is equivalent to 1 mile of a hiking trail. So, the number of miles represented by 2 inches on the map, for example, would be $2 \div \frac{1}{4}$. Provide students with local maps to explore this concept.

# Guided Instruction

**Connect:** **What you know about dividing whole numbers by unit fractions to write and solve story problems** This type of open-ended question helps students to interpret the division of a whole number by a unit fraction, rather than just computing the quotient.

■ Refer students to previous presentations for ideas on situations where division of a whole number by a unit fraction is necessary.

■ The process of finding the quotient before writing the text of the problem can help students to formulate all the parts of the problem that need to be communicated and lead the reader into the solution.

✏ Have a few volunteers share their division story with the class and solve one as a class for an example. Then, have students trade problems with a partner and solve. Students should be able to verbally explain their solution process and model to their partners. If students are struggling to create an appropriate problem, have partners work together to fix and solve the problem.

---

## Guided Instruction

**Connect:** **What you know about dividing whole numbers by unit fractions to write and solve story problems**

> Write a story problem that can be modeled by the expression $16 \div \frac{1}{2}$. Give the solution to your problem.

**Step 1**

Think of a situation in which you have to divide a whole-number amount by a unit fraction.

For example, you might have 16 cups of cereal in a storage container and want to know how many $\frac{1}{2}$-cup servings this is.

**Step 2**

Find the quotient.

Dividing by $\frac{1}{2}$ is the same as multiplying by 2.     $16 \div \frac{1}{2}$

So, rewrite the division expression as a multiplication expression.     $16 \times 2$

> There are 2 halves in 1. So, there are $16 \times 2$ halves in 16.

Find the product.     32

**Step 3**

Write a story problem.

Use the cereal example.

➤ Jaycee has 16 cups of cereal. She wants to pack $\frac{1}{2}$-cup servings into snack bags to share with her classmates. How many snack bags can she make? Jaycee can make 32 snack bags of cereal.

✏ Alex uses $\frac{1}{5}$ meter of wired ribbon to make a little picture frame. Use this idea to write a division story. Draw a number line or a model and include the solution in your story. Possible answer: Alex uses $\frac{1}{5}$ meter to make a frame. How many frames can he make with 2 meters of wired ribbon? Since $2 \div \frac{1}{5} = 10$, Alex can make 10 frames.

200   Unit 3 ■ Focus on Number and Operations—Fractions

---

## Math-to-Math Connection

**Inverse Operations in Equation Solving** A strong understanding of the relationship between division by a whole number and multiplication by its multiplicative inverse (for example, division by 3 is the same as multiplication by $\frac{1}{3}$ and division by $\frac{1}{3}$ is the same as multiplication by 3) will help students when they are exposed to inverse operations for solving equations.

Lesson 23

Guided Practice

**Complete the problems below each model.**

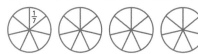

1. How many $\frac{1}{7}$s are there in 4? __28__

2. What is value of the expression $4 \div \frac{1}{7}$? __28__

3. How many $\frac{1}{5}$s are there in 3? __15__

4. What is the value of the expression $3 \div \frac{1}{5}$? __15__

5. How many $\frac{1}{6}$s are there in 5? __30__

6. What is the value of the expression $5 \div \frac{1}{6}$? __30__

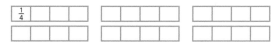

7. How many $\frac{1}{4}$s are there in 6? __24__

8. What is the value of the expression $6 \div \frac{1}{4}$? __24__

### Think•Pair•Share

MP4  9. Write a division story problem about one of the models on this page. Then ask a classmate to solve your problem.
Story problems will vary. Possible story: Barbara cuts a regular hexagon into 6 equilateral triangles. How many triangles can she cut from 5 hexagons? Since $5 \div \frac{1}{6} = 30$, she can cut 30 triangles.

## Mathematical Practices

Mathematical Practice Standards underline the teaching and understanding of all concepts and skills presented. The emphasis of specific practices is noted throughout the guided and independent practice of this lesson.

| MP4 | **Model with mathematics.** |
| --- | --- |

**Item 9:** By writing a division story, students are relating the mathematical process of dividing a whole number by a unit fraction to an everyday problem. By sharing with a classmate, students are interpreting the solution in the context of the story.

## Observational Assessment

Use page 201 to assess whether students are able to use a model to interpret division of a whole number by a unit fraction. Ensure that students are making the connection between the first question after each model and the second question showing the division.

### Think•Pair•Share

**Peer Collaboration** Have students work individually to write their division story problem. Then, break the class into pairs. Have students trade their story problem with their partner and solve. Finally, ask several volunteers to share what strategy they used to solve their partner's problem. Ask questions, such as:

- *What strategy did you use to solve your problem?*

- *How could you use a different strategy to answer the question?*

### Return to the Essential Question

Reread the Lesson 23 Essential Question on page 198: *How can you divide a whole number by a unit fraction?*

Ask volunteers to use what they learned in this lesson to answer this question. (Possible response: I can use the whole number of models divided into unit fraction parts. The total number of pieces is the quotient. I can use a number line from 0 to the whole number with each whole divided into unit fraction parts. The number of parts is the quotient. I can write the division equation as an equivalent multiplication equation by multiplying the denominator of the unit fraction by the whole number.)

# Independent Practice

## Concept Application

Students may work independently on these pages in the classroom or at home. They may refer to the first four pages of the lesson to revisit the instruction or to see a worked-out example.

**Common Errors** and **Teaching Tips** may help you support student learning either in the classroom or as a follow-up for work done at home.

## Common Errors

### Items 1–3

Ensure that students' answers have units that are appropriate for the context of the question. Writing answers as complete sentences can help students interpret the context.

## Teaching Tips

### Items 1–3

Help students make the connection between the text of the division stories, the number lines or models, and the division expressions. Point out that the part of the model given represents 1 whole (1 mile, 1 box of flour, and 1 square). Students must extend the models to represent all the wholes in the situation.

### Independent Practice

**Solve each problem.**

MP4   1. A tortoise is moving at a speed of $\frac{1}{3}$ mile an hour. At this speed, how long will it take the tortoise to go 5 miles?

   a. Complete this number line model for the story situation.

   b. How many $\frac{1}{3}$s are there in 5? __15__

   c. What is the value of the expression $5 \div \frac{1}{3}$? __15__

   **Answer** It will take the tortoise 15 hours to go 5 miles.

MP4   2. Hal works in a bakery. He used $\frac{1}{6}$ of a large box of flour for a batch of muffins. How many batches can he make with 4 boxes of flour?

   a. Complete this model for the story situation.

   b. How many $\frac{1}{6}$s are there in 4? __24__

   c. What is the value of the expression $4 \div \frac{1}{6}$? __24__

   **Answer** Hal can make 24 batches with 4 boxes.

MP4   3. Agnes is cutting squares into triangles for a quilt project. Each triangle is $\frac{1}{4}$ of a square. How many triangles can she cut from 5 squares?

   a. Complete this model for the story situation.

   b. How many $\frac{1}{4}$s are there in 5? __20__

   c. What is the value of the expression $5 \div \frac{1}{4}$? __20__

   **Answer** Agnes can cut 20 triangles from 5 squares.

**202**   Unit 3 ▪ Focus on Number and Operations—Fractions

## Mathematical Practices

| MP4 | **Model with mathematics.** |
| --- | --- |

**Items 1–3:** Students use number lines and area models to represent division situations.

## Independent Practice

**Fill in the blanks to write a division problem. Then write and solve a division equation for the problem.**

4. _____Max_____ cuts a ____pizza____ into ____8____ equal pieces.
   [name]                [thing]              [whole number]

   Each piece is ____$\frac{1}{8}$____ of a whole. How many pieces can be cut
                   [unit fraction]

   from ____3____ whole ____pizzas____?
        [whole number]      [thing]

   **Division Equation** ____$3 \div \frac{1}{8} = 24$____

   **Answer** Max can cut 24 pieces from the 3 pizzas.

5. _____Sue_____ uses ____$\frac{1}{3}$____ of a bag of ____corn____ to make a
   [name]              [unit fraction]              [ingredient]

   ____corn bread____. How many ____corn breads____ can be made from
        [thing]                    [thing]

   ____4____ bags?
   [whole number]

   **Division Equation** ____$4 \div \frac{1}{3} = 12$____

   **Answer** Sue can make 12 corn breads from 4 bags of corn.

**For exercises 6–7, choose the best answer.**

6. It took Marsha 15 minutes to cut 20 pizzas into ninths. How many slices of pizza does she have? Choose the division expression that gives the answer.

   a. $\frac{1}{9} \div 20$          b. $9 \div 20$

   c. $20 \div \frac{1}{9}$          d. $(20 - 15) \div 9$

7. Ed plants trees in city parks. He used $\frac{1}{10}$ of a bag of fertilizer around the base of a newly planted tree. How many trees can Ed fertilize with 40 bags of fertilizer?

   a. 4          b. 10

   c. 40          d. 400

## Common Errors

### Item 4
Some students might not realize that the whole number in the third blank determines the unit fraction in the fourth blank. Students cannot simply choose any unit fraction. For example, if the "thing" is divided into 5 equal pieces, then each piece is $\frac{1}{5}$ of a whole. Work with students to help them make this connection.

### Item 6
Note that extraneous information is given in this problem. Help students identify it as such and guide them to only use the necessary information to answer the question.

### Item 7
Some students may multiply 40 by $\frac{1}{10}$ instead of dividing 40 by $\frac{1}{10}$, and choose 4 as the answer. Ask students if 4 is a reasonable answer. Ask: How many trees can Ed fertilize with 1 bag if he uses $\frac{1}{10}$ bag for each tree? So, if he has 40 bags, how many trees can he fertilize?

## Writing About Math

▸ **Write an Explanatory Text** Ask students to write a paragraph about the similarities and differences between the strategies of using a number line versus using a model to divide a whole number by a unit fraction. Students should support their thoughts by using an example and applying both strategies. Ask them to include vocabulary such as *whole number, unit fraction,* and *division* or *divide.*

Ask a few volunteers to read their paragraphs aloud. While the paragraphs are being read, ask another volunteer to create a diagram in front of the class detailing the similarities or differences being mentioned.

# Independent Practice

## Teaching Tips

### Items 9-10

Be sure students are using the model above exercise 8 as the guide for these questions. Help students see that, in problem 9, each rectangle represents a display board. And, in problem 10, each rectangle represents a container of fruit salad.

## Independent Practice

**For exercises 8–10, use the model below.**

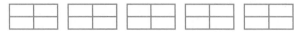

8. Explain how the model shows both $5 \div \frac{1}{4}$ and $5 \times 4$.

   Possible explanation for $5 \div \frac{1}{4}$: The 5 rectangles are divided into fourths. The total number of fourths is $5 \div \frac{1}{4}$.

   Possible explanation for $5 \times 4$: Each rectangle has 4 sections. So, the total number of sections equals 5 times 4.

9. Complete this story situation for the model.

   Each student in an art class gets $\frac{1}{4}$ of a display board to present his or her project. How many students can display projects if . . .

   Possible answer: the teacher has 5 display boards?

10. Complete a different story situation for the model.

    Fred has 5 containers of fruit salad for the family reunion. Each person will get . . .
    Possible answer: $\frac{1}{4}$ of a container. How many people will the fruit salad serve?

**Complete the division equation to solve each problem.**

11. Each rhombus is $\frac{1}{6}$ of this star.

    How many rhombuses are there in 50 of these stars?

    $\underline{50} \div \underline{\frac{1}{6}} = \underline{300}$

12. Each circle is $\frac{1}{21}$ of this pyramid.

    How many balls are there in 12 of these pyramids?

    $\underline{12} \div \underline{\frac{1}{21}} = \underline{252}$

## Digital Connection

**Digital Video Camera** Have students work in groups of three or four and use a video device to create a short video clip modeling a situation that involves dividing a whole number by a unit fraction. Students may use a situation from this lesson or create one of their own. In the video, students should creatively introduce the situation with characters. Then, they should use a physical model to solve the division problem, such as cutting whole pieces of paper into unit fraction pieces or using a whole number of linking blocks that break apart into unit fraction pieces. Have them demonstrate on the video how they found the quotient, then present their answer in the context of the story.

Lesson 23

**Independent Practice**

**Solve the problems.**

MP4  **13.** Use the large circle to model $\frac{1}{2} \div 4$. Use the four small circles to model $4 \div \frac{1}{2}$. Explain why the two expressions have different meanings.

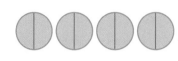

Possible answer: When $\frac{1}{2}$ is divided by 4, each little piece is $\frac{1}{8}$ of the whole circle. So, $\frac{1}{2} \div 4 = \frac{1}{8}$. When 4 circles are each divided into halves, there are 8 halves. So, $4 \div \frac{1}{2} = 8$.

MP2  **14.** It takes Camilla $\frac{1}{4}$ hour to make a customized basket. How many baskets can she make in 6 hours?

⬛▶ **Show your work.**

Possible answer: $6 \div \frac{1}{4} = 6 \times 4 = 24$; She can make 4 baskets per hour. So, in 6 hours she can make 6 times that many.

**Answer** Camilla can make 24 baskets.

MP2  **15.** The distance traveled by a moving object equals the rate of speed multiplied by the time. This can be represented by the formula $d = r \times t$. Find the speed of a moving car that goes 11 miles in $\frac{1}{5}$ of an hour.

⬛▶ **Show your work.**

I used the formula $d = r \times t$, substituted the given numbers, and solved for $r$:
$d = r \times t$, $11 = r \times \frac{1}{5}$, $r = 11 \div \frac{1}{5}$, $r = 11 \times 5$, $r = 55$

**Answer** The speed of the car is 55 miles per hour.

**Unit 3 ▪ Focus on Number and Operations—Fractions  205**

## Teaching Tips

### Item 13
Students may need help using the large circle to model the first expression. Encourage them to first divide it in half, and then divide that half into 4 equal parts. Call their attention to the difference in the order of division in the two expressions.

### Item 15
Help students identify which part of the formula each number represents by calling attention to the units as clues. Coach them to substitute what they know into the formula, and then look for ways to solve for the unknown part. Some students may not directly use division by a unit fraction in their solution process. Ensure that students return to the problem context to choose appropriate units for their answer.

## Mathematical Practices

| MP2 | **Reason abstractly and quantitatively.** |
|---|---|

**Item 14:** Students make sense of the quantities in a real-world problem to determine what calculation is required to find the answer.

**Item 15:** Students use a symbolic formula to represent a real-world situation. They manipulate the symbols, using the relationship between multiplication and division, to find the solution.

| MP4 | **Model with mathematics.** |
|---|---|

**Item 13:** Students use models to explain how dividing a fraction by a whole number is different from dividing the whole number by the fraction.

## OBJECTIVE
Use unit fractions and whole numbers in computations, models, and equations to solve real-world problems.

## ESSENTIAL QUESTION
Explain that students will use computations, models, and equations to solve real-world problems that involve division with unit fractions and whole numbers.

## FLUENCY PRACTICE
Fluency practice is available at **sadlierconnect.com**.

## Concept Development

### Understand: How to solve problems that involve more than one step

■ Students should realize that they need to divide the number of bags of crackers used by the fraction of a bag in each snack box. Have students explain why this division represents the total number of snack bags made.

■ The final step of this problem is finding how much money was earned by selling 50 snack bags at $2.50 each. Remind students to keep track of the decimal point in order to avoid making a mistake.

### Understand: How to solve problems using a picture

■ Without a picture, students might use the numbers from the problem and think there are 10 spaces. By drawing 10 trees, they can count the spaces to see that there are only 9 spaces between the trees.

---

### Lesson 24 — Problem Solving: Divide Unit Fractions and Whole Numbers

**Essential Question:** How can you use division with unit fractions and whole numbers to solve real world problems?

#### Guided Instruction

In this lesson you will solve problems using division with unit fractions and whole numbers.

**Understand:** How to solve problems that involve more than one step

> Bert and Betty made snack boxes to sell at a school picnic. Each snack box had an apple and crackers and sold for $2.50. They put $\frac{1}{10}$ of a bag of crackers in each box. They used 5 bags of crackers and sold all the boxes they made. How much money did they earn?

First, divide to find the number of snack boxes Bert and Betty made with 5 bags.

$5 \div \frac{1}{10} = 5 \times 10 = 50$

Then, multiply the 50 snack boxes you determined above by $2.50 per box.

$2.50 \times 50$ snack boxes $= \$125$

➡ Bert and Betty earned $125.

**Understand:** How to solve problems using a picture

> The city has 10 trees to plant along a stretch of road that is $\frac{1}{4}$ mile long. The trees will be equally spaced. How far apart should the trees be?

To solve, first make a sketch showing the 10 trees.

Notice there are only 9 spaces between the 10 trees. Divide the $\frac{1}{4}$ mile road into 9 equal parts, *not* 10.

Write a division equation and solve. $\frac{1}{4} \div 9 = \frac{1}{9} \times \frac{1}{4} = \frac{1}{36}$

➡ The trees should be $\frac{1}{36}$ mile apart.

**Remember!**
Drawing pictures can help you better understand a problem situation and avoid incorrect calculations.

---

## Support English Language Learners

A common mistake at this grade level is incorrectly writing a division from a word problem. For example, students may write the dividend as the divisor, and visa versa. It may be helpful for English language learners to practice with a few examples of how to correctly write divisions from sentences.

Write a few sentences that represent real-world division situations on the board, and have students say the division calculation that matches each sentence. For example, write *Divide a $\frac{1}{2}$ pizza into 5 equal slices.* Students should understand and say that they need to calculate $\frac{1}{2} \div 5$ to solve. For *Divide 5 cups of yogurt into $\frac{1}{2}$-cup servings,* students should understand that the calculation is $5 \div \frac{1}{2}$.

**Understand: How to use division to solve a comparison problem**

> Kai has 4 cousins. This is $\frac{1}{6}$ as many cousins as Lucca has. How many cousins does Lucca have?

To find how many cousins Lucca has, start by writing a comparison statement in words.

The number of cousins Kai has is $\frac{1}{6}$ *times* as many cousins as Lucca has.

Use the statement to write a multiplication equation.

Let $c$ represent the number of cousins Lucca has.

Multiplication equation: $4 = \frac{1}{6} \times c$

Use the fact that multiplication and division are inverse operations to write an equivalent division equation.

Division equation: $c = 4 \div \frac{1}{6}$

Now, solve.

$c = 4 \div \frac{1}{6}$
$c = 4 \times 6$ ⟵ There are 6 sixths in 1, so there are $4 \times 6$ sixths in 4.
$c = 24$

▷ Lucca has 24 cousins.

✏ It took Kara $\frac{1}{3}$ hour to finish a crossword puzzle. This is 4 times as long as it took Andre to complete the crossword puzzle. How long did it take Andre to complete the crossword puzzle?
Possible answer: The amount of time Kara took is 4 times the amount Andre took. The equation is $\frac{1}{3} = 4 \times a$. This is equivalent to $a = \frac{1}{3} \div 4$, which is the same as $a = \frac{1}{4} \times \frac{1}{3} = \frac{1}{12}$. It took Andre $\frac{1}{12}$ hour to complete the crossword puzzle.

**Understand: How to use division to solve a comparison problem**

■ Remind students that a comparison statement can be written in the form "*a* is *n* times as many (or as much) as *b*." This can be expressed as the equation $a = n \times b$. In a comparison problem, one of the values *a*, *n*, or *b*, is not known.

■ In this problem, the comparison statement is "The number of cousins Kai has is $\frac{1}{6}$ times as many as Lucca has." Kai has 4 cousins. The number Lucca has is unknown. If *c* is the number of cousins Lucia has, the equation is $4 = \frac{1}{6} \times c$.

■ Discuss using the inverse relationship between multiplication and division to rewrite the equation as a division: $4 = \frac{1}{6} \times c$ is equivalent to $c = 4 \div \frac{1}{6}$.

■ Help students recall that dividing a number by a unit fraction is the same as multiplying the number in the denominator of the unit fraction by the whole number.

✏ The previous problem was solved by dividing a whole number by a unit fraction. This problem is solved by dividing a unit fraction by a whole number. After students have answered the question, ask a few volunteers to demonstrate how they solved the problem and compare and contrast their methods. You may wish to ask the class to determine how many minutes it took Andre to complete the crossword puzzle.

## Math-to-Social Studies Connection

**Co-op Gardens** Many people in the U.S. buy their fruits and vegetables at supermarkets; however, cooperative gardens, or co-op gardens, have become very popular in some cities and towns.

Have students research co-op gardens and if there are any co-op gardens in their community. Then have each student plan a co-op garden for the class. Ensure that part of the planning involves dividing the class up by a unit fraction. Students can model their division with any of the models they have encountered, and they should support their model with a division statement. For an extra challenge, have student planners divide each group's piece of the garden into growing vegetables, fruits, and flowers.

**Connect: What you know about division with unit fractions and whole numbers to solve problems** Use this page to help students strengthen their understanding of how division with unit fractions can be used to solve real-world problems.

■ Remind students that models can be used to represent problem situations, solve equations, and verify solutions.

■ Help students understand that dividing a fraction by a whole number is the same as multiplying the fraction by the multiplicative inverse of the whole number.

■ If students demonstrate a clear understanding of the content, you may wish to ask for volunteers to use their knowledge of customary units from 4th grade to determine the volume of lemonade in each glass in cups. Students will revisit customary units of measure in subsequent lessons.

---

Lesson 24  Problem Solving: **Divide Unit Fractions and Whole Numbers**

### Guided Instruction

**Connect: What you know about division with unit fractions and whole numbers to solve problems**

> For the last 2 days, Juan and Kim have been selling lemonade for 50¢ a glass. They have $\frac{1}{2}$ gallon left and pour an equal amount of the remaining lemonade into 8 glasses. What fraction of a gallon is in each glass?

**Step 1**

Identify the key information.

Juan and Kim are dividing $\frac{1}{2}$ gallon into 8 equal parts.

**Step 2**

Choose the operation you will use to solve. Write an equation.
Let $x$ = the fraction of a gallon in each of the 8 glasses.

$$\frac{1}{2} \div 8 = x$$

**Step 3**

Use a model to visualize the division.

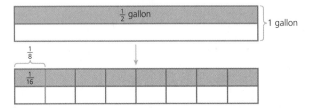

**Step 4**

Solve the equation. Verify your answer using the model.

$$\frac{1}{2} \div 8 = x$$
$$\frac{1}{8} \times \frac{1}{2} = x$$
$$\frac{1}{16} = x$$

➡ Each glass contains $\frac{1}{16}$ of a gallon.

---

## Math-to-History Connection

**Egyptian Fractions** Ancient Egyptians wrote fractions as sums of unit fractions where all the unit fractions were different. This method, though infrequently used now, made it easy to compare fractions and divide quantities into equal portions. As an example, $\frac{2}{3}$ written as an Egyptian fraction would be $\frac{1}{2} + \frac{1}{6}$.

Divide students into groups of three or four. Ask each group to try and find a sum of unit fractions to represent a simple fraction, for example $\frac{3}{4}$, $\frac{2}{5}$, or $\frac{7}{8}$. Ask each group to share their Egyptian fraction with the class and discuss their solutions and the strategies they used.

Lesson 24

**Use the problem below to answer exercises 1 and 2.**
Vern and Tina are each planting $\frac{1}{2}$ of a rectangular garden. Tina plants vegetables in her half. Vern divides his half into 6 equal parts and plants marigolds in one of these sections. How much of the entire rectangular garden will be marigolds?

1. Will the answer to the problem be a fraction less than 1 or a whole number? Explain how you know.
   A fraction less than 1. Possible explanation: $\frac{1}{2}$ is being divided into smaller pieces. Each piece will be less than $\frac{1}{2}$ of the garden.

2. Write an equation to represent the problem. Then solve.
   $\frac{1}{2} \div 6 = m$, $\frac{1}{6} \times \frac{1}{2} = m$; $m = \frac{1}{12}$.
   The entire rectangular garden will be $\frac{1}{12}$ marigold flowers.

**Use the problem below to answer exercises 3–5.**
Ruth is making pillows. She uses $\frac{1}{2}$ yard of fabric for each pillow. Her grandmother gives her a box of 15 spools of thread, 6 yards of fabric, and 40 zippers. How many pillows can Ruth make from the fabric?

3. What information is *not* needed to solve the problem?
   15 spools of thread, 40 zippers

4. Explain how division can be used to solve the problem.
   Possible explanation: $6 \div \frac{1}{2} = 12$. There are 2 halves in 1 yard, so there are 12 halves in 6 yards.

5. Explain how multiplication can be used to solve the problem.
   Possible explanation: $6 \times 2 = 12$. Each yard will make 2 pillows. There are 6 yards, so she can make 12 pillows.

♛ **Think▪Pair▪Share**

MP7  6. Compare the equations used to solve the garden and pillow problems. How are they the same? How are they different?
   Possible response: Both problems use the numbers $\frac{1}{2}$ and 6. In the garden problem, $\frac{1}{2}$ is divided by 6. In the pillow problem, 6 is divided by $\frac{1}{2}$.

Unit 3 ▪ Focus on Number and Operations—Fractions  **209**

## Observational Assessment
Use page 209 to assess whether students are able to use division of unit fractions and whole numbers to solve real-world problems.

♛ **Think▪Pair▪Share**

**Peer Collaboration**  Give students time to complete their response. Then divide the class into partners. Have student partners discuss their answers with each other. Ask for student pairs to present their conclusions to the class. As they present, start a discussion by asking:

- *Did you and your partner notice any patterns in the problems besides that the two numbers in each equation are the same?*

- *How did the fraction as the divisor affect your answer? How did the fraction as the dividend affect your answer?*

To summarize, the quotient is affected whether the unit fraction is the dividend or the divisor.

## Return to the Essential Question
Reread the Lesson 24 Essential Question on page 206: *How can you use division with unit fractions and whole numbers to solve real world problems?*

Ask volunteers to use what they learned in this lesson to answer this question. (Possible response: I can use diagrams and models to write and solve equations with unit fractions and whole numbers.)

Invite as many volunteers as possible to express ideas about solving real-world problems using unit fractions and whole numbers in their own words.

## Mathematical Practices

Mathematical Practice Standards underline the teaching and understanding of all concepts and skills presented. The emphasis of specific practices is noted throughout the guided and independent practice of this lesson.

| MP7 | **Look for and make use of structure.** |
| --- | --- |

**Item 6:** Students identify a pattern in equations to solve a problem.

# Independent Practice

## Concept Application

Students may work independently on these pages in the classroom or at home. They may refer to the first four pages of the lesson to revisit the instruction or to see a worked-out example.

**Common Errors** and **Teaching Tips** may help you support student learning either in the classroom or as a follow-up for work done at home.

## Teaching Tips

### Items 1-4

Help students recognize that there is sometimes extra information in real-world problems. A good first step when approaching these problems is to determine the information that is needed.

---

### Independent Practice

**Use the problem below to answer exercises 1–4.**
Paul uses $\frac{1}{5}$ liter of chicken broth and $\frac{1}{2}$ packet of noodles for a bowl of soup. How many bowls of soup can he make from 4 liters of chicken broth?

1. What numerical information is needed to solve the problem?
$\frac{1}{5}$ liter, 4 liters

2. Which numbers should you divide to solve the problem? Explain why.
Divide 4 by $\frac{1}{5}$. This will give the number of $\frac{1}{5}$ liters in 4 liters.

3. Write and solve an equation to answer the question in the problem.
$4 \div \frac{1}{5} = b$; $b = 20$
Paul can make 20 bowls of soup from 4 liters.

4. Explain how to use multiplication to check your answer.
Dividing by $\frac{1}{5}$ is the same as multiplying by 5; $4 \times 5 = 20$.

**Use the problem below to answer exercises 5 and 6.**
A quilt is made from squares, rectangles, and right triangles. One-third of the pieces are each shape. Sur divides the square pieces into 4 equal groups and makes one group from red fabric. What fraction of the quilt pieces will be red squares?

5. Complete this visual model to illustrate the problem.

| | red | | |
|---|---|---|---|
| squares | $\frac{1}{12}$ | | |
| rectangles | | | |
| right triangles | | | |

6. Explain how to use equivalent fractions and logical reasoning to solve the problem.
$\frac{1}{3}$ is equal to $\frac{4}{12}$, and $\frac{4}{12}$ divided by 4 equals $\frac{1}{12}$.
$\frac{1}{12}$ of the number of pieces will be red squares.

---

## Writing About Math

· **Write an Opinion Piece** Ask students to write an opinion paragraph on whether they think drawing a diagram to represent given information in a real-world situation is helpful or not. Students should state an opinion, justify their opinion using facts and details, and provide a concluding statement.

Ask volunteers to read their paragraphs aloud. Remind students that these are opinion paragraphs, so there is no right or wrong answer.

Lesson 24

Independent Practice

| Problem Solving Strategies | |
| --- | --- |
| Draw a Picture or Diagram | Find a Pattern |
| Guess, Check, and Revise | Use Objects |
| Make an Organized List | Make a Table |
| Use a Number Sentence or Equation | Work Backwards |
| Use Logical Reasoning | Solve a Simpler Problem |

**Choose a problem solving strategy and explain how you use it.**

7. An art teacher plans to give each student $\frac{1}{3}$ of a jar of paint. How many students can sign up for the art classes if the teacher has 20 paint jars?

   **Strategy:** Possible answer: Use logical reasoning.

   **Show your work.**
   Possible answer: I need to find the number of $\frac{1}{3}$'s in 20, so I will divide 20 by $\frac{1}{3}$. There are 3 thirds in 1, so there are 20 × 3 thirds in 20.

   **Answer** The teacher has enough paint for 60 students.

   a. Explain a way to check your answer.
   Possible answer: Three students can use each jar so 3 × 20, or 60 students can use 20 jars.

8. Charlie has $\frac{1}{3}$ yard of gold braid to trim a jacket. He divides the braid into 2 equal pieces and uses 1 piece for the each sleeve. How long is the trim on each sleeve?

   **Strategy:** Possible answer: Draw a picture.

   **Show your work.**

   Possible answer: I marked the number line in thirds. Then I divided each third in 2 pieces. One of these pieces is $\frac{1}{6}$.

   **Answer** The trim on each sleeve is $\frac{1}{6}$ yard.

Unit 3 ■ Focus on Number and Operations—Fractions **211**

## Digital Connection

**Interactive Whiteboard** Use a whiteboard to write a division word problem intended to use whole numbers and unit fractions. Leave out several pieces of information, including both the whole number and the unit fraction. For example, *Alex and his _____ (type of animal, plural) went _____ (activity) yesterday. Alex planned to share _____ (unit fraction) of his _____ (type of food) with each of them. If there are _____ (whole number) of them, does he have enough?*

Without showing students the problem, ask volunteers for each of the missing pieces of information. Have students then complete the word problem by solving as a division. Then, have students explain how and why a multiplication could be used to solve the problem. Complete the word problem with the information provided, and find the solution as a class.

## Teaching Tips

### Items 7-8
Help students understand that there are no specific strategies that are correct for these items, but emphasize that some strategies may lend themselves more than others to a particular situation.

# Independent Practice

## Common Errors

### Item 9

Be sure that students understand that the decimeter is the larger unit of measure.

## Teaching Tips

### Items 9-10

Students may wish to use models or a diagram to complete these items.

---

**Independent Practice**

9. A centimeter is equal to $\frac{1}{10}$ decimeter. How many centimeters are in 2 decimeters?

   **Strategy:** <u>Possible answer: Use logical reasoning.</u>

   **Show your work.**
   There are 10 centimeters in 1 decimeter, so there are 20 centimeters in 2 decimeters.

   **Answer** <u>There are 20 centimeters in 2 decimeters.</u>

   a. Explain a way to check your answer.

      Possible answer: $2 \div \frac{1}{10} = 2 \times 10 = 20$

10. Gayle has enough gravel to cover 40 square yards. She is putting the gravel on a walkway that is $\frac{1}{2}$ yard wide. How much of the path can she cover with the gravel?

    **Strategy:** <u>Possible answer: Use an equation</u>

    **Show your work.**
    $A = \ell \times w$
    $40 = \ell \times \frac{1}{2}$
    $\ell = 40 \div \frac{1}{2}$
    $\ell = 80$

    **Answer** <u>Gayle can cover 80 yards of the path with the gravel.</u>

**Choose the best answer.**

11. What information is *not* needed to solve this problem?

    Larry buys large bags of birdseed for $9.87 per bag. He uses $\frac{1}{6}$ bag of birdseed each week. He has 4 full bags of birdseed now. How long will it last?

    (a.) The birdseed costs $9.87 per bag.  b. He uses $\frac{1}{6}$ bag per week.

    c. He has 4 bags right now.  d. All this information is needed.

---

## Math-to-Measurement Connection

**Rates** In later grades, students will work with rates. A rate compares two measurements with different units, such as $4 for 2 hamburgers or 10 miles in 2 hours. A unit rate uses division to find the rate for 1 unit such as $2 per hamburger or 5 miles per hour.

Sometimes rates are given as fractions. Students will need to know how to divide by a unit fraction to find the unit rate of a person running 3 miles in $\frac{1}{2}$ hour: $3 \div \frac{1}{2} = 6$ miles per hour.

MORE ONLINE sadlierconnect.com

Lesson 24

## Independent Practice

**Solve the problems.**

MP4 **12.** John divides his food budget into 2 equal parts and spends one part on fruits and vegetables. He divides his book budget into 3 equal parts and uses one part for science books.

John's Budget

What fractional part of John's budget did he spend on fruits and vegetables and science books? Compare the fractional parts. Use both computation and a visual model in your answer.

➤ **Show your work.**

Possible answer: John spends $\frac{1}{12}$ on fruits and vegetables because $\frac{1}{6} \div 2 = \frac{1}{12}$.

He also spends $\frac{1}{12}$ on the science books because $\frac{1}{4} \div 3 = \frac{1}{12}$. The given model

shows both parts are $\frac{1}{12}$ of the total budget.

**Answer** Fruits & vegetables: $\frac{1}{12}$; Science books: $\frac{1}{12}$; Both parts equal $\frac{1}{12}$ of the budget.

MP2 **13.** Explain how dividing something into thirds is different from dividing it by $\frac{1}{3}$. Create two story situations to illustrate your answer.

Possible answer: To divide a number in thirds, divide it by 3 or multiply it by $\frac{1}{3}$. To divide a number by $\frac{1}{3}$, multiply it by 3.

**Story: Dividing into thirds** Possible story: Ed has 24 inches of twine and divides it into thirds. Each piece is 8 inches long.

**Story: Dividing by $\frac{1}{3}$** Possible story: Alice uses $\frac{1}{3}$ cup of milk to make a loaf of bread. She can make 18 loaves from 6 cups of milk because $6 \div \frac{1}{3} = 6 \times 3$.

MP5 **14.** Solve the problem below two ways, once using the fraction $\frac{1}{50}$ and once using its decimal equivalent.

A metal machine cuts very small parts that are $\frac{1}{50}$ of an inch long. How many of these parts can be cut from a 3-inch strip of metal?

**Method 1: Use $\frac{1}{50}$:** $3 \div \frac{1}{50} = 3 \times 50 = 150$

**Method 2: Use a decimal:** $3 \div 0.02 = 150$

## Teaching Tips

### Item 12

After dividing the food and book portions, some students may wish to divide the entire circle into twelfths to help them name the fractions.

### Item 14

Emphasize to students that $\frac{1}{50}$ and 0.02 are equivalent, so the answer should be the same regardless of the method used.

## Return to the

Progress Check

Remind students to return to the Progress Check self-assessment, page 131, to check off additional items they have mastered during the unit.

## Mathematical Practices

| | |
|---|---|
| **MP2** | **Reason abstractly and quantitatively.** |

**Item 13:** Students explain the difference between dividing into thirds and dividing by $\frac{1}{3}$ both by using mathematical language and reasoning and by using real-world contexts.

| | |
|---|---|
| **MP4** | **Model with mathematics.** |

**Item 12:** Students use a model to represent and analyze John's budget.

| | |
|---|---|
| **MP5** | **Use appropriate tools strategically.** |

**Item 14:** Students use appropriate tools to solve a problem.

The Unit 3 Review covers all the standards presented in the unit. Use it to assess your students' mastery of the unit's concepts and skills.

## Depth of Knowledge

The depth of knowledge is a ranking of the content complexity of assessment items based on Webb's Depth of Knowledge (DOK) levels. The levels increase in complexity as shown below.

**Level 1:** Recall and Reproduction
**Level 2:** Basic Skills and Concepts
**Level 3:** Strategic Reasoning and Thinking
**Level 4:** Extended Thinking

| Item | DOK |
|------|-----|
| 1 | 2 |
| 2 | 2 |
| 3 | 2 |
| 4 | 2 |
| 5 | 2 |
| 6 | 2 |
| 7 | 2 |
| 8 | 3 |
| 9 | 2 |
| 10 | 3 |
| 11 | 2 |
| 12 | 4 |
| 13 | 2 |
| 14 | 2 |
| 15 | 2 |
| 16 | 3 |
| 17 | 3 |
| 18 | 2 |
| 19 | 2 |
| 20 | 2 |

**For exercises 1–4, evaluate. Show your work.**

1. $3\frac{1}{2} \times 1\frac{3}{4}$
   $\frac{7}{2} \times \frac{7}{4}$
   $\frac{49}{8}$
   $6\frac{1}{8}$

2. $\frac{3}{4} \times 3 \times 5\frac{1}{3}$
   $\frac{3}{4} \times 3 \times \frac{16}{3}$
   $\frac{144}{12}$
   $12$

3. $\frac{1}{8} \div 2$
   $\frac{1}{2} \times \frac{1}{8}$
   $\frac{1}{16}$

4. $24 \div \frac{1}{3}$
   $24 \times 3$
   $72$

5. Write $23 \div 3$ as both a fraction and a mixed number.
   Fraction: $\frac{23}{3}$    Mixed number: $7\frac{2}{3}$

6. Two-thirds of a science class is going on a field trip. One-fifth of this group is bringing cameras. What fraction of the class will be bringing cameras on the trip?
   Two-fifteens of the class will be bringing cameras.

7. What is the area of a park that is $\frac{1}{2}$ mile wide and $\frac{7}{8}$ mile long?
   The area is $\frac{7}{16}$ square miles.

**For exercises 8–9, choose the correct answer.**

8. In a number-guessing game, Paula chooses a fraction between 0 and 1. She multiplies 50 by her fraction. What must be true of the product?

   (a.) It is less than 50.

   b. It is greater than $\frac{1}{2}$ of 50.

   c. It is greater than 50.

   d. There is not enough information to decide.

9. Which expression is equivalent to $\frac{7}{9} - \frac{1}{6}$?

   a. $\frac{7}{9} - \frac{7}{18}$

   b. $\frac{7}{9} - \frac{1}{18}$

   (c.) $\frac{14}{18} - \frac{3}{18}$

   d. $\frac{7}{12} - \frac{2}{12}$

UNIT **3** Review

10. Describe a method for estimating this difference.

$5\frac{1}{3} - 2\frac{7}{8}$

Possible answer: Round $2\frac{7}{8}$ up to 3. The difference is about $5\frac{1}{3} - 3$, or $2\frac{1}{3}$.

11. Barb gets 6 pizzas to divide equally among 4 people. How much of a pizza can each person have?

Each person gets $1\frac{1}{2}$ pizzas.

12. Write an example problem for the rule below. Then, explain why the product is greater than the original number.

When you multiply a number by a fraction *greater than* 1, the product is *greater than* that number.

Possible answer: $\frac{3}{2} \times 20 = 30$. $\frac{2}{2} \times 20 = 20$ because $\frac{2}{2} = 1$.
Since $\frac{3}{2}$ is greater than $\frac{2}{2}$, $\frac{3}{2} \times 30$ must be greater than 20.

13. A work crew is planting flowers along a stretch of road that is $\frac{3}{4}$ mile long. They plant $\frac{1}{3}$ mile the first day and $\frac{1}{4}$ mile the second day. How much of the job is left to complete on the final day? Show the equation you use.

▸ **Show your work.**

Equation: $\frac{3}{4} - (\frac{1}{3} + \frac{1}{4}) = n$

**Answer** They have $\frac{1}{6}$ mile left to complete.

14. Ms. Tompkins flies to San Francisco for a business trip. She decides to drive home. She drives $\frac{1}{3}$ of the way the first day, and then $\frac{3}{8}$ of the way the second day. How much of the trip has Ms. Tompkins completed so far?

▸ **Show your work.**

$\frac{1}{3} + \frac{3}{8} = \frac{8}{24} + \frac{9}{24} = \frac{17}{24}$

**Answer** Ms. Tompkins has completed $\frac{17}{24}$ of the trip.

15. There are 24 students in Rob's class. One-third of the students walk or ride a bike to school. How many students do not walk or ride a bike?

▸ **Show your work.**

$\frac{1}{3} \times 24 = \frac{24}{3} = 8$; $24 - 8 = 16$

**Answer** 16 students do not walk or ride bikes.

Unit 3 ▪ Focus on Number and Operations—Fractions  **215**

This chart correlates the Unit 3 Review items with the lessons in which the concepts and skills are presented.

| Item | Lesson |
| --- | --- |
| 1 | 21 |
| 2 | 21 |
| 3 | 22 |
| 4 | 23 |
| 5 | 17 |
| 6 | 18 |
| 7 | 19 |
| 8 | 20 |
| 9 | 15 |
| 10 | 16 |
| 11 | 17 |
| 12 | 20 |
| 13 | 16 |
| 14 | 16 |
| 15 | 18 |
| 16 | 22 |
| 17 | 18 |
| 18 | 17 |
| 19 | 19 |
| 20 | 24 |

## Writing About Math

🖊️ Direct students to respond to the Unit 3 Essential Question. (This can also be found on student page 133.)

**Essential Question:**
How can you use models and equivalent fractions to perform all operations with fractions or mixed numbers?

Possible responses:
- Use equivalent fractions to add and subtract fractions.
- Models can help show what happens when multiplying or dividing with fractions.

| Unit Assessment |
| --- |
| • Unit 3 Review, *pp. 214–216* |
| • Unit 3 Performance Task (ONLINE) |

| Additional Assessment Options |
| --- |
| • Performance Task 1, *pp. 217–222* (ALSO ONLINE) |

**Optional Purchase:**
- iProgress Monitor (ONLINE)
- Progress Monitor Student Benchmark Assessment Booklet

---

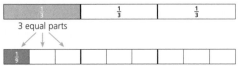

UNIT 3 Review

MP4 **16.** Explain how this model shows $\frac{1}{3} \div 3$. Include the quotient in your answer.

| $\frac{1}{3}$ | $\frac{1}{3}$ | $\frac{1}{3}$ |

3 equal parts

| $\frac{1}{9}$ | | | | | | | | |

Possible explanation: The top strip shows thirds. Each third is divided into 3 equal parts. The blue part is $\frac{1}{9}$ of the whole strip. So, $\frac{1}{3} \div 3 = 9$.

MP4 **17.** Explain how this model shows $\frac{2}{5} \times 15$. Include the product in your response.
Possible explanation: 15 is split into 5 groups of 3. Each group is $\frac{1}{5}$ of the total. So, 2 groups are $\frac{2}{5}$ of the total, so $\frac{2}{5} \times 15 = 6$.

MP6 **18.** Greg has 60-inches of braided leather. He plans to cut 8-inch pieces to make leather key chains. Does Greg have enough to make 8 key chains? Explain.
No. Possible explanation: $60 \div 8 = 7\frac{1}{2}$. He can make 7 key chains, but not 8.

MP1 **19.** Gina has a square garden that is 20 yards on each side. She uses a rectangular area $\frac{1}{2}$ yard wide and 6 yards long for tulips. How much of the garden can be used for other plants?
🖊️ **Show your work.**
$(20 \times 20) - (\frac{1}{2} \times 6) = 400 - 3 = 397$

**Answer** Gina can use 397 square yards for other plants.

MP1 **20.** Janine is using an old silk dress for part of a quilt. She will make $\frac{1}{4}$ of the quilt from the dress. Janine divides this area into 2 equal parts and adds fancy stitching to one part. What fraction of the quilt will have dress fabric with fancy stitching?
🖊️ **Show your work.**
$\frac{1}{4} \div 2 = \frac{1}{2} \times \frac{1}{4} = \frac{1}{8}$

**Answer** $\frac{1}{8}$ of the quilt will have dress fabric with fancy stitching.

**216** Unit 3 ■ Focus on Number and Operations—Fractions

---

| Mathematical Practices | |
| --- | --- |
| **MP1** | **Make sense of problems and persevere in solving them.** |
| **Item 19:** Students analyze a problem and plan a solution. | |
| **Item 20:** Students explore the meaning of a problem and solve. | |
| **MP4** | **Model with mathematics.** |
| **Item 16:** Students explain the relationship between quantities in two models. | |
| **Item 17:** Students explain an equation by using a model. | |
| **MP6** | **Attend to precision.** |
| **Item 18:** Students precisely express an answer for a problem context. | |

## Performance Tasks

Performance Tasks show your understanding of the Math that you have learned. You will be doing various Performance Tasks as you complete your work in this text.

### Beginning This Task

The next five pages provide you with the beginning of a Performance Task. You will be given 5 items to complete, and each item will have two or more parts. As you complete these items you will:

I   Demonstrate that you have mastered mathematical skills and concepts

II  Reason through a problem to a solution, and explain your reasoning

III Use models and apply them to real-world situations.

### Extending This Task

Your teacher may extend this Performance Task with additional items provided in our online resources at sadlierconnect.com.

### Scoring This Task

Your response to each item will be assessed against a rubric, or scoring guide. Some items will be worth 1 or 2 points, and others will be worth more. In each item you will show your work or explain your reasoning.

---

**ONLINE** Customize Performance Task 1

Performance Task 1 in *Progress Mathematics* also provides students with additional practice. You can use the online items of Performance Task 1 to customize the amount and kind of performance task practice based on your ongoing evaluation of your students. You may choose to challenge some students, to give extra experience with a particular kind of task for other students, or to extend exposure to performance assessments for the entire class.

Go to **sadlierconnect.com** to download the following resources for Performance Task 1.

- Additional Items
- Additional Teacher Support
- Additional Scoring Rubrics

---

## Performance Task 1 Overview

Performance Task 1 in *Progress Mathematics* provides students with practice for the types of items that may be found on standardized performance assessments.

Various item formats, including short- and extended-response items and technology-enhanced items, are included in the tasks. All items connect mathematical content correlated to the mathematical practices.

Items in Performance Task 1 are based on three primary types of tasks.

**Type I**   Mastery of mathematical concepts, skills and procedures

**Type II**  Using and explaining mathematical reasoning

**Type III** Modeling problem situations in a real-world context

Performance Task 1 begins with a collection of five self-contained items in the Student Book and continues with additional items online at **sadlierconnect.com**.

**Introduce Performance Task 1** Read student page 217 with the class. Explain that Performance Task 1 may cover any of the math they have learned in Units 1–3. Orient students to each item and communicate helpful reminders that will enable students to approach each item successfully. Once students have completed each item, go over the correct responses with them.

**Recommended Pacing** Administer Performance Task 1 on Student Book pages 218-222 over five 20-minute sessions.

**Teacher Resources** For each task, the teacher materials include:

- Item types and purposes
- Correlations to *Standards for Mathematical Practice*, and Depth of Knowledge (DOK) levels
- Suggested administration procedures
- Scoring Rubric

# Item 1: Yummy Strawberries at the Farmers Market

| Item | Type | Purpose |
|------|------|---------|
| **1.a.** | II | Explain an error in a solved expression. |
| **1.b.** | I | Evaluate an expression. |
| **1.c.** | III | Write an expression for a real-world problem. |
| **1.d.** | I | Evaluate the expression from item 1.c. |

| Item | MP | DOK |
|------|-----|-----|
| **1.a.** | 3 | Level 3 |
| **1.b.** | 2 | Level 1 |
| **1.c.** | 2 | Level 2 |
| **1.d.** | 6 | Level 1 |

## Administering Item 1 (Pacing: 20 minutes)

Ask a volunteer to read the introductory paragraph. Have others describe the situation in their own words.

**Item 1.a.** (7 minutes)

Students should understand that Olga is only buying strawberries for the children that eat them.

**Item 1.b.** (3 minutes)

Remind students to line up their factors correctly when multiplying.

**Item 1.c.** (6 minutes)

Encourage a discussion on which members of the class are going to be eating strawberries at the class party. Students should explain that they need to multiply the number of students eating strawberries by 3.

**Item 1.d.** (4 minutes)

Have students compare their answers from items 1.b. and 1.d. Encourage a discussion on why the answers are different.

---

### Yummy Strawberries at the Farmer's Market

1. Olga goes to the farmer's market to buy strawberries for a class party. There are 27 children in her class, but 9 of them do not like strawberries. Olga wants to buy 3 strawberries for each classmate who likes strawberries.

   a. Olga writes the expression $(3 \times 27) - 9$ to find the number of strawberries she should buy. What error did Olga make when she wrote the expression?

   Possible answer: Olga put the parentheses in the wrong place. The parentheses should be around $27 - 9$, the operation that she needs to do first.

   b. Evaluate the expression that Olga wrote in item 1.a. above: $(3 \times 27) - 9$.

   The value of Olga's expression is 72.
   $(3 \times 27) - 9$
   $81 - 9$
   $72$

   c. Write a correct expression Olga can use to find the number of strawberries she should buy.

   $3 \times (27 - 9)$ or $(27 - 9) \times 3$

   d. Evaluate the expression you wrote in item 1.c. above. How many strawberries should Olga buy?

   $3 \times (27 - 9)$
   $3 \times 18$
   $54$
   $54$

   Olga should buy 54 strawberries.

---

## Scoring Rubric

| Item | Points | Student Responses |
|------|--------|-------------------|
| **1.a.** | 2 | Correctly identifies the error. |
| | 1 | Does not clearly state reasoning. |
| | 0 | Does not identify the error. |
| **1.b.** | 2 | Evaluates the expression correctly. |
| | 1 | Makes a minor error when evaluating the expression. |
| | 0 | Makes a major error when evaluating the expression. |
| **1.c.** | 2 | Writes a correct expression. |
| | 1 | Minor error in writing expression. |
| | 0 | Major error in writing expression. |
| **1.d.** | 2 | Evaluates the expression correctly. |
| | 1 | Minor error in evaluating the expression. |
| | 0 | Major error in evaluating the expression. |

## Performance Task 1

### Boxes of Granola Bars

2. Ms. Sandino, the owner of a health food super store, receives 14 boxes of granola bars. Each box contains 248 bars.

   a. Find the total number of granola bars Ms. Sandino receives.

   Ms. Sandino receives 3,472 granola bars.

   Possible solution:

   ```
      1 3
      248
   ×   14
      992
   + 2 480
   ─────────
    3,472
   ```

   b. Ms. Sandino wants to put an equal number of granola bars on each of 8 display racks. Find the number of granola bars she should put on each display rack. Use your answer from item 2.a. above.

   Ms. Sandino should put 434 granola bars on each display rack.

   Possible solution:

   | | 400 | 30 | 4 |
   |---|---|---|---|
   | 8 | 3,472<br>−3,200 | 272<br>−240 | 32<br>−32 |
   | | 272 | 32 | 0 |

   c. Show how you can use the relationship between multiplication and division to check your answer to item 2.b. above.

   Possible work:

   ```
      2 3
      434
   ×    8
   ─────────
    3,472
   ```

## Scoring Rubric

| Item | Points | Student Responses |
|---|---|---|
| 2.a. | 2 | Correctly multiplies 14 boxes by 248 bars. |
| | 1 | Makes a minor computational error when multiplying. |
| | 0 | Does not use multiplication and finds an incorrect answer. |
| 2.b. | 2 | Correctly divides 3,472 bars by 8 display racks. |
| | 1 | Makes a minor computational error when dividing. |
| | 0 | Does not use division and finds an incorrect answer. |
| 2.c. | 2 | Correctly multiplies 434 bars by 8 display racks to check answer. |
| | 1 | Makes a minor computational error when multiplying. |
| | 0 | Does not use multiplication and answer does not check out. |

# Item 2: Boxes of Granola Bars

| Item | Type | Purpose |
|---|---|---|
| 2.a. | I | Solve a real-world multiplication problem. |
| 2.b. | I | Solve a real-world division problem. |
| 2.c. | II | Use related multiplication and division facts to check a solution. |

| Item | MP | DOK |
|---|---|---|
| 2.a. | 1 | Level 1 |
| 2.b. | 1 | Level 1 |
| 2.c. | 6 | Level 3 |

## Administering Item 2 (Pacing: 20 minutes)

Ask a volunteer to read the introductory paragraph. Have others describe the situation in their own words.

### Item 2.a. (7 minutes)

Students should see that they need to multiply to find the number of total granola bars in the 248 boxes.

### Item 2.b. (7 minutes)

Encourage a discussion on determining which operation to use when finding how many equal groups can be made from a group of objects.

### Item 2.c. (6 minutes)

Students should check their division by multiplying their quotient by the number of display racks, 8.

## Item 3: Bean Stew

| Item | Type | Purpose |
|------|------|---------|
| 3.a. | II | Evaluate an estimate to determine its reasonableness. |
| 3.b. | III | Add two mixed numbers. |
| 3.c. | II | Explain how the procedures used help to solve the problem. |
| 3.d. | III | Subtract a mixed number and a fraction. |

| Item | MP | DOK |
|------|-----|------|
| 3.a. | 3 | Level 2 |
| 3.b. | 5 | Level 2 |
| 3.c. | 3 | Level 3 |
| 3.d. | 1 | Level 2 |

## Administering Item 3 (Pacing: 20 minutes)

Ask a volunteer to read the introductory paragraph. Have others describe the situation in their own words.

### Item 3.a. (5 minutes)

Suggest that students use benchmark fractions to help them solve the problem.

### Item 3.b. (5 minutes)

Encourage a discussion on how to use equivalent fractions to solve the problem.

### Item 3.c. (5 minutes)

Suggest to students that they think about what to do to explain to another student how to use equivalent fractions to add.

### Item 3.d. (5 minutes)

Students should see that they need to use equivalent fractions to solve.

---

**Bean Stew**

3. Andrew purchases two kinds of beans to make stew. He buys $2\frac{1}{2}$ pounds of pinto beans and $1\frac{5}{8}$ pounds of kidney beans.

   a. Andrew estimates that he purchases about 3 pounds of beans altogether. Do you agree or disagree with his estimate? Explain.

   Possible answer: I disagree with Andrew's estimate. I know $\frac{5}{8}$ pound is more than $\frac{4}{8}$ pound, or $\frac{1}{2}$ pound. So $2\frac{1}{2} + 1\frac{5}{8}$ would be a little more than $2\frac{1}{2} + 1\frac{1}{2}$, which is 4. A better estimate would be 4 pounds.

   b. Find the exact weight of the beans Andrew purchases.
   Andrew purchases $\frac{33}{8}$ or $4\frac{1}{8}$ pounds of beans.
   Possible solution:
   $2\frac{1}{2} + 1\frac{5}{8}$
   $\frac{5}{2} + \frac{13}{8}$
   $\frac{20}{8} + \frac{13}{8} = \frac{33}{8}$ or $4\frac{1}{8}$

   c. Explain how knowing about equivalent fractions helped you find the exact weight of the beans in item 3.b. above.
   Possible answer:
   To add fractions, the fractions must have like denominators. So, knowing that $\frac{1}{2}$ and $\frac{4}{8}$ (or $\frac{5}{2}$ and $\frac{20}{8}$) were equivalent fractions made it possible for me to add the fractions.

   d. Andrew uses $\frac{3}{4}$ pound of the beans he buys to make a stew. How many pounds of beans does Andrew have left?
   Andrew has $\frac{27}{8}$ or $3\frac{3}{8}$ pounds of beans left.
   Possible solution:
   $\frac{33}{8} - \frac{3}{4}$
   $\frac{33}{8} - \frac{6}{8} = \frac{27}{8}$ or $3\frac{3}{8}$

---

### Scoring Rubric

| Item | Points | Student Responses |
|------|--------|-------------------|
| 3.a. | 2 | Correctly reasons that the estimate is too low. |
|      | 1 | Identifies the error but does not provide reasoning. |
|      | 0 | Does not identify the error. |
| 3.b. | 2 | Finds the exact weight. |
|      | 1 | Makes a minor error when adding fractions. |
|      | 0 | Does not find an answer. |
| 3.c. | 2 | Correctly explains reasoning. |
|      | 1 | Explanation lacks clarity. |
|      | 0 | Cannot explain reasoning. |
| 3.d. | 2 | Finds the weight of remaining beans. |
|      | 1 | Makes a minor error when subtracting fractions. |
|      | 0 | Does not find an answer. |

## Advertising a Sale on Organic Avocados

4. Ms. Sandino makes a rectangular sign to advertise an unexpected bulk shipment of organic avocados. The sign is $\frac{3}{10}$ meter wide and $\frac{4}{5}$ meter long.

a. What is the area of the sign?
The area of the sign is $\frac{12}{50}$, or $\frac{6}{25}$, square meter.
Possible solution:
$A = \ell \times w$
$= \frac{4}{5} \times \frac{3}{10}$
$= \frac{12}{50}$, or $\frac{6}{25}$

b. The store manager looks at the sign and says, "I think you should make a new sign. The area of the new sign should be $\frac{5}{4}$ the area of this sign." Does the store manager want the new sign to be larger or smaller than the sign Ms. Sandino made? Explain how you know.
The store manager wants the sign to be larger. Possible explanation: Multiplying a number by a fraction greater than 1 results in a product greater than that number. Since $\frac{5}{4}$ is greater than 1, $\frac{5}{4} \times$ the area of the sign will be greater than the area of the sign.

c. Find the area for the sign that the store manager would like to have.
The area that the store manager would like the sign to have is $\frac{30}{100}$, or $\frac{3}{10}$, square meter.
Possible solution:
$\frac{5}{4} \times \frac{6}{25} = \frac{30}{100}$ or $\frac{3}{10}$

d. Find the length and width of a sign that would have an area $\frac{5}{4}$ the area of Ms. Sandino's sign.
Answers will vary. The two numbers in the answer must have a product of $\frac{30}{100}$ or $\frac{3}{10}$. Possible answers: $\frac{3}{5}$ meter and $\frac{1}{2}$ meter; $\frac{5}{10}$ meter and $\frac{6}{10}$ meter; $\frac{2}{25}$ meter and $\frac{15}{4}$ meters; $\frac{3}{20}$ meter and $\frac{10}{5}$ meters.

### Scoring Rubric

| Item | Points | Student Responses |
|---|---|---|
| 4.a. | 2 | Correctly multiplies two fractions. |
| | 1 | Makes a minor error when multiplying two fractions. |
| | 0 | Incorrectly multiplies fractions. |
| 4.b. | 2 | States the correct answer with correct reasoning. |
| | 1 | States the correct answer with reasoning that is not entirely clear. |
| | 0 | States incorrect answer with incorrect reasoning. |
| 4.c. | 2 | Correctly multiplies two fractions. |
| | 1 | Makes minor multiplication error. |
| | 0 | Incorrectly multiplies fractions. |
| 4.d. | 2 | Correctly identifies two sides. |
| | 1 | Identifies one correct side. |
| | 0 | Does not identify sides. |

## Item 4: Advertising a Sale on Organic Avocados

| Item | Type | Purpose |
|---|---|---|
| 4.a. | III | Find the area of a rectangle with fractional dimensions. |
| 4.b. | II | Explain that multiplication by a fraction greater than one results in a product greater than the original number. |
| 4.c. | III | Find the area of a rectangle with fractional dimensions. |
| 4.d. | III | Determine possible dimensions given an area and a scale factor. |

| Item | MP | DOK |
|---|---|---|
| 4.a. | 5 | Level 2 |
| 4.b. | 3 | Level 3 |
| 4.c. | 1 | Level 2 |
| 4.d. | 7 | Level 4 |

### Administering Item 4 (Pacing: 20 minutes)

Ask a volunteer to read the introductory paragraph. Have others describe the situation in their own words.

**Item 4.a.** (5 minutes)
Students should see that they need to multiply the two fractions to find the area.

**Item 4.b.** (3 minutes)
Encourage a discussion on multiplying a number by a fraction greater than 1. Students should know that the product will be greater than the original number.

**Item 4.c.** (5 minutes)
Students understand that they need to multiply the area from item 4.a. by the scale factor.

**Item 4.d.** (7 minutes)
Have students make a table to show all of the possibilities of the sign's dimensions.

## Item 5: The Deli Counter

| Item | Type | Purpose |
|------|------|---------|
| 5.a. | IIII | Draw a model of a problem situation and explain how the model shows the solution. |
| 5.b. | I | Write an equation that matches the model from item 5.a. |
| 5.c. | II | Use the relationship between multiplication and division to show the equation is correct. |
| 5.d. | III | Write a problem situation to match the expression. |

| Item | MP | DOK |
|------|-----|------|
| 5.a. | 4 | Level 1 |
| 5.b. | 4 | Level 2 |
| 5.c. | 6 | Level 3 |
| 5.d. | 2 | Level 3 |

## Administering Item 5 (Pacing: 20 minutes)

Ask a volunteer to read the introductory paragraph. Have others describe the situation in their own words.

### Item 5.a. (7 minutes)

Suggest that students think how many pounds of turkey there are and how much is needed for each sandwich.

### Item 5.b. (3 minutes)

Have students study their model to help them determine the equation.

### Item 5.c. (3 minutes)

Remind students that the relationship between multiplication and division does not change because they are working with fractions.

### Item 5.d. (7 minutes)

Suggest to students look at item 5.a. to help them think of a situation.

### The Deli Counter

5. Terrence works the late afternoon shift at the deli counter. He uses 3 pounds of turkey breast to make sandwiches. He puts $\frac{1}{4}$ pound of turkey breast in each sandwich.

   a. Draw a model that Terrence could use to find how many sandwiches he can make. Explain how your model shows the number of sandwiches Terrence can make.

Possible explanation: Each circle represents 1 pound of turkey breast partitioned into 4 equal parts. Each part represents $\frac{1}{4}$ pound, the amount of turkey in each sandwich. To find the number of sandwiches, count the number of equal parts. There are 12 equal parts. So, Terrence can make 12 sandwiches.

   b. Write a division equation that your model in item 5.a. above shows.
$3 \div \frac{1}{4} = 12$

   c. Use the relationship between multiplication and division to show that your division equation is correct.
$3 \div \frac{1}{4} = 12$ because $12 \times \frac{1}{4} = \frac{12}{4}$ or 3.

   d. After Terrence finishes making the sandwiches, he begins to slice some cheddar cheese. He writes the expression $\frac{1}{2} \div 10$. Write and solve a story problem that matches Terrence's expression.

Possible problem and solution: Terrence has $\frac{1}{2}$ pound of cheddar cheese. He slices the cheddar cheese into 10 equal-weight slices. What is the weight of each slice?
$\frac{1}{2} \div 10 = \frac{1}{20}$ because $\frac{1}{20} \times 10 = \frac{10}{20}$ or $\frac{1}{2}$.
Each slice weighs $\frac{1}{20}$ pound.

### Scoring Rubric

| Item | Points | Student Responses |
|------|--------|-------------------|
| 5.a. | 2 | Draws an accurate model and gives a clear explanation. |
|      | 1 | Explanation lacks some clarity. |
|      | 0 | Draws and explains incorrectly. |
| 5.b. | 2 | Writes a correct equation. |
|      | 1 | Minor error in equation. |
|      | 0 | Writes an incorrect equation. |
| 5.c. | 2 | Uses correct reasoning. |
|      | 1 | Explanation lacks clarity. |
|      | 0 | Does not use relationship. |
| 5.d. | 2 | Interprets a correct situation. |
|      | 1 | Interprets a correct situation but reasoning lacks clarity. |
|      | 0 | Does not interpret situation. |

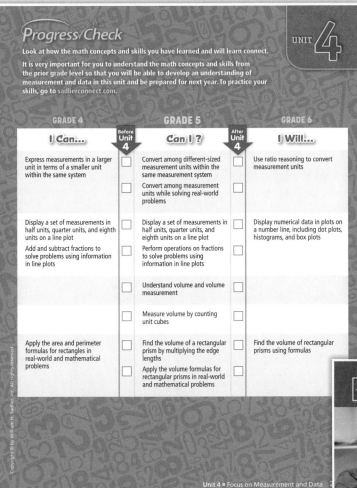

**Progress Check**

Look at how the math concepts and skills you have learned and will learn connect.

It is very important for you to understand the math concepts and skills from the prior grade level so that you will be able to develop an understanding of measurement and data in this unit and be prepared for next year. To practice your skills, go to sadlierconnect.com.

UNIT 4

| GRADE 4 | | GRADE 5 | | GRADE 6 |
| --- | --- | --- | --- | --- |
| **I Can...** | **Before Unit 4** | **Can I ?** | **After Unit 4** | **I Will...** |
| Express measurements in a larger unit in terms of a smaller unit within the same system | ☐ | Convert among different-sized measurement units within the same measurement system | ☐ | Use ratio reasoning to convert measurement units |
| | | Convert among measurement units while solving real-world problems | ☐ | |
| Display a set of measurements in half units, quarter units, and eighth units on a line plot | ☐ | Display a set of measurements in half units, quarter units, and eighth units on a line plot | ☐ | Display numerical data in plots on a number line, including dot plots, histograms, and box plots |
| Add and subtract fractions to solve problems using information in line plots | | Perform operations on fractions to solve problems using information in line plots | ☐ | |
| | | Understand volume and volume measurement | ☐ | |
| | | Measure volume by counting unit cubes | ☐ | |
| Apply the area and perimeter formulas for rectangles in real-world and mathematical problems | ☐ | Find the volume of a rectangular prism by multiplying the edge lengths | ☐ | Find the volume of rectangular prisms using formulas |
| | | Apply the volume formulas for rectangular prisms in real-world and mathematical problems | ☐ | |

Unit 4 ■ Focus on Measurement and Data

**Student Page 223**

# Progress Check

Progress Check is a self-assessment tool that students can use to gauge their own progress. Research shows that when students take accountability for their learning, motivation increases.

Before students begin work in Unit 4, have them check any items they know they can do well. Explain that it is fine if they don't check any of the boxes; they will have the opportunity to learn and practice all the standards through the course of the unit.

Let them know that at the end of the unit they will review their checklists to check their progress. After students have completed the last lesson of the unit, before they begin the Unit 4 Review, you will be prompted to have students revisit this page.

# HOME ◆ CONNECT...

The Home Connect feature is a way to keep parents or other adult family members apprised of what their children are learning. The key learning objectives are listed, and some ideas for related activities and discussions are included.

Explain to students that they can share the Home Connect page at home with their families. Let students know there is an activity connected to their classroom learning that they can do with their families.

Encourage students and their parents to share their experiences using the suggestions on the Home Connect. You may wish to invite students to share this work with the class.

## HOME ◆ CONNECT...

**In this unit your child will:**
- Convert customary and metric measurement units.
- Use line plots.
- Understand concepts of volume measurement.
- Measure volume using a variety of strategies and formulas.

**Ways to Help Your Child**

Ask your child, "What did you learn today?" That question might sometimes be met with apathy, but be persistent. You will show that you are interested in their daily lives and care about your child's education. Additionally, it will keep you informed about what's happening in the classroom so you can help make connections at home.

If you have ever rented a truck during a move, you know how important it is to accurately estimate volume. Will all of your boxes and personal items fit into the moving truck? Not enough space presents a big problem, but so can too much extra space.

Volume is an attribute of three-dimensional space. It describes the amount of space that a solid figure like a cube occupies. There are two formulas for measuring the volume of a right rectangular prism:

**Volume = length × width × height**
**Volume = area of the base × height**

In the lessons that follow, your child will understand why these volume formulas work by obtaining a deeper conceptual understanding of volume.

**Activity:** Gather several boxes of different sizes and shapes. Ask your child to estimate the volume of each one. Then, find the volumes. Discuss together.

**ONLINE**
For more Home Connect activities, continue online at sadlierconnect.com

224   Unit 4   Focus on Measurement and Data

**Student Page 224**

## UNIT PLANNER

| Lesson | Objective |
|---|---|
| **25** Convert Customary Measurement Units | Convert customary units of liquid volume, weight, and length. |
| **26** Convert Metric Measurement Units | Convert measurements between metric units to solve real-world problems. |
| **27** Problem Solving: Use Line Plots | Solve real-world problems representing and interpreting data on line plots. |
| **28** Understand Concepts of Volume Measurement | Understand volume as the number of unit cubes in a three-dimensional figure. |
| **29** Measure Volume | Use the concept of volume and counting unit cubes to determine the volume of right rectangular prisms. |
| **30** Find Volume: Relate Packing of Unit Cubes to Multiplying | Use multiplication to find the volume of a right rectangular prism. |
| **31** Find Volume: Use the Associative Property | Use the Associative Property of Multiplication to find volumes of right rectangular prisms. |
| **32** Problem Solving: Apply Volume Formulas for Prisms | Use formulas to find volume. |
| **33** Problem Solving: Decompose Figures to Find Volume | Find the volumes of composite three-dimensional figures. |

| Essential Question | Words to Know |
|---|---|
| How can you convert a measurement from one customary unit to another? | customary units of liquid volume<br>customary units of weight<br>customary units of length |
| How can you convert a measurement from one metric unit to another? | metric units of length<br>base unit<br>metric units of liquid volume<br>metric units of mass |
| How can you solve real-world problems using line plots? | line plot |
| What is volume and how do you measure it? | unit cube<br>volume<br>cubic unit |
| How do you measure the volume of a right rectangular prism? | |
| How can you multiply to find the volume of a right rectangular prism? | |
| How is the Associative Property of Multiplication related to calculating volumes of right rectangular prisms? | Associative Property of Multiplication |
| How do you find volume using a formula? | |
| How do you find the volume of a composite figure? | |

## Unit Assessment

- Unit 4 Review, *pp. 298–300*
- Unit 4 Performance Task  ONLINE

## Additional Assessment Options

**Optional Purchase:**
- iProgress Monitor  ONLINE
- Progress Monitor Student Benchmark Assessment Booklet

### ONLINE  Digital Resources

- Home Connect Activities
- Unit Performance Tasks
- Additional Practice
- Fluency Practice
- Teacher Resources
- iProgress Monitor (optional purchase)

**Go to SadlierConnect.com to access your Digital Resources.**

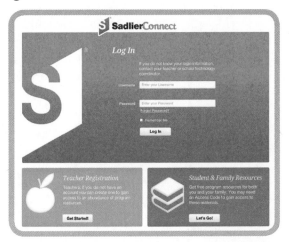

**For more detailed instructions see page T3.**

## LEARNING PROGRESSIONS

This page provides more in-depth detail on the development of math concepts and skills across the grade levels. See also the unit Progress Check page in the Student Edition for a roadmap of the Learning Progressions.

### Grade 4

- Students know the relative sizes of units within a measurement system and convert measurements from a larger unit to a smaller unit.
- Students apply the area and perimeter formulas for rectangles to solve real world and mathematical problems, including finding a missing length or width.
- Students display a set of measurements in half, quarter, and eighth units on a line plot and add and subtract fractions to solve problems based on the displayed data.

### Grade 5

- Students convert among different-sized measurement units within the same measurement system while solving mathematical and real-world problems. Conversion of units within the metric system reinforces place value concepts for whole numbers and decimals, and provides practical connections between decimals and fractions.
- Students make a line plot to display a set of measurements in half units, quarter units, and eighth units. They apply grade 5 fraction operations to solve problems involving data displayed on line plots.
- Students recognize volume as an attribute of three-dimensional figures and understand the concepts of a unit cube and volume measurement.
- Students measure volume by counting unit cubes.
- Students show that the volume found by packing a rectangular solid with unit cubes is the same as would be found by multiplying the edge lengths, or multiplying the height by the area of the base. They represent three-factor whole-number products as volumes.
- Students apply the formulas $V = \ell \times w \times h$ and $V = b \times h$ to find the volume of rectangular solids in real-world and mathematical problems.
- Students recognize volume as additive, and find the volumes of solid figures composed of two non-overlapping rectangular solids by adding the volumes of the two solids.

### Grade 6

- Students use ratio reasoning to convert measurement units.
- Students display numerical data in plots on a number line, including dot plots, histograms, and box plots.
- Students find the volume of a rectangular solid with fractional side lengths by packing it with unit cubes of appropriate side length and by multiplying edge lengths. They solve real-world and mathematical problems involving volumes of rectangular solids.

# Focus on Measurement and Data

**Essential Question:**
What strategies can you use to determine the capacity of a figure?

Unit 4 ■ Focus on Measurement and Data  225

## Essential Question:
What strategies can you use to determine the capacity of a figure?

As students become involved with the Essential Question they will learn about both the customary and metric measurement systems, including how to convert within each system. Also students will learn how to use models and how to use formulas to determine the volume.

## Conversation Starters

Have students discuss what they believe is happening in the photograph.

Ask questions such as: *Have any of you seen a scene like this? If so where did you see it? What do you think might be in the containers? Where do you think they came from and where might they be going?*

Point out that there is a lot of writing on the containers. *How might the writing help people with the containers?* (The writing could have numbers that identify what is in the containers. The writing could tell how large the containers are.)

*Suppose there were shoes in the container. How do you think the shoes are packaged so they can be put into the container?* (The shoes are put into shoeboxes and then the shoeboxes are put into cartons or bigger boxes. Then these boxes are put into the container.)

*Why do you think the items are put into containers to be sent on ships or on trucks?* (The containers will protect the items. Also, using the containers will help you send as many items as you can.)

Let pairs of students discuss how to solve problems involving measurement. Lead them to see that choosing a unit of measure is a good first step.

## Activity

Tell students that boxes of canned food are in the containers. They need to determine how many boxes will fit into a container. Have small groups of students solve these problems.

Ask students to tell how they would find the number of boxes that will fit into the container. *What if you had many same-size boxes of food? How could you use them to help find how many boxes would fit in the container? How could making models of the container and the boxes help?*

Lead a class discussion in which students share and explain their work. Students may describe how they first measured each box. Then they might describe how they grouped the boxes and measured to see if they would fit.

## OBJECTIVE
**Convert customary units of liquid volume, weight, and length.**

## ESSENTIAL QUESTION
Ask students for examples of units of measurement that are used to measure liquid volume, weight, and length. Students may share examples of customary units of measurement, such as inches and quarts. Others may even share some familiar customary unit conversions (12 inches = 1 foot, 4 quarts = 1 gallon). Tell students that they will encounter real-world problems that involve converting from one customary unit to another.

## FLUENCY PRACTICE
Fluency practice is available at **sadlierconnect.com**.

## Concept Development

### Understand: Converting larger customary units to smaller units

■ Students will be converting units within the customary unit measurement system to solve real-world problems. Students will need to use reasoning about the size of two units to choose whether to multiply or divide to perform the conversion.

■ Point out the blue box labeled "Customary Units of Liquid Volume". It may be useful for students to create a note card of conversions used throughout the lesson.

■ Make sure students understand why they should use multiplication to convert larger customary units to smaller units. Drawing a bar model will help students make the connection to what operation to use.

---

**Lesson 25 — Convert Customary Measurement Units**

**Essential Question:** How can you convert a measurement from one customary unit to another?

**Words to Know:**
- customary units of liquid volume
- customary units of weight
- customary units of length

In this lesson you will learn how to convert customary units of measurement to solve real-world problems.

**Understand: Converting larger customary units to smaller units**

> Jared buys 3 gallons of orange juice for a football team breakfast. The juice will be served in pitchers that hold 1 quart each. How many pitchers can Jared fill with juice?

To find the number of pitchers Jared can fill, you need to convert 3 gallons to the equivalent measurement in quarts. Look at the conversion chart for customary units of liquid volume. The chart shows that 1 gallon = 4 quarts.

**Customary Units of Liquid Volume**
1 pint (pt) = 2 cups (c)
1 quart (qt) = 2 pints
1 gallon (gal) = 4 quarts

**Method 1** Make a bar model.

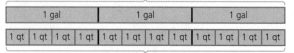

The model shows that there are 12 quarts in 3 gallons.

**Method 2** Write and solve an equation.
A gallon is larger than a quart. To convert from a larger unit to a smaller unit, multiply. *Multiply* the number of gallons of juice by the number of quarts in 1 gallon. Use *n* for the unknown number of quarts.

number of gallons × number of quarts in 1 gallon = number of quarts
$$3 \quad \times \quad 4 \quad = \quad n$$

Since 12 = *n*, 3 gallons = 12 quarts.

➡ Jared can fill 12 one-quart pitchers with juice.

---

## Words to Know

**customary units of liquid volume:** units of measure used in the customary system of measurement

**Example:** cup, pint, quart, and gallon

**customary units of weight:** units of measure used in the customary system of measurement

**Example:** ounce, pound, and ton

**customary units of length:** units of measure used in the customary system of measurement

**Example:** inch, foot, yard, and mile

**Glossary can be found on pp. 347–350.**

Lesson 25

**Guided Instruction**

**Understand:** Converting smaller customary units to larger units

> A truck loaded with building supplies weighs about 72,000 pounds. The driver wants to use a bridge whose weight limit is 35 tons per vehicle. Can the truck use this bridge?

To determine if the truck can use the bridge, you need to convert 72,000 pounds to the equivalent weight in tons. Look at the conversion chart for customary units of weight.

**Customary Units of Weight**
1 pound (lb) = 16 ounces (oz)
1 ton (t) = 2,000 pounds

A ton is larger than a pound. To convert from a smaller unit to a larger unit, divide. *Divide* the number of pounds the truck weighs by the number of pounds in 1 ton.

number of pounds ÷ number of pounds in 1 ton = number of tons
   72,000      ÷         2,000           =        $n$

Since 36 = $n$, 72,000 pounds is equivalent to 36 tons.

The loaded truck weighs about 36 tons. This is greater than the bridge weight limit of 35 tons per vehicle.

➡ The truck cannot use this bridge.

▰▰ For each problem on pages 226 and 227, compare the number in the original measurement to the number in the converted measurement. Tell what you notice about those conversions.
Possible answer: When you convert a customary measurement from a smaller unit to a larger unit, the converted measurement number becomes less than the original measurement number. When you convert a customary measurement from a larger unit to a smaller unit, the converted measurement number becomes greater than the original measurement number.

Unit 4 ▪ Focus on Measurement and Data **227**

---

**Understand: Converting smaller customary units to larger units**

■ Have students add the unit conversions in the blue box labeled "Customary Units of Weight" to their note card of conversions.

■ Make sure students understand why they should use division to convert smaller units to larger units.

■ Ask students if there is another way to solve the problem. Students should understand that they could also convert 35 tons to pounds, and then compare the weights in pounds.

▰▰▶ After students have answered this question, ask volunteers to share observations about converting from larger units to smaller units. Ask questions to direct the discussion such as: *What operation is used?* and *How does the number change?* Create a list of the observations on the board. Then, ask volunteers to share observations about converting from smaller units to larger units. Ask similar follow-up questions, if needed, and create another list of these observations. Direct students' attention to the differences between the two lists.

---

## Support English Language Learners

Most countries use the metric system. To help students who are unfamiliar with customary units, have real objects available that can demonstrate the scale and size of some standard customary units of measure. For example, display an empty gallon milk jug, an empty quart container, a 1-cup dry measuring cup, a 1-pound bag of rice, a 12-inch ruler, and a yardstick. Pick up each object, name the object and unit of measurement, and have students repeat the names and units of measurement. Place the objects around the room. Have students rotate to each object, observe the object, draw it on a sheet of paper, and label it with the appropriate unit of measurement.

# Guided Instruction

## Connect: What you know about customary units of measurement to solve real-world problems

Use this page to help students apply unit conversion within a multi-step problem-solving situation.

■ Tell students to add the "Customary Units of Length" to their note card of conversions. Students should now have a list of all of the unit conversions. Ask students how they can tell which units are the larger units and which units are the smaller units in their list.

■ Have students reread the problem statement. Ask them to circle the units in the problem and decide which direction to convert the units (feet to yards or yards to feet) and which operation should be used (multiplication or division).

■ Discuss the plan for the solution in Step 1. Ask students to identify the steps that are in this solution process. Students will have to determine their own plans as they solve multi-step real-world problems.

---

## Guided Instruction

### Connect: What you know about customary units of measurement to solve real-world problems

> Gia needs 130 feet of string. A spool of string contains 20 yards and costs $1.50. What is the total cost of the string that Gia must buy?

**Step 1**

Plan the solution.

To solve the problem, first convert 130 feet to yards. Next, determine how many spools of string Gia needs. Then multiply the number of spools by $1.50 to find the total cost of the string.

**Step 2**

Convert 130 feet of string to yards. Use the chart of customary units of length.

**Customary Units of Length**
1 foot (ft) = 12 inches (in.)
1 yard (yd) = 3 feet
1 mile (m) = 5,280 feet
1 mile (m) = 1,760 yards

You are converting from a smaller unit, feet, to a larger unit, yards, so divide.

**Remember!**
To convert from *larger units to smaller units*, multiply.
To convert from *smaller units to larger units*, divide.

number of feet ÷ number of feet in 1 yard = number of yards
$$130 \div 3 = n$$

Since $\frac{130}{3} = n$, 130 feet $= \frac{130}{3}$ yards, which equals $43\frac{1}{3}$ yards.

**Step 3**

Determine how many spools of string Gia needs. Two spools is 2 × 20, or 40 yards. This is not quite enough, therefore Gia must buy three spools.

**Step 4**

Multiply the number of spools Gia needs by the cost of one spool.

3 spools of string × $1.50 for each spool = $4.50

➩ Gia must buy $4.50 worth of string.

---

## Math-to-Science Connection

**Converting Units** Many situations in science require the skill of unit conversion. A strong understanding of the context of these units will help as reference in later math and science courses. A kinesthetic exercise that can help reinforce these conversions is to have different class members work together to carefully divide a gallon of water into quarts, pints, cups, tablespoons, etc. to determine how many of each smaller unit fits into the bigger unit.

Guided Practice

**Convert the measurements.**

1. 5 feet = ▥ inches

   1 foot = 12 inches

   An inch is smaller than a foot, so multiply.

   $5 \times 12 = \underline{60}$

   5 feet = $\underline{60}$ inches

2. 14 cups = ▥ pints

   1 pint = 2 cups

   A pint is $\underline{\text{larger}}$ than a cup, so $\underline{\text{divide}}$.

   $14 \underline{\div} \underline{2} = \underline{7}$

   14 cups = $\underline{7}$ pints

3. 1,080 seconds = ▥ minutes

   1 minute = 60 seconds

   A minute is $\underline{\text{larger}}$ than a second, so $\underline{\text{divide}}$.

   $1{,}080 \underline{\div} 60 = \underline{18}$

   1,080 seconds = $\underline{18}$ minutes

4. 176 ounces = ▥ pounds

   1 pound = 16 ounces

   A pound is $\underline{\text{larger}}$ than an ounce, so $\underline{\text{divide}}$.

   $176 \underline{\div} \underline{16} = \underline{11}$

   176 ounces = $\underline{11}$ pounds

**Solve the problem.**

5. Mariah has a new puppy that weighs 6 pounds 4 ounces. What is the weight of the puppy in ounces? Show your work.
   Change 6 pounds to ounces. 16 ounces = 1 pound. An ounce is smaller than a pound, so multiply: 6 x 16 = 96. 6 pounds is 96 ounces. Add the 4 ounces. The puppy weighs 100 ounces.

☝ Think · Pair · Share

MP6 6. Seth and Brian ran the 200-yard dash at the track meet. Brian reached the finish line in 30 seconds. Seth ran 25 feet per second. Who finished the race first? Explain your reasoning.
   Seth finished the race first. Possible explanation: Since 1 yard = 3 feet, the length of the race is 200 × 3 = 600 feet. So, it took Seth 600 ÷ 25 = 24 seconds to finish the race. 24 < 30, so Seth finished the race before Brian.

Unit 4 ▪ Focus on Measurement and Data  **229**

## Mathematical Practices

Mathematical Practice Standards underline the teaching and understanding of all concepts and skills presented. The emphasis of specific practices is noted throughout the guided and independent practice of this lesson.

**MP6  Attend to precision.**

**Item 6:** Students use measurement units appropriately and convert to a common unit in order to determine who finished first. Students explain their reasoning using precise language and justify the answer.

## Observational Assessment

Use page 229 to assess whether students are able to connect the correct operation to the conversion. They should be able to identify whether they are converting from larger units to smaller units or smaller units to larger units and choose the appropriate operation.

Note that the Guided and Independent Practice exercises for this lesson includes seconds, minutes, and hours conversions. These conversions were covered in prior academic years, but were not covered in this lesson. Students may need assistance on recalling how to make these conversions. Students will encounter real-world problems in and out of the classroom that require them to make these conversions.

☝ **Think·Pair·Share**

**Peer Collaboration** Ask each student to write a sentence describing the steps they will use to answer this question. Then ask students to share their problem-solving strategy with a partner. Ask a few partners to explain any differences between their strategies. Follow up questions could include:

- *How many seconds did it take for Seth to run the race?*

- *How fast was Brian running in feet per second? Yards per second?*

Reinforce the idea that there are multiple correct strategies for justifying the answer of who finished the race first.

### Return to the Essential Question

Reread the Lesson 25 Essential Question on page 226: *How can you convert a measurement from one customary unit to another?*

Ask volunteers to use what they learned in this lesson to answer this question.
(Possible response: If the units are going from larger to smaller, I can multiply to get the new units. If the units are going from smaller to larger, I can divide.)

# Independent Practice

## Concept Application

Students may work independently on these pages in the classroom or at home. They may refer to the first four pages of the lesson to revisit the instruction or to see a worked-out example.

**Common Errors** and **Teaching Tips** may help you support student learning either in the classroom or as a follow-up for work done at home.

## Teaching Tips

### Items 1-8

Help students recognize whether the units are going from larger to smaller or smaller to larger. Some of the larger numbers may require extended calculation time. Have students show their work for multiplication and division.

### Item 2

This exercise includes a minutes to hours conversion. Conversions between seconds, minutes, and hours were covered in prior academic years, but were not covered in this lesson. Students may need assistance on recalling how to make these conversions.

### Independent Practice

**Complete the tables to convert from one customary unit to another.**

1.

| miles | × or ÷ | feet |
|---|---|---|
| 1 | × 5,280 | 5,280 |
| 2 | × 5,280 | 10,560 |
| 3 | × 5,280 | 15,840 |

2.

| minutes | × or ÷ | hours |
|---|---|---|
| 60 | ÷ 60 | 1 |
| 300 | ÷ 60 | 5 |
| 720 | ÷ 60 | 12 |

3.

| pints | × or ÷ | cups |
|---|---|---|
| 1 | × 2 | 2 |
| 4 | × 2 | 8 |
| 8 | × 2 | 16 |

4.

| pounds | × or ÷ | tons |
|---|---|---|
| 2,000 | ÷ 2,000 | 1 |
| 6,000 | ÷ 2,000 | 3 |
| 12,000 | ÷ 2,000 | 6 |

**Convert the measurements.**

5. 45 yards = ▨ feet

   1 yard = 3 feet

   A foot is smaller than a yard, so multiply.

   45 × 3 = __135__

   45 yards = __135__ feet

6. 9 gallons = ▨ quarts

   1 gallon = 4 quarts

   A quart is __smaller__ than a gallon, so __multiply__.

   9 _×_ _4_ = _36_

   9 gallons = __36__ quarts

7. 3,000 pounds = ▨ tons

   1 ton = 2,000 pounds

   A ton is __larger__ than a pound, so __divide__.

   3,000 _÷_ _2,000_ = _1.5_

   3,000 pounds = __1.5__ tons

8. 780 inches = ▨ feet

   1 foot = 12 inches

   A foot is __larger__ than an inch, so __divide__.

   780 _÷_ _12_ = _65_

   780 inches = __65__ feet

## Writing About Math

🖍 ▸ **Write a Narrative Text** Ask students to write a narrative story about a character who experiences events that require at least two customary unit conversions. Have students brainstorm to gather ideas of real-world situations in which unit conversion would be necessary, such as cooking or driving. Students should use narrative techniques such as dialogue, description, and pacing to describe the event sequence. Once students finish their stories, ask volunteers to read their stories aloud.

## Independent Practice

**Circle every correct answer.**

9. Which of the following are equal to 440 yards?

   **(a.)** 15,840 inches

   **b.** $146\frac{2}{3}$ feet

   **(c.)** 1,320 feet

   **(d.)** $\frac{1}{4}$ mile

**Order the measurements from *largest* to *smallest*. Show your work.**

10. 15 gallons, 260 cups, 80 quarts Possible student work:
    1 gallon = 4 quarts, so 15 gallons = 15 × 4 = 60 quarts
    1 quart = 4 cups, so 260 cups = 260 ÷ 4 = 65 quarts
    80 quarts > 65 quarts > 60 quarts

    Answer <u>80 quarts, 260 cups, 15 gallons</u>

11. 0.5 ton, 1,800 pounds, 27,200 ounces Possible student work:
    1 ton = 2,000 pounds, so 0.5 ton = 0.5 × 2,000 pounds = 1,000 pounds
    1 pound = 16 ounces, so 27,200 ounces = 27,200 ÷ 16 = 1,700 pounds
    1,800 pounds > 1,700 pounds > 1,000 pounds

    Answer <u>1,800 pounds, 27,200 ounces, 0.5 ton</u>

**Complete parts a–d to solve the problem.**

12. Josiah is building a fence around the perimeter of his garden, which is shaped like a rectangle. His garden is 39 feet long and 45 feet wide. One yard of fencing costs $15. How much will Josiah spend on fencing?

    a. Find the perimeter of Josiah's garden in feet. <u>168</u> feet

    b. Convert the perimeter in feet to yards.

       A yard is <u>larger</u> than a foot, so <u>divide</u>.

       <u>168</u> ÷ 3 = <u>56</u>. So, <u>168</u> feet = <u>56</u> yards

    c. Multiply the number of yards by the cost of one yard of fencing.

       <u>56</u> yards × $<u>15</u> = <u>$840</u>

    d. Answer the question.

       Josiah will spend <u>$840</u> on fencing.

Unit 4 ■ Focus on Measurement and Data   **231**

## Common Errors

### Item 9

Make sure students are aware that multiple answers are possible.

## Teaching Tips

### Items 10–11

Help students realize the necessity of converting all measurements to the same units before comparing them. Follow up by asking which unit was chosen and why they chose to convert to that unit instead of the others.

### Digital Connection

**Online Unit Converter** Use a search engine to find an online unit converter or use a unit conversion application. Assign groups of students to work together. Have one student pick a card from one jar that has a number and another jar that has a unit conversion (feet to inches, feet to yards, seconds to minutes, quarts to gallons, etc.). The other two students will race to see who can convert fastest, one converting by hand, the other converting with the digital tool. If the customary unit conversions are not memorized, have the student converting by hand use a reference sheet or note card with conversions. The student using the digital tool must complete the conversion electronically before answering even if the answer could be found quickly without it. After several rounds, have students in the group change roles.

# Independent Practice

## Common Errors

### Item 15

Students may need support on multiplying a mixed number by a whole number. Refer students back to Lesson 21 for reminders.

## Teaching Tips

### Item 13

Note the reference to problem 12 on the previous page. It may be helpful for students to write down the important information from that problem next to this problem. Make sure students are clear that the fence is sold by the yard only.

### Item 14

This conversion will require two steps to convert from cups to quarts, then quarts to gallons (if using the conversions given on page 226) or will require students to derive the conversion 1 gallon = 16 cups.

## Independent Practice

MP2   **13.** Suppose the length of Josiah's garden from exercise 12 is 40 feet instead of 39 feet. This would change the perimeter of the garden from 56 yards to 170 feet, or 56 yards and 2 feet. How would this change affect the answer to the problem?
Possible answer: To enclose the garden, Josiah would have to buy 57 yards of fencing instead of 56 yards. So, instead of spending $840, he would have to spend 57 yards × $15 per yard = $855.

MP3   **14.** The capacity of an insulated cooler is 344 cups. Michele says the cooler will hold 22.25 gallons. Sharon says the cooler will hold only 21.5 gallons. Who is correct? Explain.
Sharon is correct. Possible explanation:
1 gallon = 4 quarts, and 1 quart = 4 cups, so 1 gallon = 16 cups.
344 cups ÷ 16 cups per gallon = 21 gallons with a remainder of one half gallon or 8 cups. 8 cups ÷ 16 cups in 1 gallon = 0.5 gallon.
21 gallons + 0.5 gallon = 21.5 gallons.

**Solve the problems.**

MP1   **15.** Nine deep potholes on Marina's street will be filled. It takes about $2\frac{3}{4}$ tons of hot mix asphalt to fill each pothole. How many pounds of hot mix asphalt will be used in all?

> **Show your work.**
Possible student work: To fill each pothole takes $2\frac{3}{4}$ tons × 2,000 pounds per ton = 5,500 pounds of hot mix asphalt. It will take 5,500 pounds × 9 = 49,500 pounds of hot mix asphalt.

**Answer** About 49,500 pounds of hot mix asphalt will be used.

| Mathematical Practices | |
|---|---|
| **MP1** | **Make sense of problems and persevere in solving them.** |
| **Item 15:** Students must analyze the information given and plan a multi-step solution. | |
| **MP2** | **Reason abstractly and quantitatively.** |
| **Item 13:** Students must use quantitative reasoning to support their answer. | |
| **MP3** | **Construct viable arguments and critique the reasoning of others.** |
| **Item 14:** Students must decide who is correct and justify the answer by explaining the approach. | |

Lesson 25

## Independent Practice

MP2  **16.** A serving of cheese weighs 3.5 ounces. How many whole servings of cheese are there in a 40-pound wheel of cheese? How much is left over?

▸ **Show your work.**

Possible student work: 40 pounds in ounces is 40 pounds × 16 ounces = 640 ounces. 640 ounces ÷ 3.5 ounces per serving = 182 servings with a remainder of 3 ounces. So, there are 182 whole servings of cheese with 3 ounces left over.

**Answer** There are 182 whole servings of cheese and 3 ounces left over.

MP3  **17.** Arun needs 3 rods of wood with lengths of 26 inches, 17 inches, and 37 inches. At the local lumberyard, wood rods are sold in 6-foot, 8-foot, and 10-foot lengths. Which length should Arun buy so that the least amount of scrap wood is left over?

**Answer** Arun should buy an 8-foot rod.

▸ **Justify your answer using words, drawings, or numbers.**

Possible justification: Arun needs a total of 26 + 17 + 37 = 80 inches of wood rods. The 6-foot rod is 72 inches long, so it is too short. The 8-foot rod is 96 inches, and the 12-foot rod is 120 inches. The 96-inch rod will leave 16 inches left over. The 120-inch rod will leave 40 inches left over. So, Arun should buy the 8-foot rod.

MP3  **18.** Michaela is mailing a 12.25-pound package to her grandmother. The shipping service charges $0.26 for every ounce mailed. Or, Michaela can use a flat-rate box that costs $25. Which is the less expensive option?

**Answer** Using the flat-rate box will cost less.

▸ **Justify your answer using words, drawings, or numbers.**

Possible justification: 12.25 pounds is 12.25 × 16 = 196 ounces. 196 × 0.26 = $50.96. $50.96 > $25, so the flat-rate box is the less expensive shipping option.

Unit 4 ■ Focus on Measurement and Data  **233**

## Teaching Tips

### Item 16

Students may have difficulty finding the amount of cheese left over. If students use long division to calculate 640 ÷ 3.5, they will get a decimal number. The whole number part of the decimal, 182, is the number of whole servings. Students can multiply 182 × 3.5 and subtract the result, 637, from the 640 ounces in the whole wheel to find that there are 3 ounces left over.

### Items 16-18

Have students circle the units in the problem as they are reading. This may help them identify the needed conversion. Ensure that students are revisiting the problem statement after doing calculations to make sure they are answering the question being asked and justifying their answers.

## Mathematical Practices

| **MP2** | **Reason abstractly and quantitatively.** |
|---|---|

**Item 16:** Students must recognize the need for unit conversion by paying attention to the units given.

| **MP3** | **Construct viable arguments and critique the reasoning of others.** |
|---|---|

**Items 17-18:** Students must explain and justify the reasoning they use to solve problems.

# Guided Instruction

## OBJECTIVE
Convert measurements between metric units to solve real-world problems.

## ESSENTIAL QUESTION
Explain that different units can be used to express the same measurement. As an example, hold up a meter stick and explain that 1 meter can also be expressed as 100 centimeters. There are real-world situations that require a specific unit and sometimes a conversion between different-sized units is needed.

## FLUENCY PRACTICE
Fluency practice is available at **sadlierconnect.com**.

## Concept Development

### Understand: Converting metric units of length

■ This lesson shows students how to convert measurements within the metric system. To do these conversions with ease, students should understand how to multiply and divide by powers of 10.

■ Relate the chart on page 234 to a place-value chart. With both metric units and place-value units, each unit is 10 times as much as the next smaller unit and $\frac{1}{10}$ as much as the next larger unit.

■ Remind students that dividing a number by 10 shifts its digits 1 place right. So, dividing 3250 by 1000, which is 10 × 10 × 10 (or 10³), shifts the digits right three places.

▸ Explain that a larger unit will have a smaller number for the measurement. A meter stick can be used as a visual to demonstrate this concept.

---

## Lesson 26 Convert Metric Measurement Units

**Essential Question:** How can you convert a measurement from one metric unit to another?

**Words to Know:**
metric units of length
base unit
metric units of liquid volume
metric units of mass

### Guided Instruction

In this lesson you will learn how to convert metric measurements to solve real-world problems.

**Understand: Converting metric units of length**

> Anari hikes 3250 meters. How many kilometers does he hike?

To solve this problem, you need to convert 3250 meters to kilometers.

The chart below shows metric units of length from largest to smallest. The meter is the base unit of length. The bottom row of the chart shows how the other units compare to 1 meter. The most commonly used units are shown in red.

| kilometer | hectometer | dekameter | meter | decimeter | centimeter | millimeter |
|---|---|---|---|---|---|---|
| km | hm | dam | m | dm | cm | mm |
| 1000 × 1 m | 100 × 1 m | 10 × 1 m | 1 m | $\frac{1}{10}$ × 1 m | $\frac{1}{100}$ × 1 m | $\frac{1}{1000}$ × 1 m |

Each metric unit is 10 times the next smaller unit and $\frac{1}{10}$ the next larger unit.

To convert from a larger unit to a smaller unit, *multiply by 10* for each unit you move in the chart.

To convert from a smaller unit to a larger unit, *divide by 10* for each unit you move in the chart.

To convert from meters to kilometers, you move three units on the chart, so divide 3250 by 10 × 10 × 10, or 1000.

3250 meters ÷ 1000 = 3.250 kilometers

▸ Anari hikes 3.25 kilometers.

▸ Rename each unit of measure.

  a. 3.78 centimeters = __37.8__ millimeter(s)

  b. 2 dekameters = __0.02__ kilometer(s)

**234** Unit 4 ■ Focus on Measurement and Data

**Remember!**
Multiplying a number by 10 shifts the digits 1 place to the left.

Dividing a number by 10 shifts the digits 1 place to the right.

---

## Words to Know

**metric units of length:** units of measure used in the metric system of measurement, includes millimeter, centimeter, meter, and kilometer

**base unit:** The standard unit of measurement for length, liquid volume, and mass in the metric measurement system. The base units are meter, liter, and kilogram.

**metric units of liquid volume:** units of measure used in the metric system of measurement, includes milliliter, liter, and kiloliter

**metric units of mass:** units of measure used in the metric system of measurement, includes milligram, gram, and kilogram

**Glossary can be found on pp. 347–350.**

Lesson 26

Guided Instruction

## Understand: Converting metric units of liquid volume

A chemist needs to convert 2.5 liters of a solution to milliliters to present an experiment. How many milliliters is 2.5 liters?

To solve this problem, you need to convert 2.5 liters to milliliters.

This chart shows the metric units of liquid volume from largest to smallest. The most commonly used units are shown in red. The liter is the base unit of liquid volume. Notice that the relationship among the units is the same as it is for the units of length.

| kiloliter | hectoliter | dekaliter | liter | deciliter | centiliter | milliliter |
|---|---|---|---|---|---|---|
| kL | hL | daL | L | dL | cL | mL |
| $1000 \times 1$ L | $100 \times 1$ L | $10 \times 1$ L | $1$ L | $\frac{1}{10} \times 1$ L | $\frac{1}{100} \times 1$ L | $\frac{1}{1000} \times 1$ L |

**Method 1**  Use the chart.

To convert from a larger unit to a smaller unit, *multiply by 10* for each unit you move in the chart.

To convert from a smaller unit to a larger unit, *divide by 10* for each unit you move in the chart.

Milliliters are smaller than liters, and to get from liters to milliliters, you move three units on the chart. So, to convert 2.5 liters to milliliters, multiply 2.5 by $10 \times 10 \times 10$, or 1000.

2.5 liters $\times$ 1000 = 2500 milliliters

**Remember!**

Multiplying a number by 10 shifts the digits 1 place to the left.

Dividing a number by 10 shifts the digits 1 place to the right.

**Method 2**  Use basic equivalences.

At the right are the basic equivalences for the most commonly used metric units of liquid volume.

**Metric Units of Liquid Volume**
1 kiloliter (kL) = 1000 liters
1 liter (L) = 1000 milliliters (mL)

Milliliters are smaller than liters, so multiply.

Number of liters $\times$ number of milliliters in 1 liter = number of milliliters
2.5 $\times$ 1000 = $n$

Since 2500 = $n$, 2.5 liters = 2500 milliliters.

➤ 2.5 liters is equal to 2500 milliliters.

Unit 4 ■ Focus on Measurement and Data  **235**

## Understand: Converting metric units of liquid volume

■ In this presentation, students convert liters to milliliters in a real-world situation.

■ Point out that the prefixes in this chart—kilo, hecto, deka, deci, centi, and milli—are the same as those in the chart for lengths. The relationship among the units is also the same. Each unit is 10 times the next smaller unit, and $\frac{1}{10}$ the next larger unit.

■ To solve the problem, students need to recognize which unit is larger and which is smaller. They then need to decide whether to multiply or divide by 10 and what power of 10 to use.

■ Help students realize that if they convert a measurement to smaller units, the number of units needed will be greater.

■ You might give students other liquid-volume measurements to convert. For example, have them 35 liters to kiloliters and 0.5 kiloliters to milliliters.

## Support English Language Learners

Have students explore the shades of meanings for the word *convert*. Write the word *convert* on the board, say the word, and have students repeat. Then, ask students to define *convert* in their own words. Some students may define the term as a change in one's beliefs or religion, or to exchange one type of currency for another.

Next, write *to change from one form to another* under *convert* on the board. Explain that in mathematics, it is sometimes necessary to convert a unit of measure to another unit of measure. Write an example of unit conversion on the board and say *I converted _____ to _____*. Then have students discuss the similarities between their definitions of *convert* with the mathematical meaning of *convert*. Write other examples on the board and have students use the sentence frame to describe the unit conversion.

**Connect:** **What you know about metric units to solve real-world problems** Use this page to help students solidify their understanding of how to convert units within the metric system.

■ This presentation demonstrates how to convert among metric units of mass.

■ Review the chart and compare and contrast it to those on the two previous pages. Point out that the base unit, gram, is different than the base units in the previous charts, but the prefixes are the same. The relationship among the units is also the same.

■ Students can also solve this problem using the chart of units. Getting from kilograms to grams requires moving right 3 units. So, to convert 5 kilograms to grams, multiply 5 by 10 × 10 × 10, or 1000.

---

**Connect:** **What you know about metric units to solve real-world problems**

> Fae has a 5-kilogram bag of corn meal. A recipe calls for 250 grams of corn meal to make one loaf of bread. How many loaves of bread can Fae make from the bag of corn meal?

**Step 1**

Plan the solution.

To solve the problem, first find the number of grams of corn meal in the 5-kilogram bag. Then, divide the answer by 250 grams to determine how many loaves of bread Fae can make.

**Step 2**

Convert 5 kilograms to grams.

The chart below shows the metric units of mass from largest to smallest. The most commonly used units are shown in red. The gram is the base unit of mass. The relationship among the units is the same as it is for units of length and liquid volume.

| kilogram | hectogram | dekagram | gram | decigram | centigram | milligram |
|---|---|---|---|---|---|---|
| kg | hg | dag | g | dg | cg | mg |
| $1000 \times 1$ g | $100 \times 1$ g | $10 \times 1$ g | $1$ g | $\frac{1}{10} \times 1$ g | $\frac{1}{100} \times 1$ g | $\frac{1}{1000} \times 1$ g |

To convert 5 kilograms to grams, you can use the chart or the basic equivalences shown at the right.

Grams are smaller than kilograms, so multiply.

5 kilograms × 1000 = 5000 grams

**Metric Units of Mass**
1 kilogram (kg) = 1000 grams
1 gram (g) = 1000 milligrams (mg)

**Step 3**

Divide the total number of grams of corn meal by the number of grams of corn meal needed for one loaf of bread.

5000 ÷ 250 = 20

➡ Fae can make 20 loaves of bread from the one bag of corn meal.

**236** Unit 4 ■ Focus on Measurement and Data

---

## Math-to-Cooking Connection

**Awful Pie** Work as a class to write a pie recipe using random ingredients measured in grams. Start the recipe by saying an ingredient and an amount, for instance 400 grams of chewing gum. As the class lists off ingredients, write them in a chart on the board with the given amount. Next, have students work as a class or in teams to convert the amounts to milligrams. If time allows, convert the ingredients to kilograms.

Guided Practice

**Convert the measurements.**

1. 20 meters = ■ centimeters

   1 meter = 100 centimeters

   A centimeter is ___smaller___

   than a meter, so ___multiply___.

   20 _×_ 100 = _2000_

   20 meters = _2000_ centimeters

2. 1700 meters = ■ kilometers

   1 kilometer = 1000 meters

   A kilometer is ___larger___

   than a meter, so ___divide___.

   1700 _÷_ _1000_ = _1.7_

   1700 meters = _1.7_ kilometers

3. 4569 grams = ■ kilograms

   1 kilogram = 1000 grams

   A kilogram is larger than a gram,

   so ___divide___.

   4569 _÷_ _1000_ = _4.569_

   4569 grams = _4.569_ kilograms

4. 1.5 kiloliters = ■ liters

   1 kiloliter = 1000 liters

   A liter is smaller than a kiloliter,

   so ___multiply___.

   1.5 _×_ _1000_ = _1500_

   1.5 kiloliter = _1500_ liters

**Solve the problem.**

5. Andrea bicycles 8.04 kilometers each day, going to and from school. How many meters does she bicycle each day?

   Andrea bicycles 8040 meters each day: 8.04 × 1000 = 8040.

### Think • Pair • Share

MP7  6. Jacob has a 15-kilogram bag of rice. A serving of rice has a mass of 200 grams. Jacob wants to find the number of servings of rice the bag contains. Should Jacob convert kilograms to grams or grams to kilograms to get the answer? Explain your reasoning.

   Jacob can do either. The answer will be the same. Possible explanation: Converting kilograms to grams: 15 kilograms × 1000 = 15,000 grams. 15,000 ÷ 200 = 75 servings. Converting grams to kilograms: 200 grams ÷ 1000 = 0.2 kilograms. 15 ÷ 0.2 = 75 servings.

## Observational Assessment

Use page 237 to assess whether students are able to convert among different-sized standard measurement units within the metric system. Look for understanding of unit size relationships and whether multiplications or divisions by powers of 10 are used to calculate the correct answer.

### Think•Pair•Share

**Peer Collaboration** Write the pertinent information from the problem on the board. Take a poll of which conversion students would have Jacob perform. Ask volunteers to give their reasoning.

- *Why is a unit conversion needed to solve this example?*

- *How does the size of a gram compare to the size of a kilogram?*

### Return to the Essential Question

Reread the Lesson 26 Essential Question on page 234: *How can you convert a measurement from one metric unit to another?*

Ask volunteers to use what they learned in this lesson to answer this question. Possible response: (I can use the chart with all the metric units. If I am converting to a larger unit, I divide by 10 for each unit I move in the chart. If I am converting to a smaller unit, I multiply by 10 for each unit I move in the chart.)

Invite students to relate how they decide which units are larger and smaller.

## Mathematical Practices

Mathematical Practice Standards underline the teaching and understanding of all concepts and skills presented. The emphasis of specific practices is noted throughout the guided and independent practice of this lesson.

| MP7 | **Look for and make use of structure.** |
|---|---|

**Item 6:** Students use the pattern in the relationship of metric units to solve a problem.

# Independent Practice

## Concept Application

Students may work independently on these pages in the classroom or at home. They may refer to the first four pages of the lesson to revisit the instruction or to see a worked-out example.

**Common Errors** and **Teaching Tips** may help you support student learning either in the classroom or as a follow-up for work done at home.

## Teaching Tips

### Items 1–8

Help students recognize the relationships between the sizes of the units in the conversions. Draw a line with arrows on both ends on the board with the terms "kilo," "hecto," "deka," "base unit," "deci," "centi," and "milli" written in order above the line and the words "larger" near the left arrow and "smaller" near the right arrow. Have students copy this on a piece of paper for reinforcement and reference.

---

### Independent Practice

**Complete the table to convert from one metric unit to another.**

1.

| centiliters | × or ÷ | milliliters |
|---|---|---|
| 1 | × 10 | 10 |
| 2 | × 10 | 20 |
| 3 | × 10 | 30 |

2.

| meters | × or ÷ | kilometers |
|---|---|---|
| 2500 | ÷ 1000 | 2.5 |
| 3500 | ÷ 1000 | 3.5 |
| 4500 | ÷ 1000 | 4.5 |

3.

| kilograms | × or ÷ | grams |
|---|---|---|
| 2 | x 1000 | 2000 |
| 4 | x 1000 | 4000 |
| 6 | x 1000 | 6000 |

4.

| grams | × or ÷ | kilograms |
|---|---|---|
| 3000 | ÷ 1000 | 3 |
| 6000 | ÷ 1000 | 6 |
| 12,000 | ÷ 1000 | 12 |

**Convert the measurements.**

5. 9845 milliliters = ▧ liters

    1 liter = 1000 milliliters

    A liter is larger than a milliliter,

    so ___divide___.

    9845 _÷_ _1000_ = _9.845_

    9845 milliliters = _9.845_ liters

6. 5.2 kilograms = ▧ grams

    1 kilogram = 1000 grams

    A gram is smaller than a kilogram,

    so ___multiply___.

    5.2 _×_ _1000_ = _5200_

    5.2 kilograms = _5200_ grams

7. 12 kilometers = ▧ meters

    1 kilometer = 1000 meters

    A meter is ___smaller___

    than a kilometer, so ___multiply___.

    12 _×_ 1000 = _12,000_

    12 kilometers = _12,000_ meters

8. 6800 grams = ▧ kilograms

    1 kilogram = 1000 grams

    A kilogram is ___larger___

    than a gram, so ___divide___.

    6800 _÷_ _1000_ = _6.8_

    6800 grams = _6.8_ kilograms

---

## Writing About Math

✏ • **Write Explanatory Text** Ask students to write a paragraph explaining the relationship between kilometers, meters, and millimeters. They should include the concepts of multiplication, division, place value, and the number 10. Sentences within the paragraph should have a coherent flow and correct grammar and punctuations should be used. Students can exchange papers and evaluate the explanations.

**Circle every correct answer.**

9. Which of the following are equal to 72 liters?

   (a.) 72,000 milliliters

   b. 720 centiliters

   c. 0.072 kilometers

   (d.) 0.072 kiloliters

**Order the measurements from *smallest* to *largest*. Show your work.**

10. 175 grams, 18,000 milligrams, 1.6 kilograms
    Possible student work: 1000 mg = 1 g, so 18,000 mg ÷ 1000 = 18 g.
    1 kg = 1000 g, so 1.6 kg = 1600 g.
    18 g < 175 g < 1600 g

    **Answer** 18,000 milligrams, 175 grams, 1.6 kilograms

11. 50 centimeters, 570 millimeters, 0.53 meter
    Possible student work: 1 cm = 10 mm, so 570 mm = 57 cm.
    1 m = 100 cm, so 0.53 m = 53 cm.
    50 cm < 53 cm < 57 cm

    **Answer** 50 centimeters, 0.53 meter, 570 millimeters

**Complete parts a–c to solve the problem.**

12. Ann is making smoothies. She uses 1.2 kilograms of apples and 600 grams of kiwi. How many kilograms of fruit does Ann use in all?

    a. Convert the 600 grams of kiwi to kilograms.

       1 kilogram = 1000 grams. A kilogram is ___larger___ than a gram,
       so you need to ___divide___.

       ___600___ ÷ 1000 = ___0.6___

       600 grams = ___0.6___ kilograms

    b. Add the number of kilograms of apples to the number of kilograms of kiwi.

       1.2 kilograms + ___0.6___ kilograms = ___1.8___ kilograms

    c. Answer the question.

       Ann uses ___1.8___ kilograms of fruit in all.

Unit 4 ■ Focus on Measurement and Data **239**

## Common Errors

### Item 9
Be sure students recognize that there may be more than one correct choice.

### Items 10-11
Students may struggle with recognizing that a smaller number may represent a greater measure because of the units. Point out to students that if they convert all the measurements to the same unit, they will be much easier to compare.

## Digital Connection

**Metric Units** Use a search engine to find other metric units that have liter, gram, and meter as their base units. Ask students to determine whether these units are larger or smaller than the units in the lesson. Have students record these other units of measure. If time allows, have students report their findings to the class.

# Independent Practice

## Teaching Tips

### Items 15 and 16

These problems are similar to those in this lesson, but they are arranged differently. If students are struggling with how to approach the problem, have them list the givens from the problem and what they need to determine. This may help them work towards a solution.

### Item 16

Encourage students to think about how many weeks are in 1 year. This may help struggling students find an approach to the problem.

---

## Independent Practice

**MP2   13.** Suppose you want to find the amount of fruit in exercise 12 in grams instead of kilograms. Without calculating, explain how you would find the answer.
Possible explanation: Convert the 1.2 kilograms of apples to grams, and then add the number of grams of apples to the number of grams of kiwi.

**MP3   14.** Compare converting units in the metric system with converting units in the customary system. How are they the same? How are they different?
Possible answer: With both systems you multiply when converting from a larger unit to a smaller unit, and you divide when converting from a smaller unit to a larger unit. With the metric system, you can also simply move the decimal point when converting between units.

### Solve the problems.

**MP1   15.** Jasper has a lemonade stand. One glass of lemonade has 4950 milligrams of sugar. One weekend, he sells 87 glasses of lemonade. How many grams of sugar does Jasper use that weekend?

▶ **Show your work.**
Possible student work:
4950 milligrams = 4.95 grams. 4.95 × 87 = 430.65.

**Answer** Jasper used 430.65 grams of sugar.

**MP1   16.** Quinn is a runner. As part of her training, she keeps detailed records about the distances she runs. Last year Quinn ran 1820 kilometers. On average, about how many meters did Quinn run each week last year?

▶ **Show your work.**
Possible student work: There are 52 weeks in a year:
1820 ÷ 52 = 35 kilometers per week.
35 kilometers = 35,000 meters.

**Answer** Quinn ran about 35,000 meters each week last year.

**240   Unit 4 ■ Focus on Measurement and Data**

---

## Mathematical Practices

| | |
|---|---|
| **MP1** | **Make sense of problems and persevere in solving them.** |
| **Items 15–16:** Students determine an approach to a conversion problem. | |
| **MP2** | **Reason abstractly and quantitatively.** |
| **Item 13:** Students make sense of the quantities in a problem and the relationship among metric units to solve a problem. | |
| **MP3** | **Construct viable arguments and critique the reasoning of others.** |
| **Item 14:** Students critique and compare methods of converting metric units to methods of converting standard units. | |

---

**MORE ONLINE** sadlierconnect.com            Lesson 26

## Independent Practice

MP2   **17.** Ryan has a rope that is 1.25 meters long. He cuts off a piece that is 33 centimeters. Then Ryan cuts off a piece that is 150 millimeters. How many centimeters of rope is left?

     **· Show your work.**
Possible student work:
1.25 meters = 125 centimeters. 150 millimeters = 15 centimeters.
125 − 33 − 15 = 77. So, Ryan has 77 centimeters of rope left.

**Answer** Ryan has 77 centimeters of rope left.

MP3   **18.** Gemma is making three candles of different sizes. She will need 125 grams, 0.65 kilograms, and 130,000 milligrams of wax to make the candles. Gemma can buy a 1000-gram block of wax or a 0.8-kilogram block of wax. Which one should Gemma buy to make her candles?

**Answer** Gemma should buy the 1000-gram block of wax.

     **· Justify your answer using words, drawings, or numbers.**
Possible justification:
0.65 kilograms = 650 grams. 130,000 milligrams = 130 grams.
125 + 650 + 130 = 905 grams. Gemma should buy the 1000-gram block of wax. The 0.8-kilogram block of wax is only 800 grams, so it will not be enough wax.

MP2   **19.** Felix says 1000 kiloliters is a million milliliters. Is Felix correct? Explain.

**Answer** No, Felix is not correct.

     **· Justify your answer using words, drawings, or numbers.**
Possible justification:
1000 kiloliters = 1,000,000 liters. 1,000,000 liters = 1,000,000,000 milliliters. 1000 kiloliters is 1 billion milliliters.

Unit 4 ■ Focus on Measurement and Data    **241**

## Teaching Tips

### Item 17
To help students determine which unit to convert to, have them write down the lengths given and the unit asked for in the answer. Ask them which unit would require the least number of conversions to obtain the correct answer.

## Mathematical Practices

| **MP2** | **Reason abstractly and quantitatively.** |
|---|---|

**Items 17 and 19:** Students make sense of quantities and the relationship among metric units to solve a problem.

| **MP3** | **Construct viable arguments and critique the reasoning of others.** |
|---|---|

**Item 18:** Students solve a problem and construct an argument to justify their answer.

## OBJECTIVE
**Solve real-world problems representing and interpreting data on line plots.**

## ESSENTIAL QUESTION
Have students share what they remember about line plots from Grade 4. Tell students that line plots are a useful way to organize and display certain types of data. The line plots in this lesson will represent data with fractional values.

## PREREQUISITE SKILLS
Use Item I on page 341 of the Foundational Skills Handbook to help students review making a line plot.

## FLUENCY PRACTICE
Fluency practice is available at **sadlierconnect.com**.

## Concept Development

### Understand: How to represent data using a line plot

■ In Grade 4, students created line plots and used them to solve real-world problems involving addition and subtraction of fractions. In Grade 5, the focus shifts to real-world problems involving all operations with fractions.

■ Be sure that students understand that the line plot must be divided into equal intervals and must include the entire range of the data set. A common mistake is for students to skip the intervals for values without any data.

✏️ ➤ Have students explain why they did not count data values of $\frac{1}{2}$.

---

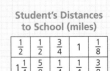

**Lesson 27 — Problem Solving: Use Line Plots**

**Essential Question:**
How can you solve real-world problems using line plots?

**Words to Know:**
line plot

### Guided Instruction

In this lesson you will learn how to solve real-world problems by representing and interpreting data on a line plot.

**Understand: How to represent data using a line plot**

As part of Mr. Hughes' health class, ten students tracked the distance they walked to school one morning. They record the distances to the nearest $\frac{1}{8}$ mile. The results are shown at the right.

Make a line plot of the data. How many students walked at least $\frac{1}{2}$ mile to school?

| Student's Distances to School (miles) | | | | |
| --- | --- | --- | --- | --- |
| $\frac{1}{2}$ | $\frac{1}{2}$ | $\frac{3}{4}$ | $1$ | $\frac{1}{8}$ |
| $1\frac{1}{4}$ | $\frac{5}{8}$ | $1\frac{1}{4}$ | $\frac{1}{4}$ | $\frac{3}{8}$ |

A line plot uses a number line to organize and display data.

To start, draw a part of a number line that includes all the values of the student's distances. Use intervals of $\frac{1}{8}$ because the distances are recorded to the nearest $\frac{1}{8}$ mile. Add a label or title below the line to show what the values on the plot will represent.

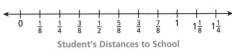

Student's Distances to School

For each value in the data set, make an X above that value on the number line. For example there is a $\frac{1}{8}$ in the data set. Therefore, there is one X above $\frac{1}{8}$.

Student's Distances to School

To answer the question, locate $\frac{1}{2}$ on the number line. Count the number of Xs above $\frac{1}{2}$ and above values greater than $\frac{1}{2}$. There are 6 Xs that represent values greater than or equal to $\frac{1}{2}$.

➡️ Six students walked at least $\frac{1}{2}$ mile to school.

✏️ ➤ How could you find the number of students who walked less than a $\frac{1}{2}$ mile to school? Possible answer: You could count the number of Xs above values to the left of $\frac{1}{2}$.

242 Unit 4 ■ Focus on Measurement and Data

---

## Words to Know

**line plot:** a display of data that uses a number line and Xs

**Example:**

X
X       X
X   X   X   X   X       X       X
←———+———+———+———+———+———+———+———+———+———+———→
    0   $\frac{1}{8}$  $\frac{2}{8}$  $\frac{3}{8}$  $\frac{4}{8}$  $\frac{5}{8}$  $\frac{6}{8}$  $\frac{7}{8}$  $\frac{8}{8}$  $\frac{9}{8}$  $\frac{10}{8}$

**Student's Distances to School**

Glossary can be found on pp. 347–350.

Lesson 27

Guided Instruction

**Connect: What you know about line plots to solve problems**

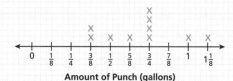

This line plot shows the amounts of punch in 10 pitchers.

**Amount of Punch (gallons)**

Javier wants to redistribute the punch so there is the same amount in each pitcher. How much punch will be in each pitcher after Javier has redistributed it?

To find how much punch will be in each pitcher after Javier has redistributed it, first find the total gallons of punch in all 10 pitchers. Do this by writing an expression that represents the total gallons of punch. Read the data values from the line plot.

$$2 \times \frac{3}{8} + \frac{1}{2} + \frac{5}{8} + 4 \times \frac{3}{4} + 1 + 1\frac{1}{8}$$

2 pitchers have $\frac{3}{8}$ gal.  4 pitchers have $\frac{3}{4}$ gal.

Evaluate the expression.

$2 \times \frac{3}{8} + \frac{1}{2} + \frac{5}{8} + 4 \times \frac{3}{4} + 1 + 1\frac{1}{8}$ ⟵ The original expression.

$\frac{6}{8} + \frac{1}{2} + \frac{5}{8} + \frac{12}{4} + 1 + 1\frac{1}{8}$ ⟵ Multiply.

$\frac{6}{8} + \frac{4}{8} + \frac{5}{8} + 3 + 1 + 1\frac{1}{8}$ ⟵ Rewrite $\frac{12}{4}$ as 3. Rewrite the other fractions so all have the denominator 8.

$5\frac{16}{8}$ ⟵ Add.

$7$ ⟵ Simplify.

Divide the total number of gallons by the 10 pitchers.

$7 \div 10 = \frac{7}{10}$

➤ Each pitcher will contain $\frac{7}{10}$ gallon of punch after Javier redistributes it.

**Connect: What you know about line plots to solve problems** Use this page to help students strengthen their understanding of line plots and develop their ability to interpret data.

■ Point out that some fractions on the number line have different denominators because they are simplified values. The intervals are still equal and every interval between 0 and 1 is included even if there are no data values.

■ Students need to follow the order of operations to properly calculate the total gallons of punch.

■ Remind students that the quotient of two whole numbers can be written as a fraction.

## Support English Language Learners

Draw a line plot on the board with tick marks and labels at intervals of $\frac{1}{4}$, beginning at 0 and ending at 2. Tell students the drawing is a *line plot* because it *plots* data on a number *line*. Have students repeat the term *line plot*. Point to the tick marks that are labeled 0, $\frac{1}{4}$, $\frac{2}{4}$, $\frac{3}{4}$, 1, and so on. Tell students that these marks divide the number line into *intervals* of $\frac{1}{4}$. Ask them what they think the word *interval* means. If necessary, explain that the interval for a plot is the equal distance between the tick marks. To further review the term *interval,* have students look at a ruler or a yardstick. Ask them how the ruler or yardstick looks like a line plot and what intervals they see.

# Guided Practice

## Observational Assessment

Use pages 244–245 to assess whether students are able to properly display data on a line plot and to interpret and use data that are presented on a line plot.

A good strategy for students to practice when creating line plots is to compare the number of data values to the number of Xs on the line plot to make sure that they plotted each value.

### Guided Practice

**Use the data set below to make a line plot.**

1.

| $\frac{1}{4}$ | $\frac{1}{2}$ | $\frac{1}{2}$ | $\frac{3}{4}$ | 1 |
|---|---|---|---|---|
| 1 | $\frac{1}{2}$ | $\frac{3}{4}$ | $\frac{1}{4}$ | $\frac{1}{2}$ |

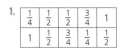

**Solve.**

2. The data set below lists the amounts of water in cups in 14 vases.

| $\frac{7}{8}$ | $\frac{1}{4}$ | 1 | $\frac{3}{4}$ | $\frac{3}{4}$ | $\frac{1}{8}$ | $\frac{5}{8}$ |
|---|---|---|---|---|---|---|
| 1 | $\frac{1}{2}$ | 1 | $\frac{1}{2}$ | $\frac{3}{4}$ | $1\frac{1}{8}$ | $1\frac{1}{4}$ |

a. Make a line plot to organize and examine the data.

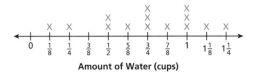

**Amount of Water (cups)**

b. How many vases have less than $\frac{3}{4}$ cup of water?
   Five vases have less than $\frac{3}{4}$ cup of water.

c. How many vases have at least $\frac{1}{2}$ cup of water?
   Twelve vases have at least $\frac{1}{2}$ cup of water.

## Math-to-Math Connection

**Data Collection** Analyzing and interpreting data on a line plot is emphasized but data collection will also be key to future study in mathematics.

Have students come up with data about the class they would like to represent on a line plot. You can suggest that students gather data on shoe size or hand size. Have students collect data about their classmates. You should teach students a strategy on how to record data, such as using tally marks when collecting data. Then have students use their data to create a line plot. Then ask students to present their findings to the class. You can also challenge students by asking if they can make a conjecture about the data they collected, or if there are any patterns they can see in the line plot.

3. Mr. Park has 10 bags of almonds. The line plot shows the weight of each bag.

**Weight of Almonds (pounds)**

Mr. Park wants to redistribute the almonds so that each bag weighs the same. What will be the weight of each bag?

a. Complete this expression for the total weight of the almonds.

$\frac{1}{8} + 2 \times \frac{1}{4} + 2 \times \frac{3}{8} + 2 \times \frac{1}{2} + \frac{3}{4} + \frac{7}{8} + 1$

b. Evaluate the expression. Show your work.

$\frac{1}{8} + 2 \times \frac{1}{4} + 2 \times \frac{3}{8} + 2 \times \frac{1}{2} + \frac{3}{4} + \frac{7}{8} + 1$

$\frac{1}{8} + \frac{1}{2} \quad + \frac{6}{8} \quad + 1 \quad + \frac{3}{4} + \frac{7}{8} + 1$

$\frac{1}{8} + \frac{4}{8} \quad + \frac{6}{8} \quad + \frac{8}{8} \quad + \frac{6}{8} + \frac{7}{8} + \frac{8}{8}$

$\frac{40}{8} = 5$

c. Divide the total weight by the 10 bags. Give the answer as a fraction.

$\frac{5 \div 10}{} = \frac{5}{10} \text{ or } \frac{1}{2}$

When the almonds are redistributed equally among 10 bags, the weight of each bag will be $\frac{1}{2}$ pound(s).

**Think · Pair · Share**

MP3 4. Cassandra wrote this expression to represent the sum of the data shown on the line plot below. Is her expression correct? Why or why not? Explain your reasoning.

$\frac{1}{4} + \frac{1}{4} + (3 \times \frac{1}{2}) + (2 \times \frac{3}{4}) + 1$

Yes, Cassandra is correct. Possible explanation: There are 2 Xs above $\frac{1}{4}$, 3 Xs above $\frac{1}{2}$, 2 Xs above $\frac{3}{4}$, and 1 X above 1.

**Think·Pair·Share**

**Peer Collaboration** After students have answered the questions, have them choose a partner and compare their explanations. As a class, discuss some of the explanations students wrote. Ask questions such as:

- *Did Cassandra represent every data value in the line plot in her expression?*
- *Could she have written a different expression to represent the sum of the data values? How?*
- *What operations should be performed first to find the sum of the data values?*

**Return to the Essential Question**

Reread the Lesson 27 Essential Question on page 242: *How can you solve real-world problems using line plots?*

Ask volunteers to use what they learned in this lesson to answer this question. (Possible responses: I can represent data on a line plot by drawing Xs for each value in the data set. I can answer questions about a line plot by using the data values that each X represents.)

## Mathematical Practices

Mathematical Practice Standards underline the teaching and understanding of all concepts and skills presented. The emphasis of specific practices is noted throughout the guided and independent practice of this lesson.

| MP3 | **Construct viable arguments and critique the reasoning of others.** |
|---|---|

**Item 4:** Students compare a data set displayed on a line plot with an expression and determine the reasonableness of the expression.

## Concept Application

Students may work independently on these pages in the classroom or at home. They may refer to the first four pages of the lesson to revisit the instruction or to see a worked-out example.

**Common Errors** and **Teaching Tips** may help you support student learning either in the classroom or as a follow-up for work done at home.

## Common Errors

### Item 1

Some students may count the value of $\frac{5}{8}$ and get the answer 6, instead of 5. Point out that the question asks about values *greater than* $\frac{5}{8}$, so $\frac{5}{8}$ should not be included.

## Teaching Tips

### Item 2

Students should count the number of data values in the table, the line plot, and their expression to make sure they included all of the data.

### Independent Practice

**Use the data set below to make a line plot.**

1.

| | | | | | |
|---|---|---|---|---|---|
| $\frac{2}{4}$ | $\frac{1}{4}$ | 1 | $\frac{3}{4}$ | $\frac{1}{4}$ | $\frac{1}{2}$ |
| $\frac{3}{4}$ | $\frac{1}{4}$ | $\frac{1}{2}$ | $\frac{3}{4}$ | 1 | $\frac{5}{8}$ |

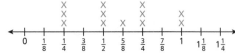

a. How many numbers on the line plot are greater than $\frac{5}{8}$? ___5___

**Solve.**

2. Mrs. Kelly has 10 square mosaic tiles. The data set below lists the side length of each tile in inches.

Lengths of Tile (inches)

| | | | | |
|---|---|---|---|---|
| $\frac{1}{2}$ | 1 | $\frac{3}{4}$ | $\frac{1}{2}$ | $\frac{1}{2}$ |
| $\frac{3}{4}$ | $\frac{3}{8}$ | $\frac{1}{4}$ | $\frac{7}{8}$ | 1 |

a. Make a line plot to organize and examine the data set.

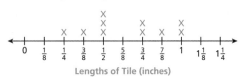

Lengths of Tile (inches)

b. What is the sum of the lengths of the 10 tiles? Show your work.
Possible student work:

$\frac{1}{4} + \frac{3}{8} + 3 \times \frac{1}{2} + 2 \times \frac{3}{4} + \frac{7}{8} + 2 \times 1 = \frac{2}{8} + \frac{3}{8} + \frac{12}{8} + \frac{12}{8} + \frac{7}{8} + 2 =$
$\frac{36}{8} + 2 = 4\frac{1}{2} + 2 = 6\frac{1}{2}$

The sum of the lengths of the 10 tiles is $6\frac{1}{2}$ inches.

## Writing About Math

✏ ▸ **Write an Opinion Text** Ask students to write a paragraph giving their opinion on whether or not they believe a line plot would be a good way to represent 100 pieces of data. Have them provide mathematical justification and examples to support their opinion. Ask students to share their examples with the class. If possible, display some examples and discuss why it may or may not be a good idea to use a line plot for so much data.

Lesson 27

Independent Practice

**For exercises 3–4, circle the correct answer. Use the line plot below.**

This line plot shows the weights of the deli meat Mr. Arlen sold to customers this morning.

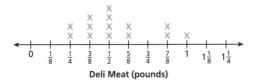

**Deli Meat (pounds)**

3. How many of the weights are less than $\frac{1}{2}$ pound?

   a. 6                             b. 7

   c. 5                             d. 9

4. How many of the weights are $\frac{3}{4}$ pound or more?

   a. 0                             b. 2

   c. 5                             d. 3

**Solve.**

5. Fourteen students in gym class ran the distances shown in the line plot below.

**Distances Ran (miles)**

a. What distance did the greatest number of students run?

   The greatest number of students ran 1 mile.

b. What is the total distance that the 14 students ran?

   The 14 students ran a total distance of $10\frac{5}{8}$ miles.

Unit 4 ■ Focus on Measurement and Data    247

## Digital Connection

**Interactive Whiteboard** Use an interactive number line. Create a data set with fractions to use to make a line plot and post it on the whiteboard. Ask a volunteer to label the number line on the whiteboard. Discuss whether the number line is labeled appropriately for the data. Have other volunteers take turns adding Xs to the number line for each fraction to generate the line plot.

As the line plot is generated on the whiteboard, have all students record it on paper. If there is time, ask students to describe what the data might represent (results of an experiment, weights of pieces of fruit, or fractions of hours spent on homework). Repeat this process to create additional line plots as time allows.

## Teaching Tips

### Items 3-4
Be sure that students carefully read the questions to determine whether or not to include the given number.

## Common Errors

### Item 7

Students may make a computational error when subtracting $3\frac{7}{8}$ from $4\frac{3}{8}$. Prompt students by pointing out that they cannot subtract $\frac{7}{8}$ from $\frac{3}{8}$, so they must rename the mixed number $4\frac{3}{8}$ as $3\frac{11}{8}$. After renaming the mixed number, students can subtract $\frac{7}{8}$ from $\frac{11}{8}$.

## Teaching Tips

### Item 6

Students need to choose an appropriate scale for the line plot. Point out that there are 10 questions, so all scores will be represented as a fraction with a denominator of 10. Make sure students know how to represent the quiz scores as fractions. For example, answering 9 quiz problems correctly is represented by a score of $\frac{9}{10}$.

### Independent Practice

6. Ms. Quentin wants to find out how many students in her class correctly answered at least half of the problems on a 10-question quiz. Explain how she can use a line plot to find the answer. What fractions could Ms. Quentin use for her number line?

   Answers will vary. Possible answer: Ms. Quentin could plot students quiz scores on a number line labeled in tenths. Each X represents a student's score. To find the number of students in her class who answered at least half of the questions correctly, Ms. Quentin can count the Xs above and to the right of the $\frac{5}{10}$ mark.

MP5  7. A tailor measures patches of fabric. The line plot shows his measurements. He wants to make a patchwork jacket, which requires $3\frac{7}{8}$ yards of fabric. Does the tailor have enough fabric to make the jacket? If so, how much fabric is left over? If not, how much additional fabric does he need?

**Lengths of Fabric (yards)**

▬▬ · **Show your work.**

Possible student work:
$\frac{3}{8} + (3 \times \frac{4}{8}) + (2 \times \frac{6}{8}) + \frac{8}{8} = \frac{3}{8} + \frac{12}{8} + \frac{12}{8} + \frac{8}{8} = \frac{35}{8} = 4\frac{3}{8}$
$4\frac{3}{8} - 3\frac{7}{8} = \frac{1}{2}$ yards left over

**Answer** Yes, the tailor has enough to make the jacket. He will have $\frac{1}{2}$ yard left over.

**248**   Unit 4 ■ Focus on Measurement and Data

| **Mathematical Practices** | |
|---|---|
| MP5 | **Use appropriate tools strategically.** |
| **Item 7:** Students use the given line plot to solve the real-world problem. | |

Lesson 27

## Independent Practice

MP6 **8.** A painter measures the amount of paint in gallons left in 5 cans: $\frac{1}{2}$, $\frac{3}{4}$, 1, $\frac{1}{4}$, $\frac{1}{2}$. She wants to combine all the paint and pour it into the fewest number of cans possible. Each can holds a maximum of one gallon of paint. Make a line plot to show the data. How many cans of paint will she need?

**Show your work.**
Possible student work:
$\frac{1}{4} + \frac{1}{2} + \frac{1}{2} + \frac{3}{4} + 1 = 3$

Amount of Paint (in gallons)

**Answer** The painter will need 3 cans.

MP1 **9.** A baker needs $7\frac{1}{8}$ pounds of strawberries for the week. One shipment includes 8 baskets weighing the recorded pounds listed at the right. Make a line plot to show the data.

He gives away the baskets of strawberries that weigh less than $\frac{3}{4}$ pound. With the remaining baskets, will he have enough for the week? If so, how many pounds will he have left over? If not, how many additional pounds will he need?

Weights of
Baskets (pounds)

| $\frac{7}{8}$ | 1 | $\frac{5}{8}$ | $\frac{3}{4}$ |
|---|---|---|---|
| 1 | $\frac{3}{4}$ | $\frac{3}{4}$ | $\frac{7}{8}$ |

**Answer** No, the baker will not have enough strawberries because he has only 6 pounds. He will need $1\frac{1}{8}$ pounds more.

**Justify your answer using words, drawings, or numbers.**
Possible justification:
$\frac{6}{8} + \frac{6}{8} + \frac{6}{8} + \frac{7}{8} + \frac{7}{8} + \frac{8}{8} + \frac{8}{8} = \frac{48}{8} = 6$ pounds total
$7\frac{1}{8} - 6 = 1\frac{1}{8}$ pounds needed

Weights of Baskets (in pounds)

MP5 **10.** Collect 10 classroom items that are 1 foot or less in length. Measure your items to the nearest inch. Record your measurements as fractions of a foot on a line plot. Make up a problem about your line plot. Give the solution to your problem.

**Answer** Answers may vary. Check students' work.

**Justify your answer using words, drawings, or numbers.**
Answers may vary. Students' work should include a line plot with a number line labeled in fractions of a foot, a word problem, and a solution.

## Common Errors

### Items 7-8
Students may struggle with finding equal intervals to use on the number line. Encourage students to write all fractions with common denominators. This will make the decision for making the scale clearer.

## Teaching Tips

### Item 10
Students will need an inch ruler to complete this problem.

## Mathematical Practices

| MP1 | **Make sense of problems and persevere in solving them.** |
|---|---|

**Item 9:** Students need to make sense of a real-world problem and use a line plot to help them solve it.

| MP5 | **Use appropriate tools strategically.** |
|---|---|

**Item 10:** Students use rulers to measure items and use those measurements as the data set for a line plot.

| MP6 | **Attend to precision.** |
|---|---|

**Item 8:** Students create equivalent fractions to determine the appropriate scale for their line plot.

## OBJECTIVE

**Understand volume as the number of unit cubes in a three-dimensional figure.**

## ESSENTIAL QUESTION

Ask students to read the Essential Question. Tell them that the next few lessons will focus on volume, which is a measure of three-dimensional figures. Have students look for similarities and differences in ways to measure volume and area.

## FLUENCY PRACTICE

Fluency practice is available at **sadlierconnect.com**.

## Concept Development

## Understand: Volume and cubic units

■ Discuss the fact that if the cubes have gaps or overlaps, then the number of unit cubes will not accurately reflect the amount of space the figure occupies.

■ Consider having students use cubes to explore the relationship between unit cubes and volume.

✏ → Have students build a prism from a single layer of six cubes. Then, have them explore the prism to determine the area of the top of the prism and compare it to the volume of the entire prism. The top of the prism is a rectangle, a two-dimensional figure. The *area* of the rectangle is 6 square units. The *volume* of the prism can be found by counting the number of unit cubes in the prism.

---

**Lesson 28 Understand Concepts of Volume Measurement**

**Essential Question:**
What is volume and how do you measure it?

**Words to Know:**
unit cube
volume
cubic unit

### Guided Instruction

In this lesson you will learn about using cubic units to measure volume.

**Understand: Volume and cubic units**

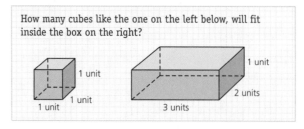

How many cubes like the one on the left below, will fit inside the box on the right?

The cube above is called a unit cube because it has edge lengths of 1 unit.

The drawing below shows that 6 unit cubes fit inside the box.

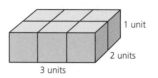

➤ 6 unit cubes will fit inside the box.

The volume of a three-dimensional figure is a measure of the amount of space the figure occupies or contains. A unit cube has a volume of 1 cubic unit. Because the box in the problem can be packed with 6 unit cubes *with no gaps or overlaps*, it has a volume of 6 cubic units.

▬▬ · What is the difference between area and volume?
Possible answer: Area is a measure of two-dimensional, or plane, figures. You can find area by counting how many unit squares cover the figure exactly, without gaps or overlaps. Area is measured in square units. Volume is a measure of three-dimensional, or solid figures. You can find volume by counting how many unit cubes can be packed exactly into the figure without gaps or overlaps. Volume is measured in cubic units.

**250** Unit 4 ■ Focus on Measurement and Data

**Remember!**
A face is a flat surface of a solid figure surrounded by line segments. An edge is a line segment where two faces of a solid figure meet.

---

## Words to Know

**unit cube:** a cube that has edge lengths of 1 unit

**volume:** a measure of the amount of space a three-dimensional figure occupies or contains

**Example:** The volume of the figure below is 6 cubic units.

**cubic unit:** the volume of a unit cube

**Glossary can be found on pp. 347–350.**

Lesson 28

**Guided Instruction**

**Understand:** Comparing volumes

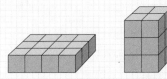

The right rectangular prisms below are made with inch cubes. How do these volumes of the prisms compare?

An inch cube has edge lengths of 1 inch. The volume of an inch cube is 1 cubic inch, which can also be written as 1 in.³

1 in.
1 in.
1 in.

To find the volume of each prism, count the number of inch cubes that *pack* each prism.

The prism on the left is made up of 3 rows with 4 inch cubes in each row. So, it contains $4 + 4 + 4$, or 12, inch cubes in all. Its volume is 12 cubic inches, or 12 in.³

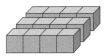

The prism on the right has 3 layers with 4 cubes in each layer. So, it contains $4 + 4 + 4$, or 12 inch cubes. Its volume is 12 cubic inches, or 12 in.³

➡ The volumes of the right rectangular prisms are the same. Both have a volume of 12 cubic inches, or 12 in.³

Unit 4 ■ Focus on Measurement and Data **251**

## Understand: Comparing volumes

■ In this presentation, students compare volumes of two rectangular prisms. Before working through the solution, ask students which prism they think has a greater volume.

■ Point out that volume is measured in cubic units. The unit can be any measure of length, such as cubic inches, cubic meters, or cubic feet.

■ Explain that just as students can count unit squares to determine area, students can count unit cubes to determine volume.

■ Provide cubes for students to use to build different rectangular prisms that have a volume of 12 cubic units. Students should describe each prism by describing the number of layers and the number of cubes in each layer.

■ Remind students that rectangular prisms have opposite faces that are congruent. An irregular shape could also have a volume of 12 cubic units, but it would not be a rectangular prism.

## Support English Language Learners

The similarity between *unit cube* and *cubic unit* may be particularly troubling for English language learners. Ask students to recall the units they have worked previously (cm, m, in., ft) and how those units are used to measure objects. Draw a picture of a cube on the board and label the length, width, and height each as *1 unit*. Write the term *1 unit cube* below the illustration and say it aloud with the students. Write the following sentence on the board for students to repeat after you: *A unit cube has a volume of 1 cubic unit.* Show other simple figures composed of unit cubes. Have students count the number of cubes in each object and say: *This figure has _____ unit cubes. It has a volume of _____ cubic units.*

# Guided Instruction

**Connect: What you know about volume and liquid volume** Use this page to help students apply what they know about volume in cubic units and units of liquid volume.

■ In this presentation, students are introduced to the fact that $1 \text{ mL} = 1 \text{ cm}^3$. They use this idea to find the liquid volume of a box filled with centimeter cubes.

■ Make sure students understand what the problem is asking. Discuss the steps students need to follow to solve the problem. They need to find the volume of the box in cubic centimeters. Then they can determine how many milliliters of water the prism can hold. Finally, they will need to determine if the prism can hold 36 milliliters of water.

■ Remind students that they can only compare measurements that are measured in the same units.

## Guided Instruction

**Connect: What you know about volume and liquid volume**

A box the size of a centimeter cube will hold 1 milliliter of water.

Marley has a plastic box filled with centimeter cubes. The box is shown at the right. She wants to remove the cubes and fill the plastic box with 36 milliliters of water. Will all the water fit?

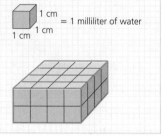

1 cm
1 cm 1 cm = 1 milliliter of water

**Step 1**

Find the volume of the plastic box in cubic centimeters.

The plastic box contains 2 layers of centimeter cubes. Each layer has 16 cubes. The total number of centimeter cubes is 16 + 16. The volume of the plastic box is 32 cm³.

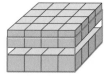

**Step 2**

Find the liquid volume of the plastic box in milliliters.

The plastic box holds 32 centimeter cubes. If each of these cubes were an empty box, it could hold 1 milliliter of water. So, the liquid volume of the plastic box is 32 milliliters.

**Step 3**

Determine whether the water will fit in the plastic box.

Marley has 36 milliliters of water, but the plastic box holds only 32 milliliters.

➡ The water will not fit in the plastic box.

**252** Unit 4 ■ Focus on Measurement and Data

## Math-to-Shopping Connection

**Packaging** Companies package products in ways that are designed to make the customer want to buy them. Some companies design containers to look as if they hold more of a product than the competitor's container. A tall slim container may look as if it holds more than a short wide container. Ask students to bring in empty liquid containers that still have labels with the liquid volume or gather some yourself. Put groups of containers that hold the same amount together. Have students decide whether they all look as if they hold the same amount. If possible, let students use water and beakers to compare the amounts that different containers can hold.

MORE ONLINE sadlierconnect.com

Guided Practice

**Complete the statements.**

1. Some unit cubes have already been placed in this box.

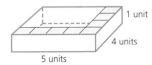

5 units · 4 units · 1 unit

a. A total of __20__ unit cubes can be packed into the box.

b. The volume of the box is __20__ cubic units.

2. This right rectangular prism is made of centimeter cubes.

a. The prism has __2__ layers of centimeter cubes.

   There are __6__ cubes in each layer.

b. The volume of the prism is __12__ cm³.

☂ **Think · Pair · Share**

MP3  3. Paulina and Jackson are measuring the volume of the same box using unit cubes. Paulina can fit 9 unit cubes inside the box without any gaps or overlaps. Jackson can fit 16 unit cubes inside the box without any gaps or overlaps. Is it possible that they are using unit cubes of the same size? Explain your reasoning.

No, Paulina's and Jackson's unit cubes cannot be the same size. Possible explanation: A solid figure that can be packed without gaps or overlaps using $n$ unit cubes has a volume of $n$ cubic units. If Paulina's measurement of volume is 9 cubic units, and Jackson's is 16 cubic units, they must be measuring using unit cubes of different sizes.

Unit 4 ■ Focus on Measurement and Data   **253**

## Observational Assessment

Use page 253 to assess whether students understand how to use cubic units to measure volume. Take note of those students who have difficulty determining the number of cubes in a layer or the number of layers in a right rectangular prism. Provide hands-on models or manipulatives for struggling students to use as they work through the problems on this page.

### ☂ Think·Pair·Share

**Peer Collaboration** Ask student partners to share their answers and explain their rationale for determining their conclusions. As students discuss their conclusions, ask these questions:

- *What do you know about the box that Paulina and Jackson are filling with unit cubes?*

- *Did you and your partner conclude that the unit cubes were the same size or different sizes? How did you and your partner come to this conclusion?*

To summarize, explain that the number of unit cubes needed to fill a box depends on the size of the unit, so the volume of the same box may be reported in different ways using different cubic units.

### Return to the Essential Question

Reread the Lesson 28 Essential Question on page 250: *What is volume and how do you measure it?*

Ask volunteers to use what they learned in this lesson to answer this question. (Possible responses: Volume is the amount of space a figure occupies. Volume can be measured by packing a container with unit cubes. Volume is measured in cubic units.)

Invite as many volunteers as possible to express ideas about volume in their own words.

---

## Mathematical Practices

Mathematical Practice Standards underline the teaching and understanding of all concepts and skills presented. The emphasis of specific practices is noted throughout the guided and independent practice of this lesson.

| MP3 | **Construct viable arguments and critique the reasoning of others.** |
|---|---|

**Item 3:** Students justify their conclusion by articulating the mathematical relationship of unit cubes and volume.

# Independent Practice

## Concept Application

Students may work independently on these pages in the classroom or at home. They may refer to the first four pages of the lesson to revisit the instruction or to see a worked-out example.

**Common Errors** and **Teaching Tips** may help you support student learning either in the classroom or as a follow-up for work done at home.

## Teaching Tips

### Item 1

Students can find the missing number of cubes by counting that there are 6 cubes in each row and 3 equal rows. Make sure students understand that the height of the prism is 1 unit, so there is just one layer of cubes.

---

### Independent Practice

**Complete the statements.**

1. Some unit cubes have already been placed in this box.

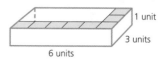

a. A total of <u>18</u> unit cubes can be packed into the box.

b. The volume of the box is <u>18</u> cubic units.

2. This right rectangular prism is made of inch cubes.

a. The prism has <u>4</u> layers of inch cubes.

There are <u>4</u> cubes in each layer.

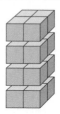

b. The volume of the prism is <u>16</u> in.³

**Fill in the blanks.**

3. <u>   Area   </u> is the amount of space that a two-dimensional figure occupies.

4. <u>   Volume   </u> is the amount of space that a three-dimensional solid occupies.

**254**   Unit 4 ■ Focus on Measurement and Data

---

## Writing About Math

⬤▬▬ ▸ **Writing an Explanatory Text** Explain the difference between area, which is measured in square units, and volume, which is measured in cubic units. Present students with several real-world objects. Ask each student to write a paragraph explaining whether he or she would describe each object's size in square units or cubic units.

Lesson 28

## Independent Practice

Circle the most appropriate unit to measure the volume of each item.

5. a glass of orange juice
   - a. square meters
   - b. cubic yards
   - c. cubic inches
   - (d.) cups

6. a brick
   - (a.) cubic centimeters
   - b. liters
   - c. ounces
   - d. miles

7. a storage unit
   - a. quarts
   - (b.) cubic meters
   - c. cubic milliliters
   - d. square centimeters

**Solve.**

8. A crate can be filled with 4 layers of unit cubes. Each layer contains 6 unit cubes.

   a. What is the total number of unit cubes that can fill the crate?

   24

   b. What is the volume of the crate? Express your answer in cubic units.

   24 cubic units

## Teaching Tips

### Items 5-7

Remind students that a cubic unit is the volume of a cube with edge lengths of 1 unit. So, for example, a cubic meter is the volume of a cube with edge lengths of 1 meter. Some students may need to review the relative sizes of metric and customary units of length, so they can visualize the corresponding unit cubes.

## Digital Connection

**Animations** Enter the key words *interactive volume of a rectangular prism* into a search engine to find animations showing how a rectangular prism can be packed with unit cubes. Seeing how the cubes fit into layers and how the layers fill the prism from bottom to top will strengthen students' comprehension of volume.

# Independent Practice

## Common Errors

### Item 9

This problem relates the number of unit cubes to the volume of the solid. Since the quantities are the same, some students will answer that Ambika is correct. Students may not consider that the unit cubes were counted incorrectly. Also, the units should be cubic units, not square units. Remind students to review all parts of a problem, including models.

### Item 10

Watch for students who do not understand that this measurement is inaccurate. Emphasize that only unit cubes that have no gaps or overlaps can represent the volume of a figure.

---

## Independent Practice

MP3 **9.** Ambika found the volume of the solid below by counting the unit cubes. Then she wrote an expression for the volume.

number of unit cubes in solid = 14
volume of solid          = 14 square units

Is Ambika correct? If not, explain how she can correct her work.

No , Ambika is not correct. Possible explanation: Ambika incorrectly counted the number of unit cubes. She also used square units instead of cubic units to express the volume. The answer should be 12 cubic units.

MP3 **10.** Kevin filled a container with unit cubes. He was able to fit 16 unit cubes into the container, as shown below. He says the volume is 16 cubic units. Is his measurement accurate? Why or why not?

No, his measurement is not accurate. Possible explanation: The unit cubes do not fill the container without gaps. To find an accurate volume measurement, he needs to find out how many unit cubes fit in the container without gaps or overlaps.

**Solve the problems.**

**11.** A solid figure is packed with 52 cubes. If the edge lengths of the cubes are 1 meter, what is the volume of the solid?

▪▪▪▪ **Show your work.**
Possible student work:
Each cube measures 1 cubic meter, so 52 cubes is 52 cubic meters.

**Answer** The volume is 52 cubic meters or 52 m³.

**12.** Joey is packing books into a box. Each book has a volume of 125 cubic inches. Joey can fit 11 books into the box without any space in between or above them. What is the volume of the box?

▪▪▪▪ **Show your work.**
Possible student work:
$125 \times 11 = 1{,}375$

**Answer** The volume of the box is 1,375 cubic inches.

**256** Unit 4 ▪ Focus on Measurement and Data

---

| **Mathematical Practices** |
|---|
| MP3 **Construct viable arguments and critique the reasoning of others.** |

**Item 9:** Students identify another student's error and explain how to correct it.

**Item 10:** Students describe and explain another student's misconception about volume.

MP1 **13.** A dresser has a volume of 120 cubic feet. A nightstand takes up exactly half the amount of space. What is the volume of the nightstand?

> **Show your work.**

Possible student work:

$\frac{120}{2} = 60$

**Answer** The volume of the nightstand is 60 cubic feet.

MP7 **14.** The volume of a stick of butter is 180 cubic centimeters. The volume of a jar of grape jam is 240 milliliters. What is the total volume of both items? Express your answer in cubic centimeters.

**Answer** The total volume is 420 cubic centimeters.

> **Justify your answer using words, drawings, or numbers.**

Possible justification: 1 milliliter equals 1 cubic centimeter. 180 + 240 = 420.

MP7 **15.** An architect is planning a building of the future. It has 27 floors. Each floor has 15 offices. The volume of 1 office is 1000 cubic meters. Hallways and other areas besides offices take up 100,000 cubic meters of space on each floor. What is the total volume of the skyscraper?

**Answer** The total volume is 3,105,000 cubic meters.

> **Justify your answer using words, drawings, or numbers.**

Possible justification: 15 × 1000 + 100,000 = 115,000; 115,000 × 27 = 3,105,000 cubic meters

## Teaching Tips

### Item 14
Remind students that cubic centimeters and milliliters are related. Refer them to page 252, where they can read about the relationship.

### Item 15
Suggest that students start by focusing on one floor, finding the total volume of its 15 offices and hallways and other spaces. They can then find the volume of the entire skyscraper by multiplying that result by 27.

## Mathematical Practices

| MP1 | Make sense of problems and persevere in solving them. |
| --- | --- |

**Item 13:** Students apply their knowledge of division to their understanding of volume.

| MP7 | Look for and make use of structure. |
| --- | --- |

**Item 14:** Students use their knowledge of the relationship between different units to solve the problem.

**Item 15:** Students interpret the pattern of a described figure and use their multiplication skills to find its volume.

## OBJECTIVE
**Use the concept of volume and counting unit cubes to determine the volume of right rectangular prisms.**

## ESSENTIAL QUESTION
Ask students to share what they learned about volume in the last lesson. Be sure to discuss the fact that the volume of a prism is the number of unit cubes that can be packed inside the prism. Tell students that, in this lesson, they will explore strategies for counting the unit cubes that pack a prism.

## FLUENCY PRACTICE
Fluency practice is available at **sadlierconnect.com.**

## Concept Development

### Understand: Counting unit cubes

■ A right rectangular prism is a prism in which all six faces are rectangles. The edges of the lateral faces are perpendicular to the bases. In this lesson, all rectangular prisms are assumed to be right rectangular prisms.

■ Remind students that when measuring length, a ruler is placed end to end with no gaps or overlaps. When measuring area, the unit squares must completely fill the area with no gaps or overlaps. Likewise when finding volume, the space must be completely filled with no gaps or overlaps.

 Have students build the box using 24 cubes so that it rests on a rectangular face. Then, have them orient the box on a square face and compare the volume in each orientation.

---

Lesson

# 29  Measure Volume

### Guided Instruction

In this lesson you will learn how to measure volume by counting unit cubes.

**Understand: Counting unit cubes**

Marnie packs a rectangular box with inch cubes as shown below. What is the volume of the rectangular box?

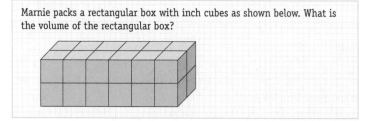

To find the volume of the rectangular box, count the number of inch cubes Marnie uses to pack the box.

There are two layers of inch cubes, like the one shown below. Each layer has 12 cubes.

| 1 | 2 | 3 | 4 | 5 | 6 |
|---|---|---|---|---|---|
| 7 | 8 | 9 | 10 | 11 | 12 |

**Remember!**
An inch cube has edge lengths of 1 inch and a volume of 1 cubic inch. This volume can be written as 1 in.³

There are 12 + 12, or 24, inch cubes in all.

➡ The volume of the rectangular box is 24 in³.

✏ Suppose Marnie's box rested on one of its square faces, rather than on a rectangular face. How would the volume change?
The volume would not change. Changing the position of the box does not change the number of inch cubes that are packed inside of it, so the volume does not change.

**258** Unit 4 ■ Focus on Measurement and Data

---

## Support English Language Learners

Explore the term *volume* with students. Most students have likely encountered volume in their everyday lives. Write the word *volume* on the board. Ask students to talk about what volume means to them. For example, volume can refer to the loudness or softness of music, or some students may define a volume as a collection of books.

Next, ask students to read the definition from the previous lesson aloud. Provide two different size transparent containers. Fill the smaller container with raw rice. Pour the rice from one container to the other to show they have different volumes because one has more space, or holds more, than the other container.

Lesson 29

Guided Instruction

**Connect:** What you know about measuring volume of right rectangular prisms with unit cubes

A sporting goods store receives a shipment of basketballs. Each basketball is packed into a box that is a foot cube. These cubic boxes are packed into a larger box as shown. What is the volume of the larger box?

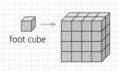

foot cube

To find the volume of the larger box, you can count the cubes layer by layer.

Count the number of foot cubes in the first layer of the box.

There are 2 rows of 4 foot cubes, or 8 foot cubes in the first layer.

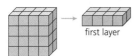

first layer

Count the number of layers of foot cubes that fill the box.

There are 4 layers.

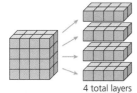

4 total layers

Add to find the total number of foot cubes in the four layers:
$8 + 8 + 8 + 8 = 32$

➡ The volume of the larger box is 32 cubic feet, or 32 ft³.

✏ Livia packs a cubic box with 27 inch cubes. What is the length of each side of the box? Make a drawing to help you answer the question.
Each side is 3 inches in length.

**Connect:** **What you know about measuring volume of right rectangular prisms with unit cubes** Use this page to help students strengthen their understanding of volume by counting the number of unit cubes in one layer, then adding to find the total volume of the prism.

■ In this presentation, a rectangular prism is decomposed into layers. The number of cubes in each layer is found and then the numbers are added to get the volume. Some students may see that the volume of one layer is its length times its width, and the volume of the whole prism is that product times the number of layers. This concept will be developed in Lesson 30.

■ You might ask students to think of the prism as two vertical layers, instead of four horizontal layers. Have them show that they get the same volume by adding the cubes in the vertical layers as they do by adding the cubes in the horizontal layers. Ask why this makes sense.

✏ Some students may have trouble drawing a three-dimensional figure. Refer them to the figures on this page and the previous page. Note that some students may draw a rectangular prism that is 1 inch by 3 inches by 9 inches. Point out that while this prism does have a volume of 27 cubic inches, it is not a *cubic* box.

## Math-to-Shopping Connection

**Refrigerators** Have students research the volumes of refrigerators advertised in weekly flyers or on the Internet. They should list at least three of the most common volumes. Ask students to discuss what other measurements should be considered when buying a refrigerator and the importance of these measurements as well as the measure of the volume.

# Guided Practice

## Observational Assessment

Use pages 260–261 to assess whether students are able to count the number of unit cubes in a rectangular prism or to partition a rectangular prism into layers and then use the volume of one layer to find the volume of the entire prism. Even though some students may be able to solve the exercises on these pages without completing each step, ask them to use each step to help strengthen their understanding of volume.

### Guided Practice

**For exercises 1–4, count the unit cubes to find the volume of each figure.**

1.

There are __5__ unit cubes.

The volume is __5__ cubic units.

2.

There are __12__ unit cubes.

The volume is __12__ cubic units.

3.

There are __8__ unit cubes.

The volume is __8__ cubic units.

4.

There are __9__ unit cubes.

The volume is __9__ cubic units.

5. This figure is made from inch cubes. Find the volume of the figure by following the instructions given in a–d.

a. Count the number of inch cubes in the first layer of the figure.

There are __6__ inch cubes in the first layer.

b. Count the number of layers. There are __3__ layers.

c. Add the cubes in each layer to find the total number of cubes.

__6__ + __6__ + __6__ = __18__

d. The volume of the figure is __18__ cubic inches.

**260**  Unit 4 ■ Focus on Measurement and Data

## Math-to-Science Connection

**Water Displacement** Place a clear metric measuring cup or beaker in a pan and partially fill the container with water. Record the measurement of the water in milliliters. Place a small object that will not float, such as a rock, into the container and record the new measurement of the water in milliliters. Ask students to discuss how these two water measurements could be used to find the volume of the rock. Point out that the difference between the beginning measurement and the ending measurement must be equal to the volume of the rock. Since 1 milliliter = 1 cubic centimeter, students can use the difference to report the volume of the rock in cubic centimeters.

Lesson 29

Guided Practice

**Find the volume of each figure by counting the unit cubes.**

6.
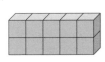

__10__ cubic units

7.

__16__ cubic units

8.

__7__ cubic units

9.
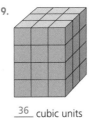

__36__ cubic units

**👑 Think · Pair · Share**

MP3 **10.** Robert wants to measure the volume of the figure below. He says there are 4 cubic units in the bottom layer of the figure. Since there are 2 layers in the figure, he thinks he can add 4 + 4 to find the total volume of the figure. Is Robert's reasoning correct? If not, explain how you can find the volume.

No. Robert's reasoning is not correct. Possible explanation: The figure is not a rectangular prism. To find the volume, you must count the unit cubes. There are 4 unit cubes in the bottom layer and 2 unit cubes in the top layer, so the volume is 6 cubic units.

**👑 Think·Pair·Share**

**Peer Collaboration** Ask students to work with a partner. One student should build a model of the figure in problem 10 using unit cubes. The other student should count the unit cubes to determine the volume of the figure. After each pair of students has done this and agreed on the volume, ask them to analyze Robert's reasoning. Some questions for students to consider are:

• *How is this figure different from the other figures on this page?*

• *How could this figure be separated into parts to determine its volume?*

• *What mistake did Robert make?*

• *How could you help Robert determine the volume of the figure?*

**Return to the Essential Question**

Reread the Lesson 29 Essential Question on page 258: *How do you measure the volume of a right rectangular prism?*

Ask volunteers to use what they learned in this lesson to answer this question. (Possible response: I can count the number of unit cubes it takes to completely fill the rectangular prism. I can separate the rectangular prism into layers, find the volume of one layer, and then add the volumes of the layers together to find the total volume.)

## Mathematical Practices

Mathematical Practice Standards underline the teaching and understanding of all concepts and skills presented. The emphasis of specific practices is noted throughout the guided and independent practice of this lesson.

| MP3 | **Construct viable arguments and critique the reasoning of others.** |
|---|---|

**Item 10:** Students analyze a peer's reasoning, determine whether the reasoning is valid, and then justify their conclusion.

# Independent Practice

## Concept Application

Students may work independently on these pages in the classroom or at home. They may refer to the first four pages of the lesson to revisit the instruction or to see a worked-out example.

**Common Errors** and **Teaching Tips** may help you support student learning either in the classroom or as a follow-up for work done at home.

## Common Errors

### Items 1-4

Some students may double or triple count the cubes on the edges by simply counting the visible faces of the cubes. It may be helpful for these students to create models of each figure using unit cubes and then count the number of unit cubes used.

## Teaching Tips

### Item 5

Students should count the number of cubes in the top layer to determine the number of cubes in each layer. Otherwise they may only count the cubes that are visible and not those that are hidden.

---

### Independent Practice

**For exercises 1–4, count the unit cubes to find the volume.**

1.

There are ___6___ unit cubes.

The volume is ___6___ cubic units.

2.

There are ___8___ unit cubes.

The volume is ___8___ cubic units.

3.

There are ___32___ unit cubes.

The volume is ___32___ cubic units.

4.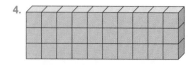

There are ___30___ unit cubes.

The volume is ___30___ cubic units.

5. This figure is made from centimeter cubes. Find the volume of the figure by following the instructions given in a–d.

   a. Count the number of centimeter cubes in the first layer of the figure.

   There are ___12___ centimeter cubes in the first layer.

   b. Count the number of layers. There are ___5___ layers.

   c. Add the cubes in each layer to find the total number of cubes.

   ___12___ + ___12___ + ___12___ + ___12___ + ___12___ = ___60___

   d. The volume of the figure is ___60___ cubic centimeters.

---

## Writing About Math

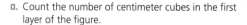 · **Explain Relationships Using a Text** Have students reread pages 250–252 and 258–259. Ask them to list at least two methods to find the volume of a rectangular prism. Then have them write a paragraph or two that shows how these methods are related. Their paragraphs should include the following:

- A clear description of each method using drawings as necessary,
- How the methods are alike and how they are different, and
- Situations in which each method might be better to use than the other(s).

Be sure students use precise language and vocabulary in their paragraphs.

Independent Practice

6. This figure is made from meter cubes. Find the volume of the figure by following the instructions given in a–d.

a. How many meter cubes are in the first layer of the figure?

___6___ meter cubes

b. How many layers of cubes are there? There are __4__ layers.

c. What is the volume of the figure?

__6__ + __6__ + __6__ + __6__ = __24__

d. The volume of the figure is __24__ cubic meters.

**Find the volume of the figures using any method.**

7.

__8__ cubic units

8.

__24__ cubic units

9.

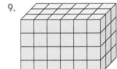

__72__ cubic units

10.

__6__ cubic units

## Common Errors

### Item 10

Some students may find the volume of the bottom layer and add this volume three times since there are three layers. Remind students that the layers are not the same and, as a result, the cubes must be counted in each layer and then added to find the total volume. Building a model with unit cubes will help students find the volume.

## Teaching Tips

### Items 7–9

Students can refer to the steps in exercise 6 to help them complete these exercises.

## Digital Connection

**Online Videos** Use online videos to motivate student learning and provide a visual approach to the concept of volume. Use this search term—*volume of rectangular prism video* with a search engine to find a selection of videos. Students may watch them in class if you have that capability for a whiteboard or with a computer or tablet. You can extend the activity by having students write a review of one of the videos they watched or create a storyboard for a video they would make about volume of a rectangular prism.

# Independent Practice

## Teaching Tips

### Item 12

Some students may not understand the term *cubic yard*. Ask students to name the number of feet in 1 yard. Then ask what the dimensions of a square yard are in feet and how many square feet are in 1 square yard. You may want to use a drawing to show the concept. Then discuss what the dimensions of a cubic yard are in feet. Students can make a drawing or a model to help them solve the problem.

---

### Independent Practice

11. Find the volume of the figure below. Express your answer in cubic units. Explain the method you used.

The volume of the figure is 27 cubic units. Possible explanation: I counted 9 unit cubes in the first layer. There are 3 layers, so I added 9 + 9 + 9 to get 27 unit cubes.

12. Amy said, "There are 3 cubic feet in a cubic yard." Explain why Amy is incorrect.
Possible answer: To pack a yard cube you need 27 foot cubes. The bottom layer would be a 3 by 3 square of foot cubes. Then, you would need to stack 3 of these layers. The total number of cubes would be 9 + 9 + 9, or 27. So, there are 27 cubic feet in a cubic yard.

**Circle the correct answer.**

13. A solid figure has 6 layers of cubes. Each layer has 8 inch cubes. What is the volume of the figure?

    a. 6 cubic inches          b. 8 cubic inches

    c. 14 cubic inches         d. 48 cubic inches

**Solve the problems.**

MP1 14. A solid figure has a volume of 18 cubic centimeters. The figure has 3 layers of centimeter cubes. If each layer has the same number of centimeter cubes, how many centimeter cubes are in each layer?

**Show your work.**
Possible student work:
18 cubic centimeter ÷ 3 layers = 6 cubes in each layer

**Answer** There are 6 centimeter cubes in each layer.

---

| Mathematical Practices |
| --- |
| MP1 **Make sense of problems and persevere in solving them.** |

**Item 14:** Students are given the total volume of a figure and must determine the volume of one layer. After solving, students can check their solution using strategies given in the lesson.

**MORE ONLINE** sadlierconnect.com                    Lesson 29

MP1  **15.** Carmella is making a model using centimeter cubes. She uses 4 cubes to build the first layer as shown below. How many more layers of 4 cubes must Carmella build so her model will have a volume of 60 cubic centimeters?

**Show your work.**
Let *n* = the number of layers, and *n* × 4 = 60. To solve for *n*, write the equivalent division equation: *n* = 60 ÷ 4, and divide. *n* = 15. Since the first layer is already built, Carmella needs to build 14 more layers. 4 cubes on the first layer and another 14 layers of 4 cubes equals 60 cubes total.

**Answer** Carmella must add another 14 layers of 4 cubes to get a volume of 60 cubic centimeters.

MP7  **16.** Below is one possible rectangular prism that can be made from 16 unit cubes. Describe two different rectangular prisms you could make from 16 unit cubes.

**Answer** Possible answer: You could make 1 layer with 2 rows of 8 cubes. Or you could make 4 layers, with each layer being 2 rows of 2 cubes.

**Justify your answer using words, drawings, or numbers.**
Check students' work.

MP7  **17.** Each cube in the figure below measures 1 cubic meter. What is the total volume of the figure?

**Answer** 44 cubic meters

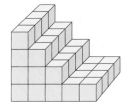

**Justify your answer using words, drawings, or numbers.**
The bottom layer has 20 cubes.
The next layer has 12 cubes.
The next layer has 8 cubes.
The top layer has 4 cubes.
20 + 12 + 8 + 4 = 44

## Common Errors

### Item 15
After dividing to see that there will be 15 layers, some students may give an incorrect answer of 15 layers. Remind students to reread the problem carefully and to always check their answers to see if they satisfy the facts given in the problem.

## Teaching Tips

### Item 16
Students may benefit from using unit cubes to build possible models.

In their justifications, students should include their computation showing that each rectangular prism they created has a volume of 16 cubic units.

| **Mathematical Practices** | |
|---|---|
| **MP1** | **Make sense of problems and persevere in solving them.** |

**Item 15:** Students analyze given information, and then determine a plan to solve the problem.

| **MP7** | **Look for and make use of structure.** |
|---|---|

**Item 16:** Students shift perspective and create rectangular prisms given a volume.

**Item 17:** Students can use patterns in the layers of a cube figure to help them calculate its volume efficiently.

## OBJECTIVE
**Use multiplication to find the volume of a right rectangular prism.**

## ESSENTIAL QUESTION
Students will learn strategies for finding volumes of rectangular prisms by using multiplication.

## PREREQUISITE SKILLS
Use Item J on page 341 of the Foundational Skills Handbook to review using the area formula.

## FLUENCY PRACTICE
Fluency practice is available at **sadlierconnect.com**.

## Concept Development

### Understand: How to find the volume of a right rectangular prism by packing it with unit cubes

■ Students must grasp the concept that a right rectangular prism can be decomposed into layers of arrays of unit cubes.

■ Preview the next problem by informing students that the volume is the product of the box's dimensions. Ask students why this makes sense. If students have difficulty explaining, tell them they will revisit this idea in the next problem.

➤ Explain that in a right rectangular prism, it does not matter which face of the prism is considered the base.

---

**Lesson**

**30** Find Volume: Relate Packing of Unit Cubes to Multiplying

**Essential Question:**
How can you multiply to find the volume of a right rectangular prism?

### Guided Instruction

In this lesson you will learn how counting unit cubes to find the volume of a right rectangular prism is related to multiplying side lengths of the prism.

**Understand: How to find the volume of a right rectangular prism by packing it with unit cubes**

A jewelry box is shaped like a right rectangular prism with the dimensions shown. Use unit cubes to find the volume of the jewelry box.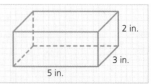

To find the volume of the jewelry box, pack the box with inch cubes.

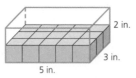 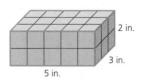

$3 \times 5 = 15$ inch cubes     $2 \times 15 = 30$ inch cubes

The bottom layer of inch cubes has 3 rows of 5 cubes, or 15 cubes. Two layers of cubes can be packed into the jewelry box, so there are $2 \times 15$, or 30, inch cubes in the box.

➤ The volume of the jewelry box is 30 cubic inches.

▭ Luke solved the problem above by visualizing 5 vertical columns of inch cubes, instead of 2 horizontal layers. What do you think Luke did?
Possible answer: Luke found the number of cubes in each column, which is $2 \times 3$, or 6. Then, he multiplied by the number of columns to get $5 \times 6$, or 30 cubes in all.

**266** Unit 4 ■ Focus on Measurement and Data

---

## Support English Language Learners

The expression *packing it with unit cubes* is used throughout this lesson. Students may benefit from a review of the term *unit cube*. English language learners may already be familiar with the meaning of *packing*. Talk about everyday uses of the word *pack*, for example, *packing* a suitcase or lunch box. Ask students to demonstrate or act out how they would pack their backpacks. Use cubes to demonstrate how they can be *packed* into a rectangular prism. Stress that when packing a figure with unit cubes to find its volume, the figure is filled completely with no gaps or overlaps in the unit cubes. Repeat the process as necessary until students have fully grasped the review.

---

**Understand:** How to find the volume of a right rectangular prism using multiplication

Find the volume of the right rectangular prism by packing it with unit cubes. Then explain why you can find the volume simply by multiplying the dimensions of the prism.

4 cm

3 cm

6 cm

Visualize packing the right rectangular prism with centimeter cubes.

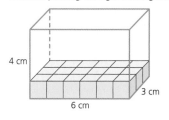

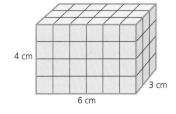

3 × 6 = 18 centimeter cubes

4 × 18 = 72 centimeter cubes

The bottom layer has 3 rows of 6 centimeter cubes, or 18 centimeter cubes. Four layers of cubes can be packed into the prism. So, there are a total of 4 × 18, or 72 centimeter cubes.

➡ The volume of the right rectangular prism is 72 cm³.

The product of the length and the width, 3 × 6, is the number of cubes in each layer. The height is the number of layers. So, you can find the volume by multiplying the dimensions.

volume  =  length  ×  width  ×  height
              3      ×    6    ×    4
            └────── number of cubes ──────┘     number of
                    in each layer              layers

**Understand:** How to find the volume of a right rectangular prism using multiplication

■ In this presentation, students examine the relationship between the number of unit cubes in a right rectangular prism and the formula for volume.

■ If possible, have students build their own 3 by 6 by 4 unit prism with unit cubes as you discuss the solution in the student book.

■ Be sure students see that the number of unit cubes that fit in the bottom layer is the same as the length of the prism times its width, and the number of layers of unit cubes that fit in the prism is the height. So, the volume of the prism is the length times the width times the height.

■ The volume formula is presented in words after the solution. You might show students how this formula can be written in symbols: $V = l \times w \times h$.

## Math-to-Math Connection

**Scale Factor and Volume** Scale factor is the ratio of the corresponding parts of two similar figures. Using the figure on page 267, ask students to find the volume of a similar figure that is scaled by a factor of 2. In the new figure, each dimension is multiplied by 2, so the volume would be 12 × 6 × 8 = 576 cm cubes. The formula for the volume of the scale figure can be written as $(l \times 2) \times (w \times 2) \times (h \times 2)$. Use the Commutative and Associative Properties of Multiplication to rewrite the formula as $(l \times w \times h) \times (2 \times 2 \times 2)$, or $(l \times w \times h) \times 2^3$. Using substitution, $(6 \times 3 \times 4) \times 2^3 = 72 \times 8 = 576$ cm cubes. Discuss the pattern and state a general rule to find the volume of a right rectangular prism with any scale factor greater than 1: Multiply the volume of the original figure by the scale factor to the third power.

**Connect:** Multiplying dimensions to multiplying base area times height Use this page to help students strengthen their understanding that prisms can have different dimensions, but the volume is the same.

■ In this presentation, students are not given all the dimensions of a prism. They need to recognize that the area of the base is the product of two dimensions. As students work through the steps, they will observe that a prism can have a variety of dimensions and still have the same volume.

■ Point out that the prism has *whole number dimensions*. This makes it possible to list all the possible length/ width combinations in Step 2. It also makes it easy to visualize whole unit cubes filling the prism

■ The objective of Step 2 is to demonstrate that you can find volume by multiplying the area of the base by the height. Have students think about a prism filled with unit cubes. Even though students do not know the dimensions of the base, they know that the prism has 16 unit cubes in the bottom layer, no matter how the cubes are arranged in rows and columns.

✏ Have students share their explanations with the class. Point out that area is a two-dimensional measurement, length × width. This two-dimensional measurement can be used to find the volume of the first layer of unit cubes because the height of one layer of cubes is 1. Any number multiplied by 1 is equal to itself, so the area of the base and the volume of the first layer of cubes have the same numeric value; although technically, one is a measurement of square units and the other is a measurement of cubic units.

---

**Connect:** Multiplying dimensions to multiplying base area times height

> A right rectangular prism has whole number dimensions. The area of the base of the prism is 16 square feet, and the height of the prism is 3 feet. Find the volume of the right rectangular prism.

**Step 1**

Plan the solution.

You can find the volume of a right rectangular prism by multiplying the dimensions. However, in this problem, you are not given the length or the width only the height of 3 feet. Since the area of the base of the right rectangular prism is 16 square feet, you know that length × width = 16 square feet.

You can try listing all the possible lengths and widths and finding the volume for each possibility.

**Step 2**

Make a table and calculate the volume of each possible prism.

| length (ft) | width (ft) | height (ft) | volume (ft³) |
|---|---|---|---|
| 1 | 16 | 3 | (1 × 16) × 3 = 48 |
| 2 | 8 | 3 | (2 × 8) × 3 = 48 |
| 4 | 4 | 3 | (4 × 4) × 3 = 48 |
| 8 | 2 | 3 | (8 × 2) × 3 = 48 |
| 16 | 1 | 3 | (16 × 1) × 3 = 48 |

The volume of each possible right rectangular prism is 48 cubic feet. The specific length and width do not matter.

➡ The volume of the right rectangular prism is 48 cubic feet.

✏ Use the idea of packing with unit cubes to explain why the volume of a right rectangular prism is the area of the base times the height. Possible explanation: The area of base is the number of unit cubes in the first layer, and the height is the number of layers. To get the total number of unit cubes in the right rectangular prism, which is the volume, you multiply these two numbers.

**268** Unit 4 ■ Focus on Measurement and Data

---

## Math-to-Construction Connection

**Models** Developers often make three-dimensional models of their construction plans to show investors what the projects will look like when they're completed. An image search on the Internet for *scale construction models* will provide many examples. Explain that a *net* is a two-dimensional pattern that can be folded up to form a model of a three-dimensional geometric shape. The nets above can be folded to make unit cubes. Transfer these nets to grid paper and show students how to cut and fold the nets to form unit cubes. Provide students with grid paper, scissors, and tape, and have them work in pairs to find other nets that can be used to form unit cubes. There are 11 different nets in all.

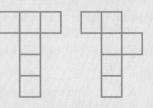

Lesson 30

Guided Practice

**The diagrams below show a right rectangular prism being packed with foot cubes. Complete exercises 1–2 using the prism.**

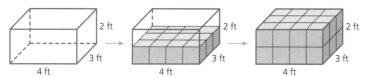

1. Cubes in one layer: __12__    Number of layers: __2__

2. Find the product below to determine the number of unit cubes that can be packed in the prism. This is the volume of the prism.

    2 × __12__ = __24__; The volume of the prism is __24 ft³__.

**For exercises 3–4, use this right rectangular prism given below. Each cube that the prism is packed with has a side length of 1 inch.**

3. Multiply to find the number of cubes in the prism.

    cubes in one layer × number of layers = number of cubes

    (__3__ × __3__) × __4__ = __36__

4. What is the volume of the prism? __36 in.³__

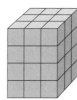

### ☝☝ Think ▪ Pair ▪ Share

MP3  5. Preeti says that the volume of the right rectangular prism shown can be found by multiplying the unit cubes in the front layer by the number of layers from front to back.

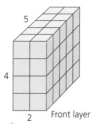

5

4

2    Front layer

   a. Use her method to find the volume of the prism.
      8 × 5 = 40. The volume is 40 cubic units.

   b. Explain how you can check your answer without having to count any unit cubes. Possible answer:
      Multiply length × width × height, 5 × 2 × 4 = 40 cubic units.

## Observational Assessment

Use page 269 to assess whether students recognize that the number of unit cubes in one layer of a rectangular prism is the length times the width (or the area of the base), and the number of layers is the height. Therefore, the volume is the product of the dimensions. Take note of those students who still try to count the individual unit cubes in each diagram.

### ☝☝ Think▪Pair▪Share

**Peer Collaboration** Break the class into student pairs. Remind students that this problem starts with the number of cubes in the front layer of a right rectangular prism, not in the bottom layer, as students are used to. This may confuse some student pairs. While they work, prompt students with questions such as:

• *Can you think of another method to find volume?*

• *What if you started with the number of unit cubes in the right layer? Would you get the same volume?*

### Return to the Essential Question

Reread the Lesson 30 Essential Question on page 266: *How can you multiply to find the volume of a right rectangular prism?*

Ask volunteers to use what they learned in this lesson to answer this question. (Possible response: I can multiply the length by the width by the height. I can multiply the area of the base by the height.)

Invite as many volunteers as possible to express ideas in their own words about multiplying to find the volume of a right rectangular prism.

---

## Mathematical Practices

Mathematical Practice Standards underline the teaching and understanding of all concepts and skills presented. The emphasis of specific practices is noted throughout the guided and independent practice of this lesson.

| MP3 | **Construct viable arguments and critique the reasoning of others.** |
|---|---|

**Item 5:** Students use another student's method to compute the volume of a prism and then explain how to use a different method to check the answer.

# Independent Practice

## Concept Application

Students may work independently on these pages in the classroom or at home. They may refer to the first four pages of the lesson to revisit the instruction or to see a worked-out example.

**Common Errors** and **Teaching Tips** may help you support student learning either in the classroom or as a follow-up for work done at home.

## Common Errors

### Item 1

Students may want to use the layer facing forward to count the number of cubes in one layer. Tell students to read through the problem before answering any part. Since the number of cubes in one layer is multiplied by 3, the layer of cubes that is counted does not include the side that measures 3 m.

## Teaching Tips

### Items 1-2

Remind students that they can use multiplication to find the number of cubes in one layer. They do not have to count individual cubes.

---

### Independent Practice

**Each right rectangular prism is packed with unit cubes. Find the volume of each prism by counting the unit cubes.**

1. 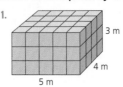   3 m, 4 m, 5 m

Cubes in one layer: __20__

Number of layers: __3__
Total number of cubes:

$3 \times$ __20__ $=$ __60__

Volume of prism: __60 m³__

2. 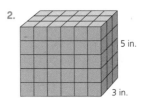   5 in., 3 in., 6 in.

Cubes in one layer: __18__

Number of layers: __5__
Total number of cubes:

__5__ $\times$ __18__ $=$ __90__

Volume of prism: __90 in.³__

**For exercises 3–6, use the right rectangular prism given below.**

3. The unit cubes in the prism have a side length of 1 millimeter. Label the length, width, and height of the prism, using the appropriate units.

4. Multiply to find the number of unit cubes in the prism.
   $5 \times 4 \times 7 = 20 \times 7 = 140$

   _140 unit cubes_

5. What is the volume of the prism? __140 mm³__

6. Which expression does not represent the total number of unit cubes in the prism?

   a. $20 + 20 + 20 + 20 + 20 + 20 + 20$

   b. $(5 \times 4) + (5 \times 4) + (5 \times 4) + (5 \times 4) + (5 \times 4) + (5 \times 4) + (5 \times 4)$

   c. $5 \times 4$

   d. $7 \times (5 \times 4)$

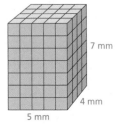   7 mm, 4 mm, 5 mm

---

## Writing About Math

▸ **Provide Reasons to Support a Method** Ask students to give reasons why there cannot be any gaps or overlaps in the unit cubes used to measure the volume of a right rectangular prism. They should include information about how unit cubes are used to measure volume. You can have students draw two diagrams, one with gaps between the unit cubes, and one with overlaps, to help them visualize and formulate their reasoning.

## Independent Practice

**For exercises 7–9, use the given right rectangular prism.**

7. Multiply the length and width.

   <u> 9 </u> × <u> 3 </u> = <u> 27 ft² </u>

8. Multiply your answer to exercise 7 by the height to find the volume of the prism.

   <u> 27 </u> × <u> 6 </u> = <u> 162 ft³ </u>

6 ft
3 ft
9 ft

9. Explain how you would use the number of unit cubes to check your answer to exercise 8. Is your answer correct? Possible answer: Count the number of unit cubes in one layer (27) and multiply by the number of layers (6) to find the volume (27 × 6 = 162 ft³). Yes, my answer is correct.

**For exercises 10–11, find the volume of each box. Each box below is a right rectangular prism.**

10.

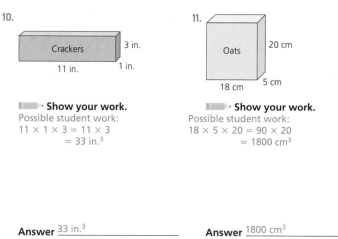

Crackers    3 in.
11 in.      1 in.

🖊 · **Show your work.**
Possible student work:
11 × 1 × 3 = 11 × 3
            = 33 in.³

**Answer** <u>33 in.³</u>

11.

Oats    20 cm
18 cm   5 cm

🖊 · **Show your work.**
Possible student work:
18 × 5 × 20 = 90 × 20
            = 1800 cm³

**Answer** <u>1800 cm³</u>

Unit 4 ■ Focus on Measurement and Data    **271**

## Teaching Tips

### Items 10 and 11

Students may struggle with which lengths to multiply first. Remind them that the Associative Property of Multiplication says that the order of multiplication does not change the product.

---

## Digital Connection

**Random Number Generator** Find a random number generator Web site. Show students how to use it to generate whole numbers between 1 and 12. Have students work in pairs to generate three numbers, sketch and label a prism with those three numbers as dimensions, and then calculate the volume of the prism. Have pairs share their work with the class and explain how they calculated the volume.

## Teaching Tips

### Item 13

Students may be confused because they are given no information about the dimensions of the bed. Point out that the volume of the bed and the volume of each bag of soil are given. Ask if it is necessary to know the dimensions in order to calculate the number of bags needed to fill the bed.

### Item 15

If students struggle with this problem, suggest that they list the information they are given in the problem and the information they know from problem 14. Some students may find it easier to find the answer first and then explain how they·came to that conclusion.

---

### Independent Practice

12. Describe two methods you can use to find the volume of this right rectangular prism shown at the right.

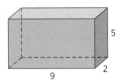

**Method 1** Possible answer: Sketch unit cubes to cover the base and count them (18). Then multiply the unit cubes in one layer by the height (5).

**Method 2** Possible answer: Multiply the length (9) by the width (2) and then multiply by the height (5).

13. A raised planting bed in the shape of a right rectangular prism has a volume of 30 cubic feet. A large bag of potting soil contains 2 cubic feet of soil. Explain how to determine the number of bags of soil that are needed to fill the planting bed.
Possible explanation: Divide the volume of the planting bed (30 ft³) by the volume of one bag of soil (2 ft³).

**Solve the problems.**

14. A water tank is shaped like a right rectangular prism and has the dimensions shown.
Find the volume of the tank.

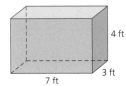

▌▌▌· **Show your work.**
Possible student work:
7 ft × 3 ft × 4 ft = 84 ft³

**Answer** 84 ft³

15. The tank in exercise 14 is filled with water. A cubic foot of water weighs about 62 pounds. Explain how to determine the weight of the water in the tank, and then find it.
Multiply the volume of the container by the weight of water per cubic foot; 84 × 62 = 5,208 pounds.

---

## Math-to-Economics Connection

**Real Estate Listings** In the real estate market, houses are described according to the number of square feet of livable space. Print out some real-estate listings for students to look at. Point out that the size of a room is described by giving the dimensions of the floor. For example, a 12 × 11 bedroom has a floor that measures 12 feet by 11 feet. Discuss the fact that the height of the room is not given. Ask students to find the dimensions of a room in one of the listings. Have them calculate the volume if the room has 10-foot ceilings and if it has 12-foot ceilings. Then, have them compare the two volumes: How much greater is the volume of the room with higher ceilings?

Lesson 30

**Independent Practice**

MP1 **16.** There is a landing pit shaped like a right rectangular prism at the end of a ramp in an indoor skate park as shown. The pit is filled with foam cubes that have a side length of 1 foot.

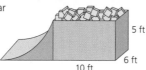

5 ft

6 ft

10 ft

The number of foam cubes in the landing pit is equal to $\frac{3}{4}$ of the volume of the landing pit. How many foam cubes are in the landing pit?

✏ **Show your work.** Possible student work:
Volume of landing pit = $10 \times 6 \times 5 = 300$ ft³
Number of foam cubes = $\frac{3}{4} \times 300 = 225$

**Answer** There are 225 foam cubes in the landing pit.

MP7 **17.** Zachary uses the expression $10 + 10 + 10$ to find the volume of a right rectangular prism. Mia uses the expression $3 \times (5 \times 2)$ to find the volume of a right rectangular prism. Is it possible that they are finding the volume of the same right rectangular prism?

**Answer** Yes, it is possible that they are finding the volume of the same right rectangular prism.

✏ **Justify your answer using words, drawings, or numbers.**
Possible justification:
The right rectangular prism shown has 3 layers of $2 \times 5 = 10$ cubes. This can be written as $10 + 10 + 10 = 30$ or $3 \times (5 \times 2) = 30$.

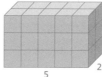

3

5

2

MP3 **18.** Suppose that the dimensions of a right rectangular prism are doubled. Is the volume of the larger prism double the volume of the smaller prism?

**Answer** No, the volume of the larger prism is not double the volume of the smaller prism.

✏ **Justify your answer using words, drawings, or numbers.**
Possible justification:
Suppose a right rectangular prism has a length of 6 feet, a width of 5 feet, and a height of 8 feet. Its volume is:
$6 \times 5 \times 8 = 240$ ft³
If you double the dimensions, the prism has a length of 12 feet, a width of 10 feet, and a height of 16 feet. Its volume is:
$12 \times 10 \times 16 = 1{,}920$ ft³
The new volume is not double the original volume; it is 8 times the original volume.

Unit 4 ■ Focus on Measurement and Data **273**

## Teaching Tips

### Item 16
Students may be confused by the foam cubes that fill the pit. Explain that although these are unit cubes, they are not "packed" in the pit, so the number of these cubes is not the same as the volume of the pit. Students should use the dimensions of the pit to calculate its volume, and then use the volume to figure out how many foam cubes are in the pit.

### Item 18
Suggest that students begin by exploring a specific example.

| **Mathematical Practices** | |
|---|---|
| **MP1** | **Make sense of problems and persevere in solving them.** |
| **Item 16:** Students formulate a plan for solving a multi-step problem. | |
| **MP3** | **Construct viable arguments and critique the reasoning of others.** |
| **Item 18:** Students construct an argument that explains why doubling the dimensions of a prism does not double its volume. | |
| **MP7** | **Look for and make use of structure.** |
| **Item 17:** Students use the structure of two expressions that represent volumes of prisms to determine what the shape of the prisms might be. | |

## OBJECTIVE

Use the Associative Property of Multiplication to find volumes of right rectangular prisms.

## ESSENTIAL QUESTION

Ask students to share what they know about calculating the volume of a rectangular prism. Discuss that it does not matter which face of a prism is considered the base; the volume will be the same. Tell students that, in this lesson, they will apply the Associative Property of Multiplication.

## PREREQUISITE SKILLS

Use Item J on page 341 of the Foundational Skills Handbook to review the area formula for a rectangle.

## FLUENCY PRACTICE

Fluency practice is available at **sadlierconnect.com**.

## Concept Development

### Understand: How to relate the Associative Property of Multiplication to the volume of a right rectangular prism

■ Using a physical model, show students that there are three possible bases in a right rectangular prism.

■ Show students that in each of the three cases, multiplying the area of the base by the height produces the same result.

---

Lesson

# 31 Find Volume: Use the Associate Property

## Guided Instruction

In this lesson, you will relate the Associative Property of Multiplication to finding volumes of right rectangular prisms.

**Understand:** How to relate the Associative Property of Multiplication to the volume of a right rectangular prism

> Explain why $(5 \times 7) \times 9 = 5 \times (7 \times 9)$ by considering the factors to be the edge lengths of a right rectangular prism.

To find the volume of a right rectangular prism, you can multiply the area of the base by the height. Any face of the prism can be considered to be the base.

➡ Consider a right rectangular prism with edge lengths of 5 units, 7 units, and 9 units.

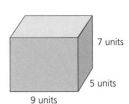

If you think of a 5 unit by 7 unit face as the base, then multiply $5 \times 7$ first to find the area of the base and then multiply the product by the height, 9. This can be represented as:

$$(5 \times 7) \times 9$$

If you think of a 7 unit by 9 unit face as the base, then multiply $7 \times 9$ first to find the area of the base and then multiply the product by the height, 5. This can be represented as:

$$5 \times (7 \times 9)$$

Because the volumes are the same in both cases, $(5 \times 7) \times 9 = 5 \times (7 \times 9)$.

This equation $(5 \times 7) \times 9 = 5 \times (7 \times 9)$ is an example of the Associative Property of Multiplication. The property states that changing the grouping of the factors in a multiplication expression does not change the product. Thinking about a right rectangular prism can help you visualize this property.

**274**   Unit 4 ■ Focus on Measurement and Data

---

## Words to Know

**Associative Property of Multiplication:** Changing the grouping of the factors in a multiplication expression does not change the product.

**Example:** $(5 \times 7) \times 9 = 5 \times (7 \times 9)$

**Glossary can be found on pp. 347–350.**

MORE ONLINE sadlierconnect.com

Lesson 31

Guided Instruction

**Connect:** What you know about the Associative Property of Multiplication to help you find the volume of a right rectangular prism

Carmen's new laptop computer was shipped in this box, which is a right rectangular prism.

Find the volume of the box using the Associative Property of Multiplication.

40 cm

25 cm

18 cm

**Step 1**

Plan a solution

To find the volume of the box, first write an equation that determines the volume. Then, use the Associative Property of Multiplication and mental math to solve.

**Step 2**

Write an equation for the volume of a right rectangular prism.

The volume is the area of the base times the height:

$$(18 \times 25) \times 40 = \blacksquare$$

area of base    height

**Step 3**

Multiply to calculate the volume.

Notice that if you regroup the factors to multiply $25 \times 40$ first, you can use mental math.

$(18 \times 25) \times 40 = 18 \times (25 \times 40)$ ⟵ Use the Associative Property to regroup.

$= 18 \times 1000$ ⟵ Multiply in parentheses.

$= 18,000$ ⟵ Multiply.

➡ The volume of the box is 18,000 cubic centimeters.

Unit 4 ■ Focus on Measurement and Data  **275**

**Connect: What you know about the Associative Property of Multiplication to help you find the volume of a right rectangular prism** Use this page to help students strengthen their understanding of how the Associative Property of Multiplication can be used to calculate volume.

■ In this presentation, students use the Associative Property of Multiplication to simplify a volume calculation.

■ Be sure students see that we can multiply the three factors in any order. However, multiplying $25 \times 40$ first makes the calculation easier.

■ Some students may want to verify that the result is the same if $18 \times 25$ is calculated first.

## Support English Language Learners

*Associative* is a term that is not often used in everyday language. Write the word on the board and read it aloud. Ask students to repeat the word back to you. Relate the word to the verb *associate* and define it as "to connect." Give examples of some things you *associate* with school: children, teaching, math, and the classroom. Ask students to tell what they *associate* with going to bed at night: brushing their teeth or doing their homework. Explain that the Associative Property is used to connect numbers. Model how parentheses are used to show the Associative Property. Have students practice using parentheses to model the Associative Property.

# Guided Practice

## Observational Assessment

Use pages 276–277 to assess whether students understand the Associative Property of Multiplication and how it relates to the volume of a rectangular prism. Watch for those students who make computational errors when multiplying the dimensions of a prism. These students may need additional practice of multiplication.

### Guided Practice

1. Which equation *best* illustrates the Associative Property of Multiplication?

    a. $(9 \times 7) \times 10 = (10 \times 7) \times 9$     (b.) $(9 \times 7) \times 10 = 9 \times (7 \times 10)$

    c. $(9 + 7) \times 10 = 16 \times 10$     d. $(9 \times 7) \times 10 = 63 \times 10$

**Evaluate the expressions on both sides of the equation to show they are equivalent.**

2. $(13 \times 5) \times 3 = 13 \times (5 \times 3)$
   $65 \times 3 = 13 \times 15$
   $\underline{195} = \underline{195}$

3. $(5 \times 6) \times 9 = 5 \times (6 \times 9)$
   $\underline{30} \times 9 = 5 \times \underline{54}$
   $\underline{270} = \underline{270}$

4. $(3 \times 13) \times 7 = 3 \times (13 \times 7)$
   $\underline{39} \times 7 = 3 \times \underline{91}$
   $\underline{273} = \underline{273}$

5. $(3 \times 6) \times 7 = 3 \times (6 \times 7)$
   $\underline{18} \times 7 = 3 \times \underline{42}$
   $\underline{126} = \underline{126}$

**Use parentheses to show two ways of grouping the factors in the expression. Do not evaluate.** Answers will vary. Possible student responses are given for each.

6. $3 \times 19 \times 6$
   $\underline{(3 \times 19) \times 6, 3 \times (19 \times 6)}$

7. $13 \times 4 \times 2$
   $\underline{(13 \times 4) \times 2, 13 \times (4 \times 2)}$

8. $9 \times 10 \times 5$
   $\underline{(9 \times 10) \times 5, 9 \times (10 \times 5)}$

9. $1 \times 8 \times 21 \times 4$
   $\underline{(1 \times 8) \times 21 \times 4, 1 \times (8 \times 21) \times 4}$

10. A model of a school ring box is shown. One expression that represents the volume of the box is $(8 \times 4) \times 12$.

    a. Use the Associative Property of Multiplication to write a second expression for the volume of the box.

       Possible answer: $8 \times (4 \times 12)$

    b. Find the volume of the box.

       $384 \text{ cm}^3$

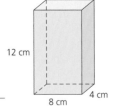

12 cm

4 cm

8 cm

## Math-to-Math Connection

**Properties of Multiplication and Mental Math** Multiplication properties can be used to simplify expressions by breaking apart numbers by place value, changing the order of the factors, and altering the order of the operations. These strategies facilitate using mental math to find solutions. For example, consider problem 9 on page 276. Using the Identity Property, eliminate the 1 from the expression. Using the Commutative Property, rewrite the expression: $8 \times 4 \times 21$. Use mental math to simplify the first two factors: $32 \times 21$. Break one of the factors apart by place value: $32 \times (20 + 1)$. Again using mental math, apply the Distributive and Identity Properties: $640 + 32$. Use mental math to add the partial products. Encourage students to demonstrate these strategies as they find the volume of figures with greater side lengths.

Use the Associative Property of Multiplication to write a second expression for the volume of each right rectangular prism. Then, find the volume of each prism.

**11.**

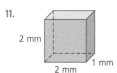
2 mm
2 mm    1 mm

$(1 \times 2) \times 2$
$1 \times (2 \times 2)$
4 mm³

**12.**

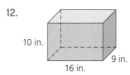
10 in.
16 in.    9 in.

$(9 \times 16) \times 10$
$9 \times (16 \times 10)$
1,440 in³

**13.**

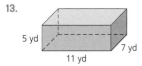
5 yd
11 yd    7 yd

$(7 \times 11) \times 5$
$7 \times (11 \times 5)$
385 yd³

**14.**

5 cm
14 cm
12 cm

$(12 \times 5) \times 14$
$12 \times (5 \times 14)$
840 cm³

👑 **Think ● Pair ● Share**

MP2  **15.** Find the volume of each box with the dimensions in the table below. Then, use the Associative Property of Multiplication to explain why the volumes of the two boxes are equivalent.

|        | Box 1  | Box 2  |
|--------|--------|--------|
| Length | 3.5 cm | 2 cm   |
| Height | 2 cm   | 5 cm   |
| Width  | 5 cm   | 3.5 cm |

Possible answer: The volume of Box 1 is $3.5 \times 2 \times 5 = 35$ cm³.
The volume of Box 2 is $2 \times 5 \times 3.5 = 35$ cm³. Possible explanation:
Applying the Associative Property of Multiplication,
$(3.5 \times 2) \times 5 = 3.5 \times (2 \times 5)$.

Unit 4 ■ Focus on Measurement and Data  **277**

## Mathematical Practices

Mathematical Practice Standards underline the teaching and understanding of all concepts and skills presented. The emphasis of specific practices is noted throughout the guided and independent practice of this lesson.

**MP2**  **Reason abstractly and quantitatively.**

**Item 15:** Students reason quantitatively to determine how the Associative Property of Multiplication relates to volume.

👑 **Think●Pair●Share**

**Peer Collaboration**  Have students work with a partner. Instruct each student to complete the problem first, and then discuss their ideas about why the volumes of the two boxes are equivalent with their partner. Prompt discussions by asking these types of questions:

- *What bases did you use to compute the volume of each box?*

- *What expressions did you write to represent the volumes of the boxes? Are the expressions the same ones your partner wrote?*

- *What property says that you can groups factors in different ways to multiply?*

To summarize, explain that as a result of the Associative Property of Multiplication, you can multiply the three dimensions of a right rectangular prism in any order and obtain the same result.

## Return to the Essential Question

Reread the Lesson 31 Essential Question on page 274: *How is the Associative Property of Multiplication related to calculating volumes of right rectangular prisms?*

Ask volunteers to use what they learned in this lesson to answer this question. (Possible responses: To find the volume of a prism, multiply the dimensions of the base times the height. Because any face can be considered the base, the dimensions can be grouped in any order in the calculation. The Associative Property of Multiplication says the factors in a multiplication expression can be grouped in any order. So, calculating the volume of a prism in different ways illustrates the Associative Property.)

Invite as many volunteers as possible to express ideas about the use of the Associative Property of Multiplication in their own words.

## Concept Application

Students may work independently on these pages in the classroom or at home. They may refer to the first four pages of the lesson to revisit the instruction or to see a worked-out example.

**Common Errors** and **Teaching Tips** may help you support student learning either in the classroom or as a follow-up for work done at home.

## Common Errors

### Items 11–14

Some students confuse the Associative and the Commutative Properties of Multiplication. Draw a distinction between these properties and remind students that they do not need to change the order of the factors when grouping the factors.

---

### Independent Practice

**Evaluate the expressions on both sides of the equation to show they are equivalent.**

1. $(8 \times 2) \times 9 = 8 \times (2 \times 9)$
   $16 \times 9 = 8 \times 18$
   $\underline{144} = \underline{144}$

2. $(7 \times 8) \times 6 = 7 \times (8 \times 6)$
   $\underline{56} \times 6 = 7 \times \underline{48}$
   $\underline{336} = \underline{336}$

3. $(20 \times 6) \times 3 = 20 \times (6 \times 3)$
   $\underline{120} \times 3 = 20 \times \underline{18}$
   $\underline{360} = \underline{360}$

4. $(6 \times 3) \times 4 = 6 \times (3 \times 4)$
   $\underline{18} \times 4 = 6 \times \underline{12}$
   $\underline{72} = \underline{72}$

5. $12 \times (27 \times 10) = (12 \times 27) \times 10$
   $12 \times \underline{270} = \underline{324} \times 10$
   $\underline{3,240} = \underline{3,240}$

6. $5 \times (11 \times 7) = (5 \times 11) \times 7$
   $5 \times \underline{77} = \underline{55} \times 7$
   $\underline{385} = \underline{385}$

**For exercises 7–10, show an equivalent expression using the Associative Property of Multiplication.**

7. $(9 \times 5) \times 10 = 9 \times (\underline{5} \times \underline{10})$

8. $9 \times (12 \times 4) = (\underline{9} \times \underline{12}) \times \underline{4}$

9. $(31 \times 7) \times 18 = \underline{31} \times (\underline{7} \times \underline{18})$

10. $(8 \times 13) \times 15 = \underline{8} \times (\underline{13} \times \underline{15})$

**Use parentheses to show two ways of grouping the factors in the expression. Do not evaluate.** Answers will vary. Possible student responses are given for each.

11. $8 \times 25 \times 2$
    $(8 \times 25) \times 2, 8 \times (25 \times 2)$

12. $\frac{7}{11} \times 5\frac{1}{4} \times 4$
    $(\frac{7}{11} \times 5\frac{1}{4}) \times 4,$
    $\frac{7}{11} \times (5\frac{1}{4} \times 4)$

13. $0.65 \times 20 \times 2.2$
    $(0.65 \times 20) \times 2.2,$
    $0.65 \times (20 \times 2.2)$

14. $19 \times 8\frac{2}{7} \times 2 \times 24$
    $(19 \times 8\frac{2}{7}) \times 2 \times 24,$
    $19 \times (8\frac{2}{7} \times 2) \times 24$

---

## Writing About Math

**Writing an Explanatory Text** Provide or ask students to bring in real-world examples of right rectangular prisms, such as empty boxes of cereal, laundry soap tabs, and facial tissues. Have each student choose a container and measure its dimensions to the nearest whole centimeter. Using those measurements, have students find the volume of the containers. Then have students write paragraphs explaining how to apply the Associative Property of Multiplication to find the volume of a right rectangular prism. Encourage students to also include any other properties they may have used in the calculations.

MORE ONLINE  sadlierconnect.com | Lesson 31

Use the **Associative Property of Multiplication** to write a second expression for the volume of each right rectangular prism. Then, find the volume of each prism.

**15.**

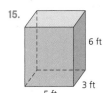

6 ft
5 ft
3 ft

(5 × 3) × 6
5 × (3 × 6)
90 ft³

**16.**

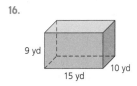

9 yd
15 yd
10 yd

(10 × 15) × 9
10 × (15 × 9)
1,350 yd³

**17.**

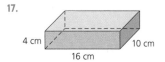

4 cm
16 cm
10 cm

(16 × 10) × 4
16 × (10 × 4)
640 cm³

**18.**

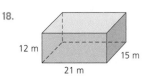

12 m
21 m
15 m

12 × (21 × 15)
(12 × 21) × 15
3780 m³

**Solve.**

**19.** A sign at a commuter train station states that no passenger can bring suitcases any larger than 28 inches by 22 inches by 14 inches on a train.

   **a.** Apply the Associative Property of Multiplication to write two expressions for the volume of the largest suitcase a train passenger can bring.
   (28 × 22) × 14, 28 × (22 × 14)

   **b.** Find the volume of the suitcase.
   8,624 cubic inches

Unit 4 ■ Focus on Measurement and Data   **279**

## Common Errors

### Items 15-18

Students may forget to write the units in their answers. Remind students that an answer without units would be incorrect. The units for volume are always cubed (unit³) because volume requires three different dimensions.

## Digital Connection

**Online Drawing Tools** Have students use an online drawing tool to create a right rectangular prism with sides of different lengths. Encourage students to copy each prism, rotate the copy 90° clockwise, and compare the height and the base of the original prism to the height and base of the rotated prism. Ask students to determine the volume of both prisms to show the volumes are the same.

# Independent Practice

## Teaching Tips

### Item 20

Suggest that students consider the given dimension to be the height. Then, ask them what they know about the area of the base.

### Items 22-23

Suggest that students eliminate unreasonable choices first. They may be able to choose the correct answers without doing any calculations.

## Independent Practice

MP3   **20.** A box has a volume of 56 cubic inches, and each dimension is a whole number of inches. If one dimension of the box is 8 inches, explain how you can find the other two dimensions.
Possible explanation: You can divide the volume by 8 to get 7. The product of the other two dimensions is 7. The only whole number factors of 7 are 1 and 7. So, the other two dimensions are 1 inch and 7 inches.

MP2   **21.** Write two expressions to represent the volume of a storage unit with a length of 14 feet, a width of 18 feet, and a height of 10 feet.
Possible answer: $(14 \times 18) \times 10$ *or* $14 \times (18 \times 10)$

**Circle the correct answer.**

**22.** What is the volume of the right rectangular prism below?

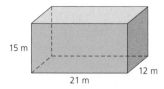

15 m

21 m

12 m

  a. 180 m³              b. 252 m³

  c. 3600 m³             (d.) 3780 m³

**23.** What is the volume of a walk-in refrigerator that is 13 feet long, 11 feet wide, and 10 feet high?

  a. 143 cubic feet          b. 153 cubic feet

  c. 260 cubic feet          (d.) 1,430 cubic feet

| Mathematical Practices | |
|---|---|
| **MP2** | **Reason abstractly and quantitatively.** |
| **Item 21:** Students use the Associative Property of Multiplication to write two equivalent expressions to represent volume in a real-world situation. | |
| **MP3** | **Construct viable arguments and critique the reasoning of others.** |
| **Item 20:** Students explain how they can find the possible dimensions of a rectangular prism given its volume and one dimension. | |

Lesson 31

**Independent Practice**

## Teaching Tips

### Item 26
Some students may need to review the order of operations in order to evaluate the expressions.

**Solve the problems.**

MP3 **24.** Logan says he wrote three equivalent expressions to represent the volume of a right rectangular prism with a length and width of 17 cm and a height of 4 cm. Are his expressions all correct?

    **a.** $17 \times (17 \times 4)$

    **b.** $2 \times (17) \times 4$

    **c.** $17 \times 17 \times 4$
Possible answer: Expression c is correct. It finds the area of the base and then multiplies by the height. Expression a is equivalent to expression c by the Associative Property, so it is also correct. Expression b is incorrect, because it is the volume of a prism with the dimensions 2 cm, 17 cm, and 4 cm.

MP1 **25.** Multiply the factors 12, 4, 8, and 7. Because of the Associative and Commutative Properties of Multiplication, you can multiply the factors in any order. Explain in which order you multiplied the factors, and why.

    ▸ **Show your work.** Possible student work:
$(12 \times 4) \times (7 \times 8)$
$48 \times 56$
$2,688$

    **Answer** Answers will vary. Possible answer: I chose factors that I could multiply easily 12 and 4, and 7 and 8.

MP3 **26.** Tyrone says he used the Associative Property of Multiplication to write two expressions equivalent to $8 \times 1.25 \times 9 - 5$. Evaluate all three expressions to see if they are equivalent. If they are not equivalent, explain the error Tyrone made.

    **a.** $8 \times (1.25 \times 9) - 5$         **b.** $8 \times 1.25 \times (9 - 5)$

    ▸ **Show your work.** Possible student work:
$8 \times (1.25 \times 9) - 5 = 85$
$8 \times 1.25 \times (9 - 5) = 40$
$8 \times 1.25 \times 9 - 5 = 85$

    **Answer** Possible answer: Expression a is equivalent to the original expression because both have value 85. Expression b is not equivalent. Tyrone tried to apply the Associative Property to an expression that involves subtraction. Additionally, Tyrone did not properly recall the order of operations, which states multiplication is completed before subtraction.

Unit 4 ■ Focus on Measurement and Data   **281**

## Mathematical Practices

| **MP1** | **Make sense of problems and persevere in solving them.** |
|---|---|

**Item 25:** Students examine the factors they must multiply and determine how to order and group the factors to simplify the calculation.

| **MP3** | **Construct viable arguments and critique the reasoning of others.** |
|---|---|

**Item 24:** Students analyze three expressions another student wrote for the volume of the prism and explain why each is or is not correct.

**Item 26:** Students analyze two expressions that another student claims are equivalent, and use the order of operations and mathematical properties to explain why they are not equivalent.

## OBJECTIVE
**Use formulas to find volume.**

## ESSENTIAL QUESTION
Discuss the fact that the volume of a right rectangular prism can be calculated by multiplying the length, width, and height or by multiplying the area of the base by the height. Tell students that in this lesson, they will see how these methods can be expressed as formulas, and they will use the formulas to solve real-world problems.

## PREREQUISITE SKILLS
Use Item J on page 341 of the Foundational Skills Handbook to review the area formula for rectangles.

## FLUENCY PRACTICE
Fluency practice is available at **sadlierconnect.com**.

## Concept Development

### Understand: How to solve problems using formulas for volume

■ To help students see why the two formulas are equivalent, remind them that the area of the base *is* its length times its width.

■ Point out that for any rectangular prism, there are three possible bases. You might ask students to identify the three possible bases for the given prism and then give the corresponding height for each one.

✏ ⁃ If any students chose to define the bases differently, discuss the different approaches and why they are correct.

---

Lesson
**32**  Problem Solving:
**Apply Volume Formulas for Prisms**

**Essential Question:**
How do you find volume using a formula?

### Guided Instruction

In this lesson you will solve real-world problems using formulas for volume.

**Understand: How to solve problems using formulas for volume**

Mr. Bower's new post office mailbox is 12 inches tall, 9 inches long, and 6 inches wide. What is the volume of the mailbox?

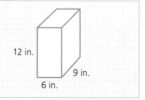

12 in.

9 in.

6 in.

To find the volume of the mailbox, you can use a formula for the volume of a right rectangular prism. There are two equivalent volume formulas.

In this formula, $V$ is the volume, $\ell$ is the length, $w$ is the width, and $h$ is the height:

$$V = \ell \times w \times h$$

In this formula, $V$ is the volume, $B$ is the area of the base, and $h$ is the height:

$$V = B \times h$$

You know all three dimensions, so you can use the formula $V = \ell \times w \times h$. In this case, $\ell = 9$ in., $w = 6$ in., and $h = 12$ in.

$V = \ell \times w \times h$ ◀——— Start with the formula.
$V = 9 \times 6 \times 12$ ◀——— Substitute values for $\ell$, $w$, and $h$.
$V = 648$ ◀——— Multiply to find the value of $V$.

➡ The volume of Mr. Bower's post office mailbox is 648 in.³

▭ ⁃ How would you find the volume of the mailbox using the formula $V = B \times h$?
Possible answer: I would find the area of the base first, which is $6 \times 9$, or 54 square inches. Then, I would multiply by the height: $54 \times 12 = 648$ cubic inches.

---

## Support English Language Learners

The term *formula* is used frequently in mathematics. Write the word *formula* on the board and ask students to provide examples of where they have heard this word. Students might mention a secret formula, or recipe, or a type of racecar. Relate to students that in this lesson, and throughout most of mathematics, *formula* means a mathematical relationship expressed in symbols. On the board, write the two formulas for volume using variables. Write the formulas out in words below each one. For example, *the volume of a rectangular prism is equal to its length times its width times its height.* Have students repeat the sentence as a class, identifying which variable correlates to each word.

Lesson 32

## Guided Instruction

**Connect:** What you know about formulas for volume
to solve problems

> There are two empty sandboxes on a school playground. Sandbox 1 has a
> base with dimensions 4 feet by 6 feet and is 2 feet high. Sandbox 2 has a
> base area of 35 square feet and is 1 foot high. The school maintenance
> crew has 90 cubic feet of sand. Is this enough to fill both sandboxes?

**Step 1**

Plan a solution.

Find the volume of each sandbox and then add to find the total volume.
Compare this volume to 90 cubic feet to see if the crew has enough sand
to fill both sandboxes.

**Step 2**

Use formulas to calculate the volumes.

**Sandbox 1:** You know all three
dimensions, so you can use the
formula $V = \ell \times w \times h$.

$$V = \ell \times w \times h$$
$$V = 4 \times 6 \times 2$$
$$V = 48$$

The volume is 48 ft$^3$.

**Sandbox 2:** You know the base area
and the height, so you can use the
formula $V = B \times h$.

$$V = B \times h$$
$$V = 35 \times 1$$
$$V = 35$$

The volume is 35 ft$^3$.

**Step 3**

Find the total volume and compare to 90 cubic feet.

48 ft$^3$ + 35 ft$^3$ = 83 ft$^3$

The total is less than 90 cubic feet.

➡ 90 cubic feet of sand is enough to fill both sandboxes.

Unit 4 ■ Focus on Measurement and Data  **283**

**Connect:** **What you know about
formulas for volume to solve
problems** Use this page to help
students strengthen their understanding
of how to solve real-world problems
involving volume.

■ In this problem, both volume formulas—
$V = \ell \times w \times h$ and $V = B \times h$—are used.
Point out that, because we are given only
the base area and height of Sandbox 2,
and not its length and width, we have to
use $V = B \times h$ to find its volume.

■ You might ask students how they
would solve this problem before
discussing the given solution.

## Math-to-Leisure Connection

**Swimming Pools** Students are likely familiar with the shallow swimming
pools for young children found in many parks. As a class, explore how
the formula for volume can be used to calculate the amount of water in
these swimming pools. Use the Internet or other resources to find the
dimensions of a local pool. Some students may want to make or draw a
model of the swimming pool and find its volume. Remind students to use
the correct units of measure as they work.

# Guided Practice

## Observational Assessment

Use pages 284–285 to assess whether students are able to apply formulas to find volumes of prisms and solve problems. Remind students to look for numbers that are easy to multiply first when evaluating the volume of each given prism. Be mindful of those students who struggle to determine the dimensions of the given volumes from the given prisms.

Lesson 32   Problem Solving: **Apply Volume Formulas for Prisms**

### Guided Practice

**Use the formulas to find the volume of the right rectangular prisms.**

1.

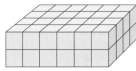

$V = \ell \times w \times h$

$\quad = 6 \text{ units} \times \underline{\ 4\ } \text{ units} \times \underline{\ 2\ } \text{ units}$

$\quad = \underline{\ 48\ } \text{ cubic units}$

2.

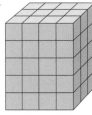

$V = \ell \times w \times h$

$\quad = 4 \text{ units} \times \underline{\ 3\ } \text{ units} \times \underline{\ 5\ } \text{ units}$

$\quad = \underline{\ 60\ } \text{ cubic units}$

3. Anna builds a spice drawer that is 40 cm long, 15 cm wide, and 10 cm tall. What is the volume of the spice drawer that Anna built?

$V = \ell \times w \times h$

$\quad = 40 \times 15 \times \underline{\ 10\ }$

$\quad = \underline{\ 6000\ } \text{ cm}^3$

The volume of the spice drawer is $\underline{\ 6000\ }$ cm³.

4. Skye is mailing a present and needs a box that has a volume of at least 200 cubic inches. Is this box big enough? Explain.

6 in.

7 in.   5 in.

$V = B \times h$

$\quad = (7 \times 5) \times \underline{\ 6\ }$

$\quad = \underline{\ 210\ } \text{ in.}^3$

Possible answer: The volume of the box is 210 in.³ So it is big enough.

## Math-to-Landscaping Connection

**Volumes of Materials** Many of the materials used by landscapers are sold in units of cubic feet or cubic yards. Discuss as a class some of the materials landscapers use: top soil, peat moss, and mulch.

Provide students with a landscaping scenario to solve as a class. For example, give the three dimensions of a flower bed and ask students to find the amount of dirt needed to fill the flower bed. Be sure to remind students to address any unit conversions that you might include in the scenario.

**Find the volume of each figure.**

5.

10 in.

5 in.    4 in.

_200 in.³_

6.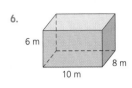

6 m

10 m    8 m

_480 m³_

**Solve.**

7. Todd wants to use organic soil to fill his flower boxes. Each box is a right rectangular prism that has a base area of 3 ft² and a height of 2 ft. How many cubic feet of organic soil does Todd need to fill one of the flower boxes?

Todd needs ___6 ft³___ of organic soil to fill one of the flower boxes.

8. Which box has the greater volume?

**Box A**

15 ft²

6 ft

$V = B \times h$

$V = \underline{15}\ ft² \times \underline{6}\ ft$

$V = \underline{90}\ ft³$

Box _B_ has the greater volume.

**Box B**

8 ft

3 ft    4 ft

$V = \ell \times w \times h$

$V = \underline{3} \times \underline{4} \times \underline{8}$

$V = \underline{96}\ ft³$

**Think·Pair·Share**

MP4  9. Joy needs a container that is a right rectangular prism. The container has to have a volume between 600 cubic inches and 800 cubic inches. It has to be longer than it is tall. What could the dimensions of her container be? Possible answer: Find 3 numbers that have a product between 600 and 800, such as 7 × 10 × 10. Since the length must be greater than the height, the dimensions of the container could be: length 10 in., width 10 in., and height 7 in.

## Mathematical Practices

Mathematical Practice Standards underline the teaching and understanding of all concepts and skills presented. The emphasis of specific practices is noted throughout the guided and independent practice of this lesson.

| MP4 | **Model with mathematics.** |
| --- | --- |

**Item 9:** Students use approximations to simplify a complicated word problem.

**Think·Pair·Share**

**Peer Collaboration** Ask students to find one potential option for the dimensions of the container. Have students divide into groups of three or four and compile a list of all of the different sets of dimensions they found. Remind students to read the problem carefully to determine any criteria that might affect their lists. Ask each group to share at least one set of dimensions with the class. While student groups present, ask:

- *How many different sets of dimensions did your group have?*

- *How many different sets of dimensions do you think are possible?*

- *What is one set of dimensions that does not meet the criteria in the problem statement? Explain why.*

### Return to the Essential Question

Reread the Lesson 32 Essential Question on page 282: *How do you find volume using a formula?*

Ask volunteers to use what they learned in this lesson to answer this question. (Possible response: If I know the base area and the height of the prism, then I can use the formula $V = B \times h$. I substitute the base area for $B$ and the height for $h$ and multiply to find $V$, which is the volume. If I know the length, width, and height, then I can use either $V = \ell \times w \times h$ or $V = B \times h$. For $V = \ell \times w \times h$, I substitute the dimensions for $\ell$, $w$, and $h$ and multiply to get $V$. For $V = B \times h$, I first have to multiply the length and width to get the base area.)

Invite as many volunteers as possible to express ideas about using formulas to find volume in their own words.

# Independent Practice

## Concept Application

Students may work independently on these pages in the classroom or at home. They may refer to the first four pages of the lesson to revisit the instruction or to see a worked-out example.

**Common Errors** and **Teaching Tips** may help you support student learning either in the classroom or as a follow-up for work done at home.

## Teaching Tips

### Items 1–3

Struggling students might benefit from building the prisms with cubes.

### Item 3

Help students understand that the base area given in the problem statement is $B$ in the formula $V = B \times h$.

---

**Independent Practice**

Use formulas to find the volume of the right rectangular prisms.

1.
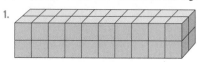

$V = \ell \times w \times h$

   = 10 units × __2__ units × __2__ units

   = __40__ cubic units

2.
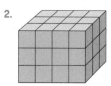

$V = \ell \times w \times h$

   = 4 units × __3__ units × __3__ units

   = __36__ cubic units

3. Each of the containers, labeled A and B, has a base with an area of 12 m². Find the volume of each. Then find the difference in the volumes of the two containers.

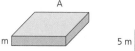 

A             B

2 m          5 m

The volume of container A is __24 m³__.

The volume of container B is __60 m³__.

The difference in volumes is __36 m³__.

---

## Writing About Math

⟍▬▬▶ **Compare and Contrast** Ask students to write a paragraph about the two formulas they have used to find volume. Students should include the measures that each variable represents. Remind students to describe both the similarities and differences between the two formulas. Ask for volunteers to share their paragraphs and discuss the similarities and differences as a class.

**For exercises 4–7, circle the correct answer.**

4. Erin built the box shown. What is its volume?

   a. 42 m³          ⓑ 72 m³

   c. 108 m³         d. 144 m³

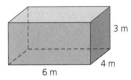

5. Luke bought the reptile tank shown. What is the volume of the tank?

   a. 440 in.³       b. 1,200 in.³

   c. 2,000 in.³     ⓓ 2,400 in.³

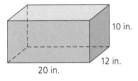

6. A storage chest has a base with an area of 25 square feet and is 5 feet tall. What is the volume of the bin?

   a. 15 ft³         b. 25 ft³

   ⓒ 125 ft³         d. 125 ft²

7. Shelley has a pencil case that is 30 cm long, 4 cm wide, and 3 cm deep. What is the volume of Shelley's pencil case?

   a. 210 cm³        ⓑ 360 cm³

   c. 720 cm³        d. 1200 cm³

**Solve.**

8. Mr. Kim has a man-made pond that is shaped like a right rectangular prism with a base area of 72 square meters. The pond has a volume 72 cubic meters. What is the pond's depth?

   The pond has a depth of ___1 meter___.

## Common Errors

### Item 6

Some students may circle choice d, which has the correct number, but the wrong unit. Remind students that volume is measured in cubic units.

## Teaching Tips

### Item 8

Suggest to students that they may wish to write the formula for volume, and then fill in the quantities that they know in order to find the solution.

## Digital Connection

**Internet Resources** Use a search engine and key words *interactive volume games* to find Web sites that use virtual manipulatives and require students to calculate volumes, rather than counting units. Have students take turns completing the activities or playing the games individually. If possible, have a couple of different options available for students to use to allow students to rotate to each type activity.

# Independent Practice

## Common Errors

### Item 9

Some students may struggle to find a solution because they do not notice that the units of the dimensions of the cube and the crate are different. Point this out and suggest that students convert 6 inches to feet or convert the dimensions of the crate to inches.

### Item 10

Students who do not convert yards to feet (or cubic feet to cubic yards) will get the answer 54. Ask students if this answer is reasonable. (It is unreasonable, whether students interpret it as 54 feet or 54 yards.) Point out to these students that the dimensions of the patio are given in yards, while the volume of the shed is given in cubic feet.

## Teaching Tips

### Items 9–10

Suggest that students make and label sketches to represent these problems. This will help them better understand how the measurement given in the problem are related.

### Item 11

Point out to students that the lengths and heights of the prisms remain constant; only the width changes.

---

### Independent Practice

MP2 **9.** Leonard is packing boxes that are cubes with 6-inch sides into a crate. The crate is 2 feet wide by 3 feet long by 2 feet tall. How many cubes can Leonard pack into the crate? Show your work.
Possible student work:
Approach 1: Change feet to inches.
Number of cubes = $(24 \times 36 \times 24) \div (6 \times 6 \times 6) = 96$
Approach 2: Find how many cubes fit along each side.
Number of cubes = $4 \times 6 \times 4 = 96$

Leonard can pack __96__ cubes into the crate.

MP1 **10.** Alexandra's house has a backyard patio that is 4 yards long by 5 yards wide. Alexandra's mother is building a rectangular storage shed with a volume of 1,080 cubic feet and with the entire patio as its base. What is the height of the shed Alexandra's mother is building? Give your answer in feet and then in yards. Show your work.
Possible student work: Change yards to feet. 4 yards = 12 feet; 5 yards = 15 feet. Height = $1,080 \div (12 \times 15) = 6$. Or, change feet to yards. 1,080 cubic feet = $1,080 \div 27 = 40$ yards. Height = $40 \div (4 \times 5) = 2$

The height of the shed is __6__ feet or __2__ yards.

**In exercise 11, the chart shows various dimensions and volumes of right rectangular prisms. Complete the chart, then answer the question below.**

**11.**

| Length | Width | Height | Volume |
|---|---|---|---|
| 50 in. | 10 in. | 10 in. | 5,000 in.$^3$ |
| 50 in. | 8 in. | 10 in. | 4,000 in.$^3$ |
| 50 in. | 5 in. | 10 in. | 2,500 in.$^3$ |
| 50 in. | 3 in. | 10 in. | 1,500 in.$^3$ |

Describe what happens to the volume of the right rectangular prisms above as the base area changes.
Possible answer: As the dimensions of the width get smaller or narrower, the base area decreases in each prism resulting in a volume that decreases as well.

---

## Mathematical Practices

| | |
|---|---|
| **MP1** | **Make sense of problems and persevere in solving them.** |

**Item 10:** Students analyze the given information and relationships to solve the problem.

| | |
|---|---|
| **MP2** | **Reason abstractly and quantitatively.** |

**Item 9:** Students make sense of quantities and relationships to solve the problem.

MORE ONLINE **sadlierconnect.com**

Lesson 32

**Independent Practice**

**Solve. Use the figure.**

MP6 **12.** A manufacturer makes juice boxes that are 12 cm tall, 10 cm wide, and 5 cm deep. What is the volume of each juice box in cubic centimeters?

The volume of each juice box is ___600 cm³___.

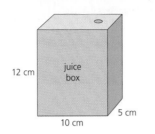

12 cm

juice box

5 cm

10 cm

MP7 **13.** What is the liquid volume of the juice box in milliliters?

The liquid volume of each juice box is ___600 mL___.

MP4 **14.** The juice box company decides to make three different juice box sizes. They want to have a mini juice box, a regular sized juice box, and a large sized juice box. Use the rules given below to choose the new dimensions of each box and find its liquid volume in milliliters.

Rules: The mini box should hold no more than 300 mL. The regular sized box should hold between 450 and 550 mL. The large sized box must hold at least 800 mL.

Sketch each new box, showing the dimensions and volume. Explain your choices. Answers will vary. Possible student responses are shown for each.

**a.** Mini juice box

**b.** Regular sized juice box

**c.** Large sized juice box

Possible answer:
9 cm by 3 cm by 10 cm; liquid volume = 270 mL

Possible answer:
10 cm by 5 cm by 10 cm; liquid volume = 500 mL

Possible answer:
10 cm by 8 cm by 15 cm; liquid volume = 1200 mL

Unit 4 ■ Focus on Measurement and Data **289**

## Teaching Tips

### Items 12–13

Students may need to be reminded that 1 cm³ = 1 mL.

### Item 14

Point out to students that there are several possible answers for each part of this problem. Suggest that students think about the look of the box and how easy it would be to hold and drink from, and not just whether its volume follows the rules.

| Mathematical Practices | |
|---|---|
| **MP4** | **Model with mathematics.** |
| **Item 14:** Students make sketches to model juice boxes of different sizes. | |
| **MP6** | **Attend to precision.** |
| **Item 12:** Students calculate accurately to solve a problem. | |
| **MP7** | **Look for and make use of structure.** |
| **Item 13:** Students use the relationship between cubic centimeters and milliliters to do a conversion. | |

## OBJECTIVE
**Find the volumes of composite three-dimensional figures.**

## ESSENTIAL QUESTION
Explain to students that a *composite figure* is a figure that can be broken up into other, simpler figures. Tell students that, in this lesson, they will find volumes of three-dimensional composite figures that can be broken into rectangular prisms.

## PREREQUISITE SKILLS
Use Item J on page 341 of the Foundational Skills Handbook to review the area formula for rectangles.

## FLUENCY PRACTICE
Fluency practice is available at **sadlierconnect.com**.

## Concept Development

### Understand: Breaking apart a figure made from unit cubes into right rectangular prisms to find volume

■ Students worked with composite two-dimensional figures in Grade 3. This knowledge is now extended to finding the volume of three-dimensional composite figures. Students should recognize that the total volume of two right rectangular prisms is equal to the sum of their individual volumes. In other words, volume is *additive*.

▸ Have students compare the results using the formula to the results in the example.

---

Lesson

# 33  Problem Solving: Decompose Figures to Find Volume

**Essential Question:**
How do you find the volume of a composite figure?

## Guided Instruction

In this lesson you will find volumes of three-dimensional figures by breaking them into right rectangular prisms.

**Understand:** Breaking apart a figure made from unit cubes into right rectangular prisms to find volume

Jason uses cubes to construct a model of a building with two sections. Each cube is 1 cubic meter. What is the volume of the model?

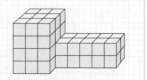

To find the volume of the model, break apart the figure into two separate right rectangular prisms and find the volume of each. Count the cubes to determine each prism's length, width, and height.

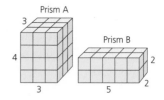

Prism A

Prism B

Use the formula for the volume of a right rectangular prism
$V = \ell \times w \times h$.

**Volume of Prism A**
$V = \ell \times w \times h$
$= 3 \times 3 \times 4$
$= 36 \text{ m}^3$

**Volume of Prism B**
$V = \ell \times w \times h$
$= 5 \times 2 \times 2$
$= 20 \text{ m}^3$

Add to find the total volume: $36 \text{ m}^3 + 20 \text{ m}^3 = 56 \text{ m}^3$.

➡ The volume of the model is $56 \text{ m}^3$.

▸ Find the volumes of Prisms A and B using the formula $V = B \times h$. Possible answer: Base area of first prism: $3 \times 3 = 9 \text{ m}^2$. Base area of second prism: $5 \times 2 = 10 \text{ m}^2$. Volume of first prism: $9 \text{ m}^2 \times 4 \text{ m} = 36 \text{ m}^3$. Volume of second prism: $10 \text{ m}^2 \times 2 \text{ m} = 20 \text{ m}^3$.

**290**  Unit 4 ■ Focus on Measurement and Data

---

## Support English Language Learners

English language learners may be unfamiliar with the words *decompose* and *composite*. Most students will not have encountered these two terms in their every day language. Write the words on the board. Then, point to each word and practice saying each term aloud together. Explain that both words come from the word *compose*. Compose means "to come together to form or make (something)." *Composite* has the same meaning as compose. Discuss the meaning of *composite figure*. The prefix *de-* means "opposite." Discuss the meaning of *decompose*: to take apart. Ask students to apply the definitions to explain the meaning of *decompose a composite figure*.

## Guided Instruction

**Understand:** How to find the volume of a figure composed of two right rectangular prisms

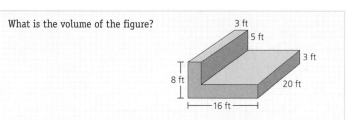

What is the volume of the figure?

3 ft
5 ft
3 ft
8 ft
20 ft
16 ft

To find the volume of the figure, you can break it into right rectangular prisms. Be sure the prisms do not overlap. One way to break up the figure is shown at the right.

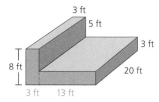

3 ft
5 ft
3 ft
8 ft
20 ft
3 ft    13 ft

Find the volume of each prism using the volume formula.

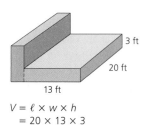

3 ft
20 ft
13 ft

$V = \ell \times w \times h$
$= 20 \times 13 \times 3$
$= 780 \text{ ft}^3$

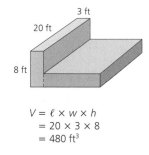

3 ft
20 ft
8 ft

$V = \ell \times w \times h$
$= 20 \times 3 \times 8$
$= 480 \text{ ft}^3$

Add the two volumes to find the volume of the composite figure.
$780 \text{ ft}^3 + 480 \text{ ft}^3 = 1{,}260 \text{ ft}^3$

➡ The volume of the composite figure is 1,260 cubic feet.

Unit 4 ■ Focus on Measurement and Data    **291**

**Understand:** How to find the volume of a figure composed of two right rectangular prisms

■ In this presentation, a composite three-dimensional figure is decomposed into two rectangular prisms to find its total volume. Emphasize that when a figure such as this is decomposed, the resulting individual figures must not overlap.

■ Some students may see that the composite figure could have been decomposed in a different way. The horizontal prism could have included the entire width. In this case, the upright prism would be 5 × 3 × 20. Point out that this would also be correct since the entire composite figure would be included with no gaps or overlaps.

## Math-to-Architecture Connection

**Buildings** Have students search the Internet, magazines, or other printed materials for examples of buildings that are composite figures. Ask students to look for buildings that are composed of two or more right rectangular prisms. Have them print a copy of the picture or a make a drawing of the building and then use two differently colored highlighters to outline each rectangular prism.

## Connect: What you know about finding the volume of composite figures

■ In this presentation, students solve a real-world problem involving a composite three-dimensional figure. This presentation may confuse some students because the drawing appears to represent a two-dimensional figure. Students may benefit from a discussion of what the third dimension is and why it is not shown.

■ In Step 1, it may be helpful to make a three-dimensional drawing of each rectangular prism and have students label the dimensions of each prism.

---

**Lesson 33** Problem Solving: **Decompose Figures to Find Volume**

## Guided Instruction

### Connect: What you know about finding the volume of composite figures

Nan just bought an air conditioner. The manual says it will cool a space with a volume up to 1,000 cubic feet.

The diagram at the right represents the floor plan of Nan's bedroom. The height of the room is 12 feet.

Will the air conditioner be powerful enough to cool Nan's room?

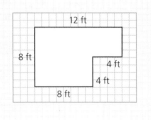

To solve this problem, find the volume of Nan's room and compare it to 1,000 cubic feet.

**Step 1**

Break apart the bedroom into two right rectangular prisms and find the volume of each one.

Separate the diagram into two squares as shown. Each square is the base of a prism with a height of 12 feet. Find the volume of each prism.

| Larger prism | Smaller prism |
|---|---|
| $V = \ell \times w \times h$ | $V = \ell \times w \times h$ |
| $V = 8 \times 8 \times 12$ | $V = 4 \times 4 \times 12$ |
| $V = 768 \text{ ft}^3$ | $V = 192 \text{ ft}^3$ |

The two prisms have volumes of 768 ft³ and 192 ft³.

**Step 2**

Add the volumes of the prisms to find the volume of the bedroom.

Volume of Nan's bedroom = 768 ft³ + 192 ft³ = 960 ft³.

**Step 3**

Compare the volume to 1,000 ft³. The volume, 960 ft³, is less than 1,000 ft³.

➡ Yes, the air conditioner will be powerful enough to cool Nan's bedroom.

**292** Unit 4 ■ Focus on Measurement and Data

---

## Math-to-Math Connection

**Logical Reasoning** Point out that the volume of composite figures can also be found by using subtraction. Consider the diagram at the top of page 292. Ask students to find the volume if the figure were a solid rectangular prism measuring 12 by 8 by 12 ft. Discuss how this volume might be used to find the volume of the actual figure. Point out that the missing portion of the base has an area of 4 by 4 ft. Multiply that area by the 12 ft height of the figure, and students should reason that the area of the actual figure is 4 by 4 by 12 ft less than the entire rectangular prism. Have students subtract the difference to find the actual volume. Discuss the pros and cons of this strategy.

Guided Practice

**For exercises 1–3, use the figure shown at the right, which is made from centimeter cubes.**

1. volume of top prism
   $V = \ell \times w \times h$
   $V = 2 \times 2 \times \underline{6}$
   $V = \underline{18}$ cm³

2. volume of bottom prism
   $V = \ell \times w \times h$
   $V = 5 \times 6 \times \underline{2}$
   $V = \underline{60}$ cm³

3. volume of composite figure
   $\underline{18}$ cm³ + $\underline{60}$ cm³ = $\underline{78}$ cm³

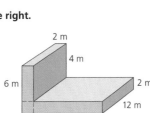

**For exercises 4–7, use the figure shown at the right.**

4. volume of bottom prism
   $14 \times 12 \times 2 = \underline{336\ m^3}$

5. volume of top prism
   $2 \times 4 \times 12 = \underline{96\ m^3}$

6. total volume
   $\underline{336\ m^3} + \underline{96\ m^3} = \underline{432\ m^3}$

2 m
4 m
6 m          2 m
             12 m
   14 m

**Think•Pair•Share**

MP4  7. Find the volume of the figure in exercises 4–6 by separating it into two different prisms. Describe the dimensions of the new prisms. What is the volume of the figure? Is it the same? Explain.
Yes, the volume is still the same. Possible explanation: Break apart the figure so that one prism measures 6 × 2 × 12 and the other prism measures 12 × 12 × 2. The volume is still the same, 432 m³.

Unit 4 ■ Focus on Measurement and Data  **293**

---

## Observational Assessment

Use page 293 to assess whether students are able to find the volume of composite three-dimensional figures by adding the volumes of the parts that compose it. Even though some students may be able to solve exercises 1 and 2 without completing each step, ask them to use each step to help solidify their understanding of the concept.

### ☝☝ Think•Pair•Share

**Peer Collaboration** Ask students to form groups of three. Read the problem aloud to the class. Before having groups determine the dimensions of the new prisms and computing the volume, discuss the following:

- *Describe how you separated the figure into two prisms.*

- *Are there any parts of the composite figure that could be part of more than one prism? If so, how did you include those parts in the volume?*

- *How will you find the length of the 14 m side after separating the prisms.*

### Return to the Essential Question

Reread the Lesson 33 Essential Question on page 290: *How do you find the volume of a composite figure?*

Ask volunteers to use what they learned in this lesson to answer this question. (Possible response: I can separate composite figures into parts, find the volume of each part, and then add these volumes to find the volume of the composite figure.)

---

## Mathematical Practices

Mathematical Practice Standards underline the teaching and understanding of all concepts and skills presented. The emphasis of specific practices is noted throughout the guided and independent practice of this lesson.

**MP4    Model with mathematics.**

**Item 7:** Students decompose a three-dimensional figure differently than previously shown to demonstrate their understanding of composite figures and their volumes.

# Independent Practice

## Concept Application

Students may work independently on these pages in the classroom or at home. They may refer to the first four pages of the lesson to revisit the instruction or to see a worked-out example.

**Common Errors** and **Teaching Tips** may help you support student learning either in the classroom or as a follow-up for work done at home.

## Common Errors

### Items 10-12

Students may mistakenly think that the height of the purple rectangular prism is 3 inches. Point out that this label applies to the additional height above the white rectangular prism. To find the height of the purple prism, they must add the height of the non-shaded prism.

## Teaching Tips

### Items 7-12

Draw students' attention to the shading in the figures. This is provided to show them how the figures can be decomposed. Students may need to draw and label each rectangular prism separately before finding the volume of each.

---

### Independent Practice

Find the volume of the green figure, which is made from centimeter cubes. Use the figure at the right to help you.

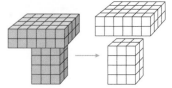

1. top prism: $V =$ ___48 cm³___

2. bottom prism: $V =$ ___24 cm³___

3. volume of composite figure:

   ___48 cm³___ + ___24 cm³___ = ___72 cm³___

Find the volume of the blue figure, which is made from centimeter cubes. Use the figure at the right to help you.

4. top prism: $V =$ ___60 cm³___

5. bottom prism: $V =$ ___60 cm³___

6. volume of composite figure:

   ___60 cm³___ + ___60 cm³___ = ___120 cm³___

Find the volume of the figure by adding the volumes of the two right rectangular prisms. The measures are in inches.

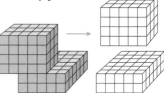

7. white prism: $V =$ ___288 in.³___

8. red prism: $V =$ ___24 in.³___

9. total volume:

   ___288 in.³___ + ___24 in.³___ = ___312 in.³___

Find the volume of the figure by adding the volumes of the two right rectangular prisms. The measures are in inches.

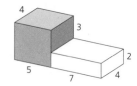

10. white prism: $V =$ ___56 in.³___

11. purple prism: $V =$ ___100 in.³___

12. total volume:

   ___56 in.³___ + ___100 in.³___ = ___156 in.³___

**294** Unit 4 ■ Focus on Measurement and Data

---

## Writing About Math

✏ **· Write an Explanatory Paragraph** Have students write a paragraph that includes the steps needed to find the volume of a composite three-dimensional figure that can be decomposed into rectangular prisms. The paragraph should begin with the sentence "I can find the volume of a composite figure by…" The paragraph should end with the sentence "So the volume of a composite figure is…" Their paragraphs should include logically ordered steps that are supported by fact and details. Be sure students use precise language and vocabulary in their paragraphs.

Lesson 33

**Independent Practice**

For exercises 13–14, draw the base of each figure on the grid provided. Separate the base into rectangles to represent the bases of two right rectangular prisms. Find the volume of the figure by finding and adding the volumes of the two right rectangular prisms.

**13.** This box has an open top. Lengths are in inches.
Possible answer is shown.

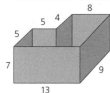
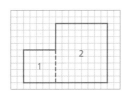

Prism 1: $V = \ell \times w \times h$
$V = 5 \times 5 \times 7$
$V = 175 \text{ in.}^3$

Prism 2: $V = \ell \times w \times h$
$V = 9 \times 8 \times 7$
$V = 504 \text{ in.}^3$

Volume of box = $175 \text{ in.}^3 + 504 \text{ in.}^3 = 679 \text{ in.}^3$

**14.** This figure is a solid piece of wood. Lengths are in centimeters.

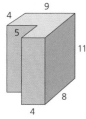
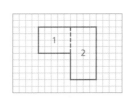

Prism 1: $V = \ell \times w \times h$
$V = 4 \times 5 \times 11$
$V = 220 \text{ cm}^3$

Prism 2: $V = \ell \times w \times h$
$V = 4 \times 8 \times 11$
$V = 352 \text{ cm}^3$

Volume of solid piece of wood = $220 \text{ cm}^3 + 352 \text{ cm}^3 = 572 \text{ cm}^3$

Unit 4 ■ Focus on Measurement and Data   **295**

## Teaching Tips

### Items 13-14

Point out to students that there is more than one way to separate the base into rectangles. Point out that students may also find the volume of the composite figure by first finding the area of the composite base and then using the formula $V = B \times h$.

## Digital Connection

**Use Digital Photography**  Provide students with unit cubes and ask them to create a composite figure made of two or more rectangular prisms. Then have them take a digital photograph of the figure with a camera or cell phone. If available, ask students to use photo-editing software to label the dimensions of the prisms. You may want to have students post the labeled pictures on your class Web site. Ask students to find the volumes of the composite figures the class created.

# Independent Practice

## Teaching Tips

### Item 15

Encourage students to draw dashed segments on the figure to show how they would break it apart. Then they can draw each rectangular prism separately and label it.

### Item 16

Be sure students realize that this problem is referring to the situation in problem 15.

### Item 17

Some students may not know where to begin. Suggest that they start by dividing the figure into two prisms. Have them list the three dimensions for each prism—length, width, and height. Then they should determine one dimension at a time for each prism, labeling the figure as they go and checking off the dimension from the list. It also may be helpful for students to shade the two decomposed prisms in different colors.

### Item 18

Be sure that students include all of the steps in their explanation and use the correct units in their answers.

---

### Independent Practice

**Use the figure to solve.**

MP2 **15.** Mr. Arthur dug this foundation for a building. Describe two different ways to find the volume of this figure by breaking it apart into two prisms.
Break it apart with a vertical cut into prisms with dimensions of 12 yd × 13 yd × 20 yd and 28 yd × 25 yd × 20 yd.

Break it apart with a horizontal cut into prisms with dimensions of 40 yd × 20 yd × 13 yd and 12 yd × 20 yd × 28 yd.

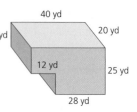

MP1 **16.** What is the volume of soil removed to pour this foundation?

    · **Show your work.**
Volume of one prism is 12 × 13 × 20, or 3,120 yd³. Volume of other prism is 28 × 25 × 20, or 14,000 yd³. The total volume is 3,120 + 14,000 = 17,120 yd³.

**Answer** <u>17,120 cubic yards of soil was removed to pour this foundation</u>

**For exercise 17, find the missing lengths to solve.**

MP2 **17.** The shaded face of the figure is square. Lengths are in feet. Find the volume of the figure.

Label the figure to show missing lengths. Show how you divide it into two prisms.

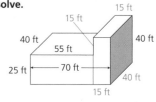

**Answer** <u>The volume is 79,000 ft³.</u>

MP3 **18.** Explain how you used the given information to solve the problem.
Possible answer: Knowing that the shaded face is a square gave me the lengths for the other sides. Then I found the width of the right prism and the length and height of the left prism. Volume of left prism is 55 ft × 25 ft × 40 ft. Volume of right prism is 15 ft × 40 ft × 40 ft.

**296**   Unit 4 ■ Focus on Measurement and Data

---

## Mathematical Practices

| **MP1** | **Make sense of problems and persevere in solving them.** |
|---|---|

**Item 16:** Students analyze a situation involving a composite three-dimensional figure, plan a solution, solve, and show their work.

| **MP2** | **Reason abstractly and quantitatively.** |
|---|---|

**Items 15 and 17:** Students use basic operations and drawings to solve problems involving composite three-dimensional figures.

| **MP3** | **Construct viable arguments and critique the reasoning of others.** |
|---|---|

**Item 18:** Students explain how they used information given in a real-life problem to solve it.

MORE ONLINE sadlierconnect.com                    Lesson 33

## Independent Practice

**Solve. Use the figure.**

MP2 **19.** A purple cube that measures 4 cm on each edge sits on top of a green right rectangular prism with an edge of length 11 cm as shown. The volume of the green prism is 88 cm³. Find the total height of the figure.

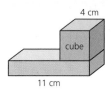
4 cm
cube
11 cm

**Answer** The height is 6 cm.

• **Justify your answer using words, drawings, or numbers.**
Justifications will vary. Possible justification: The green prism is 4 cm wide, so the height of the green prism is 88 ÷ (4 × 11) = 2 cm. The height of the figure is 2 cm + 4 cm = 6 cm.

MP6 **20.** Show how to break apart the figure from exercise 19 into two right rectangular prisms so that neither prism is a cube. Make a drawing and mark the dimensions or lengths of each prism.

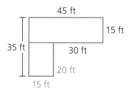
4 cm
2 cm
6 cm
7 cm   4 cm   4 cm

**Solve.**

MP1 **21.** The drawing shows the floor plan of a 7-story building. Each story is 11 ft tall. How many cubic feet are in this building?

Label the drawing to show the missing dimensions. Show the steps in your solution.

45 ft
15 ft
35 ft   30 ft
20 ft
15 ft

• **Show your work.**
Possible student work: 35 ft − 15 ft = 20 ft, 45 ft − 30 ft = 15 ft; areas are 20 × 15 and 15 × 45. Height is 7 × 11 = 77 ft. Volume is (20 × 15 × 77) + (15 × 45 × 77) = 23,100 ft³ + 51,975 ft³ = 75,075 ft³.

**Answer** The building has 75,075 cubic feet.

## Mathematical Practices

| | |
|---|---|
| **MP1** | **Make sense of problems and persevere in solving them.** |

**Item 21:** Students use written and visual information to solve a problem.

| | |
|---|---|
| **MP2** | **Reason abstractly and quantitatively.** |

**Item 19:** Students are given facts about a composite three-dimensional figure and reason quantitatively to determine missing information.

| | |
|---|---|
| **MP6** | **Attend to precision.** |

**Item 20:** Students make and label a drawing using accurate and appropriate measurements.

---

# Independent Practice

## Common Errors

### Item 21

Some students may label one of the unlabeled dimensions as 11 feet. Tell them that 11 feet is the height of one story and cannot be labeled in the two-dimensional drawing of a floor plan. After finding the missing dimensions, students may find the volume of one story, forgetting to multiply by 7, the number of stories. Remind them to check their answers for reasonableness.

## Teaching Tips

### Item 19

Students need to work backward to solve this multi-step problem. It may be helpful for them to first list what they know and then list what they need to know. Note that some students may need a reminder of the definition of a cube. Be sure their justifications clearly demonstrate an understanding of the relationship of volume to the dimensions—length, width, and height.

### Item 21

Students may also find the area of the composite floor plan and then multiply by 77 to find the volume of the building. In either case, be sure students have shown and justified all of their steps.

## Return to the

*Progress Check*

Remind students to return to the Progress Check self-assessment, page 223, to check off additional items they have mastered during the unit.

The Unit 4 Review covers all the standards presented in the unit. Use it to assess your students' mastery of the unit's concepts and skills.

## Depth of Knowledge

The depth of knowledge is a ranking of the content complexity of assessment items based on Webb's Depth of Knowledge (DOK) levels. The levels increase in complexity as shown below.

**Level 1:** Recall and Reproduction
**Level 2:** Basic Skills and Concepts
**Level 3:** Strategic Reasoning and Thinking
**Level 4:** Extended Thinking

| Item | DOK |
|------|-----|
| 1 | 1 |
| 2 | 1 |
| 3 | 2 |
| 4 | 1 |
| 5 | 2 |
| 6 | 2 |
| 7 | 2 |
| 8 | 2 |
| 9 | 3 |
| 10 | 2 |
| 11 | 2 |
| 12 | 2 |
| 13 | 3 |
| 14 | 4 |
| 15 | 3 |
| 16 | 3 |

UNIT 4 Review

**Convert the measurements from one metric unit to another.**

1. 1.6 kilograms = ■ grams

   ___1600___ grams

2. 32,000 centimeters = ■ kilometers

   ___0.32___ kilometers

**Circle the correct answer.**

3. Which of the following is more than 2 gallons?

   a. 8 quarts    b. 25 cups    (c.) 20 pints    d. 200 fluid ounces

4. Which of the following is a unit cube?

   a. 2 in. 2 in. 2 in.    (b.) 1 cm 1 cm 1 cm    c. 2 ft 2 ft 1 ft    d. 2 m 1 m 2 m

**Count the unit cubes to find the volume of each figure.**

5.

There are __12__ unit cubes.

The volume is __12__ cubic units.

6.

There are __18__ unit cubes.

The volume is __18__ cubic units.

**Show how to use the formula $V = \ell \times w \times h$ to find the volume of each figure.**

7.

$V = \underline{5} \times \underline{3} \times \underline{2}$

Volume __30__ cubic units

8.

$V = \underline{4} \times \underline{2} \times \underline{2}$

Volume __16__ cubic units

UNIT **4** Review

**Solve.**

MP1  **9.** Jamil needs 200 inches of beaded braid for a craft project. The braid is sold in 2-yard spools that cost $6.50 each, or by the foot at $1.25 per foot. Find the least amount Jamil can spend to get the braid he needs.

**Answer** The least amount Jamil can spend is $19.25.

▸ **Justify your answer using words, drawings, or numbers.**

Possible justification: Jamil needs $200 \div 12 = 16\frac{2}{3}$ feet. If he buys 3 spools for $6.50 each, he'll spend $19.50 and get 18 feet, since 2 yards is 6 feet. But, he can buy 2 spools and 5 feet for $19.25: $(2 \times 6.50) + (5 \times 1.25) = 13.00 + 6.25 = 19.25$. That will give him 17 feet of braid and save him $0.25.

**10.** Ruth's grandfather kept track of how far he walked on each of the past 24 days. Ruth made the line plot below to show these distances. On how many days did Ruth's grandfather walk more than $\frac{1}{2}$ mile?

**Distance Walked (miles)**

**Answer** Ruth's grandfather walked more than $\frac{1}{2}$ mile on 10 days.

**11.** Matt kept track of how long it took to get home from school on 10 days. His data is shown below in fractional parts of an hour.

$$\frac{5}{6}, \frac{1}{3}, \frac{1}{6}, \frac{1}{2}, \frac{1}{3}, \frac{1}{2}, \frac{2}{3}, \frac{1}{2}, \frac{5}{6}, \frac{1}{2}$$

**a.** Make a line plot for the data. Plot an X to represent each value.

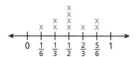

**Time to Get Home (hours)**

**b.** On how many days did it take Matt more than 30 minutes to get home from school?

It took more than 30 minutes on 3 days.

This chart correlates the Unit 4 Review items with the lessons in which the concepts and skills are presented.

| Item | Lesson |
|------|--------|
| 1 | 26 |
| 2 | 26 |
| 3 | 25 |
| 4 | 28 |
| 5 | 29 |
| 6 | 29 |
| 7 | 31 |
| 8 | 31 |
| 9 | 26 |
| 10 | 27 |
| 11 | 27 |
| 12 | 32 |
| 13 | 29 |
| 14 | 31 |
| 15 | 30 |
| 16 | 33 |

## Mathematical Practices

| | |
|---|---|
| **MP1** | **Make sense of problems and persevere in solving them.** |

**Item 9:** Students analyze a problem and plan a solution.

## Writing About Math

✏️ ▸ Direct students to respond to the Unit 4 Essential Question. (This can be found on student page 225.)

**Essential Question:**
**What strategies can you use to determine the capacity of a figure?**

Possible responses:
- Use unit cubes to find the volume of the figure.
- Use the formula $V = \ell \times w \times h$ to find the volume of a rectangular solid.

### Unit Assessment

- Unit 4 Review, *pp. 298–300*
- Unit 4 Performance Task ( ONLINE )

### Additional Assessment Options

**Optional Purchase:**
- iProgress Monitor ( ONLINE )
- Progress Monitor Student Benchmark Assessment Booklet

---

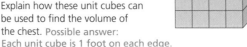

UNIT **4** Review

**MP6** **12.** Jerry built a flower box 30 inches long, 8 inches wide, and 10 inches deep. How many cubic inches of soil does Jerry need to fill the box halfway?
$(30 \times 8 \times 10) \div 2 = 2{,}400 \div 2 = 1{,}200$ cubic inches

To fill the box halfway, Jerry needs 1,200 cubic inches of soil.

**MP5** **13.** A wooden storage chest is 4 feet long, 2 feet deep, and 2 feet high. Explain how these unit cubes can be used to find the volume of the chest. Possible answer: Each unit cube is 1 foot on each edge. The model shows two layers of unit cubes, each with 8 cubes. So, the volume of the chest is 16 cubic feet.

**MP4** **14.** Explain how to use this figure to represent the Associative Property of Multiplication. Possible answer: The volume of the prism equals the area of the base times the height. If the 10 by 12 face is considered the base, then this is $(20 \times 12) \times 7$. If the 12 by 7 face is considerd the base, then this is $20 \times (12 \times 7)$. The volume is the same either way so $(20 \times 12) \times 7 = 20 \times (12 \times 7)$.

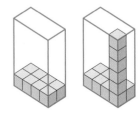

**MP5** **15.** Use the model to find the volume of a rectangular prism that is 4 units long, 2 units wide and 6 units tall. Explain your steps.
Possible answer: The bottom layer has 8 cubes, and there are 6 layers, so the volume is $8 \times 6 = 48$ cubic units.

**MP1** **16.** Find the volume of this composite figure.

✏️ ▸ **Show your work.**
right prism: $V = 3 \times 5 \times 8 = 120$ cm³;
left prism: $V = 7 \times 3 \times 5 = 105$ cm³;
volume of composite figure:
$120$ cm³ $+ 105$ cm³ $= 225$ cm³

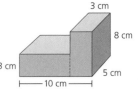

**Answer** The volume of the figure is 225 cm³.

---

## Mathematical Practices

| | |
|---|---|
| **MP1** | **Make sense of problems and persevere in solving them.** |
| **Item 16:** Students relate to a similar problem to find a solution. | |
| **MP4** | **Model with mathematics.** |
| **Item 14:** Students explain the relationship of quantities. | |
| **MP5** | **Use appropriate tools strategically.** |
| **Items 13, 15:** Students use models strategically to solve. | |
| **MP6** | **Attend to precision.** |
| **Item 12:** Students calculate accurately and use units appropriately. | |

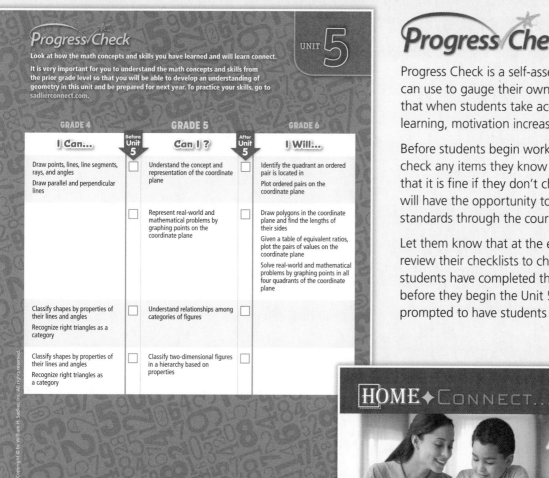

UNIT 5

Look at how the math concepts and skills you have learned and will learn connect.

It is very important for you to understand the math concepts and skills from the prior grade level so that you will be able to develop an understanding of geometry in this unit and be prepared for next year. To practice your skills, go to sadlierconnect.com.

| GRADE 4 | Before Unit 5 | GRADE 5 | After Unit 5 | GRADE 6 |
|---|---|---|---|---|
| **I Can...** | | **Can I ?** | | **I Will...** |
| Draw points, lines, line segments, rays, and angles. Draw parallel and perpendicular lines | ☐ | Understand the concept and representation of the coordinate plane | ☐ | Identify the quadrant an ordered pair is located in. Plot ordered pairs on the coordinate plane |
| | | Represent real-world and mathematical problems by graphing points on the coordinate plane | ☐ | Draw polygons in the coordinate plane and find the lengths of their sides. Given a table of equivalent ratios, plot the pairs of values on the coordinate plane. Solve real-world and mathematical problems by graphing points in all four quadrants of the coordinate plane |
| Classify shapes by properties of their lines and angles. Recognize right triangles as a category | ☐ | Understand relationships among categories of figures | ☐ | |
| Classify shapes by properties of their lines and angles. Recognize right triangles as a category | ☐ | Classify two-dimensional figures in a hierarchy based on properties | ☐ | |

Unit 5 ■ Focus on Geometry

**Student Page 301**

# Progress Check

Progress Check is a self-assessment tool that students can use to gauge their own progress. Research shows that when students take accountability for their learning, motivation increases.

Before students begin work in Unit 5, have them check any items they know they can do well. Explain that it is fine if they don't check any of the boxes; they will have the opportunity to learn and practice all the standards through the course of the unit.

Let them know that at the end of the unit they will review their checklists to check their progress. After students have completed the last lesson of the unit, before they begin the Unit 5 Review, you will be prompted to have students revisit this page.

# HOME ◆ CONNECT...

**In this unit your child will:**

- Understand points on the coordinate plane.
- Graph points to represent problem situations.
- Analyze properties to classify two-dimensional figures.

**Ways to Help Your Child**

As your child nears middle school, they will need to become more independent when it comes to completing assignments and projects. Check in with your child regularly, but avoid becoming too involved. Your support will show you are interested, but take the time to chronically reinforce that they must be responsible for their learning.

Your child will learn to use a coordinate plane to represent and solve real world problems.

You can graph a point on the coordinate plane using an ordered pair or coordinates $(x, y)$. The $x$-coordinate tells how far to travel from the origin in the direction of the $x$-axis. The $y$-coordinate tells how far to travel from the origin in the direction of the $y$-axis.

On this coordinate plane the ordered pair $(2,3)$ is graphed and labeled point $A$.

**Activity:** Ask your child to think about designing an amusement park. Have your child draw a map of the amusement park using a coordinate plane. Ask them to use ordered pairs to identify the location of rides, games, entrances, waterfalls, and eating areas. Additionally, there are many age-appropriate interactive games available that can reinforce graphing on a coordinate plane. Take the time to play those games with your child.

ONLINE
For more Home Connect activities, continue online at sadlierconnect.com

302 Unit 5 ■ Focus on Geometry

**Student Page 302**

# HOME ◆ CONNECT...

The Home Connect feature is a way to keep parents or other adult family members apprised of what their children are learning. The key learning objectives are listed, and some ideas for related activities and discussions are included.

Explain to students that they can share the Home Connect page at home with their families. Let students know there is an activity connected to their classroom learning that they can do with their families.

Encourage students and their parents to share their experiences using the suggestions on the Home Connect. You may wish to invite students to share this work with the class.

## UNIT PLANNER

| Lesson | Objective |
|---|---|
| **34** Understand Points on the Coordinate Plane | Use ordered pairs to locate and graph points on the coordinate plane. |
| **35** Graph Points to Represent Problem Situations | Use a coordinate plane to represent real-world and mathematical problems. |
| **36** Analyze Properties to Classify Two-Dimensional Figures | Classify two-dimensional figures by analyzing their properties. |

**Essential Question:** How can you represent and analyze data on a coordinate plane?

UNIT 5

| Essential Question | Words to Know |
|---|---|
| How do you use ordered pairs to locate points and draw figures on the coordinate plane? | |
| How do you use a coordinate plane to represent real-world and mathematical problems? | scale |
| How do you use properties to classify two-dimensional figures? | scalene triangle<br>isosceles triangle<br>equilateral triangle<br>acute triangle<br>right triangle<br>obtuse triangle<br>trapezoid<br>kite<br>adjacent sides<br>hierarchy diagram |

## Unit Assessment

- Unit 5 Review, *pp. 328–330*
- Unit 5 Performance Task ONLINE

## Additional Assessment Options

- Performance Task 2, *pp. 331–336*
  ALSO ONLINE

**Optional Purchase:**

- iProgress Monitor ONLINE

- Progress Monitor Student Benchmark Assessment Booklet

### ONLINE Digital Resources

- Home Connect Activities
- Unit Performance Tasks
- Additional Practice
- Fluency Practice
- Teacher Resources
- iProgress Monitor (optional purchase)

**Go to SadlierConnect.com to access your Digital Resources.**

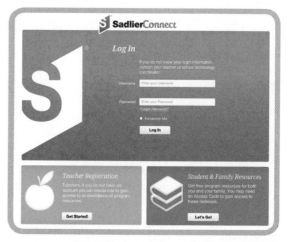

**For more detailed instructions see page T3.**

## LEARNING PROGRESSIONS

This page provides more in-depth detail on the development of math concepts and skills across the grade levels. See also the unit Progress Check page in the Student Edition for a roadmap of the Learning Progressions.

**Grade 4**

- Constructing a wide range of examples deepens understanding of geometric concepts; students draw points, lines, line segments, rays, angles (right, acute, obtuse), and perpendicular and parallel lines, and identify them in two-dimensional figures.
- Students classify shapes by properties of their lines and angles. They identify right triangles and recognize them as a category.

**Grade 5**

- Students build on previous work with number lines by using two perpendicular number lines to define a coordinate system to represent the coordinate plane. They use coordinates to identify and plot points in the first quadrant. They interpret ordered pairs, for example (3, 2), as instructions (e.g., right 3, up 2) and as positions (e.g., the point a distance 3 from the *y*-axis and a distance 2 from the *x*-axis).
- Students represent problems by graphing points in the first quadrant and connect points to represent figures with specified characteristics.
- Students understand that attributes belonging to a category of figures are shared by all subcategories of the category; for example, all rectangles have four right angles and squares are rectangles, so all squares have four right angles.
- Students classify two-dimensional figures in a hierarchy based on their properties.

**Grade 6**

- Students identify the quadrant an ordered pair is located in from the signs of the numbers in the ordered pair.
- Students understand that if two ordered pairs differ only by signs, their locations on the coordinate plane are related by reflections across one or both axes.
- Students make tables of equivalent ratios relating quantities with whole number measurements and plot the pairs of values on the coordinate plane.
- Students graph points in any quadrant of the coordinate plane to solve real-world and mathematical problems, including use of coordinates and absolute value to find distances between points with the same first or the same second coordinate.
- Students draw polygons in the coordinate plane for given vertices and use coordinates to find the length of a side with the same first coordinate or the same second coordinate.

# Focus on Geometry

UNIT 5

**Essential Question:**
How can you represent and analyze data on a coordinate plane?

Unit 5 ■ Focus on Geometry  303

## Activity

**Materials:** Drawing paper and pencils
Tell students to make drawings or maps of their neighborhood. Remind them to label streets, buildings, schools, and stores.

Have partners explain their drawing or map to each other. They can give their partner a quiz on how to get to different places on the map. You may wish to have students show how they would do this on the map or have them write the answer. Ask students how having a map can make it easy to show people how to get to school or the store?

Have a whole-class discussion in which students share and explain their work. Students may explain how using the map not only showed them what they were talking about, they could also see the direction or way to go.

**Essential Question:**
How can you represent and analyze data on a coordinate plane?

As students become involved with the Essential Question they will understand how to plot points in the first quadrant on a coordinate plane. They will understand the naming convention for these points, and also learn how to solve problems that involve graphing and analyzing data.

## Conversation Starters

Have students discuss the photograph. Ask questions such as: *What do you think is happening? Has anyone ever been in a hot air balloon? What was it like? If you haven't been in a hot air balloon, what do you think it is like?*

You may ask students if they have ever flown in an airplane and what the ground looked like from the airplane. *What do you think the ground will look like?* (The things on the ground would look much smaller. I could see shapes made on the ground by fields and buildings.)

*How do you think the block or the street you live on would look like in the air?* (The block I live on might look like a rectangle from the air.)

*Do you think if you were in a balloon you might see something that would look like a circle or a triangle? What do you think they would be?* (A swimming pool might look like a circle. A park could look like a triangle.)

*How would looking at the ground from a balloon be like looking at a map?* (When you look at a map it is like you are looking down at the ground.)

Let student pairs discuss how they can find other geometric shapes. Lead them to see that looking for shapes and patterns is a good strategy to use for viewing objects around them geometrically.

## OBJECTIVE
Use ordered pairs to locate and graph points on the coordinate plane.

## ESSENTIAL QUESTION
Have students look at and describe the coordinate grids on this page.

## FLUENCY PRACTICE
Fluency practice is available at sadlierconnect.com.

## Concept Development

### Understand: Points on a coordinate plane

■ To find the ordered pair for point *B*, move right 6 units and up 4 units. So, the coordinates of point *B* are (6, 4). Have a volunteer describe how to find the ordered pair for point *C*.

■ Be sure students understand how the coordinates relate to a point's location. The first coordinate describes how far to move horizontally on the *x*-axis. The second coordinate describes how far to move vertically.

■ Explain that point *A* (3, 5) is 3 units from the *y*-axis, and 5 units from the *x*-axis. Ask students how far points *B* and *C* are from each axis.

---

**Lesson**

# 34 Understand Points on the Coordinate Plane

**Essential Question:**
How do you use ordered pairs to locate points and draw figures on the coordinate plane?

## Guided Instruction

In this lesson you will learn how to locate and graph points on the coordinate plane.

**Understand:** Points on a coordinate plane

> Rosa randomly puts points on a coordinate plane. She labels them *A*, *B*, and *C*. How can Rosa describe the location of each point?

Rosa can describe the location of points *A*, *B*, and *C* using an ordered pair of numbers, called the coordinates of the point. Each ordered pair, (*x*, *y*), consists of an *x*-coordinate and a *y*-coordinate. The ordered pairs for points *A*, *B*, and *C* are all in the first quadrant, or top right quarter, of the coordinate plane.

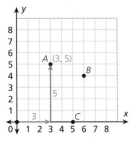

To find the ordered pair for points *A*, *B*, and *C*, begin at the origin, (0, 0). Move right and then up until you reach the point. If you start at the origin and move 3 units to the right and 5 units up, you will be at point *A*. So, the *x*-coordinate of point *A* is 3 and the *y*-coordinate is 5. Write the ordered pair as (3, 5).

The ordered pair for point *B* is (6, 4).
The ordered pair for point *C* is (5, 0).

➤ Rosa can describe the location of the points using these ordered pairs.
point *A*: (3, 5)      point *B*: (6, 4)      point *C*: (5, 0)

▭▸ Can either (5, 0) or (0, 5) be used to describe the location of point *C*? Explain.   Possible answer: No. Point *C* is on the *x*-axis. The ordered pair (0, 5) describes the location of a point on the *y*-axis.

---

## Support English Language Learners

Write the term *ordered pair* on the board and break the term into two words: *order* and *pair*. Ask students what *order* means. Most students will define order as an arrangement of things in relation to each other. Next, discuss the fact that *pair* refers to two things that go together. Explain that an *ordered pair* is two numbers that are arranged, or ordered, in a particular way. Give students the ordered pairs (3, 5) and (5, 3). Explain that the *order* of the numbers in these *pair* is very important. Demonstrate this by plotting each point, emphasizing that the *first* number tells how far to move to the right, and the *second* number tells how far to move up. When you are finished, point out that the points are different because the order of the numbers in the two ordered pairs is different.

Guided Instruction

**Understand: Using ordered pairs to graph a figure on a coordinate plane**

Ethan graphs these points on a coordinate plane.
**point A:** (1, 2)     **point B:** (2, 5)     **point C:** (7, 5)     **point D:** (6, 2)

He connects the points in order, and then connects point D back to point A. What geometric figure does Ethan graph?

To find the geometric figure Ethan graphs using points A, B, C, and D, plot and label each point on the coordinate plane.

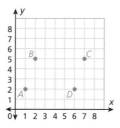

Connect the points A, B, C, and D in order and then connect point D back to point A.

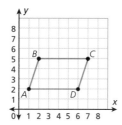

You can see that line segments AB and DC are always the same distance apart. Line segments AD and BC are also always the same distance apart. The figure is a quadrilateral with two pairs of parallel sides, so it is a parallelogram.

➡ Ethan graphs parallelogram ABCD.

✏️ Draw another quadrilateral that is a parallelogram. Explain how you know that it is a parallelogram.
Possible explanation: The line segments of parallel sides are always the same distance apart and would never meet if extended into lines.

## Understand: Using ordered pairs to graph a figure on a coordinate plane

■ In this presentation, students graph points on the plane and connect them to form a geometric figure. They classify the figure based on its properties. It may be useful to review the names and attributes of various quadrilaterals such as parallelograms, rectangles, squares, and trapezoids. Review the meanings of parallel and perpendicular lines.

✏️ After students have answered this question, ask students how they decided where to place the points to achieve the desired results. Have students share whether they plotted the points correctly the first time, or if they had to redraw part of their figure.

## Math-to-Math Connection

**Pythagorean Theorem and the Distance Formula** The Pythagorean Theorem addresses the relationship between the side lengths of a right triangle. Simply put, $a^2 + b^2 = c^2$. Since any two points on a coordinate plane can be expressed as vertices of a right triangle, the Pythagorean Theorem can be used to find the distance between those points. This application of the Pythagorean Theorem is commonly referred to as the distance formula. The value of $a$ is the distance between the $y$-values of the two points. The value of $b$ is the distance between the $x$-values of the two points. The sum of those squared values is equal to $c^2$. Taking the square root of both sides of the equation results in the diagonal distance, $c$, between the two points.

**Connect: What you know about points on a coordinate plane** Use this page to help students strengthen their understanding of coordinates and plotting points to draw figures on the coordinate plane.

■ This presentation introduces students to representing ordered pairs in a table and a graph. Students will use this understanding throughout their mathematics career to represent relations and functions.

■ Remind students to start at the origin as they graph each point. Then move *x*-units to the right and *y*-units up on the coordinate plane to graph the point.

■ After students have graphed the letter, have them identify the points that have the same *x*-coordinates and the points that have the same *y*-coordinates. Ask them what they notice about these points.

✏ Have students identify any parallel or perpendicular lines in the letter.

---

**Lesson 34   Understand Points on the Coordinate Plane**

### Guided Instruction

**Connect:** What you know about points on a coordinate plane

Rajia uses a coordinate plane to graph the points for the ordered pairs given in the table. She then connects them in order.

What letter does Rajia form?

| x | y | ( x, y ) |
|---|---|----------|
| 1 | 3 | (1, 3) |
| 1 | 8 | (1, 8) |
| 5 | 3 | (5, 3) |
| 5 | 8 | (5, 8) |

**Step 1**

Graph the point for (1, 3). Then graph the point for (1, 8). Next graph the point for (5, 3). Finally graph the point for (5, 8).

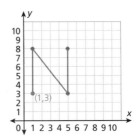

**Remember!**
Start at the origin for each point. Then move *x* units to the right and *y* units up on the coordinate plane to graph the point.

**Step 2**

Connect the points in the order they were graphed above.

Draw a line segment to connect the point for (1, 3) and the point for (1, 8).
Then draw a line segment to connect the point for (1, 8) and the point for (5, 3).
Finally draw a line segment to connect the point for (5, 3) and the point for (5, 8).
The line segments form a letter of the alphabet.

What is the letter? __N__

➤ Rajia connects the points to form the letter __N__.

✏ Graph the points for (2, 2), (2, 6), (4, 2), (6, 6), and (6, 2) on a coordinate plane. Then connect the points in the order they are given above. What letter do you form? I form the letter M.

**306   Unit 5 ■ Focus on Geometry**

---

## Math-to-Geography Connection

**Plotting Points and Reading Maps** Provide students with a county or state map. Tell students that finding a town or other location on a map is similar to plotting points. Point out the letters and numbers along the sides of the map. Give students the coordinates of a city on the map and show them how to locate the city. For example, if the city's location is B3, have students locate B and 3 on the sides of the map and follow the marked intervals from each letter and number to find where they intersect. Ask students to find the city in this overlapping region. Compare and contrast locating a city on a map to locating a point in the coordinate plane.

**MORE ONLINE** sadlierconnect.com    Lesson 34

Guided Practice

**For exercises 1–4, use the coordinate plane.**

1. Graph the following points.
   point *A*: (3, 1)    point *B*: (3, 6)    point *C*: (5, 8)
   point *D*: (8, 5)    point *E*: (8, 1)

   Connect points *A* through *E* in alphabetical order.
   Then connect point *E* back to point *A*.

   What polygon do you form when the points are
   connected? ___pentagon___

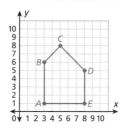

2. Which pair of sides of the polygon are parallel? ___Side *AB* is parallel to side *DE*.___

3. Which pairs of sides of the polygon are perpendicular?
   ___Side *AB* is perpendicular to side *AE* and side *DE* is perpendicular to side *AE*.___

4. How do you know when a pair of sides is perpendicular?
   ___Possible answer: The line segments that form the perpendicular sides meet at___
   ___a right angle to form a square corner.___

**Solve the problem.**

5. Garrett graphs the points for the ordered pairs (4, 6) and (4, 9) on a coordinate plane. Then he connects the points to form a line segment. Is the line segment parallel to the *x*-axis or parallel to the *y*-axis?

   **Answer** ___The line segment is parallel to the *y*-axis.___

👑 **Think•Pair•Share**

MP2  6. Elena graphs the point for the ordered pair (5, 2) on a coordinate plane. She says that the *x*-coordinate of the ordered pair, 5, means that the point is a distance of 5 units from the *y*-axis and the *y*-coordinate of the ordered pair, 2, means that the point is a distance of 2 units from the *x*-axis. Is Elena correct? Explain your reasoning.
   Yes, Elena is correct. Possible explanation: When you move 5 units to the right from the origin, you are moving a distance of 5 units away from the *y*-axis. When you then move up 2 units, you are moving a distance of 2 units up from the *x*-axis.

## Mathematical Practices

Mathematical Practice Standards underline the teaching and understanding of all concepts and skills presented. The emphasis of specific practices is noted throughout the guided and independent practice of this lesson.

| MP2 | **Reason abstractly and quantitatively.** |
| --- | --- |

**Item 6:** Students analyze the reasoning of a peer and determine whether the reasoning is correct. Students then justify their conclusion.

## Observational Assessment

Use page 307 to assess whether students are able to graph points on the coordinate plane to solve real-world and mathematical problems.

👑 **Think•Pair•Share**

**Peer Collaboration** After giving students an opportunity to consider the problem on their own, have them discuss their answer with another student. Guide their observations by asking:

- *When you locate the x-coordinate are you moving away from the x-axis or the y-axis?*

- *When you locate the y-coordinate are you moving away from the x-axis or the y-axis?*

### Return to the Essential Question

Reread the Lesson 34 Essential Question on page 304: *How do you use ordered pairs to locate points and draw figures on the coordinate plane?*

Ask volunteers to use what they learned in this lesson to answer this question. (Possible response: I can use ordered pairs to plot points by first moving to the right along the *x*-axis the first number of spaces, then moving up along the *y*-axis the second number of spaces. I can draw figures on the coordinate plane by connecting the points in the order they in which they were plotted.)

# Independent Practice

## Concept Application

Students may work independently on these pages in the classroom or at home. They may refer to the first four pages of the lesson to revisit the instruction or to see a worked-out example.

**Common Errors** and **Teaching Tips** may help you support student learning either in the classroom or as a follow-up for work done at home.

## Common Errors

### Item 1

A quick survey of students' work will enable you to identify students who are switching the coordinates when graphing the ordered pairs.

## Teaching Tips

### Items 2–3

Ask students how they know the lines are parallel or perpendicular.

### Item 5

If students simply give the answer "triangle," ask if they can be more specific. When connected, the points do form a triangle, but it is also a *right* triangle since it contains one right angle.

---

### Independent Practice

**For exercises 1–3, use the coordinate plane.**

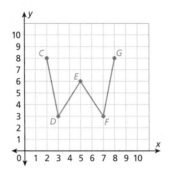

1. Graph the following points.
   point *C*: (2, 8)   point *D*: (3, 3)   point *E*: (5, 6)
   point *F*: (7, 3)   point *G*: (8, 8)

   Connect points *C* through *G* in alphabetical order.

   What letter is formed when the points are connected? __W__

2. Are any pairs of line segments that form the letter parallel? __No.__

3. Are any pairs of line segments that form the letter perpendicular? __No.__

**For exercises 4–5, use the coordinate plane.**

4. Graph the following points.
   point *J*: (1, 1)
   point *K*: (1, 4)
   point *L*: (3, 4)

5. Connect points *J*, *K*, and *L* in alphabetical order. Then connect point *L* back to point *J*.

   What polygon is formed when the points are connected? __triangle or right triangle__

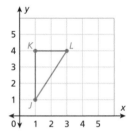

**308**  Unit 5 ■ Focus on Geometry

---

## Writing About Math

▸ **Write a Narrrative** Ask students to imagine the coordinate plane as a map of a city with the origin being the location of their home. Have them plot two points to represent places they might visit in a day, such as the school, the library, a store, or other various locations. Have the students write about their journeys for the day, including specific directions from one place to the next described as a pair of moves, first horizontal and then vertical, from their homes (the origin). Prompt students to use a clear event sequence. As time permits, allow students to read their narratives while the class plots the destinations described in the story.

## Teaching Tips

### Item 10
Ask students to notice if there are any pairs of parallel sides. Ask what shape has only one pair of parallel sides.

## Independent Practice

**For exercises 6–8, use the coordinate plane.**

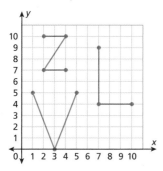

6. Graph the points for the following ordered pairs. Connect them in order.
   (7, 9)     (7, 4)     (10, 4)

   What letter do you form? __L__

7. Graph the points for the following ordered pairs. Connect them in order.
   (1, 5)     (3, 0)     (5, 5)

   What letter do you form? __V__

8. Graph the points for the following ordered pairs. Connect them in order.
   (2, 10)     (4, 10)     (2, 7)     (4, 7)

   What letter do you form? __Z__

**For exercises 9–10, use the coordinate plane.**

9. Graph the following points.
   point $Q$: (1, 5)     point $R$: (5, 5)
   point $S$: (4, 2)     point $T$: (2, 2)

10. Connect points $Q$, $R$, $S$, and $T$ in alphabetical order. Then connect point $T$ back to point $Q$.

    What polygon is formed when the points are

    connected? quadrilateral or trapezoid

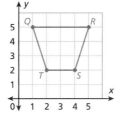

## Digital Connection

**Random Number Generator** Provide students with blank coordinate planes while displaying a coordinate plane on the Interactive Whiteboard. Use a search engine to find a random number generator and set the parameters to select two whole numbers between 1 and 10. Provide students with the random *x*- and *y*-coordinate pairs to graph. Ask volunteers to plot the point on the grid on the board, while the rest of the class plots the point on their own coordinate planes and evaluates the graphs for accuracy. Instruct students to label each point with its coordinates using the proper form *(x, y)*.

# Independent Practice

## Teaching Tips

### Item 12

Encourage students to graph the points. Some students may try just to visualize the problem, in order to avoid graphing. Remind students that the focus of this lesson is to plot points on the coordinate plane.

### Independent Practice

11. Graph the following points on the coordinate plane.
   point $L$: (2, 0)
   point $M$: (0, 4)

   When a point is located on the $x$-axis on a coordinate plane, what is the $y$-coordinate of the point? When a point is located on the $y$-axis on a coordinate plane, what is the $x$-coordinate of the point? Explain your thinking.

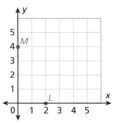

   **Answer** Possible answer: The y-coordinate of a point on the x-axis is always 0 since you do not move any units in the y direction when the point is on the x-axis. The x-coordinate of a point on the y-axis is always 0 since you do not move any units in the x direction when the point is on the y-axis.

**Solve the problems.**

MP5 12. Hong Kun graphs a quadrilateral on a coordinate plane. The vertices of the quadrilateral are (1, 1), (3, 6), (6, 6), and (8, 1). What quadrilateral does Hong Kun draw when he connects the points? How do you know?

   **Answer** Hong Kun draws a trapezoid. Possible explanation: I graphed the points and connected them in the order listed to create a quadrilateral. The quadrilateral has one pair of parallel sides so it is a trapezoid.

MP6 13. A designer graphs the model of a window on a coordinate plane. The vertices on this model are represented by the following points: $A$ (2, 2), $B$ (2, 5), $C$ (3, 7), $D$ (6, 7), $E$ (7, 5), and $F$ (7, 2). Connect the points in order, and then connect point $F$ back to point $A$, to find the shape of the window. What attributes did you use to identify the shape? Does the window have any pairs of sides that are parallel or perpendicular? If so, which pairs are they?

   **Answer** Possible answer: The window is shaped like a hexagon because it has 6 straight sides and 6 angles. Side AF is parallel to side CD, side AB is parallel to FE, side AB is perpendicular to side AF, and side EF is perpendicular to side AF.

## Mathematical Practices

| | |
|---|---|
| **MP5** | **Use appropriate tools strategically.** |

**Item 12:** Students use the coordinate plane as a tool to visualize and classify a quadrilateral.

| | |
|---|---|
| **MP6** | **Attend to precision.** |

**Item 13:** Students carefully formulate a full description of the relationships among the sides of the polygon.

Lesson 34

Independent Practice

MP8  14. Draw three different vertical line segments on the coordinate plane.

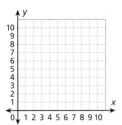

Check students' graphs.

For each vertical line segment, what conclusion can you draw about the *x*-coordinates of the ordered pairs that represent the endpoints? For horizontal line segments, can you draw a similar conclusion about the *y*-coordinates of the ordered pairs that represent the endpoints? If so, explain.

**Answer** For each vertical line segment, the x-coordinates of the endpoints are the same. For each horizontal line segment, the y-coordinates of the endpoints are the same.

MP4  15. Gaia draws a line segment to connect the points at (2, 1) and (7, 4). She draws a second line segment that is parallel to the first one by connecting the points at (2, 3) and (7, 6). If she wants to draw a third line segment parallel to the ones she has already drawn, what ordered pairs could she use?

**Answer** Ordered pairs may vary. Possible answer: (2, 5) and (7, 8)

**▸ Justify your answer using words, drawings, or numbers.**
Possible justification: I graphed the line segments on a coordinate plane. Since the line segments must always be the same distance apart, I counted up the same number of units from each endpoint to find the ordered pairs.

MP7  16. Jules draws a line segment to connect the points at (3, 6) and (8, 6). Then he graphs two more points that he connects to form a second line segment that is perpendicular to the first line segment. What could be the ordered pairs of the points he graphs?

**Answer** Ordered pairs may vary. Possible answer: (4, 8) and (4, 3)

**▸ Justify your answer using words, drawings, or numbers.**
Possible justification: I graphed the line segments on a coordinate plane. Since the line segments intersect to form right angles, they are perpendicular.

Unit 5 ▪ Focus on Geometry  **311**

## Teaching Tips

### Items 15 and 16
Explain to students that it is acceptable to draw the line segments first, and then determine the end points of the line segments they have drawn.

| Mathematical Practices | |
|---|---|
| **MP4** | **Model with mathematics.** |
| **Item 15:** Students use plotting points to make a concrete representation of the problem. | |
| **MP7** | **Look for and makes use of structure.** |
| **Item 16:** Students may apply the pattern they discovered in item 14 to help them give the coordinates of a vertical segment. | |
| **MP8** | **Look for and express regularity in repeated reasoning.** |
| **Item 14:** Students identify and describe patterns in the coordinates of the endpoints of horizontal and vertical segments. | |

## OBJECTIVE

**Use a coordinate plane to represent real-world and mathematical problems.**

## ESSENTIAL QUESTION

Have students look at the picture of the coordinate plane on page 312. Read the Essential Question and discuss how the coordinate plane might be used to determine the route from one location to another.

## FLUENCY PRACTICE

Fluency practice is available at **sadlierconnect.com**.

## Concept Development

### Understand: Locating points on a coordinate plane

■ The student page provides answer blanks for students to record the ordered pairs for the locations on the graph. Give students an opportunity find and record the ordered pairs before you discuss them as a class.

■ Be sure students understand that when they are graphing points or naming ordered pairs, they should begin at the origin. However, when they are describing a path from one point to another point, they begin at the starting point.

■ In this problem, students will also describe movement on the coordinate plane going left and down in addition to moving right and up. Have students describe another path from the School to the Deli. Students should see that they can go 3 blocks up and then 1 block left.

---

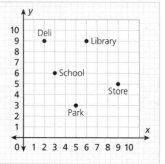

# Graph Points to Represent Problem Situations

**Essential Question:**
How do you use a coordinate plane to represent real-world and mathematical problems?

**Words to Know:**
scale

## Guided Instruction

In this lesson you will learn how to use a coordinate plane to represent real-world and mathematical problems.

**Understand:** Locating points on a coordinate plane

Ms. Linton's class uses a coordinate plane to make a map of the area near their school. Each unit on the map, or grid, represents 1 block.

Which ordered pair represents the location of each place included on the map? Describe a possible route from the School to the Deli and from the School to the Park.

To locate the ordered pair for the Deli, start at the origin, (0, 0). Move along the *x*-axis 2 units. Then move up the vertical line parallel to the *y*-axis until you reach the point that represents the Deli at (2, 9).

Repeat the process to find the ordered pairs for all the other locations.

**School:** (3, 6)　**Park:** (5, 3)　**Library:** (6, 9)　**Store:** (9, 5)

To find a possible route from one point to another, try to find a route by moving horizontally right or left first and then vertically up or down.

To go from the School to the Deli, start at the School. You can go 1 block left and 3 blocks up. To go from the School to the Park, you can go 2 blocks right and 3 blocks down.

➡ The ordered pairs for the locations are: Deli (2, 9), School (3, 6), Park (5, 3), Library (6, 9), and Store (9, 5). A possible route from the School to the Deli is 1 block left and 3 blocks up. A possible route from the School to the Park is 2 blocks right and 3 blocks down.

---

### Words to Know

**scale:** the intervals on each axis on a coordinate plane

**Example:** the *x*-axis shows a scale of 1, and the *y*-axis shows a scale of 5.

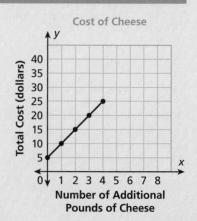

Cost of Cheese

**Glossary can be found on pp. 347–350.**

## Guided Instruction

**Understand:** Drawing a line graph to represent a real-life situation

> Andy buys a pound of cheese for $5. He needs to buy more of the same kind of cheese. What will be the total cost of all of the cheese if Andy buys two more pounds? Four more pounds? Draw a line segment on a coordinate plane to show the relationship between the number of additional pounds of cheese Andy buys and the total cost of the cheese in dollars.

To find the total cost of the cheese, make a table. In the table (0, 5) represents the original pound of cheese Andy bought for $5. Use the rule + 1 for each additional pound of cheese he buys, and + 5 for the corresponding total cost in dollars.

| Cost of Cheese | | | | | |
| --- | --- | --- | --- | --- | --- |
| Additional Pounds of Cheese | 0 | 1 | 2 | 3 | 4 |
| Total Cost (dollars) | 5 | 10 | 15 | 20 | 25 |

Next, use the table and a coordinate plane to draw a line segment that represents the relationship between the number of additional pounds of cheese and the total cost in dollars for all of the cheese. Include a title above the grid: "Cost of Cheese."

Label the horizontal axis "Number of Additional Pounds of Cheese." Label the vertical axis "Total Cost (dollars)." Since the cheese costs $5 per pound, use a scale of 5 to label the units of the vertical axis.

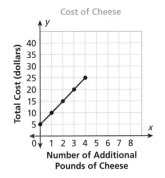

Cost of Cheese

Plot the points for the ordered pairs in the table: (0, 5), (1, 10), (2, 15), (3, 20), and (4, 25).Then draw a line segment to connect the points on the graph.

➡ The graph shows the relationship between the number of additional pounds of cheese Andy buys and the total cost in dollars for all of the cheese. He will spend a total of $15 if he buys two more pounds and a total of $25 if he buys four more pounds.

✏ How can you use the graph to find the amount Andy will spend if he buys five more pounds of cheese? Seven more pounds of cheese? Possible answer: Extend the line segment to include points with x-coordinates 5 and 7. The ordered pairs are (5, 30) and (7, 40). So, Andy will spend $30 if he buys five more pounds and $40 if he buys seven more pounds.

## Support English Language Learners

Write *coordinate* on the board. Say the term and have students repeat after you. Explain that coordinates are used to read maps and identify the position of objects in the world. GPS devices use coordinates. In geometry a coordinate is a number used to describe the position of a point. Two coordinates work together to tell the exact location of a point on a grid.

Write *plane* on the board. Say the term and have students repeat after you. Have students discuss different meanings of the term. Explain that one definition of *plane* is a flat surface. Point out examples of planes in the classroom, such as the floor or the board. Summarize by showing a coordinate plane pointing out the coordinates on the axes.

**Understand:** Drawing a line graph to represent a real-life situation

■ Explain to students how to write ordered pairs from the table. Point out that the values in the first row are the *x*-coordinates, and the values in the second row are the *y*-coordinates. Show students that by placing the number of additional pounds of cheese on the *x*-axis, they can easily see how the total cost increases as the amount purchased increases. Note that the row headings in the table are the same as the labels on the axes.

■ Students may argue that the point (1, 5) should represent the 1 pound of cheese Andy bought for $5. Point out that the table represents *additional* pounds of cheese purchased after the first pound and the total cost of all the cheese.

■ Discuss the scale on the graph. Tell students that they must look at the data given and apply logic when scaling both axes to make sure all data points can be represented on the graph. Graphs can be difficult to read and interpret if they are not carefully made.

■ Point out the title of the graph and the labels on the *x*- and the *y*-axes. Tell students that they should include these features on any data graph they make.

✏ After students answer the question, discuss what the coordinates mean in the context of the problem. The ordered pair (5, 30) represents purchasing 5 additional pounds of cheese for a total cost of $30.

# Guided Instruction

**Connect:** **What do you know about real-life situations represented on a coordinate plane** Use this page to help students strengthen their understanding of how to read a line graph to answer real-life questions.

■ Remind students to pay close attention to the labels on the *x*- and *y*-axes to be sure they are reading the graph and interpreting the ordered pairs correctly. Since age is represented on the *x*-axis and weight is represented on the *y*-axis, the ordered pairs are written as (age, weight). So, the ordered pair (8, 20) tells you that when Nelson was 8 years old, he weighed 20 pounds.

■ Have students identify the scale on each axis. Ask students how they would graph a point with an *x*-coordinate of 3 or a *y*-coordinate of 10. Students should understand that the axes represent continuous number lines and there are numerical values between the numbered lines on the grid.

✏ Have students explain how the graph shows the ages when Nelson's weight was increasing and the ages where it was decreasing. Extend the question by asking students to use the graph to predict Nelson's weight at age 14. Students should support their predictions.

---

## Guided Instruction

**Connect:** **What you know about real-life situations represented on a coordinate plane**

Leia makes a line graph on a coordinate plane to show the weight of her dog Nelson over his lifetime. How much did Nelson weigh when Leia first brought him home? How much did he weigh when he was 4 years old? What was Nelson's greatest weight and how old was he?

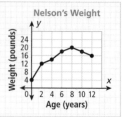

**Nelson's Weight**

**Step 1**

The ordered pair for the first point is (0, 4) and it represents Nelson's weight when Leia first brought him home. How much did Nelson weigh?

___4___ pounds

**Step 2**

To find Nelson's weight when he was 4 years old, find 4 on the *x*-axis, or the horizontal axis. Move up the vertical line parallel to the *y*-axis until you reach the point that lies on the graph. The point is exactly between 12 and 16 on the *y*-axis. The ordered pair for the point is ___(4, 14)___.

How much did Nelson weigh when he was 4 years old? ___14___ pounds

**Step 3**

To find Nelson's greatest weight, look for the highest point on the graph.

The ordered pair for the highest point is ___(8, 20)___.

What was Nelson's greatest weight? ___20___ pounds

How old was he? ___8___ years old

➡ Nelson weighed ___4___ pounds when Leia first brought him home.

He weighed ___14___ pounds when he was 4 years old. His greatest weight

was ___20___ pounds at ___8___ years old.

✏ Describe how Nelson's weight changed over his lifetime. Possible answer: Nelson gained weight until he was 8 years old. Then he lost weight until he was

**314** Unit 5 ■ Focus on Geometry          12 years old.

---

## Math-to-Math Connection

**Graphing and Algebra** Coordinate planes are often used to plot and evaluate data based on algebraic expressions. For example, a baker's dozen is thirteen items. For example, a linear equation, $13 \cdot x = y$, can be used to find the total number of items, *(y)*, in any number of baker's dozens, *(x)*. Model how to set up and complete a table of values, using a linear equation. Have students choose values for *x* and solve the equation to find the corresponding *y*-value to identify the *(x, y)* coordinates of points. Have students draw a coordinate plane, including a title, scales, and labels on both axes. Guide students as they graph the points, then use the data and graph to discuss any patterns or trends.

**For exercises 1–6, use the coordinate plane. The coordinate plane shows the location of some landmarks in Cynthia's town.**

1. Which ordered pair represents the location of the Park? __(2, 1)__

2. Which ordered pair represents the location of the Museum? __(3, 6)__

3. Which ordered pair represents the location of the Lake? __(6, 4)__

4. Which ordered pair represents the location of the Trail? __(7, 7)__

5. Describe a possible path from the Museum to the Lake.

   Possible answer: From the Museum, go 3 units right and 2 units down.

6. Describe a possible path from the Park to the Trail.

   Possible answer: From the Park, go 5 units right and 6 units up.

**Solve the problem.**

7. Rajeev has $12 saved for a vacation. He adds $4 to his savings each week. How much money will he have after 5 weeks? Use the coordinate plane to make a line segment that shows the relationship between the numbers of weeks he adds $4 and the amount of money Rajeev has saved.

   **Answer** After 5 weeks, Rajeev will have saved $32.

**Rajeev's Savings**

Check students' graphs.

**Think•Pair•Share**

MP7  8. Look back at the graph of the line segment you made to show Rajeev's savings. How is the graph useful in analyzing the data?
Possible answer: It provides a visual representation of Rajeev's savings. It shows the amount Rajeev started with and how his savings are increasing over time.

Unit 5 ■ Focus on Geometry  **315**

## Mathematical Practices

Mathematical Practice Standards underline the teaching and understanding of all concepts and skills presented. The emphasis of specific practices is noted throughout the guided and independent practice of this lesson.

**MP7  Look for and make use of structure.**

**Item 8:** Students identify a pattern in a graph of a real-world relationship and discuss what the pattern reveals about the situation.

## Observational Assessment

Use page 315 to assess whether students are able to interpret information presented on a coordinate plane and to use a coordinate plane to represent information. Be sure that students do not write the *y*-coordinate first. It may be helpful to remind students to always start along the *x*-axis first.

## Think•Pair•Share

**Peer Collaboration**  Ask students to write individual answers, and then share their responses with a partner. Facilitate student discussion by asking questions such as:

- *How does the graph represent the information given in the problem?*

- *How can you use the graph to make a prediction?*

- *What questions could you answer by using the graph?*

## Return to the Essential Question

Reread the Lesson 35 Essential Question on page 312: *How can you use a coordinate plane to represent real-world and mathematical problems?*

Ask volunteers to use what they learned in this lesson to answer this question. (Possible response: I can make a table of related values and then graph the related values as ordered pairs. I can use the points and patterns in the graph to answer questions and make predictions about the situation.)

Record student responses to these questions along with any items not noted to create a student checklist. This may be used for students to set goals in the areas where they are still struggling, or it may also be used as a checklist for students in preparation for an assessment of this skill.

## Concept Application

Students may work independently on these pages in the classroom or at home. They may refer to the first four pages of the lesson to revisit the instruction or to see a worked-out example.

**Common Errors** and **Teaching Tips** may help you support student learning either in the classroom or as a follow-up for work done at home.

## Common Errors

### Item 1

As students are recording answers, be sure that they are not reversing the coordinates. It may be helpful to remind them that in all of these items, they must record the movement along the *x*-axis or horizontal move first. Making the repeated verbal connection between horizontal and *x*-axis is important in this lesson.

## Teaching Tips

### Item 6

You may need to remind students that *vertices* are the "corners" of a figure.

---

**Lesson 35  Graph Points to Represent Problem Situations**

### Independent Practice

**For exercises 1–5, use the coordinate plane. The coordinate plane shows where Trisha and her friends live. Each unit on the coordinate plane represents 1 block.**

1. Write the ordered pair that identifies where each friend lives.

   Tricia ___(1, 6)___

   Ugo ___(2, 3)___

   Asia ___(5, 2)___

   Kyle ___(5, 5)___

   Ross ___(6, 4)___

   Barbara ___(7, 6)___

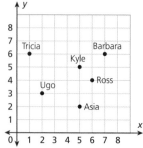

2. Describe a possible path from Tricia's home to Barbara's home.

   Possible answer: From Tricia's home, go 6 blocks right.

3. Describe a possible path from Kyle's home to Asia's home.

   Possible answer: From Kyle's home, go 3 blocks down.

4. Describe a possible path from Barbara's home to Ugo's home.

   Possible answer: From Barbara's home, go 5 blocks left and 3 blocks down.

5. Describe a possible path from Ugo's home to Kyle's home.

   Possible answer: From Ugo's home, go 3 blocks right and 2 blocks up.

6. Three of the vertices of rectangle *JKLM* are shown below.
   point *J*: (2, 3)
   point *K*: (2, 7)
   point *L*: (7, 7)

   What is the ordered pair for the missing vertex, point *M*?

   ___(7, 3)___

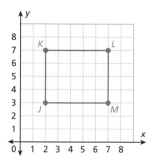

---

## Writing About Math

· **Write an Informative Text** Ask students to write a paragraph explaining how to create and use a coordinate plane to solve real-world problems. Students should begin with how to choose the scale, graph the ordered pairs, and how to read the graph. Provide students with data to use in explaining this process. Remind students to use proper vocabulary and all necessary details. Have students include a title and ask them to underline vocabulary words.

7. Three of the vertices of square *QRST* are shown below.
   point *R*: (7, 6)
   point *S:* (7, 3)
   point *T*: (4, 3)
   What is the ordered pair for the missing vertex, point *Q*?

   _____(4, 6)_____

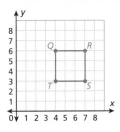

8. Three of the vertices of parallelogram *ABCD* are shown below.
   point *A*: (2, 7)
   point *C*: (5, 3)
   point *D*: (2, 2)
   What is the ordered pair for the missing vertex, point *B*?

   _____(5, 8)_____

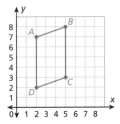

**For exercises 9–12, use the graph. The graph shows the relationship between the number of hours Hannah works and the amount she earns.**

9. How much money does Hannah earn after working for 2 hours?_____$20_____

10. How much money does Hannah earn after working for 6 hours? _____$60_____

11. How much money does Hannah earn after working for 5 hours? _____$50_____

12. How much money does Hannah earn for each hour she works? _____$10_____

13. How much money will Hannah earn after working 10 hours? _____$100_____

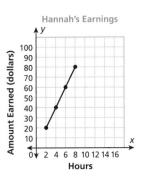

Hannah's Earnings

## Teaching Tips

### Item 8
Students may need a quick review of the properties of a parallelogram in order to complete the question.

### Item 11
The point needed to solve this problem, (5, 50), is not one of the "plotted points" on the graph. Remind students that connecting plotted points allows us to find values between the points. Suggest that students locate 5 on the *x*-axis and move straight up until they meet the segment. Students can mark a "point" at this location. The coordinates of the point are (5, 50), which indicates that Hannah earns $50 for working 5 hours.

### Item 12
Students can solve this problem by extending the line "backward" and finding the point on the line with *x*-coordinate 1. Or, they can reason that if Hannah earns $20 in 2 hours, then she must earn $20 ÷ 2, or $10 in 1 hour.

### Item 13
There is no point on the graph with an *x*-coordinate of 10. Point out that the plotted points follow an obvious pattern. Suggest that students extend this pattern to find the amount Hannah will earn after working 10 hours.

## Digital Connection

**Internet and Interactive Whiteboard** Use the Internet to gather several line graphs to display on the Interactive Whiteboard. Display two graphs at a time, labeling them *A* and *B*. Have half of the students create a question using graph *A* and the other half create a question using graph *B*. Repeat this process with additional graphs. After students have completed their questions, have students from group *A* switch papers with students from group *B*. Display the pairs of graphs again, allowing students time to answer each question using the corresponding line graph. If time allows, have students switch back to check each other's work for accuracy.

# Independent Practice

## Common Errors

### Item 15

Students may graph the coordinates incorrectly causing an error in determining the final vertex. Having students check the graph of the first three vertices may be helpful before continuing to solve the problem.

## Teaching Tips

### Item 14

Some students may struggle with choosing the appropriate scale for the temperature. Suggest that students consider the greatest value they need to display on each axis. What will each interval have to represent in order to fit all the values? Suggest that students count first to determine if their axes will include the necessary data values before labeling the scale.

### Item 15

Some students may be able to solve this problem without graphing. However, if students are having difficulty, encourage them to plot the points on a grid.

### Independent Practice

**Solve the problems.**

MP3  **14.** The table shows the temperature of a liquid as it cools. Draw a line segment on the coordinate plane below to show the relationship between the temperature and the number of minutes the liquid cools.

| Liquid Temperature Change | | | | | |
|---|---|---|---|---|---|
| Time (minutes) | 0 | 2 | 4 | 6 | 8 |
| Temperature (degrees Celsius) | 32 | 28 | 24 | 20 | 16 |

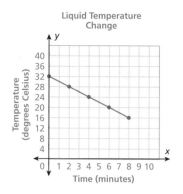

Liquid Temperature Change

Use your graph to find the temperature of the liquid after

5 minutes. __22 degrees Celsius__

What information about the temperature change does the graph show?

Possible answer: The graph shows that the temperature falls from 32 degrees Celsius to 16 degrees Celsius over 8 minutes.

**Answer** The temperatures falls 4 degrees Celsius every 2 minutes.

MP5  **15.** Sammy graphs a rectangle on a coordinate plane. Three vertices of the rectangle are at (2, 2), (2, 7), and (6, 2). What is the ordered pair for the remaining vertex of the rectangle? How do you know?

(6, 7); Possible answer: I graphed the points and then drew a

**Answer** rectangle using the points. The missing vertex was at (6, 7).

**318**   Unit 5 ■ Focus on Geometry

## Mathematical Practices

| MP3 | **Construct viable arguments and critique the reasoning of others.** |
|---|---|

**Item 14:** Students examine and interpret the graph to make a statement about the trend of the data displayed.

| MP5 | **Use appropriate tools strategically.** |
|---|---|

**Item 15:** Students determine the third vertex of a rectangle by plotting the other three vertices on a coordinate plane.

## Independent Practice

MP6 **16.** Draw a square with an area of 25 square units on the coordinate plane. Label the vertices of the square A, B, C, and D. Then, starting with vertex A, describe how to travel from one vertex to the next on the coordinate plane. Check students' squares.

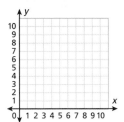

**Answer** Answers will vary.

▸ **Justify your answer using words, drawings, or numbers.**
Justifications will vary.

MP2 **17.** Today Claire cycles 5 miles to meet her friends. Then they go for a long bike ride together. The group of riders cycle 15 miles each hour for 6 hours. What is the total distance Claire cycles today after 3 hours of cycling with her friends? After 5 hours of cycling with her friends? Draw a line segment on the coordinate plane below to show the relationship between the number of hours Claire rides with her friends and her total cycling distance in miles. What does the graph show about the relationship?

**Answer** After 3 hours with her friends, Claire has cycled 50 miles. After 5 hours, she has cycled 80 miles.

Claire's Ride

▸ **Justify your answer using words, drawings, or numbers.**
Possible justification: The graph shows that Claire has cycled 50 miles after 3 hours with her friends and 80 miles after 5 hours. It shows that her distance increases steadily the more hours she rides.

Unit 5 ■ Focus on Geometry    **319**

## Common Errors

### Item 16

Students may confuse 25 square units with having a side length of 25 units. Reminding students that the area is equal to 25 square units and not the side length may help them avoid this common mistake.

### Item 17

Students may think the distance value for 1 hour should be 15 miles. Explain that the graph should show the total distance Claire cycled, including the 5 miles she rode *before* meeting her friend. After 1 hour, she cycled 20 miles, not 15, so the graph should include the point (1, 20).

## Teaching Tips

### Item 17

Suggest that students make a table of related time and distance values before making the graph. Tell them that the x-column (time) of the table should show hours *after* Claire starts cycling with her friends. The y-column (distance) should show the total miles she cycled, *including* the initial 5 miles. So, the first pair of values in the table should be (0, 5).

| Mathematical Practices | |
|---|---|
| **MP2** | **Reason abstractly and quantitatively.** |

**Item 17:** Students analyze a situation to determine how to make a proper line graph and utilize it to solve a problem.

| **MP6** | **Attend to precision.** |
|---|---|

**Item 16:** Students use a drawing on a coordinate plane to accurately describe movements between vertices.

## OBJECTIVE
**Classify two-dimensional figures by analyzing their properties.**

## ESSENTIAL QUESTION
Students will learn to analyze the properties of two-dimensional figures and use those properties to classify figures.

## PREREQUISITE SKILLS
Use Item L on page 342 of the Foundational Skills Handbook to review using angle measurement to classify two-dimensional figures.

## FLUENCY PRACTICE
Fluency practice is available at **sadlierconnect.com**.

## Concept Development

### Understand: Using properties to classify triangles

■ Explain to students that any triangle can be classified by both its side lengths and its angle measures.

■ Point out that an equilateral triangle is also isosceles.

■ A right triangle always has one right angle and two acute angles, and an obtuse triangle always has one obtuse angle and two acute angles.

■ The angles of an equilateral triangle are all acute. Point out that in an equilateral triangle, all sides are the same length and all angles have the same measures. Because its angles have the same measure, an equilateral triangle can also be called an equiangular triangle.

---

**Essential Question:**
How do you use properties to classify two-dimensional figures?

**Words to Know:**
scalene triangle
isosceles triangle
equilateral triangle
acute triangle
right triangle
obtuse triangle
trapezoid
kite
adjacent sides
hierarchy diagram

### Guided Instruction

In this lesson you will learn how to use properties to classify two-dimensional figures.

**Understand:** Using properties to classify triangles

> Renzo draws a triangle with two sides that are the same length. The triangle has one obtuse angle. How can Renzo classify the triangle?

A triangle can be classified by the lengths of its sides.

| A triangle with no sides that are the same length is a scalene triangle. | A triangle with at least two sides that are the same length is an isosceles triangle. | A triangle with three sides that are the same length is an equilateral triangle. |
|---|---|---|
|  |  |  |

A triangle can also be classified by the measures of its angles.

| A triangle with three acute angles is an acute triangle. | A triangle with a right angle is a right triangle. | A triangle with an obtuse angle is an obtuse triangle. |
|---|---|---|
|  |  | |

Renzo's triangle is an isosceles triangle because two sides are the same length.

Renzo's triangle is an obtuse triangle because it has one obtuse angle.

➡ Renzo's triangle is an isosceles obtuse triangle.

---

## Words to Know

**scalene triangle:** a triangle with no sides that are the same length

**isosceles triangle:** a triangle with at least two sides that are the same length

**equilateral triangle:** a triangle with three sides that are the same length

**acute triangle:** a triangle with three acute angles

**right triangle:** a triangle with a right angle

**Glossary can be found on pp. 347–350.**

Guided Instruction

**Understand:** Using properties to classify quadrilaterals

> Natalie wants to cut out a parallelogram to use in her collage.
> What types of quadrilaterals can Natalie use?

Examine the properties of these quadrilaterals below
to decide which are parallelograms.

**Remember!**
A quadrilateral is a polygon with
4 sides and 4 angles.

### Special Quadrilaterals

A trapezoid has
• at least 1 pair of
  parallel sides

A kite has
• 2 pairs of adjacent
  sides that are the same
  length

A parallelogram has
• 2 pairs of parallel sides
• 2 pairs of opposite sides
  that are the same length

A rectangle has
• 2 pairs of parallel sides
• 2 pairs of opposite
  sides that are the same
  length
• 4 right angles

A rhombus has
• 2 pairs of parallel sides
• 4 sides that are the
  same length

A square has
• 2 pairs of parallel sides
• 4 sides that are the
  same length
• 4 right angles

Look at the properties given for a parallelogram. Which other special
quadrilaterals above also have those properties?

____rectangle____ , ____rhombus____ , and ____square____

➤ Natalie can use a parallelogram, a rectangle, a rhombus, or a square.

✏ What if Natalie wants a parallelogram with no right angles?
What types of quadrilaterals are parallelograms that Natalie can use?
Natalie can use a parallelogram or a rhombus.

Unit 5 ■ Focus on Geometry   **321**

---

## Understand: Using properties to classify quadrilaterals

■ Help students understand that some quadrilaterals have more than one classification. For example, a *rectangle* is also a *parallelogram.*

■ Point out that squares and rhombi are also kites. Because all the sides of a square have the same length, two pairs of adjacent sides are the same length. The same is true for a rhombus.

■ Point out that kites and parallelograms both have two pairs of congruent sides. However, in a kite, the congruent pairs are adjacent, or next to each other, while in a parallelogram, they are opposite, or across from each other.

■ In this text the inclusive definition of trapezoid is used. According to the inclusive definition, a trapezoid has *at least* one pair of parallel sides. Using this definition, a parallelogram is a special case of a trapezoid. The exclusive definition of trapezoid considers a trapezoid to have *exactly* one pair of parallel sides, and so excludes parallelograms. You might use the term "strict trapezoid" to distinguish a trapezoid with only one pair of parallel sides from a parallelogram.

✏ After students have answered this question, ask a few volunteers to describe how they approached the problem. Discuss which classifications are the most specific. Have students explain why they chose the quadrilaterals they did.

---

## Words to Know

**obtuse triangle:** a triangle with an obtuse angle

**trapezoid:** a quadrilateral that has at least one pair of parallel sides

**kite:** a quadrilateral that has two pairs of adjacent sides that are the same length

**adjacent sides:** sides of a polygon that are next to each other

**hierarchy diagram:** a diagram that uses the property of figures to relate them from the most general category to the most specific category

**Glossary can be found on pp. 347–350.**

# Guided Instruction

**Connect:** **What you know about properties of two-dimensional figures** Use this page to help students strengthen their understanding of the properties of two-dimensional figures and how they are classified.

■ Help students connect the concept of hierarchy to a real-world application. For example, all poodles are dogs, but all dogs are not necessarily poodles. In a hierarchy diagram, poodles would be under dogs.

■ Discuss and clarify the placement of rhombi and rectangles in the hierarchy diagram. Both have two pairs of parallel sides, so they are parallelograms. So, both should be placed under parallelograms in the diagram. Because all rectangles are not rhombi and all rhombi are not rectangles, they are on the same level of the hierarchy and are connected to parallelograms by separate segments.

■ Squares are rectangles because they have four right angles, and squares are rhombi because they have four sides of equal length. So, in the diagram, squares is under and connected to both rectangles and rhombi.

## Guided Instruction

**Connect:** **What you know about properties of two-dimensional figures**

> Make a hierarchy diagram using these two-dimensional figures: quadrilaterals, trapezoids, parallelograms, rectangles, rhombi, and squares.

A hierarchy diagram uses the properties of figures to relate them from the most general category to the most specific category.

**Step 1**

Start by choosing the most general category.

Which name in the list can be applied to all of the figures? ___quadrilaterals___

**Step 2**

Decide how the other quadrilaterals are related.

Is a trapezoid a parallelogram? __No.__ Is a parallelogram a trapezoid? __Yes.__ Each of these will be on a separate line in the diagram. Trapezoid will be above parallelogram.

Rectangles, rhombi, and squares are parallelograms.

Is a rectangle a square? __No.__ Is a square a rectangle? __Yes.__
Is a rhombus a square? __No.__ Is a square a rhombus? __Yes.__

**Step 3**

Use your answers to complete the hierarchy diagram.

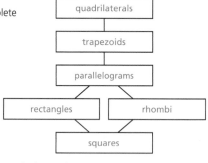

➡ A possible hierarchy diagram is shown above.

**322**  Unit 5 ■ Focus on Geometry

## Support English Language Learners

This lesson introduces a number of specialized terms for polygons. One focus in this lesson is triangles. Show and say several examples of objects that have the *tri-* prefix in their names: tricycle, triathlon, tripod, and tri-corner hat. Ask students what these objects have in common. Explain that *tri-* means three. Triangles have three angles.

The other figures in this lesson are quadrilaterals. Show and say the name of several shapes that are and are not quadrilaterals: A square (kite, rectangle, trapezoid) is a quadrilateral. A triangle (circle, hexagon, octagon) is not a quadrilateral. Ask students what characteristic each of the quadrilaterals has that the other shapes do not. Explain that *quad-* means four. Quadrilaterals have four sides.

**For exercises 1–6, write the most specific classification of the two-dimensional figure.**

1. A polygon with three sides has an angle that measures 135°. The sides of the polygon are different lengths. <u>obtuse scalene triangle</u>

2. A polygon with four sides has one pair of adjacent sides, each of which measure 8 inches. It has a second pair of adjacent sides, each of which measure 15 inches. None of the sides are parallel. <u>kite</u>

3. A polygon with five sides has three sides that are the same length. <u>pentagon</u>

4. A polygon with four sides has one pair of parallel sides that are 6 inches long. It has a second pair of parallel sides that are 9 inches long. <u>parallelogram</u>

5. A polygon with four sides has four right angles. All the sides of the polygon are the same length. <u>square</u>

6. A polygon with four sides has one right angle. None of the sides of the polygon are the same length. No pairs of sides are parallel. <u>quadrilateral</u>

**Solve the problem.**

MP7   7. Colter earned a polygonal community service badge. The badge has three sides that are each the same length. Each angle in the triangle measures 60 degrees. What is the shape of Colter's badge?

    **Answer** <u>Colter's badge is an equilateral triangle. All angles are acute.</u>

**Think•Pair•Share**

MP5   8. Olivia has a puzzle piece that is shaped like a quadrilateral. The puzzle piece has two right angles and one pair of parallel sides. What type of quadrilateral is the puzzle piece? Draw a diagram to support your answer. The puzzle piece is a trapezoid. Drawings will vary.

Unit 5 ■ Focus on Geometry   **323**

## Mathematical Practices

Mathematical Practice Standards underline the teaching and understanding of all concepts and skills presented. The emphasis of specific practices is noted throughout the guided and independent practice of this lesson.

| **MP5** | **Use appropriate tools strategically.** |
| --- | --- |

**Item 8:** Students may use paper and pencil to sketch a figure that fits a given description in order to classify the figure.

| **MP7** | **Look for and make use of structure.** |
| --- | --- |

**Item 7:** Students sort through given information to classify a triangle.

## Observational Assessment

Use page 323 to assess whether students are able to use properties to classify two-dimensional figures. Have students refer to the properties on the first two pages of the lesson if they need help.

## Think•Pair•Share

**Peer Collaboration** Asks students to complete the item individually. Then pair students to compare solutions. Ask each pair to share their strategy for arriving at that solution.

- *What information did you know about the quadrilateral? How did this information help you determine your answer?*

- *Did each of you use a similar approach when you were working individually?*

- *When you were working individually, did you arrive at the same conclusion? If not, how did you agree on an answer as a pair?*

To summarize, point out that students may approach the solution in different ways, but there is only one type of quadrilateral that meets the criteria given in the problem statement.

### Return to the Essential Question

Reread the Lesson 36 Essential Question on page 320: *How do you use properties to classify two-dimensional figures?*

Ask volunteers to use what they learned in this lesson to answer this question. (Possible response: I can classify a triangle as scalene, isosceles, or equilateral based on the number of equal-length sides it has. I can also classify a triangle as acute, obtuse, or right according to the size of its angles. I can classify a quadrilateral by considering how many parallel and equal-length sides it has and whether it has right angles. Some quadrilaterals go in more than one category.)

# Independent Practice

## Concept Application

Students may work independently on these pages in the classroom or at home. They may refer to the first four pages of the lesson to revisit the instruction or to see a worked-out example.

**Common Errors** and **Teaching Tips** may help you support student learning either in the classroom or as a follow-up for work done at home.

## Teaching Tips

### Items 1 and 6

You may need to remind students what pentagons and hexagons are. These figures were studied in Grade 4.

### Item 9

Students may need to be reminded that, if a figure has an edge that is not straight, it is not a polygon. You might also need to remind students of the meaning of *line of symmetry*.

### Independent Practice

**For exercises 1–5, write the most specific classification of the two-dimensional figure.**

1. A polygon with six sides has two sides that are the same length. ___hexagon___

2. A triangle has one right angle. Two of the sides of the triangle are the same length. ___isosceles right triangle___

3. A quadrilateral has exactly one pair of parallel sides. ___trapezoid___

4. A polygon with four sides that are the same length. ___rhombus___

5. A polygon with four sides and four right angles. ___rectangle___

**For exercises 6–11, write all of the possible classifications of the two-dimensional figure.**

6. A two-dimensional figure has five sides and five angles.
   polygon, pentagon

7. A two-dimensional figure has four sides that are the same length and two lines of symmetry.
   polygon, quadrilateral, trapezoid, parallelogram, rhombus

8. A two-dimensional figure has two pairs of opposite sides that are parallel and the same length.
   polygon, quadrilateral, trapezoid, parallelogram

9. A two-dimensional figure that has no straight sides and an infinite number of lines of symmetry. Each point on this figure is the same distance from its center.
   circle

10. A two-dimensional figure that has three sides and three acute angles.
    polygon, triangle, acute triangle

11. A two-dimensional 4-sided figure that has two pairs of adjacent sides that are the same length.
    polygon, quadrilateral, kite

## Math-to-Architecture Connection

**Geometric Shapes** Builders, designers, and landscapers often incorporate geometric figures in their designs. These shapes provide balance and order to building exteriors, windows, floor tiles, gardens, and walkways. Have students search the Web for images of geometric shapes in man-made structures. If possible, have students print the images and use a marker to outline and name each shape they found. As time permits, have students share and compare their results with the class.

Lesson 36

## Independent Practice

**Decide whether each statement is true or false. Draw an example or a counterexample to support your answer.**

12. A triangle with at least two sides that are the same length has at least one line of symmetry.

    _____true_____

    Sample drawing:

13. A quadrilateral with two right angles must be a rectangle.

    _____false_____

    Sample drawing:

14. A pentagon always has at least one line of symmetry.

    _____false_____

    Sample drawing:

15. A quadrilateral with two pairs of opposite sides that are the same length is a parallelogram.

    _____true_____

    Sample drawing:

16. A parallelogram may have no lines of symmetry so a rhombus has no lines of symmetry.

    _____false_____

    Sample drawing:

17. A hexagon with sides that are the same length has six lines of symmetry.

    _____true_____

    Sample drawing:

Unit 5 ■ Focus on Geometry   **325**

## Teaching Tips

### Items 12-17

Remind students that a counterexample is an example that shows that a statement is false. Only one counterexample is needed to prove a statement is false. However, drawing an example of a figure that supports a statement does not prove that the statement is always true.

### Item 17

A hexagon with sides that are all the same length is regular, so all the angles are also equal.

## Writing About Math

▶ **Write an Informative Text** Ask students to write about the types of quadrilaterals discussed in this lesson. Have students start from the least specific quadrilaterals to the most specific quadrilaterals, and write a paragraph describing the possible relationships between different quadrilaterals.

# Independent Practice

## Common Errors

### Item 21

Some students may answer *never*. Students may need to be reminded that a rectangle is a kite when it is a square, because squares are also rectangles.

## Teaching Tips

### Items 18-24

Encourage students to make sketches to help them reason through these items.

### Item 26

Point out to students that there are three distinct ways of classifying a triangle by its angles and more than one angle classification will never apply.

---

**Lesson 36  Analyze Properties to Classify Two-Dimensional Figures**

## Independent Practice

**For exercises 18–24, write *sometimes*, *always*, or *never*.**

18. A quadrilateral is a polygon. ___always___

19. A triangle has at least two acute angles. ___always___

20. A triangle has exactly one line of symmetry. ___sometimes___

21. A rectangle is a kite. ___sometimes___

22. A rhombus has four right angles. ___sometimes___

23. A polygon with six sides is a pentagon. ___never___

24. A trapezoid is a square. ___sometimes___

**Solve the problems.**

MP6 25. The window in Keisha's room is a quadrilateral with four right angles and four lines of symmetry. Is this enough information to determine the shape of the window in Keisha's room? Explain.

**Answer** Yes, this is enough information to determine the shape of the window. Possible explanation: Since the quadrilateral has four right angles, it must be a rectangle. Since the rectangle has four lines of symmetry, it must be a square.

MP3 26. LeVar says that a right triangle can be acute, scalene, or isosceles. Is he correct? Explain.

**Answer** No, LeVar is not correct. Possible explanation: A right triangle can be scalene or isosceles but it cannot be acute since an acute triangle has three acute angles. A right angle is not an acute angle.

---

| **Mathematical Practices** | | |
|---|---|---|
| MP3 | **Construct viable arguments and critique the reasoning of others.** | |
| **Item 26:** Students use definitions of different types of triangles to construct arguments and support their conclusions. | | |
| MP6 | **Attend to precision.** | |
| **Item 25:** Students use clear, precise language to explain their reasoning. | | |

Lesson 36

Independent Practice

MP8 **27.** What three and four sided polygons have all sides equal in length, and all angles equal in measure?

**Answer** The three-sided polygon is an (acute) equilateral triangle, and the four-sided polygon is a square.

▸ **Justify your answer using words, drawings, or numbers.**

Answers may vary. Possible justification: Students may draw diagrams or they may explain that an equilateral triangle has three acute angles that have the same measure and three sides that are the same length. A square has four right angles and four sides that are the same length.

MP3 **28.** What are the similarities among a parallelogram, a trapezoid, and a square? What are the differences?

Possible answer: All three are polygons with four sides and four angles. All three have at least one pair of parallel sides. Parallelograms and squares have two pairs of parallel sides and opposite sides that are the same length. The sides of a trapezoid may be the same length. A square has four right angles. A trapezoid

**Answer** and a parallelogram may have right angles.

▸ **Justify your answer using words, drawings, or numbers.**

Students should include diagrams of a trapezoid, parallelogram, and square to support their answers. Check student's drawings.

MP7 **29.** Make a hierarchy diagram for the following two-dimensional figures: quadrilaterals, triangles, parallelograms, polygons, rhombi, right triangles, and rectangles.

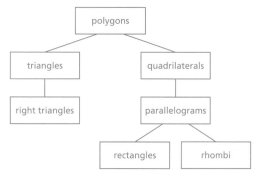

## Teaching Tips

### Item 27

Students may recognize that these must be regular polygons and may know that equilateral triangles and squares are regular.

### Item 28

It may help to review the *inclusive* and *strict* definitions for trapezoids prior to students completing this item.

## Return to the

Remind students to return to the Progress Check self-assessment, page 301, to check off additional items they have mastered during the unit.

## Mathematical Practices

| **MP3** | **Construct viable arguments and critique the reasoning of others.** |
|---|---|
| **Item 28:** Students use definitions to construct an argument and justify their conclusions. | |
| **MP7** | **Look for and makes use of structure.** |
| **Item 29:** Students use patterns and relationships among a given group of figures to create a hierarchy. | |
| **MP8** | **Look for and express regularity in repeated reasoning.** |
| **Item 27:** Students attend to details to find a solution. | |

The Unit 5 Review covers all the standards presented in the unit. Use it to assess your students' mastery of the unit's concepts and skills.

## Depth of Knowledge

The depth of knowledge is a ranking of the content complexity of assessment items based on Webb's Depth of Knowledge (DOK) levels. The levels increase in complexity as shown below.

**Level 1:** Recall and Reproduction
**Level 2:** Basic Skills and Concepts
**Level 3:** Strategic Reasoning and Thinking
**Level 4:** Extended Thinking

| Item | DOK |
|------|-----|
| 1 | 1 |
| 2 | 1 |
| 3 | 1 |
| 4 | 1 |
| 5 | 1 |
| 6 | 2 |
| 7 | 2 |
| 8 | 2 |
| 9 | 1 |
| 10 | 1 |
| 11 | 2 |
| 12 | 3 |
| 13 | 2 |
| 14 | 2 |
| 15 | 2 |
| 16 | 2 |
| 17 | 2 |
| 18 | 4 |
| 19 | 3 |
| 20 | 4 |

---

**For exercises 1–4, draw an example of the following.** Check students' drawings.

1. right isosceles triangle

   Students' triangles should have one right angle and two congruent sides.

2. rhombus

   Students' rhombi should have opposite sides parallel and four congruent sides.

3. hexagon

   Students' hexagons should have six sides.

4. obtuse scalene triangle

   Students' triangles should have one obtuse angle and each side a different length.

**For exercises 5–8, use the coordinate plane.**

5. Label the x-axis and y-axis.

6. Graph the following points on the coordinate plane.
   point A: (1, 4)    point B: (2, 7)
   point C: (5, 7)    point D: (5, 2)
   point E: (2, 2)

   Connect points A through E in order. Complete the figure by connecting point E to point A. What polygon did you make?

   ___pentagon___

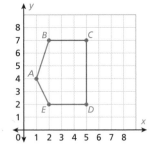

7. Which line segments are parallel? ___line segments BC and ED___

8. Which line segments are perpendicular? ___line segments: BC and CD, ED and CD___

**Circle the correct answer.**

9. Which is *not* an example of a parallelogram?

   a. rectangle

   b. rhombus

   c. trapezoid

   d. square

UNIT **5** Review

This chart correlates the Unit 5 Review items with the lessons in which the concepts and skills are presented.

**For exercises 10–12, use the map. Each unit on the map represents one block.**

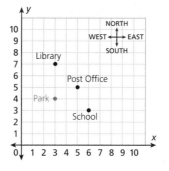

10. Which ordered pair represents the location of the Library?

    (3, 7)

11. The Park is located at (3, 4). Graph the location of the Park on the map.

12. Melanie wants to walk from School to the Post Office and then to the Library. Describe a possible path she can take.

    Paths will vary. Possible answer: The School is at (6, 3). Starting at that point, Melanie can walk 2 blocks north and 1 block west to go to the Post Office at (5, 5). Then she can walk 2 blocks west and 2 blocks north until she reaches the Library at (3, 7).

**For exercises 13–17, write *sometimes*, *always*, or *never*.**

13. A kite is a square. _sometimes_

14. A quadrilateral is a trapezoid. _sometimes_

15. A square is a rectangle. _always_

16. A triangle has two obtuse angles. _never_

17. A rhombus is a parallelogram. _always_

**Solve the problems.**

MP4 18. Owen has saved $15. He earns $9 for each hour he works. If Owen saves all of his money, how much will he have after working 2 hours? 4 hours? 10 hours? Make a graph to show the relationship between the hours Owen works and the amount of money he has saved.

    **Answer** After 2 hours of work, Owen will have $33. After 4 hours of work, he will have $51. After 10 hours of work, Owen will have $105.

Unit 5 ▪ Focus on Geometry **329**

| Item | Lesson |
| --- | --- |
| 1 | 36 |
| 2 | 36 |
| 3 | 36 |
| 4 | 36 |
| 5 | 34 |
| 6 | 34 |
| 7 | 34 |
| 8 | 34 |
| 9 | 36 |
| 10 | 35 |
| 11 | 35 |
| 12 | 35 |
| 13 | 36 |
| 14 | 36 |
| 15 | 36 |
| 16 | 36 |
| 17 | 36 |
| 18 | 35 |
| 19 | 34 |
| 20 | 36 |

## Mathematical Practices

| MP4 | Model with mathematics. |
| --- | --- |

**Item 18:** Students explain the relationship between quantities.

## Writing About Math

✏️ ▸ Direct students to respond to the Unit 5 Essential Question. (This can also be found on student page 303.)

### Essential Question:
How can you represent and analyze data on a coordinate plane?

Possible responses:
- Plot points on a coordinate plane.
- Connect the points that I have plotted on a coordinate plane to see trends and solve problems.

### Unit Assessment

- Unit 5 Review, *pp. 328–330*
- Unit 5 Performance Task ( ONLINE )

### Additional Assessment Options

- Performance Task 2, *pp. 331–336* ( ALSO ONLINE )

**Optional Purchase:**
- iProgress Monitor ( ONLINE )
- Progress Monitor Student Benchmark Assessment Booklet

UNIT 5 Review

MP7 **19.** Sal draws a line segment from (1, 4) to (5, 8). He then draws another segment from (2, 3) to (6, 7). If Sal wants to draw another line segment that is parallel to those two segments, what points can he use?

**Answer** Answers may vary. Possible answers: Sal can draw a line segment from (3, 2) to (7, 6) or from (4, 1) to (8, 5).

✏️ ▸ **Justify your answer using words, drawings, or numbers.**

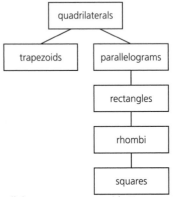

Possible answer: To answer the question, I can draw the first two line segments on the grid, then find another line segment that is parallel to the first two. One possibility is a line segment from (3, 2) to (7, 6).

MP3 **20.** Layla drew this hierarchy diagram to classify quadrilaterals. There are two errors in the diagram. Find the errors and explain how to correct them.

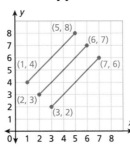

All parallelograms are trapezoids. To correct the error, Layla can place trapezoids directly under quadrilaterals and place parallelograms directly under trapezoids. Rhombi are parallelograms, but they are not rectangles. To correct the error, Layla can draw two line segments from parallelograms, one to rectangles and then on to squares, and

**Answer** the other to rhombi and then on to squares.

**330** Unit 5 ▪ Focus on Geometry

### Mathematical Practices

| MP3 | Construct viable arguments and critique the reasoning of others. |
|---|---|

**Item 20:** Students analyze a problem situation and share their reasoning with others.

| MP7 | Look for and make use of structure. |
|---|---|

**Item 19:** Students evaluate and extend a pattern in a problem.

## Performance Tasks

Performance Tasks show your understanding of the Math that you have learned. You will be doing various Performance Tasks as you complete your work in this text.

### Beginning This Task

The next five pages provide you with the beginning of a Performance Task. You will be given 5 items to complete, and each item will have two or more parts. As you complete these items you will:

I  Demonstrate that you have mastered mathematical skills and concepts

II  Reason through a problem to a solution, and explain your reasoning

III  Use models and apply them to real-world situations.

### Extending This Task

Your teacher may extend this Performance Task with additional items provided in our online resources at sadlierconnect.com.

### Scoring This Task

Your response to each item will be assessed against a rubric, or scoring guide. Some items will be worth 1 or 2 points, and others will be worth more. In each item you will show your work or explain your reasoning.

---

## ONLINE  Customize Performance Task 2

Performance Task 2 in *Progress Mathematics* also provides students with additional practice. You can use the online items of Performance Task 2 to customize the amount and kind of performance task practice based on your ongoing evaluation of your students. You may choose to challenge some students, to give extra experience with a particular kind of task for other students, or to extend exposure to performance assessments for the entire class.

Go to **sadlierconnect.com** to download the following resources for Performance Task 2.

- Additional Items
- Additional Teacher Support
- Additional Scoring Rubrics

---

## Performance Task 2 Overview

Performance Task 2 in *Progress Mathematics* provides students with practice for the types of items that may be found on standardized performance assessments.

Various item formats, including short- and extended-response items and technology-enhanced items, are included in the tasks. All items connect mathematical content correlated to the mathematical practices.

Items in Performance Task 2 are based on three primary types of tasks.

**Type I**  Mastery of mathematical concepts, skills and procedures

**Type II**  Using and explaining mathematical reasoning

**Type III**  Modeling problem situations in a real-world context

Performance Task 2 begins with a collection of five self-contained items in the Student Book and continues with additional items online at **sadlierconnect.com**.

**Introduce Performance Task 2**  Read student page 331 with the class. Explain that Performance Task 2 may cover any of the math they have learned in Units 1–5. Orient students to each item and communicate helpful reminders that will enable students to approach each item successfully. Once students have completed each item go over the correct responses with them.

**Recommended Pacing**  Administer Performance Task 2 on Student Book pages 332–336 over five 20-minute sessions.

**Teacher Resources**  For each task, the teacher materials include:

- Item types and purposes
- Correlations to State Standards for Mathematical Practice, and Depth of Knowledge (DOK) levels
- Suggested administration procedures
- Scoring Rubric

# Item 1: Modeling an Underground Parking Garage

| Item | Type | Purpose |
|------|------|---------|
| 1.a. | III | Make a line plot for the given data. |
| 1.b. | III | Analyze information in a line plot. |
| 1.c. | III | Use information from a line plot to solve a real-world problem. |
| 1.d. | I | Convert measures within the customary system. |

| Item | MP | DOK |
|------|----|----|
| 1.a. | 4 | Level 2 |
| 1.b. | 2 | Level 2 |
| 1.c. | 1 | Level 2 |
| 1.d. | 1 | Level 1 |

## Administering Item 1 (Pacing: 20 minutes)

Ask a volunteer to read the introductory paragraph. Have others describe the situation in their own words.

### Item 1.a. (7 minutes)

Remind students to first choose their mixed-number intervals. Make sure they check their line plots by crossing off the numbers in the data table.

### Item 1.b. (3 minutes)

Suggest students use what they know about writing expressions to solve this problem.

### Item 1.c. (6 minutes)

Encourage students to divide the total weight of all sandbags by the number of sandbags.

### Item 1.d. (4 minutes)

Remind students to look carefully at their answer to item 1.c. They can use the whole number part of the answer and the fraction separately to solve the problem.

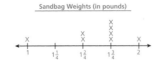

## Modeling an Underground Parking Garage

1. The students in Harold's art class are making drawings and models. Harold makes a model of an underground parking garage.

   a. Harold uses sandbags to make his model. The data set at the right shows the weights of the sandbags in pounds.

   Make a line plot of the data shown.

   **Sandbag Weights (in pounds)**

   | 2 | $1\frac{3}{4}$ | $1\frac{3}{4}$ | 1 |
   |---|---|---|---|
   | $1\frac{3}{4}$ | $1\frac{1}{2}$ | $1\frac{1}{2}$ | $1\frac{3}{4}$ |

   Sandbag Weights (in pounds)

   b. What is the total weight of the sandbags?

   The total weight of the sandbags is 13 pounds.
   Possible solution: $1 + (2 \times 1\frac{1}{2}) + (4 \times 1\frac{3}{4}) + 2$
   $= 1 + 3 + 7 + 2$
   $= 13$

   c. Suppose the sandbags were re-filled so that each of the sandbags weighed the same. How many pounds would each bag weigh?

   Each bag would weigh $\frac{13}{8}$ or $1\frac{5}{8}$ pounds.
   Possible solution:
   $13 \div 8$
   $\frac{13}{8}$ or $1\frac{5}{8}$

   d. Use your answer to item 1.c. above. How many ounces would each bag weigh?

   Each bag would weigh 26 ounces.
   Possible solution: 1 pound = 16 ounces;
   $\frac{5}{8}$ pound = $\frac{5}{8} \times 16 = 10$ ounces; $16 + 10 = 26$.

332   Performance Task 2

## Scoring Rubric

| Item | Points | Student Responses |
|------|--------|-------------------|
| 1.a. | 2 | Correctly makes a line plot. |
|      | 1 | Minor error in line plot. |
|      | 0 | Makes an incorrect line plot. |
| 1.b. | 2 | Correctly calculates weight. |
|      | 1 | Makes minor calculation error. |
|      | 0 | Makes major calculation error. |
| 1.c. | 2 | Chooses the correct operation and performs calculations correctly. |
|      | 1 | Chooses the correct operation but makes a minor error. |
|      | 0 | Makes a major error when writing the expression. |
| 1.d. | 2 | Correctly converts measurement. |
|      | 1 | Makes minor conversion error. |
|      | 0 | Does not convert the measurement. |

## Performance Task 2

### Modeling an Apartment Building

2. Rebecca builds a model of an apartment building.

   a. Rebecca plans to use foot cubes to make the model. She begins by making the sketch below. Draw cubes in this sketch to help Rebecca find the total number of foot cubes she needs.

   4 ft
   2 ft
   2 ft

   b. How many foot cubes will Rebecca need?
   Rebecca will need 16 foot cubes.

   c. Multiply to find the volume of Rebecca's apartment building model.
   Possible multiplication:
   $\ell \times w \times h$
   $2 \times 2 \times 4$
   16
   The volume of the model is 16 cubic feet.

   d. Jarred also makes a model of an apartment building. His model is a cube with edge lengths of 1 yard. Whose model has the greater volume, Rebecca's or Jarred's? How much greater?
   Jarred's model has the greater volume. Its volume is 11 cubic feet greater than the volume of Rebecca's model.
   Possible solution: One yard is equivalent to 3 feet. The volume of Jarred's model is 3 ft × 3 ft × 3 ft or 27 cubic feet, and 27 cubic feet is greater than 16 cubic feet. 27 − 16 = 11.

Performance Task 2    333

## Item 2: Modeling an Apartment Building

| Item | Type | Purpose |
|------|------|---------|
| 2.a. | III | Draw lines on a model to help show its volume. |
| 2.b. | I | Determine the number of cubes in a model. |
| 2.c. | I | Find the volume of a model using a formula. |
| 2.d. | III | Determine the difference in the volumes of two models that involves the conversion of measures. |

| Item | MP | DOK |
|------|----|----|
| 2.a. | 4 | Level 1 |
| 2.b. | 4 | Level 1 |
| 2.c. | 2 | Level 1 |
| 2.d. | 6 | Level 2 |

### Administering Item 2  (Pacing: 20 minutes)

Ask a volunteer to read the introductory paragraph. Have others describe the problem situation in their own words.

**Item 2.a.**  (3 minutes)
Remind students that these are cubes. Since they are cubes, all sides are equal.

**Item 2.b.**  (3 minutes)
Students may count the cubes in the model. Remind them to also count the cubes that are not visible.

**Item 2.c.**  (5 minutes)
Encourage a discussion on how to use the volume formula.

**Item 2.d.**  (9 minutes)
Discuss with students that there are several ways to solve this problem. Recommend that they convert yards to feet to help solve the problem.

### Scoring Rubric

| Item | Points | Student Responses |
|------|--------|-------------------|
| 2.a. | 2 | Makes a correct drawing. |
|      | 1 | Drawing has minor errors. |
|      | 0 | Does not make a correct drawing. |
| 2.b. | 2 | Correctly identifies the number of cubes. |
|      | 0 | Does not correctly identify the number of cubes. |
| 2.c. | 2 | Multiplies the correct numbers to find the volume of the model. |
|      | 1 | Makes multiplication error. |
|      | 0 | Does not find the volume. |
| 2.d. | 2 | Accurately calculates the difference. |
|      | 1 | Makes a minor calculation error. |
|      | 0 | Does not correctly state which model has the greater volume. |

## Item 3: Modeling an Office Building

| Item | Type | Purpose |
|------|------|---------|
| 3.a. | II | Critique a method for solving a problem and find the error in the method. |
| 3.b. | II | Decompose an irregular figure. |
| 3.c. | II | Explain how to solve a problem using a formula. |
| 3.d. | III | Calculate to find the volume of an irregular figure. |

| Item | MP | DOK |
|------|-----|-------|
| 3.a. | 3 | Level 2 |
| 3.b. | 7 | Level 2 |
| 3.c. | 3 | Level 3 |
| 3.d. | 6 | Level 2 |

## Administering Item 3 (Pacing: 20 minutes)

Ask a volunteer to read the introductory paragraph. Have others describe the situation in their own words.

**Item 3.a.** (5 minutes)

Students should see that the volume formula cannot be used on this figure as a whole. It must first be decomposed.

**Item 3.b.** (5 minutes)

Have students draw a picture of a right rectangular prism to see how to decompose the figure.

**Item 3.c.** (5 minutes)

Students should explain that they can find the volume of each decomposed figure and then add the volumes.

**Item 3.d.** (5 minutes)

Remind students to line up the factors and addends properly to ensure a correct answer.

### Modeling an Office Building

3. Jorge makes the model shown at the right of an office building.

a. Jorge says that he can use the formula $V = \ell \times w \times h$ to find the volume of his model. He says he will multiply $62 \times 34 \times 62$, because the length is 62 inches, the width is 34 inches, and the height is 62 inches. He says his answer will be in cubic inches. What error is Jorge making?

Possible answer: The formula $V = \ell \times w \times h$ is for right rectangular prisms. Jorge's model is made up of right rectangular prisms, but the entire model is not a right rectangular prism.

b. Draw a line segment on Jorge's model to show how you can break apart the model into two right rectangular prisms.

Students may draw a vertical line segment breaking apart the model into two side-by-side rectangular prisms (34 in. × 10 in. × 62 in. and 52 in. × 34 in. × 10 in.) or they may draw a horizontal line segment breaking apart the model into two rectangular prisms, one above the other (34 in. × 10 in. × 52 in. and 62 in. × 34 in. × 10 in.).

c. Explain how you can use the formula $V = \ell \times w \times h$ to find the volume of Jorge's model.

Possible answer: After I break apart the model into two rectangular prisms, I would use the formula to find the volume of each rectangular prism, and then add the two volumes to find the total volume of Jorge's model.

d. Find the volume of Jorge's model.

The volume of Jorge's model is 38,760 cubic inches.
Possible solution:

$$V = \ell \times w \times h \qquad\qquad V = \ell \times w \times h$$
$$= 10 \times 34 \times 62 \qquad\qquad = 52 \times 34 \times 10$$

```
      2
     34                    52              21,080
    ×62                   ×34            +17,680
     68                   208             38,760
  +2040                 +1560
  2,108                 1,768
= 10 × 2,108           = 1,768 × 10
= 21,080               = 17,680
```

### Scoring Rubric

| Item | Points | Student Responses |
|------|--------|-------------------|
| 3.a. | 2 | Correctly identifies the error. |
|      | 1 | Identifies the error but is not clear in the explanation. |
|      | 0 | Does not correctly identify the error. |
| 3.b. | 2 | Draws the line segment correctly. |
|      | 1 | Is not entirely accurate in the drawing of the line segment. |
|      | 0 | Does not draw line segment. |
| 3.c. | 2 | Correctly explains reasoning. |
|      | 1 | Explanation lacks total clarity. |
|      | 0 | Cannot explain reasoning. |
| 3.d. | 2 | Finds the correct volume. |
|      | 1 | Makes a minor error(s) when find the volume. |
|      | 0 | Does not use the proper procedure for finding the volume. |

## Modeling a Vacation Home

4. Hua makes a chart of clues for drawing her dream vacation home on a coordinate plane.

a. Complete Hua's chart.

| Point | Directions from the Origin | Ordered Pair |
|---|---|---|
| A | 2 units to the right, 1 unit up | (2, 1) |
| B | 2 units to the right, __5__ units up | (2, 5) |
| C | __4__ units to the right, 5 units up | (4, 5) |
| D | __4__ units to the right, __7__ units up | (4, 7) |
| E | 5 units to the right, 8 units up | (5, 8) |
| F | __7__ units to the right, __7__ units up | (7, 7) |
| G | 7 units to the right, 1 unit up | (7, 1) |

b. What is the meaning of the origin on a coordinate plane?
Possible answer: The origin is the point where the value of both coordinates is 0.

c. On the coordinate plane to the right, plot and label the points for the Check that ordered pairs from the chart. students have graphed and labeled each point accurately.

d. Make the outline of Hua's dream vacation home. Use the coordinate plane at the right. Draw line segments to connect the points in order. Then connect the last point to the first point.
Check students' work.

## Scoring Rubric

| Item | Points | Student Responses |
|---|---|---|
| 4.a. | 2 | Correctly completes table. |
| | 1 | Correctly completes majority of table. |
| | 0 | Makes several errors completing table. |
| 4.b. | 2 | Explains the origin correctly. |
| | 1 | Lacks clarity in explanation. |
| | 0 | Does not state the correct meaning. |
| 4.c. | 2 | Correctly plots and labels each point on the coordinate plane. |
| | 1 | Minor error(s) when plotting points. |
| | 0 | Does not correctly plot points. |
| 4.d. | 2 | Correctly connects the points. |
| | 1 | Make minor error connecting the points. |
| | 0 | Incorrectly connects points. |

# Item 4: Modeling a Vacation Home

| Item | Type | Purpose |
|---|---|---|
| 4.a. | I | Record ordered pairs and label directional units. |
| 4.b. | II | Explain the meaning of the origin on a coordinate plane. |
| 4.c. | I | Plot and label points on a coordinate plane. |
| 4.d. | I | Connect points on a coordinate plane in a specific order. |

| Item | MP | DOK |
|---|---|---|
| 4.a. | 1 | Level 1 |
| 4.b. | 6 | Level 2 |
| 4.c. | 8 | Level 1 |
| 4.d. | 1 | Level 1 |

## Administering Item 4 (Pacing: 20 minutes)

Ask a volunteer to read the introductory paragraph. Have others describe the situation in their own words.

### Item 4.a. (7 minutes)

Remind students that sometimes the ordered pair is given and not the number of units. They will need to use the ordered pair to find the number of units.

### Item 4.b. (3 minutes)

Students should understand that the origin is the point where the $x$- and $y$-axes meet.

### Item 4.c. (7 minutes)

Remind students that they can use both the directions from the origin and the numbers in the ordered pairs to help them solve this problem.

### Item 4.d. (3 minutes)

Students should label each point based on the table and then connect them in order.

## Item 5: Triangular Doors

| Item | Type | Purpose |
|------|------|---------|
| 5.a. | II | Define an isosceles triangle. |
| 5.b. | III | Draw an acute isosceles triangle and explain why it fits that definition. |
| 5.c. | III | Draw a right isosceles triangle and explain why it fits that definition. |
| 5.d. | III | Draw an obtuse isosceles triangle and explain why it fits that definition. |

| Item | MP | DOK |
|------|----|----|
| 5.a. | 6 | Level 2 |
| 5.b. | 5 | Level 3 |
| 5.c. | 3 | Level 3 |
| 5.d. | 3 | Level 3 |

## Administering Item 5 (Pacing: 20 minutes)

Ask a volunteer to read the introductory paragraph. Have others describe the situation in their own words.

### Item 5.a. (2 minutes)

Suggest to students they draw an isosceles triangle to help. Students should know that at least two sides of an isosceles triangle are equal.

### Item 5.b. (6 minutes)

Have students define *acute* and *isosceles* separately. Then have them base their drawings off of these definitions.

### Item 5.c. (6 minutes)

Have students define *right* and *isosceles* separately. Then have them base their drawings off of these definitions.

### Item 5.d. (6 minutes)

Have students define *obtuse* and *isosceles* separately. Then have them base their drawings off of these definitions.

### Performance Task 2

**Triangular Doors**

5. Ilya is designing doors for her model of an amusement park's fun house. She wants each door to have the shape of an isosceles triangle.

  a. Describe the attributes of an isosceles triangle.

    Possible answer: An isosceles triangle has three sides. At least two of those sides have the same length.

  b. Ilya wants one door to have the shape of an acute triangle. Draw an example of an acute triangle that is also an isosceles triangle. Explain how your triangle is both acute and isosceles.

    Possible drawing:     Students may also draw an equilateral triangle.

    Possible explanation: My triangle has two sides the same length and all three angles are acute.

  c. Ilya wants another door to have the shape of a right triangle. Draw an example of a right triangle that is also an isosceles triangle. Explain how your triangle is both a right triangle and an isosceles triangle.

    Possible drawing:     Possible explanation: My triangle has two sides the same length and one right angle.

  d. Ilya wants the third door of her model to have the shape of an obtuse triangle. Draw an example of an obtuse triangle that is also an isosceles triangle. Explain how your triangle is both an obtuse triangle and an isosceles triangle.

    Possible drawing:     Possible explanation: My triangle has two sides the same length and one obtuse angle.

336  Performance Task 2

## Scoring Rubric

| Item | Points | Student Responses |
|------|--------|-------------------|
| 5.a. | 2 | Describes all the attributes clearly. |
|      | 1 | Description lacks clarity. |
|      | 0 | Does not describe all the attributes. |
| 5.b. | 2 | Draws and explains accurately. |
|      | 1 | Either drawing or explanation is inaccurate. |
|      | 0 | Draws and explains inaccurately. |
| 5.c. | 2 | Draws and explains accurately. |
|      | 1 | Either drawing or explanation is inaccurate. |
|      | 0 | Draws and explains inaccurately. |
| 5.d. | 2 | Draws and explains accurately. |
|      | 1 | Either drawing or explanation is inaccurate. |
|      | 0 | Draws and explains inaccurately. |

## Foundational Skills Handbook

A review of prerequisite mathematics needed to understand the concepts and skills of Grade 5.

### A. Understand: Comparing with an unknown factor

Tyler waits 21 minutes for the school bus. Tyler's waiting time is 3 times as long as Grace's waiting time. How long does Grace wait for the bus?

To find how long Grace waits for the bus, first model the problem. Then write and solve an equation. Use $g$ to represent the unknown quantity, Grace's waiting time.

**Waiting Times**

21 minutes

Tyler $\boxed{g}\;\boxed{g}\;\boxed{g}$

Grace $\boxed{g}$

Grace's waiting time is the amount being multiplied, or the size of each group in the model.

Write a multiplication equation for the comparison.
21 = 3 times as long as Grace's waiting time
$21 = 3 \times g$

Write and solve a related division equation to find $g$, the unknown factor.
$21 \div 3 = g$
$7 = g$

**Remember!**
Multiplication and division are opposite, or *inverse*, operations.

Grace waits 7 minutes for the bus.

### B. Understand: Number patterns and pattern rules

To solve some problems, you can make a number pattern. A number pattern is an ordered list of numbers that follow a rule and repeat or change in some way. The pattern rule tells you how the pattern works.

Suppose you start with $10 and save $5 each week. To generate the pattern for the amount you will have in 5 weeks, start at 10 and follow the rule *add* 5. Each number in a number pattern is called a term. This pattern tells you that each new term *increases* by 5, so this is a growing pattern. **Rule:** Start at 10 and add 5.

| +5 | +5 | +5 | +5 | +5 |
| 10 | 15 | 20 | 25 | 30 | 35 |

In 5 weeks, you will have $35.

Foundational Skills Handbook   337

**The Foundational Skills Handbook:**
Use to provide review of prerequisite content and skills needed for Grade 5.

## Item A.

### Understand: Comparing with an unknown factor

■ Relate the model to the problem to help students connect that the unknown quantity, $g$, is the time it takes Grace to get to school and that Tyler's time is 21 minutes, or 3 of Grace's unknown quantity.

■ Review the multiplication equation for the comparison. Make sure students can relate the equation to the information in the problem.

■ Make sure students understand the concept of inverse relationships. You may wish to review inverse operations with additional equations, such as $4 \times 3 = 12$ and $12 \div 3 = 4$.

## Item B.

### Understand: Number patterns and pattern rules

■ Make sure students understand the important information while working with this number pattern. They need to know the pattern rule, the starting number, and the period of time that the person is saving.

■ Making a chart or a drawing will help students to visualize a pattern.

## Foundational Skills Handbook Contents

## Item C.

### Understand: Quotients of tens, hundreds, and thousands

■ Students should recognize that 20 tens is the same as 200. You may wish to use place-value models to reinforce the concept to students.

■ Ask students to explain the pattern of zeros in the divisions. You may wish to have students try another example, such as finding the quotient of 300 ÷ 6.

■ If students need help reading and using the number line, have the class count by 4s, then by 40s.

## Item D.

### Understand: Division and the Distributive Property

■ Have students explain what is meant when they are asked to break apart the number 2,280.

■ Help students understand why 2,000 was subtracted from 2,280. For example, pretend a person is dividing $2,280 earned at the school fair among 5 charities. The 2,000 has been divided into 5 groups of 400 so the 2,000 has already been divided. There is 280 left.

■ Have a student explain why it is necessary to add the partial quotients to find the answer.

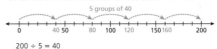

**C.** **Understand:** Quotients of tens, hundreds, and thousands

Find the quotient of 200 ÷ 5.

In this division 200 represents the dividend, the number you divide; 5 represents the divisor, the number you divide by in the division to find a quotient, the unknown number that is the answer to the problem.

$$\underset{\text{dividend}}{200} \div \underset{\text{divisor}}{5} = \underset{\text{quotient}}{n}$$

Now use the fact 20 ÷ 5 = 4 and the pattern of zeros to solve.

20 ÷ 5 = 4

20 tens ÷ 5 = 4 tens ⟶ 200 ÷ 5 = 40, so n = 40.

You can use a number line to show a model of 200 ÷ 5 = 40.

5 groups of 40

200 ÷ 5 = 40

**D.** **Understand:** Division and the Distributive Property

2,280 ÷ 5 = ■

To solve the division equation, break apart 2,280.

Choose a hundreds number that when multiplied by 5 would be close to 2,280. 5 × 400 = 2,000. Subtract.

Next choose a tens number that when multiplied by 5 would be close to 280. 5 × 50 = 250. Subtract.

Now choose a ones number that when multiplied by 5 would be close to 30. 5 × 6 = 30. Subtract.

```
  2,280
 −2,000  ← 5 × 400
    280
   −250  ← 5 × 50
     30
    − 30  ← 5 × 6
      0
```

Write 2,280 as a sum of 2,000 + 250 + 30.

You can distribute the divisor 5 the same way you distributed a factor when using the Distributive Property of Multiplication.

When dividing 2,280, each addend is divided by 5. Add these partial quotients to find the answer.

2,280 ÷ 5 = (2,000 ÷ 5) + (250 ÷ 5) + (30 ÷ 5)
= 400 + 50 + 6 ← partial quotients
= 456

2,280 ÷ 5 = 456

**E. Understand: Place value and partial products**

$924 \times 6 = $ ▨

To find the product, multiply 6 times the value of each digit in 924. Partial products are formed by multiplying the value of each digit by a factor.

Find the partial products.
Multiply the ones first.
Then multiply the tens and the hundreds.

$$
\begin{array}{r}
924 \\
\times \quad 6 \\
\hline
24 \leftarrow 6 \times 4 \text{ ones} \\
120 \leftarrow 6 \times 2 \text{ tens} \\
5{,}400 \leftarrow 6 \times 9 \text{ hundreds}
\end{array}
$$

Add all the partial products.
$924 \times 6 = 24 + 120 + 5{,}400$
$924 \times 6 = 5{,}544$

$$
\begin{array}{r}
924 \\
\times \quad 6 \\
\hline
24 \\
120 \\
+5{,}400 \\
\hline
5{,}544
\end{array}
$$

**F. Understand: Fractions and mixed numbers**

A mixed number shows the sum of a whole number and a fraction but does not have a plus (+) sign. You can write fractions as mixed numbers and you can write mixed numbers as fractions.

Write $\frac{9}{4}$ as a mixed number.

$\frac{9}{4} = \frac{4}{4} + \frac{4}{4} + \frac{1}{4}$ ← Write $\frac{9}{4}$ as a sum of fractions.

$= 1 + 1 + \frac{1}{4}$ ← Write $\frac{4}{4}$ as 1.

$= 2 + \frac{1}{4}$ ← Add the whole numbers.

$= 2\frac{1}{4}$ ← Write the sum as a mixed number.

> **Remember!**
> $\frac{4}{4} = 1$

Write $4\frac{1}{2}$ as a fraction.

$4\frac{1}{2} = 4 + \frac{1}{2}$ ← Write $4\frac{1}{2}$ as a sum of 4 plus $\frac{1}{2}$.

$= 1 + 1 + 1 + 1 + \frac{1}{2}$ ← Write 4 as a sum of 1s.

$= \frac{2}{2} + \frac{2}{2} + \frac{2}{2} + \frac{2}{2} + \frac{1}{2}$ ← Write 1 as a fraction with the denominator 2.

$= \frac{2+2+2+2+1}{2}$ ← Add the numerators.

$= \frac{9}{2}$

Foundational Skills Handbook **339**

## Item E.

### Understand: Place value and partial products

■ Review the term *partial products*. Focus on the word *partial,* which means "part of." Help students to see that they are adding all the parts to find the product.

■ Guide students through the process of finding partial products. Reinforce that the expanded form of the factor 924 is 900 + 20 + 4. Make sure students think about place value and understand that they are multiplying 6 × 4, 6 × 20, and 6 × 900.

■ Review with students that when they multiply 6 × 2 tens, the product is 12 tens, which is the same as 120. 6 x 9 hundreds is 54 hundreds, which is the same as 5,400.

## Item F.

### Understand: Fractions and mixed numbers

■ To make sure students understand the terminology used in Item 5, have them define *mixed number* and *fraction,* and give an example of each that is not already on this page.

■ Explain that since the denominator of the given fraction $\frac{9}{4}$ is 4, it makes sense to use $\frac{4}{4}$ for 1. Similarly, students should see that when writing $4\frac{1}{2}$ as a fraction, they should use $\frac{2}{2}$ for 1.

# Foundational Skills Handbook

## Item G.

### Understand: Multiplication as repeated addition

- Relate the model to 6 groups of $\frac{2}{3}$.

- Make sure students understand the steps that led from $\frac{2}{3}$ being added six times to the step that shows the fraction with $6 \times 2$ as the numerator and 3 as the denominator.

- Explain how the information in the Remember box relates to finding $\frac{12}{3} = 4$.

## Item H.

### Understand: Multiplying a fraction by a whole number

- Students may notice that both Items G. and H. are about multiplying $6 \times \frac{2}{3}$. Help students see the relationship between the multiplication in Item H and the repeated addition in Item G.

- Discuss with students that $\frac{12}{3}$ also means $12 \div 3$.

---

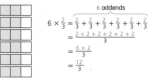

**G. Understand: Multiplication as repeated addition**

Multiply $6 \times \frac{2}{3}$.

Draw a model to show 6 groups of $\frac{2}{3}$. The model shows that multiplying $6 \times \frac{2}{3}$ is the same as adding $\frac{2}{3} + \frac{2}{3} + \frac{2}{3} + \frac{2}{3} + \frac{2}{3} + \frac{2}{3}$.

$$6 \times \frac{2}{3} = \overbrace{\frac{2}{3} + \frac{2}{3} + \frac{2}{3} + \frac{2}{3} + \frac{2}{3} + \frac{2}{3}}^{6 \text{ addends}}$$
$$= \frac{2+2+2+2+2+2}{3}$$
$$= \frac{6 \times 2}{3}$$
$$= \frac{12}{3}$$

Write the product $\frac{12}{3}$ as a whole number. You can use the fact $12 = 4 \times 3$ to help you find the whole number.

$$\frac{12}{3} = \frac{4 \times 3}{3} = \frac{3}{3} + \frac{3}{3} + \frac{3}{3} + \frac{3}{3} = 4$$
$$6 \times \frac{2}{3} = 4.$$

**Remember!**
You can break apart the numerator of a fraction in the same way as a whole number.

**H. Understand: Multiplying a fraction by a whole number**

Multiply $6 \times \frac{2}{3}$.

To multiply any fraction by a whole number, you can multiply the numerator of the fraction by the whole number. Then write the product over the denominator.

$$6 \times \frac{2}{3} = \frac{6 \times 2}{3} = \frac{12}{3} = 4$$
$$6 \times \frac{2}{3} = 4.$$

340 Foundational Skills Handbook

Copyright © by William H. Sadlier, Inc. All rights reserved.

**340** Foundational Skills Handbook

**I. Understand: Reading and using line plots**

A line plot shows measurement data in order from least to greatest.

**Maple Leaf Lengths (in inches)**

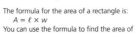

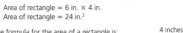

| $3\frac{1}{8}$ | $2\frac{5}{8}$ | $2\frac{1}{4}$ | $2\frac{6}{8}$ | $2\frac{1}{2}$ | 3 | $3\frac{1}{4}$ |
|---|---|---|---|---|---|---|
| 3 | $2\frac{1}{2}$ | $2\frac{4}{8}$ | $2\frac{6}{8}$ | $3\frac{3}{8}$ | $2\frac{7}{8}$ | 3 |
| $3\frac{1}{8}$ | $3\frac{1}{8}$ | $3\frac{1}{8}$ | $3\frac{3}{4}$ | $2\frac{1}{8}$ | $2\frac{5}{8}$ | |

A line plot can help you summarize data. For example:

- There are 20 X's so there are 20 measurements altogether.
- All of the leaves are between $2\frac{1}{8}$ and $3\frac{3}{4}$ inches long.
- Most leaves are between $2\frac{1}{8}$ and $3\frac{3}{8}$ inches long.
- Four leaves are $3\frac{1}{8}$ inches long.
- No leaves are $3\frac{4}{8}$ or $3\frac{5}{8}$ inches long.

**J. Understand: Area formula for rectangles**

To find the area of a rectangle, multiply its length by its width.

Area of rectangle = 6 in. × 4 in.
Area of rectangle = 24 in.²

The formula for the area of a rectangle is:
$A = \ell \times w$
You can use the formula to find the area of any rectangle, including squares.

If you know the area of a rectangle, you can also use the formula to find an unknown side length.

The area of the rectangle at the right is 15 cm². If it has a width of 3 cm, what is its length?

$A = \ell \times w$
$15 = ? \times 3$
$15 = 5 \times 3$

The length of the rectangle is 5 cm.

## Item I.

### Understand: Reading and using line plots

■ Review with students why it is important to consider the data before making the number line for a line plot.

■ Work through the process of making the line plot shown on the student page.

■ Ask students to comment on the advantages of using a line plot to show information. Discuss all the information that this line plot shows.

## Item J.

### Understand: Area formula for rectangles

■ Students should be able to explain how an array shows why the formula for area makes sense.

■ Make sure students understand that if they know the area and either the length or width of one side, they can find an unknown side length. Discuss how knowing the area and finding the unknown side length relates to inverse operations.

## Item K.

**Understand:** Identifying right, acute, obtuse, and straight angles

■ Use the figure to reinforce students' understanding of vertex, ray, and also angle types.

■ Have students identify angles in the figure and tell how the angles compare.

■ Draw student's attention to the fact that angle *BCD* is 180°. Relate angle *BCE* and angle *ECD* to straight angle *BCD*.

## Item L.

**Understand:** Using angle measurements to classify two-dimensional figures

■ Guide students as they classify each triangle.

■ Point out that the classification of triangles is based on one or more angles of the triangle. Use the figures and other drawings to discuss why a right triangle always has one right angle and two acute angles; an obtuse triangle always has one obtuse angle and two acute angles; and an acute triangle always has three acute angles.

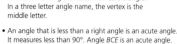

**K.  Understand:** Identifying right, acute, obtuse, and straight angles

An angle is named by its vertex, the point from which the two sides of an angle begin.

Look at the figure.

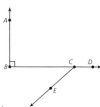

- The angle at *B* is marked by the symbol ⌐ so it is a right angle and measures 90°. It can also be named as angle *ABC*, or angle *CBA*. The letter naming the vertex names the angle. In a three letter angle name, the vertex is the middle letter.

- An angle that is less than a right angle is an acute angle. It measures less than 90°. Angle *BCE* is an acute angle.

- An angle that is greater than a right angle is an obtuse angle. It measures more than 90° and less than 180°. Angle *DCE* is an obtuse angle.

- An angle that forms a straight line is a straight angle. It measures 180°. Angle *BCD* is a straight angle.

**Remember!**
An angle is formed when two rays share the same endpoint, called the vertex. The two rays form the sides of the angle.

**L.  Understand:** Using angle measurement to classify two-dimensional figures

You can use angle measurement to classify two-dimensional figures such as triangles.

| right triangle | obtuse triangle | acute triangle |
| 1 right angle | 1 obtuse angle | 3 acute angles |

## Problem-Solving Model

You can use this model to solve problems.

**Read**

**Read the problem.**
**Focus on the facts and the questions.**

- What facts do you know?
- What do you need to find out?

**Plan**

**Outline a plan.**
**Plan how to solve the problem.**

- What operation will you use?
- Do I need to use 1 step or 2 steps?
- Will you draw a picture?
- How have you solved similar problems?

**Solve**

**Follow your plan to solve the problem.**

- Did you answer the question?
- Did you label your answer?

**Check**

**Test that the solution is reasonable.**

- Does your answer make sense? If not, review and revise your plan.
- How can you solve the problem a different way? Is the answer the same?
- How can you estimate to check your answer?

## Introducing the Problem-Solving Model

You can use the Problem-Solving Model pages to encourage students to think problems through and solve them successfully.

The Problem-Solving Model is just one way to help students master the art of problem solving. Many students intuitively see alternative methods or solutions. Their intuitive grasp of the problem/situation should not be impeded or slowed by having to use the model. Students should be asked only to demonstrate that they solved a problem using some logical plan, and not necessarily this specific model. Students should be able to explain the method they have used.

# Problem-Solving Model

## A Multiplication Problem

Making a table imposes an organized way of looking at information in a problem. It is important to expose students to the need to organize data so they can more clearly organize their thinking about what a problem asks, as well as how best to solve it. When making a table, students will use their number sense and may also guess and check.

Sometimes there can be more than one solution to a problem. Experience with problems that have more than one solution, like A Multiplication Problem, serves as readiness for later work in algebra.

### A Multiplication Problem

> Rory multiplied a two-digit number by a one-digit number greater than 1. The product was between 40 and 45. What were the factors?
>
> ■ ■
> × ■
> product

**Read**

Visualize the problem as you reread it.
Focus on the facts and the question.

**Facts:** The factors were a two-digit number and a one-digit number greater than 1. The product was between 40 and 45.

**Question:** What were the factors?

**Plan**

Make a table to record the factors and products.
To find the factors, list:
- one-digit numbers greater than 1. (2, 3, 4, . . .)
- two-digit numbers. (10, 11, 12, . . .)

Since the least two-digit number is 10 and $5 \times 10 = 50$, the one-digit number must be less than 5.
Multiply the factors to find the products that equal 41, 42, 43, or 44.

> **Remember!**
> Not all problems have just one solution.

**Solve**

| Factors | 21<br>× 2 | 22<br>× 2 | 23<br>× 2 | 13<br>× 3 | 14<br>× 3 | 15<br>× 3 | 11<br>× 4 |
|---|---|---|---|---|---|---|---|
| Product | **42** | **44** | 46 | 39 | **42** | 45 | **44** |

There is *more than one solution*.
Look at the table. The factors for a product between 40 and 45 are: $2 \times 21$, $2 \times 22$, $3 \times 14$, and $4 \times 11$.

**Check**

Go back to the problem. Reread it. Compare the completed table to the facts given in the problem.
Are all the solutions reasonable? Yes.

## A Book Problem

To solve multistep problems, such as A Book Problem, students must be able to perceive and understand the interrelatedness of the multiple parts. By using the problem-solving model, students can analyze the problem and not only choose the correct operations, but plan the correct sequence in which to do each operation.

### A Book Problem

> Marvin is reading a 341-page book. He has already read 128 pages of the book and skipped reading the foreword containing 19 pages. How many more pages does Marvin have left to read to finish the book?

**Read**

Visualize the problem as you reread it.
Focus on the facts and the question.

**Facts:** The book has 341 pages.
Marvin has read 128 pages.
Marvin skipped 19 pages.

**Question:** How many more pages does Marvin have left to read?

**Plan**

Do you need more than one step to solve this problem? Yes.
**Step 1:** Add the number of pages Marvin read and skipped.
**Step 2:** Subtract that sum from the total number of book pages.

**Solve**

Step 1: Add

```
    1
  1 2 8  ← pages read
+   1 9  ← pages skipped
  1 4 7
```

Marvin has 194 pages left to read.

Step 2: Subtract

```
    13
  2 3 11
  3 4 1  ← total number of book pages
- 1 4 7  ← pages read and skipped
  1 9 4  ← pages left to read
```

**Check**

Use the Commutative Property and addition to check your answer.

```
    1
    1 9  ← pages skipped
+ 1 2 8  ← pages read
  1 4 7
```

```
    1 1
  1 9 4  ← pages left to read
+ 1 4 7  ← pages skipped and read
  3 4 1  ← total number of book pages
```

The answer is correct.

The Standards for Mathematical Practice, identified here, are an important part of learning mathematics. They are covered in every lesson in this book.

| MP1 | **Make sense of problems and persevere in solving them.** |
|---|---|

- Analyze and plan a solution
- Relate to a similar problem
- Assess progress
- Use concrete objects or pictures
- Check solutions

| MP2 | **Reason abstractly and quantitatively.** |
|---|---|

- Pay attention to all mathematical language
- Represent problems using symbols
- Consider units in problem solving
- Use properties of operations and objects

| MP3 | **Construct viable arguments and critique the reasoning of others.** |
|---|---|

- Analyze a problem situation
- Share reasoning with others
- Explain an approach to a problem
- Construct arguments by using drawings or concrete objects

| MP4 | **Model with mathematics.** |
|---|---|

- Relate mathematics to everyday problems
- Make assumptions and estimations
- Explain the relationship of quantities
- Use concrete tools to explain operations
- Interpret the solution in the context of a situation

| MP5 | **Use appropriate tools strategically.** |
|---|---|

- Consider the range of available tools (e.g., place-value charts, graphs, clocks, etc.)
- Decide on appropriate tools to use for each situation
- Use tools carefully and strategically

| MP6 | **Attend to precision.** |
|---|---|

- Communicate with precision
- Identify the meaning of symbols
- Use measurement units appropriately
- Calculate accurately
- Carefully formulate full explanations

| MP7 | **Look for and make use of structure.** |
|---|---|

- Search for patterns or structure
- Evaluate the structure or design of a problem
- Discuss geometric shapes in terms of their similarities and differences

| MP8 | **Look for and express regularity in repeated reasoning.** |
|---|---|

- Make generalizations in computation
- Obtain fluency using patterns
- Look for patterns with shapes and designs
- Use patterns to relate operations
- Evaluate reasonableness of answers

**Key:** MP = Mathematical Practice

## A

**acute triangle** A triangle with three acute angles.

**adjacent sides** Sides of a polygon that are next to each other.

**Associative Property of Multiplication** Changing the grouping of the factors in a multiplication expression does not change the product.

For example, $(5 \times 7) \times 9 = 5 \times (7 \times 9)$

## B

**base** The number used as a factor in exponential form.

For example, $10^2$: 10 is the base.

**base unit** The standard unit of measurement for length, liquid volume, and mass in the metric measurement system. The base units are meter, liter, and gram.

**braces { }** Symbols used to group terms within expressions and equations.

For example, $\{\frac{2}{6} + [4 \times (\frac{5}{6} + \frac{2}{6})]\} \div 5$

**brackets [ ]** Symbols used to group terms within expressions and equations.

For example, $[634 - (350 + 275)] \times 5$

## C

**common denominator** The common multiple of the denominators of two or more fractions.

For example, in the addition expression $\frac{1}{8} + \frac{3}{8}$, both fractions contain the common denominator 8.

**coordinate plane** A grid formed by intersecting perpendicular number lines.

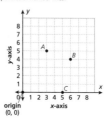

origin
(0, 0)    x-axis

**coordinates** The numbers in an ordered pair used to locate a point on a coordinate plane.

For example, (3, 5): 3 is the x-coordinate, and 5 is the y-coordinate.

**corresponding terms** Terms that are in the same position in two patterns.

For example, pairs of corresponding terms are circled in green below.

**cubic unit** The volume of a unit cube.

**customary units of length** Units of length measure used in the customary system of measurement.

For example, inch, foot, yard, and mile

**customary units of liquid volume** Units of liquid volume measure used in the customary system of measurement.

For example, cup, pint, quart, and gallon.

**customary units of weight** Units of weight measure used in the customary system of measurement.

For example, ounce, pound, and ton.

## E

**equilateral triangle** A triangle with three sides that are the same length.

**evaluate** To find the value of an expression.

For example, evaluate $4 \times (9 - 3)$. The value of the expression is 24.

**exponent** The number that tells how many times the base is used as a factor.

For example, $10^2$: 2 is the exponent.

## G

**grouping symbols** Parentheses, brackets, and braces are examples. These symbols group parts of a mathematical expression together to show which part to evaluate first.

For example, $\{\frac{2}{6} + [4 \times (\frac{5}{6} + \frac{2}{6})]\} \div 5$

## H

**hierarchy diagram** A diagram that uses the properties of figures to relate them from the most general category to the most specific category.

## I

**isosceles triangle** A triangle with at least two sides that are the same length.

## K

**kite** A quadrilateral that has two pairs of adjacent sides that are the same length.

## L

**line plot** A display of data that uses a number line and Xs symbols.

Student's Distances to School

## M

**metric units of length** Units of length measure used in the metric system of measurement.

For example, millimeter, centimeter, meter, and kilometer.

**metric units of liquid volume** Units of liquid volume measure used in the metric system of measurement.

For example, milliliter, liter, and kiloliter.

**metric units of mass** Units of mass or weight measure used in the metric system of measurement.

For example, milligram, gram, and kilogram.

## N

**numerical expression** A mathematical phrase containing only numbers and one or more operation symbols.

For example, "twice the sum of five and seven" or $(5 + 7) \times 2$.

**numerical pattern** A list of numbers that follows a constant rule.

$+3 \quad +3 \quad +3 \quad +3$

3, 6, 9, 12, 15, ...

## O

**obtuse triangle** A triangle with an obtuse angle.

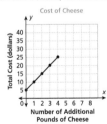

**ordered pair** Pairs of numbers in the form $(x, y)$ used to locate a point on a coordinate plane.

For example, (2, 6): 2 is the $x$-coordinate, and 6 is the $y$-coordinate.

**origin** The point at which the $x$-axis and $y$-axis of a coordinate plane intersect. The coordinates of the origin are (0, 0).

origin (0, 0)   $x$-axis

## P

**parentheses ( )** Symbols used to group terms within expressions and equations.

For example, $(6 + 9) \div 5$

**partial product** Numbers that are formed by multiplying the value of each digit by a factor.

For example, the partial products are in red.

$$
\begin{array}{r}
\overset{3}{\underset{}{2}} \\
24 \\
\times\ 86 \\
\hline
144 \leftarrow 6 \times 24 \\
+1{,}920 \leftarrow 80 \times 24 \\
\hline
2{,}064
\end{array}
$$

**partial quotient** Numbers that are formed by dividing the value of each digit by the divisor.

For example, the partial quotients are in red.

$$
\begin{array}{r}
4 \\
50 \\
300 \\
24\overline{)8{,}496} \\
-7{,}200 \\
\hline
1{,}296 \\
-1{,}200 \\
\hline
96 \\
-96 \\
\hline
0
\end{array}
$$

**power of 10** A number with a base number of 10 and an exponent.

For example, $10^2$

## R

**right triangle** A triangle with a right angle.

## S

**scale** The intervals on each axis on a coordinate plane.

For example, on the coordinate plane below the $x$-axis shows a scale of 1, and the $y$-axis shows a scale of 5.

**Cost of Cheese**

Total Cost (dollars)

Number of Additional Pounds of Cheese

**scalene triangle** A triangle with no sides that are the same length.

**scaling** Resizing a number by using multiplication.

## T

**trapezoid** A quadrilateral that has at least one pair of parallel sides.

## U

**unit cube** A cube that has edge lengths of 1 unit.

1 unit   1 unit   1 unit

**unlike denominators** The denominators of two or more fractions that are different.

For example, in the subtraction expression $\frac{5}{6} - \frac{2}{3}$, each fraction has a different denominator.

## V

**volume** A measure of the amount of space a three-dimensional figure occupies or contains.

For example, the volume of the figure below is 6 cubic units.

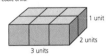

1 unit   2 units   3 units

## X

**x-axis** The horizontal number line on the coordinate plane.

**x-coordinate** The first number in an ordered pair.

For example, (3, 8): 3 is the $x$-coordinate.

## Y

**y-axis** The vertical number line on the coordinate plane.

**y-coordinate** The second number in an ordered pair.

For example, (3, 8): 8 is the $y$-coordinate.

# Notes